THE 1992 GUI...

C000041052

Con...

First published in the United Kingdom in 1992
Alan Sutton Publishing Ltd
Phoenix Mill · Far Thrupp · Stroud · Gloucestershire

British Library Cataloguing in Publication Data

Les Routiers guide to France.
647.944401

ISBN 0-7509-0085-7

Typeset in Rockwell 10/11pt.
Typesetting and origination by
Alan Sutton Publishing Limited.
Printed in Great Britain by
The Bath Press, Bath, Avon.

FOREWORD

'It is possible to eat your way through France, indulging in riotous gluttony for just a few francs – if you know about Les Relais Routiers' *Washington Post*

For the traveller in France, the red and blue Les Routiers sign has become as much a part of the scenery as the poplars, châteaux and vineyards. The restaurants and hotels recommended by Les Routiers offer local cuisine, simple accommodation and a warm welcome – all at a price you can afford.

The Les Routiers Guide provides a reliable source of reference for all those looking for real French food, an authentic atmosphere and good value. All 'Relais Routiers' are regularly inspected to ensure they provide a warm welcome, serve good quality food, offer at least one fixed price menu, and observe rules of hygiene in kitchens, bedrooms and bathrooms.

The attractions of France are many – good food, fine wine, hospitable people. Indeed, the French have a unique respect and love of food. Many visitors will find that where to eat dictates their entire holiday plans. With over 2,000 Les Routiers recommended establishments in France ranging from family restaurants to local brasseries, your Les Routiers Guide offers plenty of choice.

By venturing off the motorway, you will not only see the beauty of the French countryside, but avoid the motorway tolls and most congested routes. Let Les Routiers guide you through the vineyards of Burgundy or the sun drenched villages of Provence. Taste the world famous red and white wines and enjoy regional specialities such as coq au vin and salade nicoise.

As soon as you cross the Channel you will notice the different flavours and styles of cooking. The Routiers Guide is your guarantee of finding a cheerful greeting, homely comfort and traditional food at good value for money. The following pages will explain how to get the best from your Guide and make the most of travelling in France.

BON VOYAGE ET BON APPETIT

WHAT MAKES A RELAIS ROUTIERS

Relais Routiers have been carefully selected since 1934. With the increase in the number of travellers through France, the Routiers establishments have adapted themselves to cater more readily for families and tourists but the philosophy of Les Routiers remains unchanged – all Relais Routiers are inspected regularly to ensure they provide a warm and friendly welcome, good food and value for money.

Relais Routiers come in all shapes and sizes, from roadside café to locals' bar, pretty country hotel to lively town brasserie – but whatever the style of the establishment, quality and value are served with a generous helping of authentic French cuisine and atmosphere.

The hallmark of the French Relais Routiers is the fixed price menu. To display the red and blue Les Routiers sign, this menu must be available and be displayed on the door of the establishment. The menu will normally be for a 3 course meal and may or may not include drinks. An à la carte menu may also be offered, but this will be more expensive.

HOW TO FIND A RELAIS ROUTIERS

1. **You want to know whether there is a Relais Routiers in a certain locality.**
Look for the name of the town in question in the alphabetical list of entries. If the name is not present, there is no Relais Routiers in that town. Each establishment entry is followed by the department and number (the French equivalent of the county and postcode), the main road reference for the town and the map reference.
e.g. **Abbeville 80100 Somme RN1 Map 5–A3** This means that Abbeville is in the Somme Department on Route Nationale 1 and can be found on map 5 grid reference A3.

2. **You are following an itinerary, and you want to know where to find a Relais Routiers.**
Turn to our List of Maps of France, where you will find 25 maps covering the whole of the country. The main roads are shown on all these maps; it is easy to turn to the regional maps which are numbered when you have noted which regions the roads traverse. All the places where there are Relais Routiers are marked thereon. After that, all you have to do is turn to the alphabetical list of places, as you did before.

3. **You wish to find a hotel.**
Although the majority of Relais Routiers are restaurants, many of them also have accommodation. These are denoted in the guide by the hotel symbol followed by the number of rooms. However, as the standards in these may vary considerably, we have cited the official classification awarded by the French Tourist Board. On pages 52–60 you will find a list of Relais Routiers approved by the French Tourist Board by department. A map showing their location is on pages 50 and 51.

4. **What is a Casserole Relais?**
You will find a 'Casserole' symbol beside certain guide entries. This symbol distinguishes those Relais Routiers where particular care is taken to offer above-average meals with perhaps a special menu or specialities of the region. The 'Casserole' is the Les Routiers mark of excellence. A map showing their location can be found on pages 44–45, and a list of all 'Casseroles' on pages 46–49.

SYMBOLS USED IN THIS GUIDE

Y   RESTAURANT

⊗   BAR, CAFE, SNACKS

⌂   HOTEL – bed and breakfast available

⌂   CASSEROLE – the Les Routiers mark of excellence awarded annually to those Relais Routiers where particular care is taken to offer above average meals.

☆   OFFICIAL CLASSIFICATION OF THE FRENCH TOURIST BOARD – the number of stars (1–4) indicates the degree of comfort.

☎   TELEPHONE NUMBER

NB. All place-names given in the Guide indicate a Relais Routiers – but not its category. Do make sure you check the symbols so that on arrival at a Relais, you do not find a bar only, when what you require is a hotel.

---

1. Take your Guide with you into restaurants and hotels – it will let the owners know that you have chosen their establishments by using the Guide and that you expect a high standard of food and service.

2. There are two types of meal available – 'repas complet' and 'casse croute'. 'Repas complet' is a full meal and is served at set meal times. 'Casse croute' is a snack meal, can be served at any time and usually consists of something simple, such as an omelette, sandwich or plate of cold meats.

3. Following a change in the laws in 1987, the service charge must be included in the price of a meal. Tips are rarely expected and are usually given by rounding up the bill.

4. The price quoted for accommodation will be for the room and not per person but a small supplement will be charged if more than 2 people are sharing a room. This is usually minimal and a great help for families travelling on a budget. The price of the room is usually shown on a card on the back of the door, along with the price of breakfast.

5. French hotels are officially classified on a star system. The stars provide a rating of 1–4 (NN) and luxe, and are usually shown on a plaque by the main entrance. These are the 'Hotels de Tourisme' but there are many unclassified hotels in addition where the standards are perfectly acceptable.

6. It is normal practice to see the room offered before deciding to take it. You will therefore be able to check on the degree of cleanliness and comfort. However, if you wish to make an advance booking at a hotel before you arrive, we strongly advise you to make your selection from the approved Relais Routiers 'Tourist Hotels'.

7. If you have booked a hotel room, try to arrive before 6pm unless you have advised the hotel of your time of arrival. If you have been delayed, do try to contact the hotel. If you do not have a reservation, the chances of finding a room are far better if you arrive before 6pm.

8. Many small hotels will lock their doors quite early at night so, if you wish to go out, remember to advise the proprietors of this and they will probably make arrangements for you.

9. Many French people take their holiday between 14th July and 15th August and you may find some hotels and restaurants closed during this period. It is advisable to book accommodation well in advance if you wish to travel at this time.

The British Embassy
Ambassade de Grande-Bretagne
16 rue d'Anjou
Paris 8
France
TEL: 42 66 38 10 (prefix 010 33 1 if dialling from the UK).

A L'HOTEL . . .

Monsieur,

Votre hôtel m'a été recommandé par Les Routiers. Je vous prie de vouloir bien me retenir une chambre à un lit/pour deux personnes avec/sans salle de bain/douche pour la nuit du . . . . /du . . . . jusqu'au . . . .

Soyez assez aimable de nous confirmer cette location et de nous dire si'il vous faut une caution.

Avec nos remerciements anticipés.

Veuillez agréer, Monsieur, nos sentiments les plus distinguées.

Dear Sir

Your hotel has been recommended to me by Les Routiers. I would be grateful if you would reserve me a single/double room with/without bathroom/shower on the . . . . for one night/from . . . . to . . . .

Please could you confirm this and let me know if a deposit is required.

Thanking you in advance.

Yours faithfully

Single room – une chambre à un lit
Double room – une chambre pour deux personnes avec un grand lit
Twin room – une chambre avec deux lits
Bathroom – salle de bain
Shower – douche

Breakfast – le petit déjeuner
Half board – demi-pension
Full board – pension complète

I'd like to book/reserve . . . – Je voudrais retenir/réserver . . .
How much does the room cost? – Combien coûte/vaut la chambre?

AU RESTAURANT . . .

Choosing a restaurant and deciding what to eat can be one of the most enjoyable parts of your stay in France. One of the delights of eating in Relais Routiers lies in the discovery of authentic French cuisine and atmosphere. Providing the season is right, you can experiment with regional dishes and taste the true flavours of France. Here are a few useful points:

1. Note the difference between the 'set menu' and 'à la carte'. The set menu is a complete 3 or 4 course meal and may or may not include drinks. Many restaurants will offer more than one set menu and the lunchtime menus will often cost less than those of the evening. Please note, you are not entitled to a reduction of the cost of the set menu if you do not eat all courses. Every Relais Routiers must state if drinks are included in the menu price. In these cases a 25 cl of wine will be about 6,00 Frs.

2. Soft drinks are much more expensive in France than in the UK. 'Sirops', which are mixed with water like a cordial, are a cheaper alternative to coke and lemonade.

3. Prices in cafes must be clearly shown. Drinks are more expensive if you sit at a table as opposed to standing at the bar.

4. Tap water must be provided free by law. If you are unwilling to drink the tap water ask for 'l'eau mineral' but you will be charged for this.

5. Vin compris – ordinary or house wine is included in the price; Boisson compris – check which drinks are included. This could be a pichet (jug) of wine, a beer, or a bottle of mineral water.

BON APPETIT

EN ROUTE . . .

Traffic rules in France are very similar to Britain with the obvious exception that in France you drive on the right. When leaving a restaurant after a relaxing lunch, setting off from your hotel early in the morning, or after using a one-way street, beware momentarily forgetting – many experienced British drivers in France will have stories to tell about the times they have happily set off on the left hand side of the road.

Here are a few extra points:

1. Speed limits:
    50 km (approx 30 miles) per hour – in built up areas
    90 km (approx 56 miles) per hour – main roads
    110 km (approx 68 miles) per hour – dual carriageways
    130 km (approx 80 miles) per hour – motorways

NB: Some motorways have **a minimum** speed limit.

2. Motorways:
France has over 3,000 miles of motorways and tolls (péages) are charged on most of these. Usually a ticket is issued and a toll paid when you leave the motorway or at intermediate points during the motorway journey. Some motorway stretches have automatic collection where you throw the change into a basket (like the Dartford Tunnel). If you do not have the correct change, use the marked, separate lane. Travellers cheques are NOT accepted but Visa card can be used as an alternative. Toll charges vary according to route.

To escape the motorway tolls and the most congested routes, follow the Green Arrow routes (Itineraires Bis) marked by green arrows. Traffic should be less and the routes are designed to provide the holiday-maker with a more attractive route.

3. Insurance:
Minimum age for driving an imported car or motorbike in France is 18 and you are not permitted to drive on a provisional licence. Insurance is compulsory and a green card advisable as it will give you better cover than the minimum otherwise applicable in France. Europ Assistance do special schemes for motorists and passengers and discounts can be obtained through membership of Les Routiers' Club Bon Viveur (see page 12 for how to join).

4. Lights:
Headlights must not dazzle oncoming drivers and should
be adjusted for right hand drive. Headlamps should have a
removable yellow plastic paint added to the lenses or
deflectors with yellow lenses to ensure that a yellow beam
is emitted.

5. Breakdown:
A warning triangle and hazard warning lights are compulsory
for all vehicles in the event of accident or breakdown. Free
emergency telephones are available every 2km on
motorways and 24 hour services can be found on motorways
at regular intervals of about 40 kilometres.

6. Petrol – **L'ESSENCE**:
NB. **Petrole** translates as crude oil or paraffin.

| Super | – **de super** | ordinary | – **d'ordinaire** |
| lead-free | – **sans plomb** | diesel | – **gazole** |

Unleaded petrol is widely available in France.

During August the motorways south are very busy with
French families heading to the coast for their summer
holiday but most of the time French roads are relatively
empty. Equip yourself with a good map and driving in
France can be an enjoyable part of your holiday.

BON ROUTE/BON CONTINUATION/BON RETOUR

DISCOUNT LES ROUTIERS

Knowing the impossibility of putting a real Relais Routiers on
a motorway, we asked motorway companies to do something
about it. On production of the current edition of the Guide, or
your Club Bon Viveur membership card, you are entitled to a
price concession at many motorway restaurant chains. See
page 62 for a list of Motorway Relais Routiers.

NB. To obtain this price concession, you must show your
Guide or card to the personnel concerned before ordering
your meal. If they show ignorance of this concession, ask
for the manager.

JOIN CLUB BON VIVEUR

Have you heard of Club Bon Viveur? . . . the club which offers superb benefits for Les Routiers Guide users who enjoy good food, wine and travel.

Just look at all the full benefit package you are entitled to!

- Your Club Bon Viveur membership card which entitles you to special concessions at over 300 Les Routiers restaurants and hotels throughout Britain

- £2 off additional copies of either the Les Routiers Guide to Britain or to France (no charge for p&p)

- Discounts off motoring services and insurance with Europ Assistance

- 10% Discount off all holidays in the Paris and France brochures booked through Jet Tours and the French Travel Service

- Newsletters including promotional offers, e.g. special motoring kits for travellers

New ideas to improve club benefits and to make the club more useful are always welcome, so if you have any thoughts of your own, please let us know.

To join Club Bon Viveur, simply complete the application form on the following page and return it to us with the annual subscription fee of £12.00.

APPLICATION FORM

If you use the Guide regularly, then it would certainly be in your interest to join Club Bon Viveur and receive the numerous benefits on offer.

Remember what they are . . .

- Discounts at over 300 Les Routiers restaurants and hotels in Britain
- £2 off additional copies of both Les Routiers Guides
- Discounts off motoring services and insurance with Europ Assistance
- Discounts off holidays in the Paris and France brochures booked through Jet Tours and the French Travel Service
- Newsletters including promotional offers

We are always pleased to hear your comments on any restaurants and hotels you have visited. On the reverse of this page, there is the opportunity to give your opinion.

To join Club Bon Viveur, simply complete the form below and return it to us with the annual subscription fee of £12.00.

Name _____

Address _____

_____

_____

I enclose a cheque for £12.00 (payable to Routiers Ltd) ☐
OR
Please debit my Access/Visa Card for the amount of £12.00. ☐

Card No. .... Expiry Date _____

Signature ....

Return to: Club Bon Viveur, 25-27 Vanston Place, London SW6 1AZ.
Please allow 28 days for delivery.

YOUR OPINION

Do you have a favourite pub, restaurant or hotel which you would like to recommend to us, which is not already Les Routiers recommended? If it is worthy of nomination, please let us know on the form below so that, with their consent, we may arrange for an inspector to call.

Alternatively, if you visit a Les Routiers establishment which you think is worthy of a Les Routiers Award or, if you are dissatisfied with an establishment, we would like to hear your comments.

With your help, we can maintain Les Routiers standards, and all correspondence will be treated in strictest confidence.

Name of Establishment: _____

Address/Location: _____

_____

Type of Establishment (please circle):

Restaurant   Public House   Wine Bar/Bistro   Hotel   B&B

Please circle: Nomination   OR   Complaint

Comments: _____

_____

_____

_____

LIST OF MAPS

15

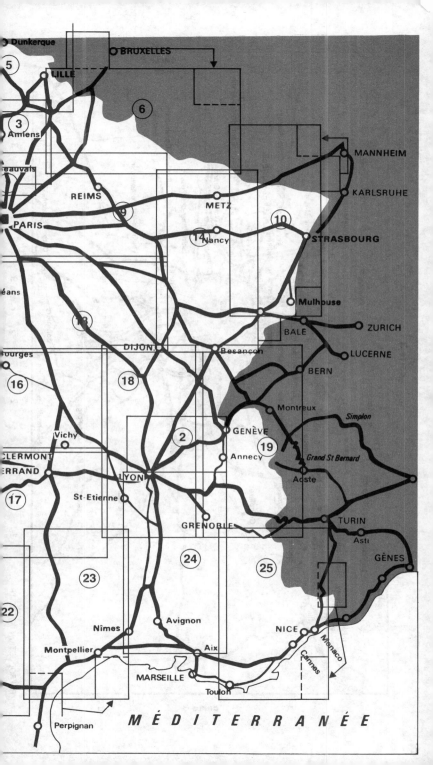

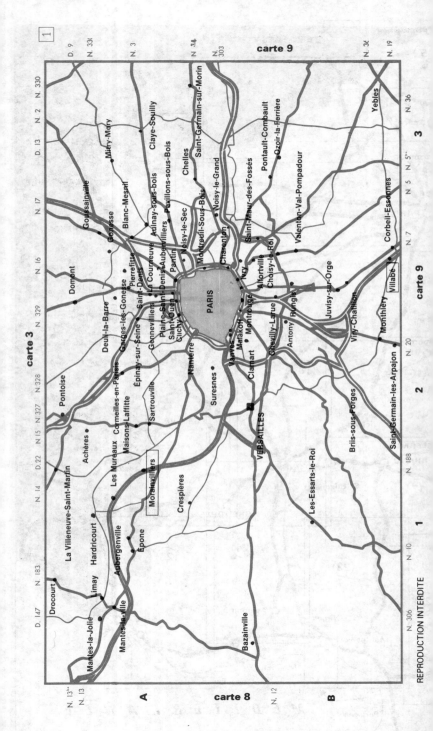

18

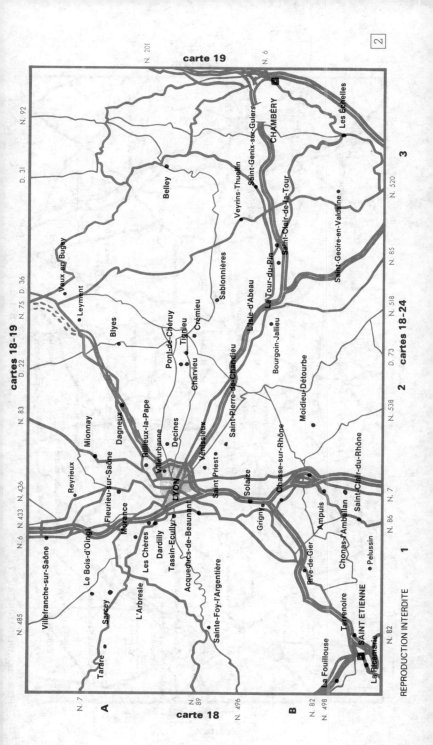

2

N. 201

N. 6

N. 92

D. 31

D. 36

N. 75

D. 22

N. 83

N. 6 N. 433 N. 436

N. 485

N. 520

N. 85

N. 518

D. 73

N. 538

N. 7

N. 86

N. 82

N. 89

N. 496

N. 498

N. 7

A

B

1   2   3

CHAMBÉRY

Les Échelles

Saint-Genix-sur-Guiers

Veyrins-Thuellin

Saint-Clair-de-la-Tour

Saint-Geoire-en-Valdaine

Belley

Sablonnières

L'Isle-d'Abeau

La Tour-du-Pin

Bourgoin-Jallieu

Moidieu-Détourbe

Vaux-en-Bugey

Leyment

Blyes

Pont-de-Chéruy

Tignieu

Crémieu

Charvieu

Saint-Pierre-de-Chandieu

Mionnay

Dagneux

Rillieux-la-Pape

Décines

Villeurbanne

Vénissieux

Reyrieux

Fleurieu-sur-Saône

Morance

Saint Priest

Solaize

Chasse-sur-Rhône

LYON

Villefranche-sur-Saône

Le Bois-d'Oingt

Sarcey

Dardilly

Les Chères

Tassin-Écully

Acqueducs-de-Beaunant

Sainte-Foy-l'Argentière

Grigny

Ampuis

Saint-Clair-du-Rhône

Chonas-l'Amballan

Pelussin

Rive-de-Gier

Tarare

L'Arbresle

Terrenoire

SAINT ETIENNE

La Ricamarie

La Fouillouse

REPRODUCTION INTERDITE

19

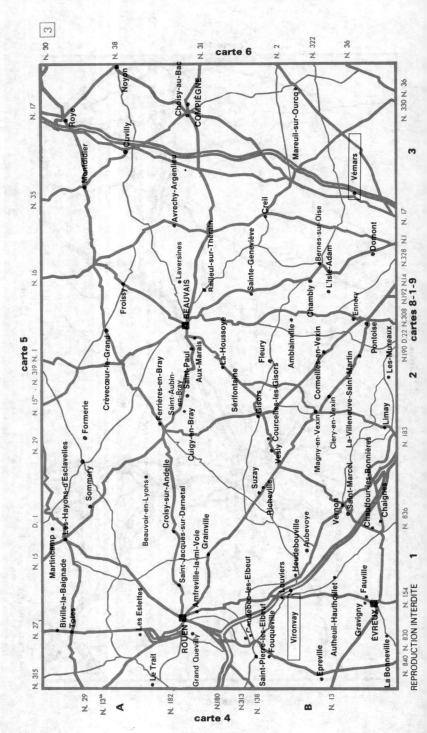

carte 6

carte 5

3

N. 30
N. 17
N. 38
N. 31
carte 6
N. 2
N. 322
N. 36

Noyon
Roye
Montdidier
Cuvilly
Choisy-au-Bac
COMPIÈGNE
Mareuil-sur-Ourcq

Avrechy-Argenlieu
Vémars

Laversines
Creil
Bernes-sur-Oise
Domont
L'Isle-Adam

Froissy
BEAUVAIS
Railleul-sur-Thérain
Sainte-Geneviève
Chambly
Ennery
Pontoise

Formerie
Crèvecoeur-le-Grand
Ferrières-en-Bray
Saint-Paul
La-Houssoye
Fleury
Amblainville
Cormeilles-en-Vexin
Les-Mureaux

Sommery
Saint-Aubin-en-Bray
Aux-Marais
Sérifontaine
Gisors
Courcelles-les-Gisors
Magny-en-Vexin
Cléry-en-Vexin
La-Villeneuve-Saint-Martin
Limay

Beauvoir-en-Lyons
Cuigy-en-Bray
Suzay
Vesly
Saint-Marcel

Martincamp
Les-Hayons-d'Esclavelles
Croisy-sur-Andelle
Grainville
Bicheville
Venon
Chaufour-les-Bonnières
Chaignes

Biville-la-Baignade
Tôtes
Saint-Jacques-sur-Darnetal
Aubevoye
Heudebouville

Les Eslettes
Amfreville-la-mi-Voie
Louviers
Vironvay
Épreville
Autheuil-Hauthoillet
Gravigny
Fauville

Le Trait
ROUEN
Grand Quevilly
Caudebec-les-Elbeuf
Saint-Pierre-les-Elbeuf
Fouqueville
ÉVREUX
La Bonneville

N. 15
D. 1
N. 29
N. 15''
N. 16
N. 35

N. 27
N. 15
N. 840 N. 830
N. 154

carte 4

A
B

N. 29
N. 13bis
N. 182
NJ80
N.313
N. 138
N. 13

N. 315

N190 D.22 N.308 NJ92 N.14   N.328 N.I   N. 17
cartes 8-1-9
N. 330 N. 36

N. 319 N. I   N. 836   N. 183

REPRODUCTION INTERDITE

20

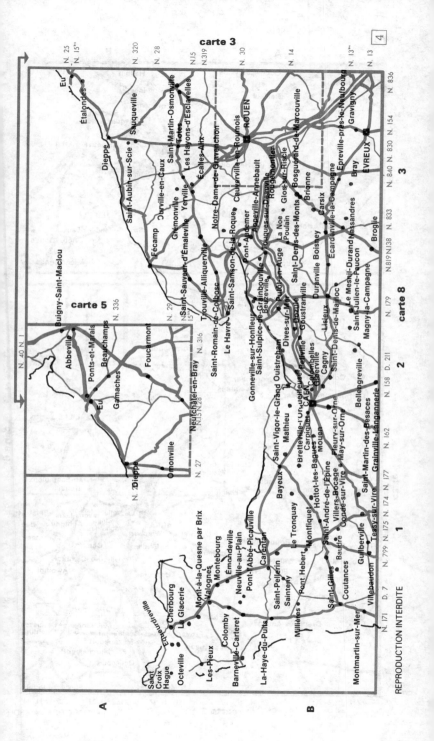

carte 3

carte 5

carte 8

N. 25
N. 15"
N. 320
N. 28
N15
N.319
N. 30
N. 14
N. 13"
N. 13

Eu
Étalondes
Sauqueville
Saint-Martin-Osmonville
Totes
Les Hayons-d'Esclavelles
Écalles-Alix
ROUEN
Gravigny
N. 836

Dieppe
Saint-Aubin-sur-Scie
Durville-en-Caux
Gremonville
Yerville
Notre-Dame-de-Gravenchon
Caudebec-en-Roumois
Epreville-près-le-Neubourg
Bray
EVREUX
N. 840 N. 830 N. 154

Fécamp
Saint-Sauveur-d'Émalleville
Trouville-Alliquerville
Saint-Samson-de-la-Roque
Appeville-Annebault
Roger-Hostier
Glos-sur-Risce
Bosguerard-de-Marcouville
Brionne
Carsix
Ecardenville-la-Campagne
N.819 N.138 N. 833

Buigny-Saint-Maclou

N. 336

N. 29
N15"
Le Havre
Saint-Romain-de-Colbosc
Beuzeville
Pont-Audemer
La Noe
Poulain
Saint-Denis-des-Monts
Duranville Boisney
Le Mesnil-Durand Vaisandres
Brogle

Abbeville
Ponts-et-Marais
Beauchamps
Foucarmont
N. 316
Gonneville-sur-Honfleur
Saint-Sulpice-de-Grainbouville
Ruel-en-Auge
Tourges-sur-Dives
Dozule
Goustranville
Lisieux
Saint-Julien-le-Faucon
Magny-la-Campagne
N. 179

Eu
Gamaches
Neufchâtel-en-Bray
NI15 N28
Saint-Vigor-le-Grand Ouistreham
Benville
Dives-sur-Mer
Colombelles
Abberville
Cagny
Saint-Denis-de-Mailloc
Bellengreville
N. 158
D. 211

Dieppe
Monville
N. 27
Bretteville-l'Orgueilleuse
CAEN
Fleury-sur-Orne
May-sur-Orne
Saint-Martin-des-Besaces
Grainville-Langannerie
N. 162

Saint-Vigor-le-Grand
Carpiquet
Mathieu
Mouen
Saint-André-de-l'Épine
Villers-Bocage
Coude-sur-Vire
Tessy-sur-Vire
N. 175 N. 174 N. 177

Bayeux
Le Tronquay
Montfiquet
Hottot-les-Bagues
Baudre
Gulberville
N. 799 N. 175

Mont-a-la-Quesne par Brix
Montebourg
Émondeville
Carentan
Pont-l'Abbé-Picauville
Pont-Hébert
Saint-Gilles
Coutances
Villebaudon
N. 171

Cherbourg
Glacerie
Valognes
Émondeville
Neuville-au-Plain
Pont-l'Abbé-Picauville
Saint-Pellerin
Saintemy
Montmartin-sur-Mer
D. 7

Saint
Croix
Hague
Octeville
Equeurdreville
Les-Pieux
Colomby
Barneville-Carteret
La-Haye-du-Puits
Millètes
N. 171

REPRODUCTION INTERDITE

N. 40 N.I

A

B

1

2

3

21

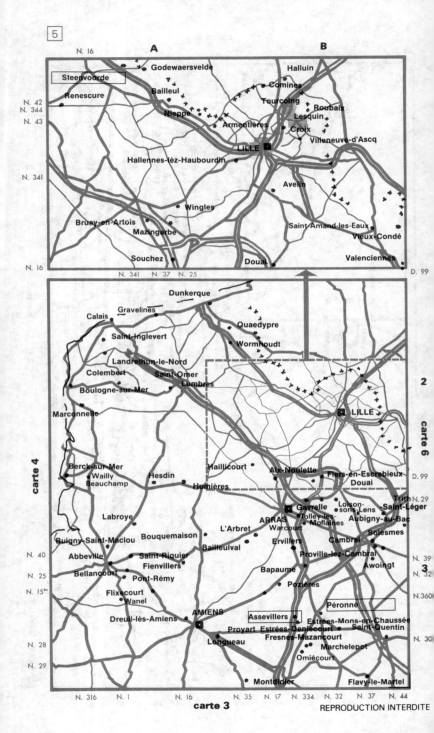

REPRODUCTION INTERDITE

22

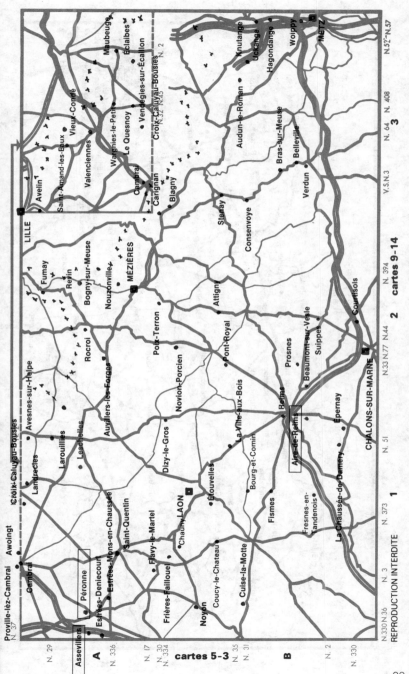

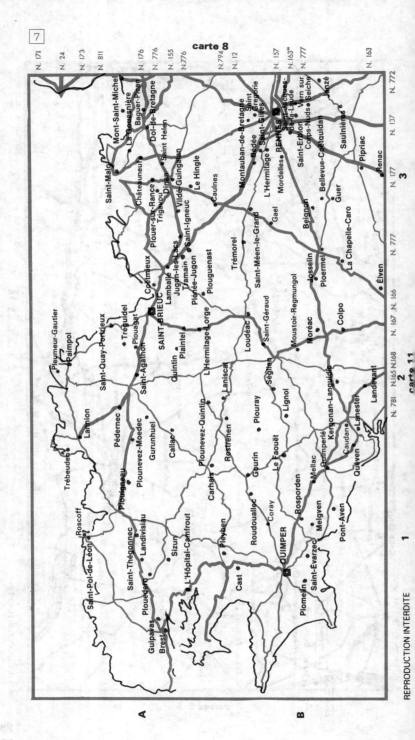

7

carte 8

N. 171
N. 24
N. 173
N. 811

N. 176
N. 776
N. 155
N.276

N.794
N. 12

N. 157
N.163ᵇⁱˢ
N. 777

N. 163

N. 772

A

Pleumeur-Gautier • Paimpol

Trébeudet •

Roscoff •
Saint-Pol-de-Léon •
Plouédern •
Guipavas •
Brest •

Lannion

Saint-Quay-Portrieux
Trégidel •
Plouagat •

Pédernec •

Plounéau
Plounevez-Moedec
Gurunhuel •

Saint-Thégonnec •
Landivisiau •

L'Hôpital-Camfrout •
Sizun •

Pleyben •

Cast •

Callac •

Plounevez-Quintin •

Carhaix •

Roudouallec •
Coray •

Saint-Agathon •
Trégueux •

SAINT-BRIEUC

Quintin •
Plaintel •

Lamballe
Jugon-les-Lacs •

Moncontour •
Trébry •

Coëtmieux •
Plouër-sur-Rance
Trigavou • Dinan •
Vildé-Guingalan •
Saint-Igneuc •

Plénée-Jugon
Plouguenast •

L'Hermitage-Lorge •

Loudéac •

Lanniscat •

Rostrenen •

Gourin •

Le Faouët •

Plouray •

Lignol •

Saint-Géraud •

Moustoir-Remungol •

Trémorel •

Saint-Méen-le-Grand •

Gaël •

Châteauneuf •

Saint-Malo

Mont-Saint-Michel •
La Gouesnière •
Baguer-Pican •

Dol-de-Bretagne •
Saint Helen •

Le Hingle •

Caulnes •

Montauban-de-Bretagne •

Bédée •
Mordelles •

L'Hermitage •
Saint-Jacques-
de-la-Lande

RENNES
Saint-Grégoire •

Saint-Gilles •

Saint-Erblon •
Corps-Nuds • Coëtquidan •

Bellevue-Coëtquidan •
Guer •

La Chapelle-Caro •

Josselin •
Ploërmel •

Elven •

Vern-sur-Seiche

Saulnières •

Piriac •

Renac •

B

Melgven •

Plomelin •

QUIMPER

Saint-Évarzec •

Rosporden •
Pont-Aven •

Quimperlé •
Mellac •

Caudan •

Quéven •

Lanester •

Kergonan-Languidic •

Landevant •

Colpo •

Moréac •

N. 781 N.165 N.168 N. 167 N. 166 N. 777 N. 177 N. 137

2
carte 11
1
3

24

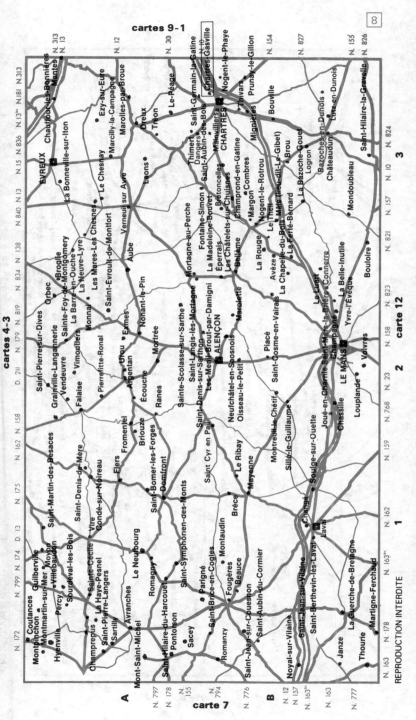

cartes 9-1

N. 313   N. 13   N. 12   N. 30   N. 10   N. 154   N. 827   N. 155   N. 826

Mantes
Chaufour-lès-Bonnières
Ezy-sur-Eure
Marolles-par-Broue
Le Péage
Saint-Germain-la-Gâtine
Chartres-Gasville
Nogent-le-Phaye
Thivars
Prunay-le-Gillon
Bouville

Dreux
Tréon
Thimert
Saint-Aubin-des-Bois
CHARTRES
Mainvilliers
Migniers

Marcilly-la-Campagne
Dangers
Bazoches-en-Dunois
Lutz-en-Dunois
Saint-Hilaire-la-Gravelle

EVREUX
La Bonneville-sur-Iton
Le Chesnay
Bréteuil
Champrond-en-Gâtine
Brétoncelles
Margon
Combres
Nogent-le-Rotrou
Mate-lieu-dit-Le-Gibet)
Brou
La Bazoche-Gouet
Logron
Châteaudun
Mondoubleau

Orbec
Broglie
Les Mares-Les Chesnes
Verneuil-sur-Avre
Laons
Aube
Mortagne-au-Perche
Fontaine-Simon
La Madeleine-Bouvet
Épernals
Bellême
Le Theil
La Chapelle-du-Bois
La Ferté-Bernard

Saint-Pierre-sur-Dives
Sainte-Foy-de-Montgomery
La Barre-en-Ouche
La Neuve-Lyre
Saint-Évroult-de-Montfort
Avèze
La Rouge
Le Luart
Saint-Mars-la-Brière
Connerré
La Belle-Inutile
Boulloire

Graineville-Langannerie
Vendeuvre
Monnai
Exmes
Nonant-le-Pin
Sainte-Scolasse-sur-Sarthe
Maroiette
Champagne
Yvré-l'Evêque

Falaise
Pierrefitte-Ronai
Urou
Argentan
Mortrée
Saint-Langis-lès-Mortagne
Saint-Denis-sur-Sarthon
ALENCON
Placé
Saint-Cosme-en-Vairais
LE MANS
Voivres

Vimoutiers
Écouché
Ranes
Les Menil-Brout-par-Damigni
Neufchâtel-en-Saosnois
Oisseau-le-Petit
Joué-en-Charnie
Chassillé
Louplande

Saint-Martin-des-Besaces
Saint-Denis-de-Méré
Flers
Fromentel
Briouze
Saint-Cyr-en-Pail
Le Ribay
Montreuil-le-Chétif
Sillé-le-Guillaume

Vire
Condé-sur-Noireau
Saint-Bomer-les-Forges
Domfront
Mayenne
Soulgé-sur-Ouette

Champreplus
Sourdeval-les-Bois
Sainte-Cécile
Le Neubourg
Saint-Symphorien-des-Monts
Bréce

Montpinchon
Guilberville
La Haye-Pesnel
Saint-Pierre-Langers
Romagny
Parigné
Montaudin
Changé
Laval

Percy
Villebaudon
Avranches
Saint-Brice-en-Cogles
Beauce
Saint-Jean-sur-Vilaine
Saint-Berthevin-lès-Laval

Coutances
Montmartin-sur-Mer
Moyon
Sartilly
Saint-Hilaire-du-Harcouët
Pontorson
Fougères
Saint-Aubin-du-Cormier
Noyal-sur-Vilaine

Hyenville
Sacey
Romanzy
Janzé
La Guerche-de-Bretagne

Mont-Saint-Michel
Saint-Jean-Couesnon
Thourie
Martigné-Ferchaud

N. 172   N. 799   N. 174   D. 13   N. 175   N. 162   N. 158   D. 211   N. 179   N. 819   N. 834   N. 138   N. 840   N. 13   N. 15   N. 836   N. 13bis   N. 181   N. 313

N. 163bis

A

B

N. 797   N. 178   N. 155   N. 794   N. 776   N. 12   N. 157   N. 163bis   N. 163   N. 777   N. 163   N. 178   N. 162   N. 159   N. 768   N. 23   N. 158   N. 823   N. 821   N. 157   N. 10   N. 824

carte 7

carte 12

1   2   3

REPRODUCTION INTERDITE

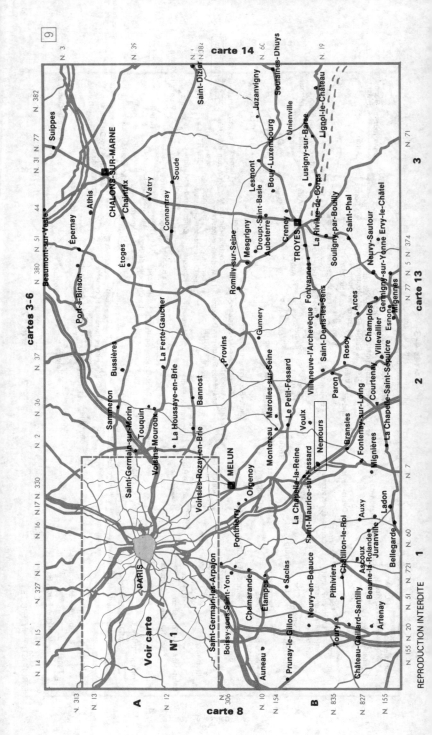

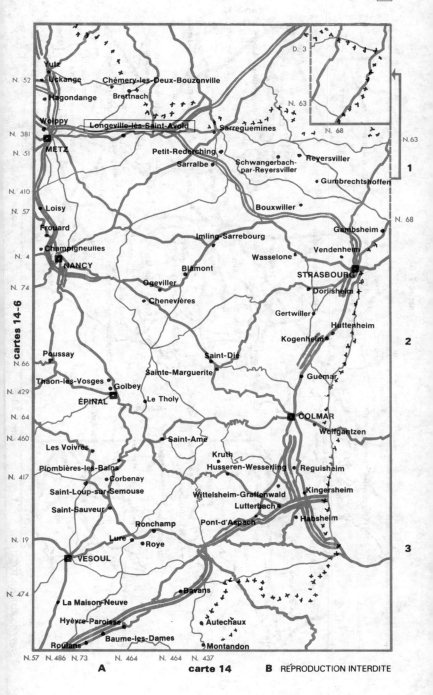

N. 52

Yutz
Uckange
Chémery-les-Deux-Bouzonville
Hagondange
Brettnach
Woippy
Longeville-lès-Saint-Avold
N. 381
Sarreguemines
N. 51
METZ

D. 3

N. 63

N. 63

N. 410
N. 57
Petit-Rederching
Sarralbe
Schwangerbach-par-Reyersviller
Reyersviller
Gumbrechtshoffen

1

N. 68

Loisy
Frouard
Bouxwiller
Champigneulles
N. 4
NANCY
Imling-Sarrebourg
Wasselone
Gambsheim
Vendenheim
N. 74
Blamont
Ogeviller
STRASBOURG
Chenevières
Dorlisheim
Gertwiller
Huttenheim
Kogenheim

cartes 14-6

2

N. 66
Poussay
Saint-Dié
Sainte-Marguerite
Thaon-les-Vosges
Golbey
Guémar
N. 429
ÉPINAL
Le Tholy
N. 64
COLMAR
N. 460
Saint-Amé
Wolfgantzen
Les Voivres
Kruth
Plombières-les-Bains
Husseren-Wesserling
Reguisheim
N. 417
Corbenay
Saint-Loup-sur-Semouse
Wittelsheim-Graffenwald
Kingersheim
Saint-Sauveur
Lutterbach
Ronchamp
Pont-d'Aspach
Habsheim
Lure
Roye
N. 19

3

VESOUL
N. 474
Bavans
La Maison-Neuve
Hyèvre-Paroisse
Autechaux
Baume-les-Dames
Roulans
Montandon

N. 57   N. 486   N. 73   N. 464   N. 464   N. 437

A   **carte 14**   **B** RÉPRODUCTION INTERDITE

27

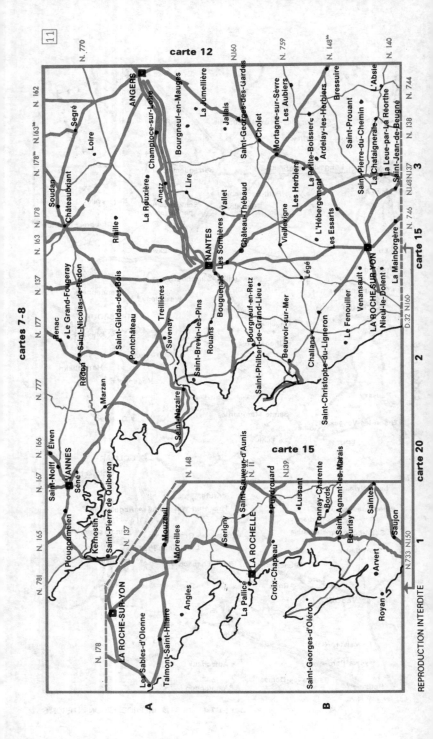

11

cartes 7-8

carte 12

N. 770   N. 162   N. 178ᵇⁱˢ   NJ.163ᵇⁱˢ   N. 178   N. 163   N. 137   N. 177   N. 777   N. 167   N. 166   N. 165   N. 781

Segré

Soudan
Châteaubriant

ANGERS

Champtocé-sur-Loire
La Meilleraie

Bourgneuf-en-Mauges

La Jumellière

Cholet

Saint-Georges-des-Gardes

Loire

NJ160

N. 759

Riaillé

Lire
Anetz

NANTES

Les Sorinières
Vallet

Château-Thébaud

Mortagne-sur-Sèvre
Les Aubiers

Les Herbiers
La Petite-Boissière

Vieillevigne
L'Hébergement

Ardelay-les-Herbiers
Saint-Pierre-du-Chemin

Bressuire

N. 148ᵇⁱˢ

L'Absie

Saint-Prouant

La Châtaigneraie
La Leue-par-La Réorthe
Saint-Jean-de-Beugné

NJ48NJ37   N. 138   N. 744

Renac

Le Grand-Fougeray

Saint-Nicolas-de-Redon

Redon

Marzan

Saint-Gildas-des-Bois

Pontchâteau

Treillières
Savenay

Saint-Nazaire

Saint-Brevin-les-Pins

Rouans
Bouguenais

Bourgneuf-en-Retz
Saint-Philbert-de-Grand-Lieu

Beauvoir-sur-Mer

Challans

Légé

Les Essarts

LA ROCHE-SUR-YON

Le Fenouiller
Venansault
Nieul-le-Dolent

La Mainborgère

N. 746

carte 15

Saint-Christophe-du-Ligneron

D.32 NJ60

3

2

Éven

VANNES

Saint-Nolff

Séné

Plougoumelen

Kerhostin

Saint-Pierre de Quiberon

N. 137

Saint-Sauveur-d'Aunis

carte 15

N. 148
N. 11

NJ39

Puydrouard

Lussant

Tonnay-Charente
Bords

Saint-Agnant-les-Marais

Saintes

Saujon

NJ150

Mouzeuil

Moreilles

Sérigny

LA ROCHELLE

La Pallice

Croix-Chapeau

Saint-Georges-d'Oléron

Beurlay

Arvert

Royan

N. 733 NJ60

1

LA ROCHE-SUR-YON

Les Sables-d'Olonne

Talmont-Saint-Hilaire

Angles

N. 178

carte 20

A

B

REPRODUCTION INTERDITE

28

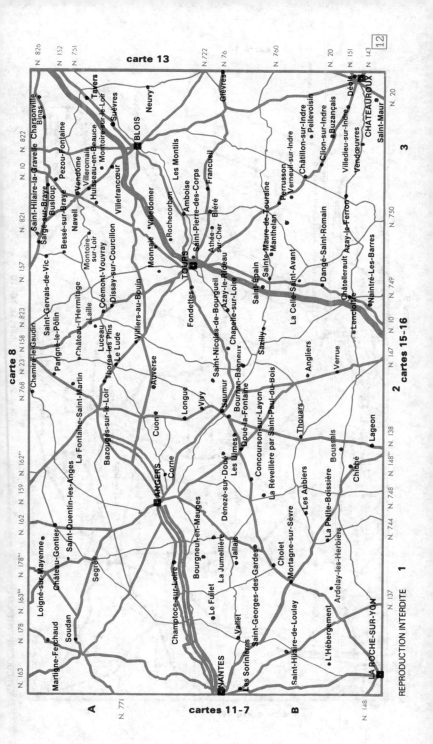

carte 13

carte 8

N 826
N 152
N 751
N 722
N 76
N 760
N 20
N 151
N 143 [12]

N 10 N 822
N 821
N 157
N 823
N 158
N 23
N 768
N 162"
N 159
N 162
N 178"
N 163"
N 178
N 163

Tavers
Neuvy
BLOIS
Charsonville
Binas
Saint-Hilaire-la-Gravelle
Pezou-Fontaine
Busloup
Sargé-sur-Braye
Bessé-sur-Braye
Navell
Montoire-sur-le-Loir
Suèvres
Villeromain
Huisseau-en-Beauce
Montoire-sur-le-Loir
Villefranceur
Les Montils
Rochecorbon
Villedômer
Amboise
Francueil
Saint-Pierre-des-Corps
Monnaie
Chemiré-le-Gaudin
Saint-Gervais-de-Vic
Montoire-sur-Loir
Laillé
Château-l'Hermitage
Parigné-le-Pôlin
Luceau
Thoirê-les-Pins
Le Lude
Athée-sur-Cher
Bléré
Villiers-au-Boin
Coémont-Vouvray
Dissay-sur-Courcillon
TOURS
Fondettes
Vendôme
Gièvres
Châtillon-sur-Indre
Pellevoisin
DÉOLS
Buzançais
Villedieu-sur-Indre
Clion-sur-Indre
Vendœuvres
CHÂTEAUROUX
Saint-Maur
N 20
N 750
Perrusson
Verneuil-sur-Indre
Sainte-Maure-de-Touraine
Manthelan
Dangé-Saint-Romain
Châtellerault
Azay-le-Ferron
Naintré-Les-Barres
Saint-Épain
La Celle-Saint-Avant
Lencloître
N 10
N 749
Saint-Nicolas-de-Bourgueil
Azay-le-Rideau
Chapelle-sur-Loire
Auverse
Saumur
Bourran-Bagneux
Doué-la-Fontaine
Sautilly
Angliers
Verrue
N 147
cartes 15-16

La Fontaine-Saint-Martin
Bazouges-sur-le-Loir
Cuon
Longue
Vivy
Corné
Les Ulmes
Dénezé-sur-Doué
Concourson-sur-Layon
La Réveillère par Saint-Paul-du-Bois
Thouars
Lageon
N 148
Chiché
Boussais
Loigné-sur-Mayenne
Château-Gontier
Saint-Quentin-les-Anges
Saint-Georges-des-Gardes
La Jumellière
Jallais
Bourgneuf-en-Mauges
ANGERS
Mortagne-sur-Sèvre
La Petite-Boissière
Les Aubiers
N 744
N 748
N 138

Martigné-Ferchaud
Soudan
Segré
Le Fuilet
Champtoce-sur-Loire
NANTES
Vallet
Saint-Georges-des-Gardes
Cholet
Saint-Hilaire-de-Loulay
Ardelay-les-Herbiers
L'Hébergement
LA ROCHE-SUR-YON
N 137
N 148

Les Sorinières

N 771
N 163

cartes 11-7

A
B

1
2
3

REPRODUCTION INTERDITE

29

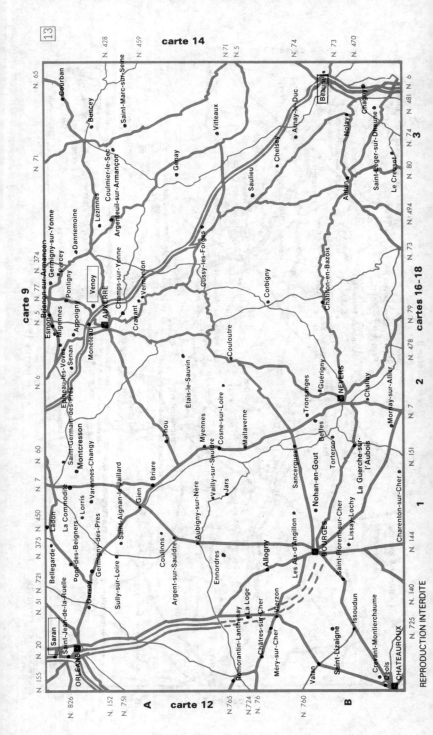

carte 9

carte 14

N. 65

N. 428

N. 459

Courban

Buncey

Saint-Marc-sur-Seine

Coulmier-le-Sec

Germigny-sur-Yonne

N. 71

Genay

Vitteaux

Beaune

N. 71

N. 5

Lezinnes

Argenteuil-sur-Armançon

Chelsy

Alnay-le-Duc

N. 74

Nolay

Saint-Léger-sur-Dheune

Chagny

N. 73

N. 481 N. 6

Dannemoine

Saulieu

Autun

Le Creusot

N. 74 3

N. 80

Espon Brienon-sur-Armançon

Percey

Pontigny

Appoigny

AUXERRE

Champs-sur-Yonne

Vermenton

Crayant

Venoy

Cussy-les-Forges

Corbigny

Châtillon-en-Bazois

N. 494

N. 374

N. 5 N. 77

Migennes

Senan

Monéteau

N. 79

N. 73

cartes 16-18

Egleau-les-Voves

Saint-Germain-des-Prés

Montcresson

Etais-le-Sauvin

Couloutre

Guerigny

NEVERS

N. 478

N. 6

Thou

Myennes

Cosne-sur-Loire

Maltaverne

Tronsanges

Challuy

Mornay-sur-Allier

N. 7 2

La Commodité

Lorris

Varennes-Changy

Briare

Vailly-sur-Sauldre

Jars

Belfes

Torteron

La Guerche-sur-l'Aubois

N. 151

N. 60

N. 7

Ladon

Germigny-des-Prés

Saint-Aignan-le-Jaillard

Gien

Aubigny-sur-Nère

Sancergues

Nohan-en-Gout

Lissay-Lochy

Charenton-sur-Cher

N. 375 N. 450

Bellegarde

Pont-des-Beigners

Coullons

Argent-sur-Sauldre

Les Aix-d'Angillon

BOURGES

Saint-Florent-sur-Cher

N. 144

N. 51 N. 721

Dorvoy

Sully-sur-Loire

Ennordes

Allogny

N. 140

Saran

Saint-Jean-de-la-Ruelle

ORLÉANS

Romorantin-Lanthenay

La Loge

Mehun

Châtres-sur-Cher

Méry-sur-Cher

Vatan

Saint-Lizaigne

Issoudun

Crevant-Montierchaume

Déols

CHATEAUROUX

N. 155

N. 20

N. 826

N. 152

N. 751

carte 12

N. 765

N. 724

N. 76

N. 760

N. 725

A

B

1

REPRODUCTION INTERDITE

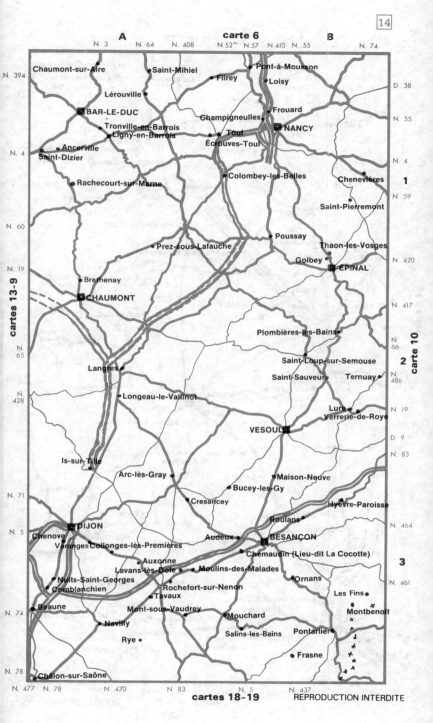

carte 6

A B

N. 3 N. 64 N. 408 N. 52ᵇⁱˢ N. 57 N. 410 N. 55 N. 74

Chaumont-sur-Aire
Saint-Mihiel
Flirey
Pont-à-Mousson
Loisy
D. 38
N. 394
Lérouville
Frouard
N. 55
BAR-LE-DUC
Champigneulles
NANCY
Tronville-en-Barrois
Toul
Ligny-en-Barrois
Écrouves-Toul
N. 4
Ancerville
Saint-Dizier
N. 4
Rachecourt-sur-Marne
Colombey-les-Belles
Chenevières
1
N. 59
Saint-Pierremont
N. 60
Poussay
Prez-sous-Lafauche
Thaon-les-Vosges
N. 19
Golbey
EPINAL
N. 420
Brethenay
CHAUMONT
N. 417
cartes 13-9
Plombières-les-Bains
N. 65
N. 66
Saint-Loup-sur-Semouse
2
carte 10
Langres
Saint-Sauveur
Ternuay
N. 486
N. 428
Longeau-le-Vallinot
Lure
N. 19
Verrerie-de-Roye
VESOUL
D. 9
Is-sur-Tille
N. 83
Arc-lès-Gray
Maison-Neuve
N. 71
Bucey-les-Gy
Cresancey
Hyèvre-Paroisse
DIJON
Roulans
N. 464
Chenôve
Varanges Collonges-lès-Premières
Audeux
BESANÇON
N. 5
Auxonne
Chemaudin (Lieu-dit La Cocotte)
3
Lavans-lès-Dole
Moulins-des-Malades
Nuits-Saint-Georges
Ornans
N. 461
Comblanchien
Rochefort-sur-Nenon
Les Fins
Tavaux
Montbenoit
Beaune
Mont-sous-Vaudrey
N. 74
Mouchard
Navilly
Pontarlier
Rye
Salins-les-Bains
N. 78
Frasne
Châlon-sur-Saône

N. 477 N. 78 N. 470 N. 83 N. 5 N. 437

cartes 18-19 REPRODUCTION INTERDITE

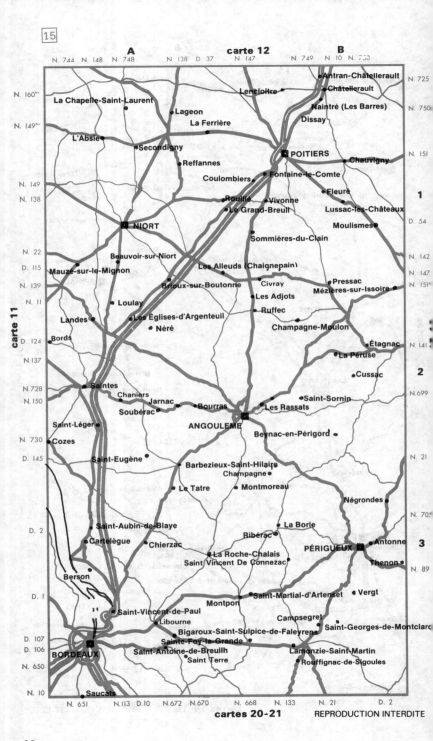

carte 12

N. 744 N. 148 N. 748   N. 138 D. 37   N. 147   N. 749   N. 10 N. 753

N. 160bis

N. 149bis

N. 149
N. 138

N. 22
D. 115
N. 139
N. 11

D. 124

N.137

N.728
N. 150

N. 730
D. 145

D. 2

D. 1

D. 107
D. 106
N. 650

N. 10

N. 725
N. 750
N. 151
1
D. 54
N. 142
N 147
N. 151bis
N 141
2
N 699
N. 21
N. 70
3
N. 89

carte 11

Antran-Châtellerault
Châtellerault
Naintré (Les Barres)
Dissay
Lencloître
POITIERS
Chauvigny
Fontaine-le-Comte
Coulombiers
Fleuré
Rouillé   Vivonne
Lussac-les-Châteaux
Le Grand-Breuil
Moulismes
NIORT
Sommières-du-Clain
Beauvoir-sur-Niort
Les Alleuds (Chaignepain)
Mauzé-sur-le-Mignon
Civray   Pressac
Brioux-sur-Boutonne   Mézières-sur-Issoire
Les Adjots
Loulay   Ruffec
Landes   Les Églises-d'Argenteuil   Champagne-Moulon
Néré
Bords   Étagnac
La Péruse
Cussac
Saintes
Chaniers   Saint-Sornin
Jarnac   Bourras   Les Rassats
Soubérac
ANGOULEME
Saint-Léger   Beynac-en-Périgord
Cozes
Saint-Eugène
Barbezieux-Saint-Hilaire
Champagne
Le Tatre   Montmoreau
Négrondes
Saint-Aubin-de-Blaye   La Borie
Cartelègue   Ribérac   Antonne
Chierzac
La Roche-Chalais   PÉRIGUEUX
Saint Vincent De Connezac   Thenon
Berson
Saint-Martial-d'Artenset   Vergt
Montpon
Saint-Vincent-de-Paul   Campsegret
Libourne   Saint-Georges-de-Montclard
Bigaroux-Saint-Sulpice-de-Faleyrens
Sainte-Foy-la-Grande
Saint-Antoine-de-Breuilh   Lamonzie-Saint-Martin
BORDEAUX   Saint Terre   Rouffignac-de-Sigoules
Saucats

La Chapelle-Saint-Laurent
Lageon
La Ferrière
L'Absie
Secondigny
Reffannes

N. 651   N.113 D.10   N.672 N.670   N. 668   N. 133   N. 21   D. 2

cartes 20-21   REPRODUCTION INTERDITE

32

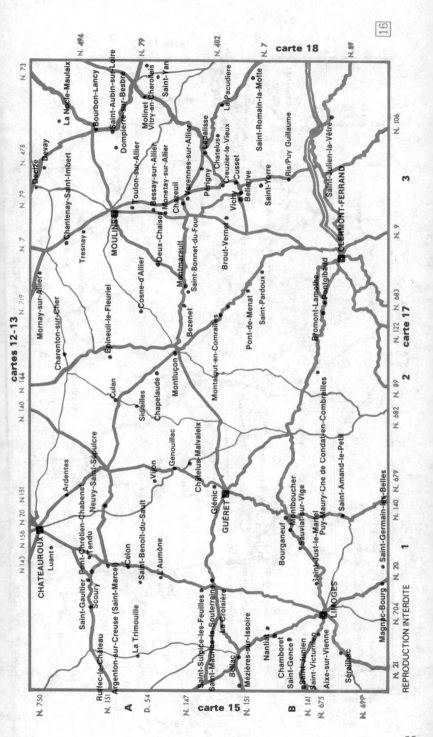

16

33

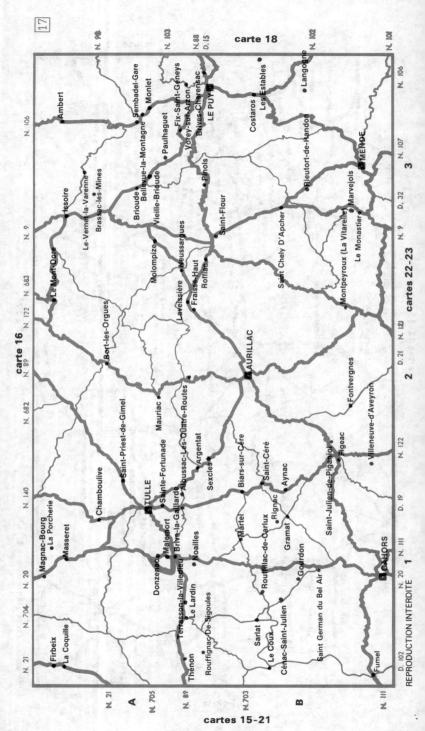

carte 16

carte 18

cartes 22-23

cartes 15-21

REPRODUCTION INTERDITE

N. 96
N. 103
N. 88
D. 15
N. 102
N. 101
N. 106
N. 107
N. 9
D. 32
N. 121
D. 21
N. 122
D. 19
N. III
N. 20
D. 102
N. III
N. 703
N. 89
N. 705
N. 21
N. 704
N. 20
N. 140
N. 682
N. 122
N. 683
N. 89
N. 9
N. 106

3
2
1
A
B

Ambert
Sembadel-Gare
Monlet
Fix-Saint-Geneys
Vorey-sur-Arzon
Brives-Charensac
LE PUY
Costaros
Les Estables
Langogne
Paulhaguet
Issoire
Le Vernet-la-Varenne
Brassac-les-Mines
Brioude
Bellevue-la-Montagne
Vieille-Brioude
MENDE
Rieutort-de-Randon
Marvejols
Le Mont-Dore
Molompize
Neussargues
Pinols
Saint-Flour
Saint Chely D'Apcher
Montpeyroux (La Vitarelle)
Le Monastier
Lavelsière
Fraisse-Haut
Roffiac
Bort-les-Orgues
AURILLAC
Fontvergnes
Saint-Priest-de-Gimel
Mauriac
Villeneuve-d'Aveyron
Magnac-Bourg
La Porcherie
Masseret
Chamboulive
TULLE
Sainte-Fortunade
Albussac-Les-Quatre-Routes
Argentat
Sexcles
Biars-sur-Cère
Saint-Céré
Aynac
Figeac
Saint-Julien-de-Piganiol
Chamboulive
Donzenac
Malemort
Brive-la-Gaillarde
Noailles
Martel
Rignac
Gramat
Terrasson-la-Villedieu
Le Lardin
Rouffilac-de-Carlux
Gourdon
CAHORS
Thenon
Rouffignac-De-Sigoules
Sarlat
Le Coux
Cénac-Saint-Julien
Saint German du Bel Air
Fumel
Firbeix
La Coquille

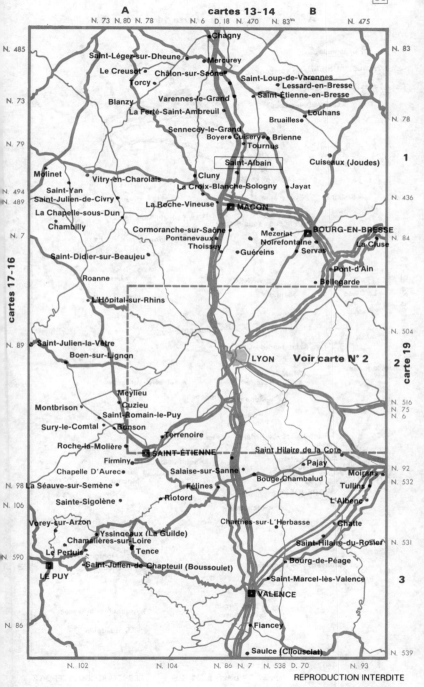

cartes 13-14

A **B**

N. 73 N. 80 N. 78 N. 6 D. 18 N. 470 N. 83 bis N. 475

N. 485

Chagny

Saint-Léger-sur-Dheune

Mercurey

Le Creusot

Châlon-sur-Saône

Torcy

Saint-Loup-de-Varennes

Lessard-en-Bresse

Saint-Étienne-en-Bresse

N. 73

Blanzy

Varennes-le-Grand

La Ferté-Saint-Ambreuil

Louhans

Bruailles

N. 78

N. 79

Sennecey-le-Grand

Boyer Cuisery Brienne

Tournus

Saint-Albain

Cuiseaux (Joudes)

1

Molinet

Vitry-en-Charolais

Cluny

N. 494

Saint-Yan

La Croix-Blanche-Sologny

Jayat

N. 489

Saint-Julien-de-Civry

La Roche-Vineuse

La Chapelle-sous-Dun

MACON

N. 436

N. 7

Chambilly

Cormoranche-sur-Saône

Mezeriat

BOURG-EN-BRESSE

Pontanevaux

Noirefontaine

Thoissey

Servas

N. 84

La Cluse

Saint-Didier-sur-Beaujeu

Guéreins

Roanne

Pont-d'Ain

Bellegarde

cartes 17-16

L'Hôpital-sur-Rhins

N. 504

N. 89

Saint-Julien-la-Vêtre

Boen-sur-Lignon

LYON

Voir carte N° 2

carte 19

2

N. 516

Meylieu

N. 75

Cuzieu

N. 6

Montbrison

Saint-Romain-le-Puy

Sury-le-Comtal

Bonson

Roche-la-Molière

Terrenoire

SAINT-ÉTIENNE

Saint Hilaire de la Côte

Firminy

Pajay

N. 92

Chapelle D'Aurec

Salaise-sur-Sanne

Bouge-Chambalud

Moirans

N. 98

La Séauve-sur-Semène

Félines

Tullins

N. 532

Sainte-Sigolène

Riotord

L'Albenc

N. 106

Charmes-sur-L'Herbasse

Chatte

Vorey-sur-Arzon

Yssingeaux (La Guilde)

Chamalières-sur-Loire

Tence

Saint-Hilaire-du-Rosier

N. 531

N. 590

Le Pertuis

Saint-Julien-de-Chapteuil (Boussoulet)

Bourg-de-Péage

LE PUY

Saint-Marcel-lès-Valence

3

VALENCE

N. 86

Fiancey

N. 539

Saulce (Cliousclat)

N. 102 N. 104 N. 86 N. 7 N. 538 D. 70 N. 93

REPRODUCTION INTERDITE

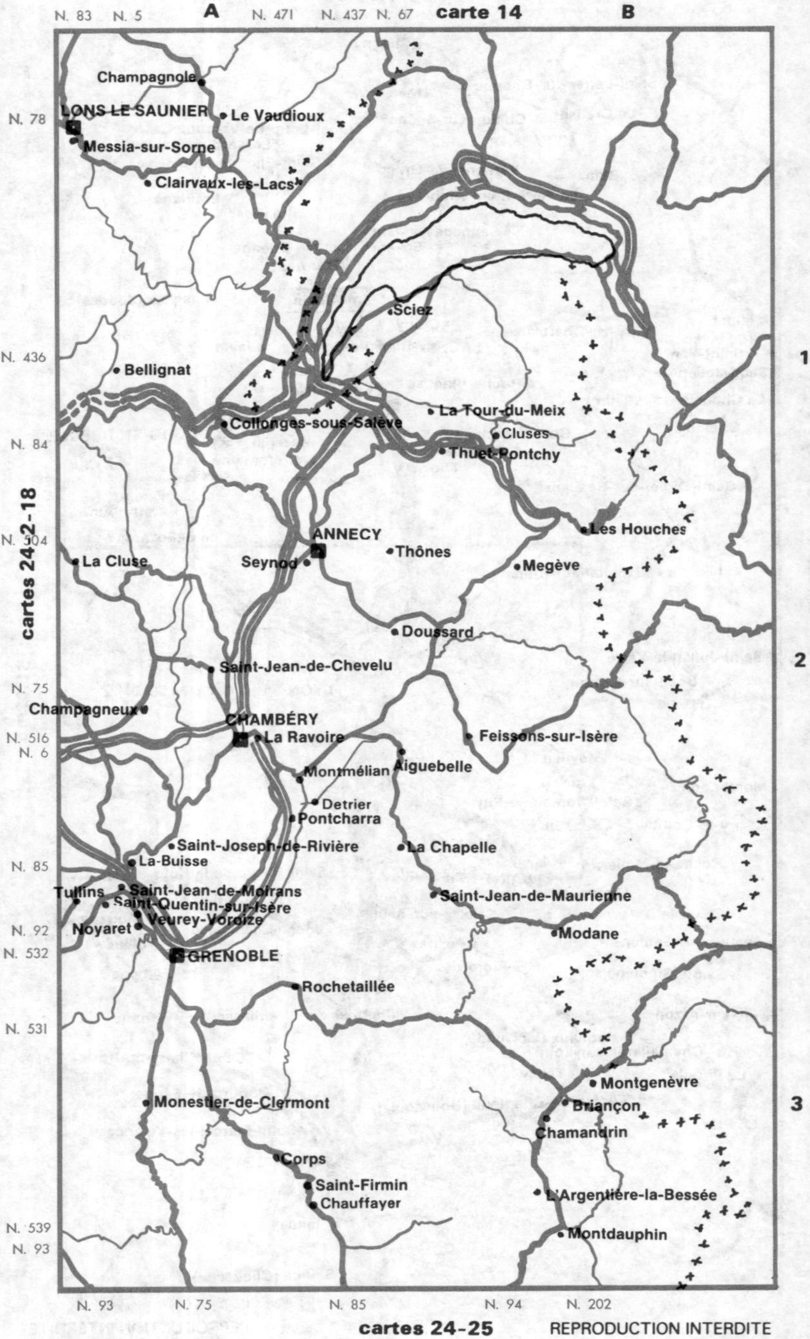
N. 83
N. 5
A
N. 471
N. 437
N. 67
carte 14
B
Champagnole
LONS LE SAUNIER
Le Vaudioux
N. 78
Messia-sur-Sorne
Clairvaux-les-Lacs
Sciez
N. 436
Bellignat
1
La Tour-du-Meix
Collonges-sous-Salève
Cluses
N. 84
Thuet-Pontchy
cartes 24-2-18
Les Houches
ANNECY
N. 504
Thônes
Seynod
La Cluse
Megève
Doussard
Saint-Jean-de-Chevelu
2
N. 75
Champagneux
CHAMBÉRY
Feissons-sur-Isère
N. 516
La Ravoire
N. 6
Aiguebelle
Montmélian
Detrier
Pontcharra
Saint-Joseph-de-Rivière
La Chapelle
N. 85
La-Buisse
Saint-Jean-de-Moirans
Tullins
Saint-Jean-de-Maurienne
Saint-Quentin-sur-Isère
Veurey-Voroize
N. 92
Noyaret
Modane
N. 532
GRENOBLE
Rochetaillée
N. 531
Montgenèvre
Monestier-de-Clermont
Briançon
3
Chamandrin
Corps
Saint-Firmin
Chauffayer
L'Argentière-la-Bessée
N. 539
Montdauphin
N. 93
N. 93
N. 75
N. 85
N. 94
N. 202
cartes 24-25

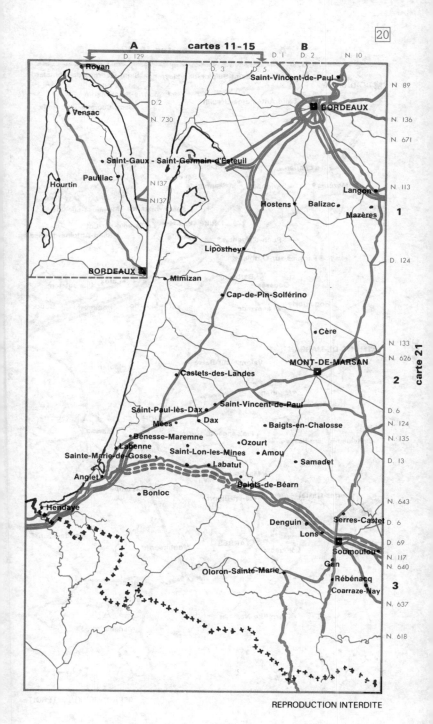

carte 21

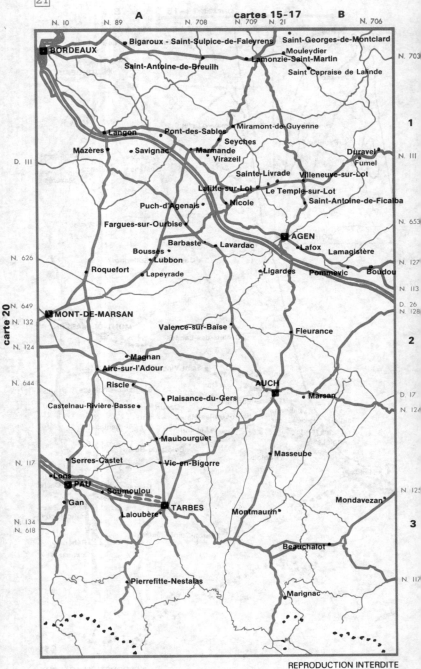

A   B

N. 10   N. 89   N. 708   N. 709   N. 21   N. 706

Bigaroux - Saint-Sulpice-de-Faleyrens

BORDEAUX   Saint-Georges-de-Montclard

Mouleydier

Lamonzie-Saint-Martin   N. 703

Saint-Antoine-de-Breuilh

Saint Capraise de Lalinde

Miramont-de-Guyenne   1

Langon   Pont-des-Sables

Seyches

Mazères   Savignac   Marmande   Duravel   N. III

Virazeil   Fumel

D. III

Sainte-Livrade   Villeneuve-sur-Lot

Lafitte-sur-Lot   Le Temple-sur-Lot

Puch-d'Agenais   Nicole   Saint-Antoine-de-Ficalba

Fargues-sur-Ourbise   N. 653

Barbaste   Lavardac   AGEN

Bousses   Lafox

N. 626   Lubbon   Lamagistère

Roquefort   Lapeyrade   Ligardes   Pommevic   Boudou   N. 127

N. 113

N. 649   D. 26

N. 132   MONT-DE-MARSAN   N. 128

Valence-sur-Baïse   Fleurance   2

N. 124

Magnan

N. 644   Aire-sur-l'Adour

Riscle   AUCH

Castelnau-Rivière-Basse   Plaisance-du-Gers   Marsan   D. 17

N. 124

Maubourguet

Masseube

N. 117   Serres-Castet   Vic-en-Bigorre

Lons   PAU   Soumoulou   Mondavezan   N. 125

Gan   TARBES

N. 134   Laloubère   Montmaurin   3

N. 618

Beauchalot

Pierrefitte-Nestalas   N. 117

Marignac

carte 20

REPRODUCTION INTERDITE

38

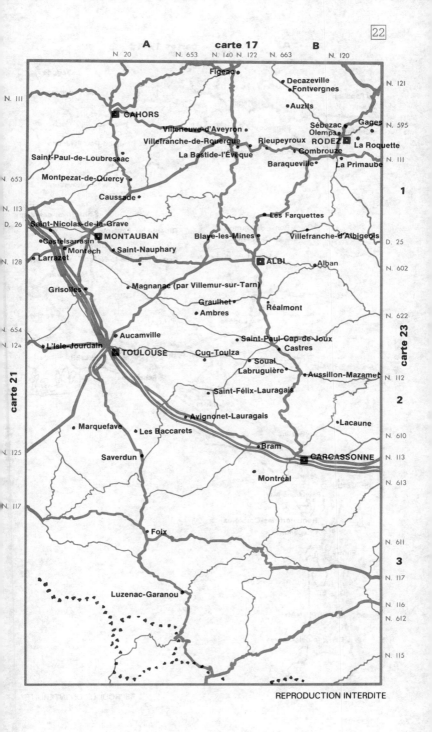

N. 20   N. 653   N. 140   N. 122   N. 663   N. 120

N. 111

N. 653

N. 113

N. 128

N. 654

N. 124

carte 21

N. 125

N. 117

Figeac

Decazeville
Fontvergnes
Auzits

CAHORS

Villeneuve-d'Aveyron
Villefranche-de-Rouergue
La Bastide-l'Évêque

Sébazac
Olemps
RODEZ
Combrouze

Gages   N. 595
La Roquette

N. 121

N. 111

Rieupeyroux

Saint-Paul-de-Loubressac

Montpezat-de-Quercy

Caussade

Baraqueville
La Primaube

Les Farquettes

Saint-Nicolas-de-la-Grave

Castelsarrasin
Montech
Larrazet

MONTAUBAN
Saint-Nauphary

Blaye-les-Mines

ALBI

Villefranche-d'Albigeois   D. 25

Alban   N. 602

Grisolles

Magnanac (par Villemur-sur-Tarn)

Graulhet
Ambres

Réalmont

N. 622

Aucamville

L'Isle-Jourdain

TOULOUSE

Saint-Paul-Cap-de-Joux

Cuq-Toulza   Castres

Soual
Labruguière

Aussillon-Mazamet   N. 112

carte 23

Saint-Félix-Lauragais

Marquefave

Avignonet-Lauragais

Les Baccarets

Saverdun

Bram

Lacaune   N. 610

CARCASSONNE   N. 113

Montréal   N. 613

Foix   N. 611

N. 117

Luzenac-Garanou

N. 116
N. 612

N. 115

1

2

3

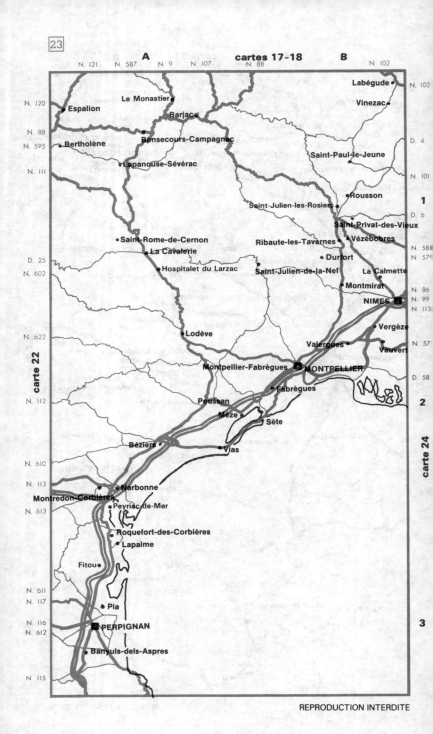

cartes 17-18

A   N. 9   N. 107   N. 88   **B**

N. 121   N. 587

N. 102

Labégude

Vinezac

N. 102

N. 120   Espalion

Le Monastier

Barjac

D. 4

N. 88
N. 595   Bertholène

Bonsecours-Campagnac

Saint-Paul-le-Jeune

N. 111

Lapanouse-Sévérac

N. 101

Rousson

1

Saint-Julien-les-Rosiers

D. 6

Saint-Privat-des-Vieux

Saint-Rome-de-Cernon

Ribaute-les-Tavernes

Vézébobres

N. 58

La Cavalerie

Durfort

N. 57

D. 25

Hospitalet du Larzac

Saint-Julien-de-la-Nef

La Calmette

N. 602

Montmirat

N. 86

NIMES

N. 99
N. 113

Vergèze

N. 622   Lodève

Valergues

Vauvert

N. 57

Montpellier-Fabrègues

MONTPELLIER

D. 58

Fabrègues

2

Poussan

N. 112

Mèze

Sète

Béziers

Vias

N. 610

N. 113

Narbonne

Montredon-Corbières

N. 613   Peyriac-de-Mer

Roquefort-des-Corbières

Lapalme

Fitou

N. 611
N. 117

Pia

3

N. 116
N. 612   **PERPIGNAN**

Banyuls-dels-Aspres

N. 115

carte 22   *carte 24*

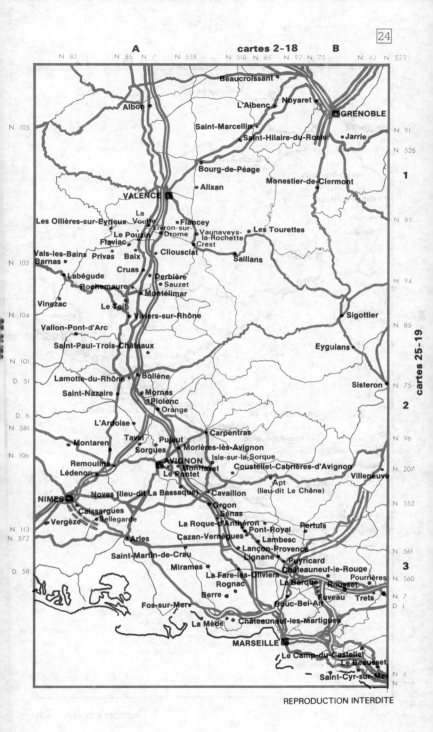

A   N 82   N 86   N 7   N 538   N 518   N 85   N 92   N 75   N 90   N 523   **B**

Beaucroissant

L'Albenc   Noyaret

GRENOBLE

Albon

Saint-Marcellin

Saint-Hilaire-du-Rosier   Jarrie   N 91

N 526

Bourg-de-Péage

Monestier-de-Clermont   **1**

Alixan

N 105

VALENCE

La Voulte

Les Ollières-sur-Eyrieux   Fiancey

Livron-sur-Drôme   Les Tourettes   N 85

Le Pouzin   Vaunaveys-la-Rochette

Flaviac   Crest

Vals-les-Bains   Privas   Baix   Cliousclat   Saillans

Barnas

N 102   Cruas

Labégude   Derbière

Rochemaure   Sauzet   N 94

Montélimar

Vinezac

Le Teil

N 104   Viviers-sur-Rhône

Vallon-Pont-d'Arc   Sigottier

N 85

Saint-Paul-Trois-Châteaux

Eyguians

N 101

D 51   Lamotte-du-Rhône   Bollène

Sisteron   N 75

Saint-Nazaire   Mornas

D 6   Piolenc   **2**

N 581   Orange

L'Ardoise

Carpentras

Montaren   Tavel   Pujaut   N 96

N 106   Sorgues   Morières-lès-Avignon

Isle-sur-la-Sorque

Remoulins   AVIGNON   Coustellet-Cabrières-d'Avignon   N 207

Lédenon   Montfavet   Villeneuve

Le Pontet

Apt

NIMES   Noves (lieu-dit La Bassaque)   Cavaillon   (lieu-dit Le Chêne)   N 552

Caissargues   Orgon

N 113   Bellegarde   Sénas

N 572   Vergèze   La Roque-d'Anthéron   Pertuis

Arles   Cazan-Vernègues   Pont-Royal

Lambesc

D 58   Saint-Martin-de-Crau   Lançon-Provence   N 561

Miramas   Lignane   Puyricard   **3**

Châteauneuf-le-Rouge

La Fare-les-Oliviers   La Barque   Pourrières   N 560

Rognac   Rousset

Berre   Fuveau   Trets   N 7

Bouc-Bel-Air   D 1

Fos-sur-Mer

La Mède   Châteauneuf-les-Martigues

MARSEILLE

Le Camp-du-Castellet

Le Beausset

Saint-Cyr-sur-Mer   N 8

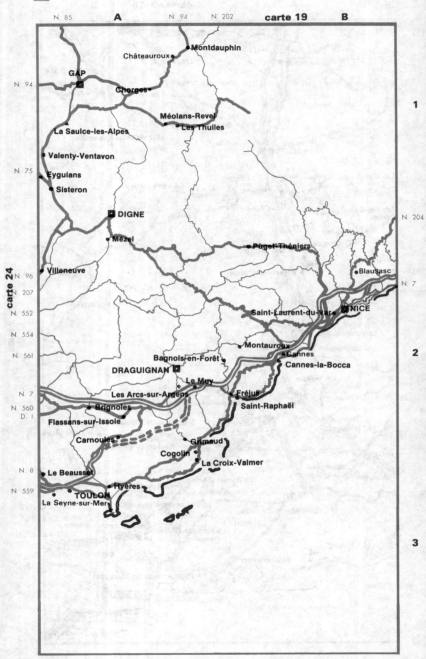

FRENCH DEPARTMENTS

Key to Departments of France

01	Ain
02	Aisne
03	Allier
04	Alpes-de-Haute-Provence
05	Hautes Alpes
06	Alpes Maritimes
07	Ardèche
08	Ardennes
09	Ariège
10	Aube
11	Aude
12	Aveyron
13	Bouches-du-Rhône
14	Calvados
15	Cantal
16	Charente
17	Charente-Maritime
18	Cher
19	Corrèze
2A	Corse-du-Sud
2B	Haute-Corse
21	Côte-d'Or
22	Côtes-du-Nord
23	Creuse
24	Dordogne
25	Doubs
26	Drôme
27	Eure
28	Eure-et-Loir
29	Finistère
30	Gard
31	Haute-Garonne
32	Gers

33	Gironde
34	Hérault
35	Ille-et-Vilaine
36	Indre
37	Indre-et-Loire
38	Isère
39	Jura
40	Landes
41	Loir-et-Cher
42	Loire
43	Haute-Loire
44	Loire-Atlantique
45	Loiret
46	Lot
47	Lot-et-Garonne
48	Lozère
49	Maine-et-Loire
50	Manche
51	Marne
52	Haute-Marne
53	Mayenne
54	Meurthe-et-Moselle
55	Meuse
56	Morbihan
57	Moselle
58	Nièvre
59	Nord
60	Oise
61	Orne
62	Pas-de-Calais
63	Puy-de-Dôme
64	Pyrénées-Atlantiques
65	Hautes-Pyrénées

66	Pyrénées-Orientales
67	Bas-Rhin
68	Haut-Rhin
69	Rhône
70	Haute-Saône
71	Saône-et-Loire
72	Sarthe
73	Savoie
74	Haute-Savoie
75	Paris
76	Seine-Maritime
77	Seine-et-Marne
78	Yvelines
79	Deux-Sèvres
80	Somme
81	Tarn
82	Tarn-et-Garonne
83	Var
84	Vaucluse
85	Vendée
86	Vienne
87	Haute-Vienne
88	Vosges
89	Yonne
90	Territoire-de-Belfort
91	Essonne
92	Hauts-de-Seine
93	Seine-St-Denis
94	Val-de-Marne
95	Val-d'Oise

CASSEROLE RELAIS ROUTIERS

01 – AIN
Cormoranche sur Saone
Auberge Chez la Mère
Martinet
Le Bourg
☎ 85-36-20-40
(JUIL 23864)

03 – ALLIER
Varennes sur Allier
Le Relais des Touristes
1, rue des Halles
☎ 70-45-00-51
(MAI 14802)

05 – HAUTES ALPES
Eyguians
Hotel de la Gare
☎ 92-66-20-08
(NOV 15439)

Guillestre
Hotel de la Gare
Montdauphin Gare
☎ 92-45-03-08
(JUN 10820)

07 – ARDECHE
Viviers sur Rhône
Le Relais du Vivarais
Route Nationale 86
Lieu-dit 'Les Sautelles'
☎ 75-52-60-41
(FEV 7485)

12 – AVEYRON
Bertholene
Hôtel Bancarel
Route Nationale 88
Laissac
Situé au pied de la
Forêt de Palanges
☎ 65-69-62-10
(AVR 21480)

Decazeville
Restaurant des Usines
23 Faubourg Desseligny
Fontvergnes
☎ 65-43-15-88
(OCT 25132)

Rodez
La Rocade
La Roquette
Route Nationale 88
☎ 65-67-10-44
(AOUT 18491)

14 – CALVADOS
Bayeux
La Colombe
13 Route de Caen
☎ 31-92-13-65
(MARS 22274)

Le Beny Bocage
La Renaissance
Saint Martin des Besaces
☎ 31-68-72-65
(FEV 20652)

Vendeuvre
Le Relais de Vendeuvre
Place de la Gare
Saint-Pierre-sur-Dives
☎ 31-40-92-77
(JUN 23836)

Vire
Hotel de France
4, rue d'Aignaux
☎ 31-68-00-35
(OCT 24705)

16 – CHARENTE
**Chateauneuf sur
Charente**
Relais de la Billette
Ladiville
☎ 45-78-57-09
(AOUT 22018)

19 – CORRÈZE
Albussac
Hostellerie Roche de
Vic
Les Quatre Routes
☎ 55-28-15-87
(MAI 11509)

22 – COTES-DU-NORD
Dinan
La Marmite
91, rue de Brest
☎ 96-39-04-42
(AOUT 23904)

Lamballe
La Tour d'Argent
2, rue du Docteur
Lavergne
☎ 96-31-03-37
(JANV 3713)

Plouer sur Rance
Le Bon Accueil Chez
Théo
La Gourbanière
☎ 96-86-91-67
(MARS 26483)

24 – DORDOGNE
Beynac et Cazenac
Hostellerie Maleville Sarl
☎ 53-29-50-06
(FEV 25804)

Cenac Saint Julien
La Promenade
Route Nationale 703
☎ 53-28-36-87
(OCT 25153)

Roche Chalais (La)
Cafe du Midi
32, avenue du Stade
☎ 53-91-43-65
(AVR 21884)

25 – DOUBS
Baume les Dames
Relais la Cremaillere
Hyèvre-Paroisse
☎ 81-84-07-88
(JUIL 13903)

Ornans
Hotel le Progres
11, rue Jacques Gervais
☎ 81-62-16-79
(AOUT 20800)

27 – EURE
Richeville
Restauroute le Balto
4, Route Nationale 14
☎ 32-27-10-55
(FEV 27173)

28 – EURE-ET-LOIRE
Mignieres
Le Relais Beauceron
Route Nationale 10
Mignières
☎ 37-26-46-21
(AVR 19743)

Chartres
Restaurant le Palmier
20, rue Saint Maurice
☎ 37-21-13-89
(FEV 26803)

Marolles
Au Relais de Marolles
44, rue Georges Bréant
☎ 37-43-20-50
(SEPT 18193)

29 – FINISTÈRE
Cast
Le Relais Saint Gildas
11 et 13, rue Kreisker
☎ 98-73-54-76
(MARS 22727)

Landivisiau
Le Terminus
94, avenue Foch
☎ 98-68-02-00
(JUN 17822)

Pont Aven
Chez Melanie et
Monique
Lieu dit Croissant-Kergos
☎ 98-06-03-09
(OCT 17916)

Sizun
Hotel des Voyageurs
2, rue de l'Argoat
☎ 98-68-80-35
(MARS 14263)

30 – GARD
Remoulins
Auberge les Platanes
Castillon du Gard
Les Croisées
☎ 66-37-10-69
(NOV 24421)

33 – GIRONDE
Langon
Restaurant Darlot
10, rue Dotézac
☎ 56-63-01-36
(MARS 14293)

Sainte Terre
Chez Regis
Avenue du Général de
Gaulle
☎ 57-47-16-21
(JANV 25783)

35 – ILLE-ET-VILAINE
Bedee
Hotel du Commerce
14, place de l'Eglise
☎ 99-07-00-37
(SEPT 13987)

Dol de Bretagne
Le Relais de Belle Lande
23, bis rue de Rennes
☎ 99-48-06-14
(OCT 23999)

Guerche de Bretagne
(La)
Le Relais du Pont
d'Anjou
11, Faubourg d'Anjou
☎ 99-96-23-10
(JUN 19813)

Montauban de Bretagne
Hotel de France
34, rue du Général de
Gaulle
☎ 99-06-40-19
(AOUT 7884)

Redon
Le Relais
Route de Rennes
☎ 99-71-46-54
(FEV 26172)

Saulnieres
La Taverne Bretonne
Le Bourg
☎ 99-44-70-61
(MAI 26540)

36 – INDRE
Argenton sur Creuse
Le Relais
7, rue du Président
Fruchon
Saint-Marcel
☎ 54-24-01-77
(NOV 17413)

37 – INDRE-ET-LOIRE
Villedomer
Le Relais des Grands
Vins de Touraine
La Grand'Vallée
☎ 47-55-01-05
(JUN 12910)

38 – ISÈRE
Corps
Le Relais du Tilleul
Rue des Fossés
☎ 76-30-00-43
(JUIL 25979)

Pajay
Ma Petite Auberge
La Côte Saint André
☎ 74-54-26-06
(JUIL 19435)

Le Bourg Doisans
Hotel Belledonne
☎ 76-80-07-04
(JANV 22965)

40 – LANDES
Escource
Au Routier
☎ 58-07-20-54
(MARS 9439)

Sainte Marie de Gosse
Les Routiers
Route Nationale 117
☎ 59-56-32-02
(AVR 12815)

41 – LOIR-ET-CHER
Theillay
Relais de la Loge
Route Nationale 20
☎ 54-83-37-20
(JANV 25249)

Suevres
Le Relais de la
Providence
1, Place de la Mairie
☎ 54-87-80-88
(SEPT 27674)

**44 – LOIRE
ATLANTIQUE**
Pontchateau
L'Auberge du Calvaire
6, Route de la Brière
Lieu-dit Le Calvaire
☎ 40-01-61-65
(NOV 20885)

Pontchateau
Le Relais de Beaulieu
☎ 40-01-60-58
(AOUT 7869)

Saint Brevin les Pins
Hotel du Marche
Place Henri Basle
☎ 40-27-22-21
(AVR 16002)

Saint Gildas des Bois
Le Relais des Routiers
27, rue du Pont
☎ 40-01-42-15
(NOV 19193)

45 – LOIRET
Chateauneuf sur Loire
Hotel de la Place
Le Bourg
Germiny des Près
☎ 38-58-20-14
(JANV 25250)

Solterre
Auberge de la Route
Bleue
☎ 38-94-90-04
(MARS 2687)

46 – LOT
Gramat
Hotel du Centre
Place de la République
☎ 65-38-73-37
(FEV 13419)

Saint Paul de Loubressac
Relais de la Madeleine
Route Nationale 20
☎ 65-21-98-08
(JUIL 9786)

49 – MAINE-ET-LOIRE
Jallais
Le Galant Vert – La
Croix Verte
Place de la Mairie
☎ 41-64-20-22
(MARS 18345)

Saumur
Hotel de la Gare
16, avenue David
d'Angers
☎ 41-67-34-24
(FEV 17188)

Vivy
Le Relais Saint Paul
30, rue Nationale
☎ 41-52-50-13
(OCT 16736)

50 – MANCHE
Coutances
Le Relais du Viaduc
25, avenue de Verdun
☎ 33-45-02-68
(JUN 16098)

Moyon
Le Super Routiers
Carrefour Paris
Route départmentale 999
☎ 30-05-59-74
(NOV 27091)

Saint Pellerin
Auberge de la
Fourchette
Carantan
☎ 33-42-16-56
(DEC 25752)

**Saint Symphorien des
Monts**
Le Relais du Bois Leger
Lapenty
☎ 33-49-01-43
(JUIL 10872)

51 – MARNE
Verzenay
La Maison du
Champagne
2, rue du Port
☎ 26-03-92-45
(MARS 2227)

**54 – MEURTHE-ET-
MOSELLE**
Nancy
Le Relais du Port
5, rue Henri Bazin
☎ 83-35-49-85
(FEV 18314)

56 – MORBIHAN
Elven
Le Relais de l'Argouet
36, avenue de l'Argouet
☎ 97-53-32-98
(AOUT 16177)

Landevant
Le Relais du Pelican
Route Nationale 14
☎ 97-56-93-12
(JUIL 6281)

Sene
Le Poulfanc
46, Route de Vannes
☎ 97-47-47-97
(FEV 16886)

58 – NIEVRE
Cosne sur Loire
Les Trois Couleurs
21, rue St-Agnan
☎ 86-28-23-50
(MARS 6751)

61 – ORNE
Domfront
Le Relais Saint Michel
5, Route du Mont Saint
Michel
☎ 33-38-64-99
(JANV 10298)

Nonant Le Pin
Le Relais des Haras
Grande Rue
☎ 33-39-93-35
(MARS 25345)

63 – PUY-DE-DOME
Menat
Les Routiers – Chez
Roger
☎ 73-85-50-17
(JUN 13786)

67 – BAS-RHIN
Bouxwiller
Au Soleil
71, Grand Rue
☎ 88-70-70-06
(AOUT 15750)

71 – SAÔNE-ET-LOIRE
Chapelle sous Dun (La)
Restaurant de la Mine
☎ 85-27-16-15
(SEPT 26660)

73 – SAVOIE
Saint Jean de Maurienne
Restaurant Relais R
Place du Champ de
Foire
☎ 79-64-12-03
(JUN 21971)

74 – HAUTE SAVOIE
Megeve
Chalet des Fleurs
Route de Sallanches au
Pont d'Arbon
☎ 50-21-21-46
(JANV 17730)

77 – SEINE-ET-MARNE
Chapelle La Reine (La)
La Salamandre
5, rue du Docteur
Battesti
☎ 64-24-30-03
(MAI 27283)

Provins
Le Relais de la Cure
d'Air
54, avenue du Général
de Gaulle
☎ 64-00-03-21
(NOV 3083)

Voulx
La Bruyère
72, Grande Rue
☎ 64-31-92-41
(AOUT 22914)

80 – SOMME
Marchelepot
Hotel du Parc Jean
Louis/Christine
Route Nationale 17
☎ 22-83-90-85
(MARS 24531)

Proyart
La Raperie
Route Nationale 336
Lieu dit 'La Raperie'
☎ 22-85-37-30
(MAI 19350)

82 – TARN-ET-GARONNE
Moissac
Relais Auvergnat
31, boulevard Camille
Delthil
Place du Palais
☎ 63-04-02-58
(AOUT 15344)

Pommevic
A la Bonne Auberge
Route Nationale 113
☎ 63-39-56-69
(OCT 12514)

83 – VAR
Saint Raphael
Le Bel Azur
247, boulevard de
Provence
☎ 94-95-14-08
(FEV 19663)

84 – VAUCLUSE
Piolenc
Le Commerce
Place Cours Corsin
☎ 90-29-60-14
(NOV 25182)

86 – VIENNE
Trimouille (La)
L'Auberge Fleurie
Rue Octave Bernard
☎ 49-91-60-64
(FEV 15533)

89 – YONNE
Auxerre
Sarl Le Sainte Nitasse
Route de Chablis
☎ 86-46-95-07
(JUN 26916)

Rosoy
La Maison Blanche
Route d'Auxerre
☎ 86-97-13-01
(JUIL 10864)

93 – SEINE-SAINT-DENIS
Pierrefitte sur Seine
Le Normandie
105, avenue Gallièni
☎ 48-26-55-62
(JUN 24982)

95 – VAL-D'OISE
Pontoise
Restaurant de la Poste
68, rue Pierre Butin
☎ 30-32-47-72
(SEPT 27016)

Saint Gratien
Le Saint Gratien
79, boulevard Pasteur
☎ 39-89-13-26
(JANV 27762)

TOURIST HOTELS

01 – AIN
Cormoranche sur Saône
Auberge Chez la Mère
Martinet
☆☆NN
Le Bourg
☎ 85-36-20-40
(JUIL 23864)

03 – ALLIER
Lapalisse
Le Chapon Dore
☆NN
2, avenue du 8 Mai 1945
☎ 70-99-09-51
(FEV 26814)

Perigny
Le Relais de Perigny
☆NN
Le Bourg
☎ 70-99-84-57
(DEC 27483)

04 – ALPES-DE-HAUTE PROVENCE
Mezel
Relais de la Place
☆NN
Place Victor Arnaux
☎ 92-35-51-05
(JUIL 22884)

05 – HAUTES ALPES
Chorges
Hôtel des Alpes
☆NN
Avenue de la Gare
☎ 92-50-60-08
(NOV 19996)

Eyguians
Hôtel de la Gare
☆NN
☎ 92-66-20-08
(NOV 15439)

Guillestre
Hôtel de la Gare
☆NN
Montdauphin Gare
☎ 92-45-03-08
(JUN 10820)

Saint Firmin
Le Relais de la Trinité
☆NN
Route Nationale 85
☎ 92-55-21-64
(NOV 19998)

06 – ALPES MARITIMES
Cannes
Le Chalet de l'Isère
☆NN
42 Avenue de Grasse
☎ 93-38-50-80
(OCT 27422)

07 – ARDECHE
Felines
Le Relais de la Remise
☆NN
Route Nationale 82
☎ 75-34-82-22
(JUN 25032)

Pouzin (Le)
Les Routiers
☆NN
64, rue Olivier de Serres
☎ 75-63-83-45
(AVR 21048)

Viviers sur Rhône
Le Relais du Vivarais
☆NN
Route Nationale 86
Lieu-dit 'Les Sautelles'
☎ 75-52-60-41
(FEV 7485)

08 – ARDENNES
Fumay
Le Relais du Lion
☆NN
41, rue de la Gare
☎ 24-41-10-27
(AVR 21465)

10 – AUBE
Bouilly
Au Relais de Montaigu
☆NN
300, rue au Fébvres
☎ 25-40-20-20
(AVR 18374)

11 – AUDE
Fitou
Relais le Parador
☆NN
Cabanne de Fitou
☎ 68-45-79-11
(MAI 27273)

12 – AVEYRON
Baraqueville
Le Palous
☆NN
184, avenue du Centre
☎ 65-69-01-89
(FEV 21398)

Bertholene
Hôtel Bancarel
☆NN
Route Nationale 88
Laissac
Situé au pied de la Forêt
de Palanges
☎ 65-69-62-10
(AVR 21480)

Gages
Le Relais de la Plaine
☆NN
☎ 65-42-29-03
(DEC 20920)

La Cavalerie
Relais Espace
☆NN
Aérodrôme Millau-
Larzac
☎ 65-62-76-22
(AVR 27243)

Laissac
Auberge du Rouergue
☆NN
Route de Rodez
☎ 65-69-60-38
(DEC 27467)

Druelle
Relais du Pas
☆NN
Route Départementale
994
Le Pas Druelle
☎ 65-69-39-11
(JUN 27300)

Rieupeyroux
Chez Pascal
☆NN
Rue de l'Hom
☎ 65-65-51-13
(OCT 23965)

Rodez
La Rocade
☆NN
La Roquette
Route Nationale 88
☎ 65-67-10-44
(AOUT 18491)

13 – BOUCHES-DU-RHÔNE
Marseille
Beaulieu-Glaris
☆NN
1 and 3 Place des
Marseillaises
☎ 91-90-70-59
(NOV 27085)

Rognac
Cadet Roussel
☆NN
Route de Berre
☎ 42-87-00-33
(AVR 25353)

14 – CALVADOS
Le Beny Bocage
La Renaissance
☆NN
Saint Martin des Besaces
☎ 31-68-72-65
(FEV 20652)

Cagny
Hôtel des Routiers
Chez Louis et Monique
☆NN
22, Route de Paris
☎ 31-23-41-27
(FEV 25806)

Villers sur Mer
Le Normand
☆NN
44, rue du Maréchal
Foch
☎ 31-87-04-23
(MAI 20735)

Vire
Hôtel de France
☆☆NN
4, rue d'Aignaux
☎ 31-68-00-35
(OCT 24705)

15 – CANTAL
Murat
Hôtel des Cimes
☆NN
Route Nationale 122
Laveissière Murat
☎ 71-20-07-42
(SEPT 26656)

Mauriac
Les Routiers
☆NN
27, rue Saint Mary
☎ 71-68-00-79
(NOV 26744)

Saint Flour
Hôtel le Progres
☆☆NN
61, rue des Lacs
☎ 71-60-03-06
(AVR 23757)

16 – CHARENTE
Champagne Mouton
Relais de Plaisance
☆NN
Place du Château
☎ 45-31-80-52
(SEPT 15354)

17 – CHARENTE MARITIME
Saujon
Hôtel de la Gare
☆NN
2, rue Clémenceau
☎ 46-02-80-33
(OCT 24404)

19 – CORRÈZE
Albussac
Hostellerie Roche de
Vic
☆☆NN
Les Quatre Routes
☎ 55-28-15-87
(MAI 11509)

21 – COTE-D'OR
Beaune
Relais de Beaune
☆☆☆NN
Aire de Service de
Beaune
Dans les deux sens
☎ 80-21-46-24

Chenove
Au Bon Coin
☆NN
54 Route de Dijon
☎ 80-52-58-17
(OCT 23957)

Nolay
Hôtel du Chevreuil
☆☆NN
Place de l'Hôtel de Ville
☎ 80-21-71-89
(AOUT 20799)

Nuits St Georges
Hôtel des Cultivateurs
☆☆NN
12, rue du Général de
Gaulle
☎ 80-61-10-41
(JUN 1894)

22 – COTES-DU-NORD
Lamballe
La Tour d'Argent
☆☆NN
2, rue du Docteur
Lavergne
☎ 96-31-03-37
(JANV 3713)

Loudeac
Restaurant les Routiers
☆☆NN
7, rue Lavergne
☎ 96-28-01-44
(JANV 26426)

Saint Agathon
Hôtel Belle Vue
☆NN
Bel Orme
☎ 96-43-80-53
(OCT 20294)

Saint Brieuc
Au Beaufeuillage
☆NN
2, rue de Paris
☎ 96-33-09-16
(JUIL 6292)

24 – DORDOGNE
Beynac et Cazenac
Hostellerie Maleville Sarl
☆☆NN
☎ 53-29-50-06
(FEV 25804)

Carlux
Aux Poissons Frais
☆☆NN
☎ 53-29-70-24
(MARS 12788)

25 – DOUBS
Baume les Dames
Relais la Cremaillere
☆☆☆NN
Hyèvre-Paroisse
☎ 81-84-07-88
(JUIL 13903)

Ornans
Hôtel le Progres
☆NN
11, rue Jacques Gervais
☎ 81-62-16-79
(AOUT 20800)

26 – DROME
Bourg de Peage
Hôtel Alpes Provence
☆☆NN
Route Nationale 532
Alixan
☎ 75-47-02-84
(JUN 25462)

Donzere
Au Bon Accueil
☆NN
Route Nationale 7
☎ 75-51-64-58
(OCT 26701)

Donzere
Le Bolo
☆NN
Route Nationale 7
☎ 75-51-61-48
(NOV 27724)

27 – EURE
Brionne
Hôtel du Havre
☆☆NN
13, rue de la Soie
☎ 32-44-80-28
(DEC 27748)

28 – EURE-ET-LOIRE
Mignieres
Le Relais Beauceron
☆☆NN
Route Nationale 10
Mignières
☎ 37-26-46-21
(AVR 19743)

Ymonville
Le Relais de L'Etoile
☆NN
31, rue du Haut Chemin
☎ 37-32-25-67
(OCT 21259)

29 – FINISTÈRE
Cast
Le Relais Saint Gildas
☆NN
11 et 13, rue Kreisker
☎ 98-73-54-76
(MARS 22727)

Saint Evarzec
Au Bon Repos
☆NN
Poullogodin
☎ 98-56-20-09
(JUN 25005)

Saint Pol de Leon
Les Routiers
☆NN
28, rue Pen Ar Pont
☎ 98-69-00-52
(JUN 26267)

Sizun
Hôtel des Voyageurs
☆NN
2, rue de l'Argoat
☎ 98-68-80-35
(MARS 14263)

30 – GARD
Remoulins
Auberge les Platanes
☆☆NN
Castillon du Gard
Les Croisées
☎ 66-37-10-69
(NOV 24421)

31 – HAUTE GARONNE
Marquefave
Le Relais Chez Roger
☆NN
Route Nationale 117
☎ 61-87-85-07
(JUIL 13851)

32 – GERS
Riscle
Relais de l'Auberge
☆NN
Place de la Mairie
☎ 62-69-70-49
(DEC 21307)

33 – GIRONDE
Libourne
Le Moulin Blanc
☆NN
132, avenue Georges
Clémenceau
☎ 57-25-01-61
(JANV 27171)

St Ciers sur Gironde
Relais du Chateau
☆NN
Route Nationale 137
Bel-Air
☎ 57-32-90-58
(SEPT 27658)

Saint Vincent de Paul
Chez Anatole
☆NN
Ambarès
☎ 56-38-95-11
(MARS 23718)

Sauveterre de Guyenne
Hôtel de Guyenne
☆NN
Route de Libourne
Pringis
☎ 56-71-54-92
(AVR 27578)

34 – HERAULT
Balaruc Les Bains
Le Garrigou
✫✫NN
Route Nationale 113
☎ 67-78-71-30
(DEC 27471)

Meze
La Vitarelle 2
✫NN
Route Nationale 113
☎ 67-43-53-89
(AVR 27261)

35 – ILLE-ET-VILAINE
Bedee
Hôtel du Commerce
✫NN
14, place de l'Eglise
☎ 99-07-00-37
(SEPT 13987)

Fougères
Aux Amis de la Route
✫NN
6, boulevard Saint-
Germain
☎ 99-99-07-62
(SEPT 23992)

Grand Fougeray (Le)
Le Relais de la Belle
Etoile
✫NN
La Belle Etoile
☎ 99-08-42-59
(MAI 25407)

Montauban de Bretagne
Hôtel de France
✫✫NN
34, rue du Général de
Gaulle
☎ 99-06-40-19
(AOUT 7884)

Montauban de Bretagne
Relais de la Hucherais
✫✫NN
La Hucherais
☎ 99-06-40-29
(SEPT 27032)

Pipriac
Hôtel de la Tour
D'Auvergne
✫NN
7, rue de l'Avenir
☎ 99-34-41-34
(NOV 22093)

Redon
Le Relais
✫NN
Route de Rennes
☎ 99-71-46-54
(FEV 26172)

Saint Brice en Cogles
Le Chateaubriant
✫✫NN
18, rue Châteaubriant
☎ 99-98-61-45
(MARS 27559)

36 – INDRE
Chateauroux
Le Rallye
✫NN
9, rue Bourdillon
☎ 54-34-37-41
(JANV 26423)

Vendoeuvres
Le Saint Louis
✫✫NN
Place Saint Louis
☎ 54-38-30-68
(FEV 27545)

37 – INDRE-ET-LOIRE
Villiers au Bouin
Le Grand Cerf
✫✫NN
La Porrerie
☎ 47-24-11-06
(SEPT 23450)

38 – ISÈRE
Corps
Le Relais du Tilleul
✫NN
Rue des Fossés
☎ 76-30-00-43
(JUIL 25979)

Le Bourg d'Oisans
Hôtel Belledonne
✫NN
☎ 76-80-07-04
(JANV 22965)

Thuellin
L'Astral
✫NN
☎ 74-33-94-27
(AVR 25874)

40 – LANDES
Aire sur l'Adour
Les Routiers – Chez
Pierrette
✫NN
15, rue du 4 Septembre
☎ 58-71-63-01
(OCT 24377)

Amou
Au Feu de Bois
✫✫NN
Avenue des Pyrénées
☎ 58-89-00-86
(JANV 26430)

Benesse Marenne
Hôtel des Pins
✫✫NN
Route Nationale 10
☎ 58-72-56-41
(JUN 25023)

Sainte Marie de Gosse
Les Routiers
✫NN
Route Nationale 117
☎ 59-56-32-02
(AVR 12815)

Saint Lon Les Mines
Hôtel du Fronton
✫NN
Au Bourg
☎ 58-57-80-45
(MAI 26880)

41 – LOIR-ET-CHER
Theillay
Relais de la Loge
✫NN
Route Nationale 20
☎ 54-83-37-20
(JANV 25249)

Romorantin Lanthenay
Les Aubiers
✫NN
1, avenue de Blois
☎ 54-76-05-59
(MARS 23703)

42 – LOIRE
Bonson
Relais des Sports
☆NN
14, avenue de la Gare
☎ 77-55-20-12
(FEV 23679)

43 – HAUTE LOIRE
Boussoulet
Auberge du Meycal
☆NN
Saint Julien de Chapteuil
☎ 71-08-71-03
(FEV 24840)

Monlet près d'Allegre
Le Roulis
☆NN
Allègre
☎ 71-00-73-54
(FEV 20650)

Puy (Le)
La Verveine
☆NN
6, Place Cadelade
☎ 71-02-00-77
(FEV 24844)

Sainte Sigolene
Le Relais de la Poste
☆NN
2, Place Leclerc
☎ 71-61-61-33
(NOV 18246)

Vieille Brioude
Les Glycines
☆☆NN
Avenue de Versailles
☎ 71-50-91-80
(NOV 25748)

**44 – LOIRE
ATLANTIQUE**
Chateaubriant
Paris-Ocean
☆NN
25 to 29, rue d'Ancenis
☎ 40-81-21-79
(FEV 27548)

Pontchateau
L'Auberge du Calvaire
☆NN
6, Route de la Brière
Lieu-dit Le Calvaire
☎ 40-01-61-65
(NOV 20885)

Saint Brevin les Pins
Hôtel du Marche
☆☆NN
Place Henri Basle
☎ 40-27-22-21
(AVR 16002)

Saint Nazaire
Les Terailles
☆NN
Route Nationale 86
☎ 66-89-66-14
(NOV 19219)

45 – LOIRET
Artenay
Le Relais d'Artenay
☆☆NN
Rue de Chartres
☎ 38-80-40-78
(SEPT 26670)

Bellegarde
Le Café du Commerce
☆NN
1, rue de la République
☎ 38-90-10-45
(AOUT 9843)

46 – LOT
Gramat
Hôtel du Centre
☆☆NN
Place de la République
☎ 65-38-73-37
(FEV 13419)

Saint Paul de Loubressac
Relais de la Madeleine
☆NN
Route Nationale 20
☎ 65-21-98-08
(JUIL 9786)

47 – LOT-ET-GARONNE
Lafox
Le Relais Toulousain
☆NN
113, route de Toulouse
☎ 53-68-54-83
(JANV 22155)

Miramont de Guyenne
Le Relais de Guyenne
☆☆NN
route de Paris
Saint Pardoux Isaac
☎ 53-93-20-76
(NOV 27097)

Sainte Livrade sur Lot
Au Bon Accueil
☆NN
route de Villeneuve
☎ 58-01-02-34
(JUIL 19426)

48 – LOZÈRE
Langogne
Hôtel du Luxembourg
☆NN
Place de la Gare
☎ 66-69-00-11
(AVR 22750)

Marvejols
Le Relais des Ajustons
☆NN
Marvejols
☎ 66-32-70-35
(MARS 20128)

49 – MAINE-ET-LOIRE
Jallais
Le Galant Vert – La
Croix Verte
☆☆NN
Place de la Mairie
☎ 41-64-20-22
(MARS 18345)

Saumur
Hôtel de la Gare
☆☆NN
16, avenue David
d'Angers
☎ 41-67-34-24
(FEV 17188)

Vivy
Le Relais Saint Paul
☆NN
30, rue Nationale
☎ 41-52-50-13
(OCT 16736)

50 – MANCHE
Coutances
Le Relais du Viaduc
☆NN
25, avenue de Verdun
☎ 33-45-02-68
(JUN 16098)

Montmartin sur Mer
Hôtellerie du Bon Vieux
Temps
☆☆NN
☎ 33-47-54-44
(JUN 26257)

Romagny
Auberge des Closeaux
☆☆NN
Les Closeaux
☎ 33-59-01-86
(OCT 24717)

Saint Symphorien des Monts
Le Relais du Bois Leger
☆NN
Lapenty
☎ 33-49-01-43
(JUIL 10872)

51 – MARNE
Verzenay
La Maison du
Champagne
☆☆NN
2, rue du Port
☎ 26-03-92-45
(MARS 2227)

Courgivaux
Auberge du Chaperon
Rouge
☆NN
Route Nationale 4
☎ 26-81-57-09
(JANV 27501)

53 – MAYENNE
Saint Berthevin
Restaurant de l'Aulne –
L'Internationnal
☆☆NN
Lieu dit 'L'Aulne'
☎ 43-69-31-74
(JUN 20761)

55 – MEUSE
Ancerville
Le Relais
☆NN
59, Route de Saint Dizier
☎ 29-75-30-13
(JUN 25958)

56 – MORBIHAN
Elven
Le Relais de l'Argouet
☆NN
36, avenue de l'Argouet
☎ 97-53-32-98
(AOUT 16177)

Lanester
La Rotonde
☆NN
120, rue Jean Jaurès
☎ 97-76-06-37
(NOV 15440)

Moreac
Le Relais du Barderff
☆☆NN
Z.I. du Barderff
☎ 97-60-18-60
(FEV 26453)

Saint Guyomard
Le Relais des Dolmens
de Lanvaux
☆NN
Lieu-dit 'Le Passoir'
☎ 97-93-81-05
(DEC 27469)

Sene
Le Poulfanc
☆NN
46, Route de Vannes
☎ 97-47-47-97
(FEV 16886)

Vannes
Le Relais de Luscanen
☆NN
Route d'Auvay
☎ 97-63-45-92
(NOV 27104)

58 – NIEVRE
Cosne sur Loire
Les Trois Couleurs
☆NN
21, rue St-Agnan
☎ 86-28-23-50
(MARS 6751)

59 – NORD
Bailleul
Auberge du Seau
☆NN
Chemin Départemental
933
☎ 20-48-62-00
(MAI 23786)

61 – ORNE
Domfront
Le Relais Saint Michel
☆NN
5, Route du Mont Saint
Michel
☎ 33-38-64-99
(JANV 10298)

Mortagne au Perche
Hôtel des Voyageurs
☆NN
60 Faubourg Saint-Eloi
☎ 33-25-25-46
(FEV 25798)

62 – PAS-DE-CALAIS
Bruay la Buissière
La Louette
(anciennement chez
Michel)
☆NN
114, rue Raoult Briquet
Place de la Gare
☎ 21-53-42-07
(MARS 26835)

63 – PUY-DE-DOME
Clermont Ferrand
Le Relais des Routiers
Auvergne Pyrénées
☆NN
12, Bis Place des
Carmes
Gare Michelin Carmes
☎ 73-92-36-73
(AVR 22778)

64 – PYRÉNÉES
ATLANTIQUES
Denguin
Les Routiers de
Denguin
☆NN
Route Nationale 117
☎ 59-68-85-15
(MARS 26846)

Gan
Hôtel Moderne
☆NN
41–43 Place de la Mairie
☎ 59-21-54-98
(DEC 23568)

Pau
Hôtel du Bois Louis
☆NN
18, avenue Gaston
Lacoste
☎ 59-27-34-98
(SEPT 23482)

65 – HAUTES
PYRÉNÉES
Laloubere
Hôtel des Pyrénées
☆NN
13, rue du Maréchal
Foch
☎ 62-93-19-62
(AOUT 16207)

Tarbes
Le Victor Hugo
☆NN
52, rue Victor Hugo
☎ 62-93-36-71
(FEV 26438)

66 – PYRÉNÉES
ORIENTALES
Banyuls dels Aspres
Hostal de Catalunya
☆NN
Route du Perthus
Km 15
☎ 68-21-81-60
(NOV 27733)

67 – BAS-RHIN
Bouxwiller
Au Soleil
☆☆NN
71, Grand Rue
☎ 88-70-70-06
(AOUT 15750)

Kogenheim
A L'Etoile
☆NN
36, route de Strasbourg
☎ 88-74-70-02
(AOUT 26624)

68 – HAUT-RHIN
Kruth
Auberge de France
☆☆NN
20, Grande Rue
☎ 89-82-28-02
(OCT 22987)

69 – RHÔNE
Decines
Hôtel de la Poste – Chez
Simone
☆☆NN
11, rue d'Alsace
☎ 78-49-19-03
(JUIL 18783)

70 – HAUTE SAÔNE
Corbenay
Au P'tit Chariot
☆NN
1, rue de Cannes
Route de Fougerolles
☎ 84-94-13-60
(OCT 27427)

Ronchamp
Le Relais de la Pomme
d'Or
☆NN
Rue le Corbusier
☎ 84-20-62-12
(FEV 18622)

71 – SAÔNE-ET-LOIRE
Mercurey
Le Mercurey
☆NN
Grande Rue
☎ 85-45-13-56
(AOUT 27372)

72 – SARTHE
Connerre
La Biche Dorée
☆NN
Route Nationale 23
☎ 43-76-70-45
(AOUT 27370)

Besse sur Braye
Le Relais de la Gare
☆NN
19, avenue de la Gare
☎ 43-35-30-22
(OCT 13181)

Joue en Charnie
Restaurant du Cheval
Blanc
☆NN
Route Nationale 157
☎ 43-88-42-13
(JUIL 23400)

73 – SAVOIE
Aiguebelle
Hôtel de la Poste
☆☆NN
Grande Rue
☎ 79-36-20-05
(NOV 27719)

Aiguebelle
Le Relais de la Poste
☆☆NN
Grande Rue
☎ 79-36-20-05
(NOV 27719)

74 – HAUTE SAVOIE
Cluses
Le Restoport du Mont
Blanc
☆NN
Autoport du Mont Blanc
La Maladière
☎ 50-96-01-08
(OCT 27411)

Doussard
La Tour du Lac
☆NN
La Tour du Lac
☎ 50-44-30-37
(OCT 26677)

Megève
Chalet des Fleurs
☆☆NN
Route de Sallanches
Pont d'Arbon
☎ 50-21-21-46
(JANV 17730)

Sciez
Le Leman
☆NN
Bonnatrait
☎ 50-72-60-04
(AVR 25358)

SEYNOD
Relais Sainte Catherine
☆NN
181, route d'Aix
☎ 50-69-00-86
(MARS 9372)

Thones
L'Hermitage
☆NN
avenue du Vieux Pont
☎ 50-02-00-31
(AVR 26523)

78 – YVELINES
Chaufour les Bonnieres
Au Bon Accueil
☆NN
Route Nationale 13
☎ 34-76-11-29
(DEC 6601)

81 – TARN
Ambres
Auberge des Pommiers
☆NN
Le Grès
☎ 63-58-05-56
(MAI 26887)

Cuq Toulza
Chez Alain 'La
Bombardière'
☆NN
☎ 63-75-70-36
(MARS 22271)

**82 – TARN-ET-
GARONNE**
Castelsarrasin
Chez Maurice
☆NN
35, Route de Toulouse
☎ 63-32-30-83
(JANV 27152)

Caussade
Relais d'Auvergne
Z.I. Meaux
☎ 63-93-03-89
(JUIL 25040)

Moissac
Relais Auvergnat
☆NN
31, boulevard Camille
Delthill
Place du Palais
☎ 63-04-02-58
(AOUT 15344)

Montpezat de Quercy
Le Relais de L'Etape de
Quercy
☆NN
Lieu dit 'La Madeleine'
Route Nationale 20
☎ 63-02-07-58
(JUN 21121)

Pommevic
A la Bonne Auberge
☆☆NN
Route Nationale 113
☎ 63-39-56-69
(OCT 12514)

83 – VAR
Fréjus
Les Trois Chènes
☆NN
Route de Cannes
☎ 94-53-20-08
(AVR 16518)

Montauroux
Le Relais du Lac
☆☆NN
Route Nationale 562
☎ 94-76-43-65
(NOV 26110)

Saint Raphael
Le Bel Azur
☆NN
247, boulevard de
Provence
☎ 94-95-14-08
(FEV 19663)

84 – VAUCLUSE
Montefavet
Relais d'Avignon
☆☆NN
Quartier la Petite
Castelette
☎ 90-88-18-06
(NOV 22100)

Montfavet
Relais de Bonpas
☆NN
Lieu dit 'Pont de Bonpas'
Route Nationale 7
☎ 90-23-07-01
(JUN 21138)

85 – VENDÉE
Herbiers (Les)
Chez Camille
☆☆NN
2, rue Monseigneur
Massé
☎ 51-91-07-57
(JANV 20079)

Herbiers (Les)
L'Orée des Bois Verts
☆NN
Route des Sables
☎ 51-91-00-18
(OCT 27044)

Roche sur Yon (La)
Hôtel Sully
☆☆NN
Boulevard Sully
☎ 51-37-18-21
(OCT 22072)

Saint Hilaire de Loulay
Le Relax
☆☆NN
Les Landes de Roussais
☎ 51-94-02-44
(JUIL 23361)

86 – VIENNE
Moulismes
La Table Ouverte
☆NN
Route Nationale 147
Montmorillon
☎ 49-91-90-68
(AVR 22752)

87 – HAUTE VIENNE
Sauviat sur Vige
Hôtel de la Poste
☆NN
☎ 55-75-30-12
(AOUT 10941)

88 – VOSGES
Arches
La Truite Renommée
☆☆NN
1, rue d'Epinal
☎ 29-32-79-13
(MARS 27574)

Plombières Les Bains
Le Relais Strasbourgeois
☆NN
3, place Beaumarchais
☎ 29-66-00-70
(AVR 6049)

Saint Pierremont
Le Relais Vosgien
☆☆NN
Rambervilliers
☎ 29-65-02-46
(NOV 14581)

Sainte Marguerite
Le Relais des Amis
☆NN
486, rue d'Alsace
☎ 29-56-17-23
(JUN 16108)

89 – YONNE
Arces
Relais de la Forêt d'Othe
☆NN
15, Place de l'Eglise
☎ 86-88-10-44
(JUN 18747)

Auxerre
Sarl le Sainte Nitasse
☆NN
Route de Chablis
☎ 86-46-95-07
(JUN 26916)

91 – ESSONNE
Chamarande
Relais de Montfort
☆NN
Route Nationale 20
☎ 60-82-20-80
(FEV 17740)

Corbeil Essonnes
L'Hermitage
☆NN
137, Boulevard de
Fontainebleau
☎ 64-96-29-42
(OCT 27037)

Montlhéry
Le Sologne
☆NN
65 Route d'Orléans
☎ 69-01-00-98
(MAI 25933)

CHAMBRES D'HOTES IN THE NORD-PAS-DE-CALAIS

Monsieur et Madame Dalle
82, rue de la Gare
Saulty
62158 L'Arbres
☎ 21-48-24-76

Monsieur et Madame de Saulieu
Château de Grand-Rullecourt
Grand-Rullecourt
62810 Avesnes-le Comte
☎ 21-58-06-37

Monsieur et Madame de Bonnières
Herlin-le-Sec
62130 St-Pol-sur-Ternoise
☎ 21-03-01-19

Sœur responsable de l'accueil
Monastère de Belbal
Troisvaux
62139 St-Pol-de-Ternoise
☎ 21-03-11-65

Monsieur et Madame Pruvost
Château de Ricquebourg
Maresquel
62990 Beaurainville
☎ 21-90-30-96

Monsieur et Madame Gézillier
Vezilier Aubin-St-Vaast
62140 Hesdin
☎ 21-86-80-48

Monsieur et Madame de Gouy
Château de Wamin
Wamin
62770 Le Parcq
☎ 21-04-81-49

Monsieur et Madame Fenet
'La Gacogne'
62130 Azincourt
☎ 21-04-45-61

Monsieur et Madame Wojtusiak
Torcy
62310 Fruges
☎ 21-90-62-51

Madame Duplouy
139, avenue des Peupliers
62780 Stella-Plage
☎ 21-94-72-69

Monsieur et Madame Desalase
135 bis, Le Mont Eventé
Menneville
62240 Desvres
☎ 21-91-77-65

Monsieur et Madame Potterie
62132 Siennes
☎ 21-36-51-71

Monsieur et Madame Behaghel
Ferme de Wolphus
Zouafques
62890 Tournehem
☎ 21-35-61-61

Monsieur et Madame Boutroy
Le Grand Maison
62179 Escalles
☎ 21-85-27-75

Monsieur et Madame Courcol
1, rue des Fusillés
59320 Emmerin
☎ 20-44-83-52

Monsieur et Madame Le Blan
133, rue Guy-Moquet
59420 Mouvaux
☎ 20-26-03-61

Madame Morelle
Château de Warnicamps
59570 Houdain-Lez-Bavay
☎ 27-66-87-61

Madame Morris
La Maison des Violettes
Rue de l'Avocat
62140 Fressin
☎ 21-81-80-94

Monsieur et Madame Augustin
Gîte rurale
Beauvoir – Wavans
62390 Auxi-le-Château
☎ 21-04-01-11

MOTORWAY RELAIS ROUTIERS

AUTOROUTE – A1

Relais Ile de France
(km 25)
Aire de service de
Vemars
Both directions
Survilliers
(95470 Val d'Oise)
☎ 34-68-39-20

L'Arche d'Asseviliers
(km 123)
Aire d'Asseviliers Ouest
Sens Paris/Lille
Peronne Asseviliers
(80200 Somme)
☎ 22-85-20-35

Relais de l'Artois
(km 165)
Aire de service de
Wancourt
Both directions
Arras
(62000 Pas-de-Calais)
☎ 21-55-97-83

AUTOROUTE – A4

Relais du Tardenois
(km 97)
Aire de Service du
Tardenois
Both directions
Fresnes en Tardenois
(02130 Aisne)
☎ 23-70-23-16

Relais Reims/
Champagne
(km 160)
Aire de service de
Reims
Both directions
Reims (51400 Marne)
☎ 26-03-93-57

L'Arche de Verdun
(km 262)
Aire de Verdun Saint
Nicolas
Sens Paris/Mezt
Verdun (55100 Meuse)
☎ 29-86-41-18

Relais de Lorraine
(km 342)
Aire de Service de
Saint Avold
Both directions
Saint Avold
(57740 Moselle)
☎ 87-92-23-89

AUTOROUTE – A6

Relais de Nemours
(km 75)
Aire de Service de
Darvault
Both directions
Nemours
(77140 Seine-et-Marne)
☎ 64-28-11-97

L'Arche de Venoy 2
(km 166)
Aire de Soleil Levant
Sens Lyon/Paris
Venoy (89290 Yonne)
☎ 86-40-35-52

L'Arche de Venoy 1
(km 166)
Aire de Grosse Pierre
Sens Paris/Lyon
Venoy (89290 Yonnne)
☎ 86-40-31-71

Relais de l'Auxois
(km 250)
Aire de Service des
Lochères
Sens Lyon/Paris
Pouilly en Auxois
(21490 Côte-d'Or)
☎ 80-90-83-28

Relais de l'Auxois
(km 255)
Aire de Service du
Chien Blanc
Sens Paris/Lyon
Pouilly en Auxois
(21490 Côte-d'Or)
☎ 80-90-74-25

Relais de Beaune
(km 311)
Aire de Service de
Beaune
Both directions
Beaune
(21200 Côte d'Or)
☎ 80-21-46-24

Truckstore Cafe
(km 311)
Aire de Service de
Beaune Tailly
Beaune
(21200 Côte d'Or)
☎ 80-21-40-78

L'Arche de Chalon la
Ferte
(km 342)
Aire de la Ferté
Sens Paris/Lyon
Sennecey le Grand
(71240 Saône-et-Loire)
☎ 85-44-21-79

L'Arche de Chalon Saint
Ambreuil
(km 343)
Aire de Saint-Ambreuil
Sens Lyon/Paris
Sennecey Le Grand
(71240 Saône-et-Loire)
☎ 85-44-20-64

Le Porte de Bourgogne
(km 375)
Aire de Saint-Aubain La
Salle
Sens Paris/Lyon
Lugny
(71260 Saône-et-Loire)
☎ 85-33-19-80

Relais du Beaujolais
(km 410)
Aire de Service de
Taponas
Sens Lyon/Paris
Belleville sur Saône
(69220 Rhône)
☎ 74-66-19-80

AUTOROUTE – A7

Relais de Montelimar
(km 150)
Aire de Service de
Montélimar
Both directions
Montelimar
(26780 Drôme)
☎ 75-46-60-00

L'Arche de Mornas
(km 185)
Aire de Mornas Village
Sens Lyon/Marseille
Mornas
(84420 Vaucluse)
☎ 90-37-03-09

Le Relais de Provence
(km 274)
Aire de Lançon
Sens Lyon/Marseille
Lancon de Provence
(13680 Bouches-du-
Rhône)
☎ 90-42-88-88

AUTOROUTE – A8

Relais Côte d'Azur
(km 67)
Aire de Service de
Cambarette
Both directions
Brignoles (83170) Var
☎ 94-69-16-81

AUTOROUTE – A9

L'Arche de Fabregues
(km 109)
Aire de Montpellier
Fabrègues
Both directions
Montpellier Fabrègues
(34690 Hérault)
☎ 67-85-15-06

AUTOROUTE – A10

Cafeteria de Limours
(km 33)
Aire de Limours Janvry
Sens Paris/Bordeaux
Briis Sous Forges
(91640 Essonne)
☎ 64-90-77-18

La Porte du Val
de Loire
(km 118)
Aire d'Orléans-Gidy
Both directions
Gidy (45520 Loiret)
☎ 38-73-31-02

La Cafeteria de Blois
(km 171)
Aire de Blois-Villerbon
Sens Paris/Bordeaux
Blois (41000 Loir-
et-Cher)
☎ 54-46-84-73

L'Arche de Tours
(km 223)
Aire de Tours Val de
Loire
Sens Bordeaux/Paris
Monnaie
(37380 Indre-et-Loire)
☎ 47-56-15-49

Grill de Touraine
(km 223)
Aire de Tours la
Longue Vue
Sens Paris/Bordeaux
Monnaie
(37380 Indre-et-Loire)
☎ 47-56-44-94

L'Arche de Saint
Leger
(km 479)
Aire de Saint-Léger
Both directions
Saint Leger
(17800 Charente-
Maritime)
☎ 46-91-95-30

Relais de Bordeaux
(km 530)
Aire de Service de
Saugon
Sens Bordeaux/Paris
Bordeaux
(33300 Gironde)
☎ 57-42-52-52

AUTOROUTE – A11

L'Arche de Chartres
Nord
(km 82)
Aire de Chartres-
Gasville
Sens Paris/Nantes
Mainvilliers
(28300 Eure-et-Loire)
☎ 37-31-62-42

L'Arche de Chartres Sud
(km 82)
Aire de Chartres-Bois
Paris
Sens Nantes/Paris
Mainvilliers
(28300 Eure-et-Loire)
☎ 37-31-62-41

L'Arche de la Ferte
Bernard
(km 166)
Aire de la Ferté Bernard
Sens Paris/Nantes
Ferte Bernard (La)
(74400 Haute-Savoie)
☎ 43-93-41-02

AUTOROUTE – A13

L'Arche de Vironvay
(km 93)
Aire de Vironvay
Sens Paris/Caen
Vironvay (27400 Eure)
☎ 32-40-21-51

AUTOROUTE – A25

Cafeteria de
Steenvoorde
(km 39)
Aire de Saint-Laurent
Both directions
Steenvoorde
(59114 Nord)
☎ 28-49-71-33

AUTOROUTE – A31

Restaurant du Relais de
l'Obrion
Aire de Service de
l'Obrion
Loisy (54700 Meurthe-et-
Moselle)
☎ 83-81-18-89

Le Mirabellier
(km 73)
Aire de Service de Toul
Dommartin
Both directions
Toul (54200 Meurthe-et-
Moselle)
☎ 83-64-64-01

Relais de Dijon Côte
D'Ôr
(km 240)
Aire de Service de Dijon
Brognon
Both directions
Dijon (21490 Côte-d'Or)
☎ 80-23-30-20

AUTOROUTE – A40

Relais du Bugey
(km 73)
Aire de Service de
Ceignes
Sens Mâcon/Chamonix
Ceignes (01430 Ain)
☎ 74-75-60-06

AUTOROUTE – A43

Le Relais de l'Arche
(km 35)
Bourgoin-Jallieu
Both directions
Isle d'Abeau (L')
(38300 Isère)
☎ 74-27-27-91

L'Arche de l'Isle
d'Abeau
(km 35)
Aire de Isle d'Abeau
Both directions
Isle d'Abeau
(38080 Isère)
☎ 74-27-10-14

AUTOROUTE – A62

Relais Agen Porte
d'Aquitaine
(km 93)
Aire de Service d'Agen
Both directions
Agen
(47310 Lot-et-Garonne)
☎ 53-68-70-75

AUTOROUTE – A71

Relais du Berry
(km 176)
Aire de Service de
Farges Allichamps
Both directions
Bourges (18000 Cher)

Relais des Volcans
d'Auvergne
(km 290)
Aire de Service des
Volcans
Both directions
Clermont Ferrand
(63000 Puy-de-Dôme)

AUTOROUTE – A86

Le Mirabellier
Aire de Service de
Pompadour
Creteil
(94000 Val-de-Marne)
☎ 48-99-77-00

ABBEVILLE 80100 Somme **RN 1 Map 5-A3**

♈⊗ **AUBERGE FLEURIE** (N° RR OCT 25 672) (M. Michel **Rubin**) 294, Côte de la Justice ☎ 22-24-88-80. Closed Sun, July. Good parking.

ABBEVILLE 80132 Somme **RN 25 Map 5-A3**

♈⊗ **AU CHEVAL NOIR** (N° RR JANV 26 779) (M. Bernard **Lafargue-Fortier**) RN 25, petit Miannay ☎ 22-24-20-17. Closed all day Fri, Sat lunch and the last week of Aug. Coaches welcome. Rest. seats 100. A little English spoken.

ABSCON 59215 Nord **RN 45 Map 5-A3**

♈⊗ **LE MOULIN D'OR** (N° RR MAR 25 846) (Mme Monique **Bauduin**)
⌂ 17, place de Gaulle ☎ 27-36-30-33 ⇥ 9. Closed Aug. Evening meals until 9pm.

ABSIE (L') 79240 Deux-Sèvres **Map 15-A1**

♈⊗ **RESTAURANT DE LA POSTE** (N° RR AOU 26 984) (M. Eugène **Bignon**) 21, rue de la Poste ☎ 49-95-90-21. Restaurant: open 8am–8.30pm. Closed Sun. Filling stations nearby.

ABZAC 33230 Gironde **Map 15-A3**

♈⊗ **LE GAULOIS** (N° RR NOV 27 721) (M. Jacques **Lacoux**) ☎ 57-49-07-54. Restaurant: family cooking. Set menu from 50–75F. Children's menu. À la carte menu. Dinner served until 10pm. Credit cards accepted. 2 dining rooms with 32 places. Parking for cars and coaches. ⇤ Service station nearby open 8am–9pm.

ACQUEDUCS DE BEAUNANT 69110 Rhône **Map 1-A1**

♈⊗ **AU REVEIL MATIN** (N° RR SEPT 27 678) (Mme Michèle **Lely**) 66, route de la Libération ☎ 78-59-03-05. Restaurant: closed Sat and Sun. Service station close by open 7am–8pm.

ADJOTS (LES) 16700 Charente **RN 10 Map 15-B2**

♈⊗ **PARIS-IRUN-CHEZ BRANGE** (N° RR JUN 19 796) (M. Jacky **Sommier**) ☎ 45-31-02-44. Closed Sat, Sun, Aug.

AGEN 47310 Lot-et-Garonne **Map 21-B1**

⊗ **RELAIS AGEN PORTE D'AQUITAINE** (N° RR 2033) Aire de Service d'Agen. On both sides of the motorway ☎ 53-68-70-75. English spoken. Restaurant: regional cooking à la carte with children's menu. A discount of 25% is given to chauffeurs routiers. Open 7am–11pm. Credit cards accepted. Dining room with 140 places. Sitting room. Terrace. ⇤ Parking for cars and coaches available. Shop with regional products. TV room. Play room for children. Tourist information bureau, meeting room, nursery. The building is built in the 'Bastides' style appropriate to the region and offers visitors a permanent exhibition of rugby and local fruit (prunes).

AIGUEBELLE 73220 Savoie **Map 19-A2**

♈⊗ ✭✭ **HOTEL DE LA POSTE** (N° RR NOV 27 719) (Mme Danielle
⌂ **Ivanoff**), Grande Rue on the road to Chambéry Maurienne et Turin ☎ 79-36-20-05. English spoken. Restaurant: regional cooking. Menus from 57–100F. Closed Sat and from 20 Dec–1 Jan. Credit cards accepted. Traditional décor. 2 dining rooms with 80 places. Hotel ⇥ 21 from 120–220F with en suite showers and toilets, television, telephone, sitting room, terrace. ⇤ Parking for cars and coaches. Service station close by open 6am–9pm.

AIGURANDE

Aiguebelle continued

℞⊗ ☆☆ **LE RELAIS DE LA POSTE** (N° RR NOV 27 719) (Mme Danielle
⌂ **Ivanoff)** Grande Rue ☎ 79-36-20-05. English spoken. Restaurant:
menu from 57–100F. Dinner served until 9pm. Closed Sat and from
20 Dec–1 Jan. Hotel ⇥ 21 from 120–210F. Parking for cars and
coaches. Service station within 100m open from 6am–9pm.

℞⊗ **SARL LE VORNAY** (N° RR FEV 27 789) (M. Bernard **Chibaudel)**
Le Chapelle ☎ 79-36-12-44. **Minitel**. English and Italian spoken.
Restaurant: menu at 56F. Open from 6am until midnight. Closed
Sun. Parking for cars and coaches. Service station close by, open
24 hours.

AIGURANDE 36140 Indre **Map 16-A1**

℞⊗ **HOTEL DE FRANCE** (N° RR SEPT 27 672) (Société Chrislau) 37,
rue Grande ☎ 54-06-32-30. English and Spanish spoken. Hotel ⇥
2. Service station within 200 metres, open 9am–7.30pm.

AIRE-SUR-L'ADOUR 40800 Landes **RN 134 Map 21-A2**

℞⊗ ☆ **NN LES ROUTIERS-CHEZ PIERRETTE** (N° RR OCT 24 377)
⌂ (M. Joël **Daste)** 15, rue du 4 Septembre ☎ 58-71-63-01 ⇥ 10 from
70–110F. Restaurant: dinner served until 9pm. Rest. seats 150. ⊦
Good parking.

AIX-D'ANGILLON (LES) 18220 Cher **Map 13-B1**

℞⊗ **LE PARISIEN** (N° RR JANV 26 153) (M. Jacques **Blanchet)** 20,
place du Général-de-Gaulle ☎ 48-64-43-62. Situated close to the
rescue centre. Traditional home cooking. Menus from 48–68F.
Lunch from noon–2pm. Dinner from 7–8.30pm. 88 places in 2
rooms. Closed Sun and Aug. Traditional décor. Hotel ⇥ 4 from
80–120F. Château de Menetou Salon and Maupas nearby.

AIXE-SUR-VIENNE 87700 Haute-Vienne **RN 21 Map 16-B1**

℞⊗ **LE RELAIS DE LA CHAUMIERE** (N° RR JUL 15 314) (M. J.-L.
⌂ **Pechalat)** 5, avenue de la Gare ☎ 55-70-12-12. **Minitel** ⇥ 5.
Restaurant: closed Wed, 15 Aug–7 Sept. Rest. seats 70 in 3 rooms.

ALBAN 81250 Tarn **Map 22-B1**

℞⊗ **LES QUATRE SAISONS** (N° RR DEC 27 127) (M. Jean-François
Galvan) 2, Grand-Rue ☎ 63-55-83-22. Arabic, Spanish, Italian
spoken. Filling stations nearby. Open 6.30am–11pm

ALBENC (L') 38470 Isère **Maps 24-B1 and 18-B3**

℞⊗ **AUBERGE DU VERCORS** (N° RR MARS 25 335) (Mme Claudette
Torri) Place Jean-Vinay ☎ 76-64-75-17. Closed Sun.

ALBI 81000 Tarn **RN 88 and D 81 Map 22-B1**

℞⊗ **AUBERGE LANDAISE DE CHEZ MARCEL** (N° RR FEV 27 189)
(M. Marcel **Gauzère)** route de Montplaisir La Rivayrolle ☎
63-45-03-11. Closed Sun. Filling station nearby.

℞⊗ **LE RELAIS FLEURI** (N° RR DEC 25 225) (M. Pedro **Casado)** 25,
avenue François-Verdier ☎ 63-54-07-09 ⇥ 3 120–150F. Closed
Sun. Restaurant: regional and family cooking. À la carte menu.
Lunch from noon–3pm. Dinner from 7–10pm. Traditional décor.
60 places in two rooms. Terrace. ⊦ Car parking. Sights: museum,
Toulouse-Lautrec and wax museum, cathedrals and the Tarn
Gorge.

♈⊗ **RELAIS CATALAN** (N° RR AVR 26 878) (M. Raymond **Tharreau**) RD 999 Route de Millau (Barrière de Montplaisir) ☎ 63-60-27-00. **Minitel** ◄ 9. Evening meal served until 10pm. Closed Sat, Sun, Aug.

ALBON 26140 Drôme **RN 7 Map 24-A1**

♈⊗ **RELAIS DE LA TOUR ALBON** (N° RR DEC 26 745) (M. Camille
⌂ **Bertrand**) Route Nationale 7 ☎ 75-03-11-22. **Minitel** ◄ 13. Closed Sun (unless by arrangement). Rest. seats 230. Open 6am–11pm. Family cooking speciality: quercynoises. ➹ Modern décor. Tourist sites nearby. Credit cards accepted. Parking.

ALBUSSAC 19400 Corrèze **D 940 RN 121 Map 17-A1**

♈⊗ ☆☆ **NN HOSTELLERIE DE ROCHE-DE-VIC** (N° RR MAI 11 509)
⌂➹ (Mme **Pailler**) Les Quatre Routes ☎ 55-28-15-87. **Minitel** ◄ 14 85–210F. Closed Mon (low season), Jan, Feb. Full-board 90–220F per night. Bed, telephone, TV. Coaches welcome. Rest. seats 100. Evening meals. Regional food. Children's menus. Open 7am–11pm. Parking. Terrace. Grill. Bar. ➹ Sights: Roche-de-Vic, Collonges la Rouge, Meyssac Turenne. English spoken. Tennis. Numerous lakes. Swimming. Golf. Waterfalls.

ALFORTVILLE 94140 Val-de-Marne **Map 1-B2/3**

♈⊗ **LA TERRASSE** (N° RR OCT 27 059) (M. Boualem **Belamri**) 173, rue Etienne Dolet ☎ 43-75-17-02. Closed Sun and Sept. English spoken. Open till 8pm. 65 places.

ALIXAN 26300 Drôme **RN 532 Map 24-A1**

♈⊗ ☆☆ **NN ALPES PROVENCE** (N° RR JUN 25 462) (M. Jean-Claude
⌂ **Bocaud**) RN 532 Alixan ☎ 75-47-02-84 ◄ 22. Closed 15 Nov–5 Dec 140–260F per night with TV and telephone. English, German spoken. Parking. ➹ Games, bowls. Shaded park. Sights: Museum de la chaussure à Romans, trips to Vercors.

ALLEX 26400 Drôme **Map 24-A1**

♈⊗ **LE DAUPHINOIS** (N° RR OCT 27 689) (M. Marcel **Pisano**) Quartier de la Butte. Directions: exit autoroute Valence–Sud in the direction of Fiancey Nle 7/Allex Dle 93 ☎ 75-62-61-69. **Minitel**. Restaurant: family cooking. Menu at 55F. Dinner served until 10pm. Credit cards accepted. 40 places. Garden terrace. ➹ Parking. 24 hour service station close by. Aquarium and bird garden nearby.

AMBENAY 27250 Eure **Map 2-A2**

♈⊗ **HOTEL DE LA RISLIE** (N° RR JAN 27 507) (M. Jean-Louis
⌂ **Marcilly**) 9, rue Guy Lacombe ☎ 32-24-63-45 ◄ 6. Closed Sun. Evening meals until 9pm.

AMBERIEU-EN-BUGEY 01500 Ain **RN 504 Map 2-A2**

♈⊗ **RELAIS DU GUBEY HUBERT-CHEZ CLAUDINE** (N° RR FEV 25 309) (Mme Denise **Hubert**) 84, au Jules-Pellaudin ☎ 74-38-10-27. Closed on Sun, Aug. Rest. seats 42. Evening meal until midnight.

AMBLAINVILLE 60110 Oise **RN 327 Map 3-B2**

♈⊗ **CHEZ MARIE-ODILE** (N° RR JUL 23 393) (Mme Marie-Odile **Prunier**) 40, rue Nationale ☎ 44-52-03-10. Closed Sun.

AMBOISE

AMBOISE 37400 Indre-et-Loire **RD 151 Map 12-A3**
Y⊗ **LE CHANTECLERC** (N° RR DEC 26 773) (M. Eric **Boitelle**) 34,
⌂ avenue de Tours ☎ 47-57-11-94 ⊷ 5. Closed Sun in winter.
English spoken.

AMBRES 81500 Tarn **RD 87 Map 22-A2**
Y⊗ ☆ **AUBERGE LES POMMIERS** (N° RR MAI 26 887) (M. Alain
⌂ **Sore**) Le Grès ☎ 63-58-05-56 ⊷ 8 70–110F with TV. Closed Fri
evenings and Feb. Spanish and English spoken. Holiday terms
(full-board 160–200F). Coaches welcome. Rest. seats 150. Parking. Bar ⌒ TV. Tourist train.

AMFREVILLE LA MI VOIE 76920 Seine-Maritime **RN 13 bis Map 3-A1**
Y⊗ **LE BOUT DU MONDE** (N° RR AOUT 26 979) (M. Rémy **Piquot**) 2,
route de Paris ☎ 35-23-31-47. Filling stations nearby. Coaches
welcome. Rest. seats 50. Evening meals to 10pm. Parking.

AMIENS 80000 Somme **RN 16 Map 5-A3**
Y⊗ **SAINT ROCH** (N° RR FEV 21 411) (Mme **Halter**) 2, place Foch ☎
⌂ 22-91-38-69 ⊷ 7. Closed Fri and Sun evenings. English spoken.
Rest. seats 60.

AMILLY 45200 Loiret **RN 443 Map 13-A1/2**
Y⊗ **LE RELAIS DU GROS-MOULIN** (N° RR SEP 19 905) (Mme
Bernadette **Grégoire**) 371, rue du Gros-Moulin ☎ 38-85-46-62.
Closed Sun, 15–31 Aug.

AMOU 40330 Landes **RD 15 Map 20-B2**
Y⊗ ☆☆ **AU FEU DE BOIS** (N° RR JANV 26 430) (M. Joël **Martinet**)
⌂ avenue des Pyrénées ☎ 58-89-00-86. Restaurant: regional
cooking. Specialities: fois gras, confit, magret de canard, Saint
Pierre à l'oseille, suckling pig. Menus from 45–150F. Children's
menu. À la carte. Dinner served until 9pm. 3 rooms offering 150
places. Closed Fri evening, Sat lunch and Jan. Credit cards
accepted. Hotel ⊷ 16 from 70–150F with showers, bathroom, TV.
Open from 8am–1am. Garden terrace. ⌒ Sights: a tour of the
Chalosse, Dax, Pau, Loudres (60km).

AMPUIS 69420 Rhône **RN 86 Map 2-B1/2**
Y⊗ **AUX PORTES DE PROVENCE** (N° RR JUN 20 215) (M. Maurice
⌂ **Terpend**) RN 86 Les Allées ☎ 74-56-10-31. **Minitel** ⊷ 11. Closed
Wed and the last 2 weeks of Feb and Aug. Rest. seats 100.
Evening meals to 9pm. Parking.

ANCERVILLE 55170 Meuse **RN 4 Map 14-A1**
Y⊗ ☆ **NN LE RELAIS** (N° RR JUN 25 958) (Mme Renée **Lange**) 59,
⌂ route de St-Dizier ☎ 29-75-30-13 ⊷ 10 95–130F with showers or
baths. Closed Sat afternoon and Sun morning and part of Sept.
Rest. seats 80. Restaurant: family cooking. Specialities: tête de
veau, andouillettes. Children's menu. À la carte. Self service.
Sights: Lac du Dër, Vancouleur, Bar-le-Duc.

ANETZ 44150 Loire-Atlantique **RN 23 Map 11 A3**
Y⊗ **LE RELAIS DE LA BARBINIÈRE** (N° RR JANV 27 169) (Mme
Sylvie **Dronet**) La Barbinière ☎ 40-83-11-25. **Minitel** ⊷ 4. Closed
Sat and Sun, and between Christmas and New Year. English
spoken. Filling station 500m open 7.30am–9pm.

ANGERS 49000 Maine-et-Loire **RN 31 Maps 12-A1 and 11-A3**
♈⊗ **CHEZ GEORGES** (N° RR AVR 24 926) (M. Georges **Janneau**) 47,
⌂ rue Guillaume-Lekeu ☎ 41-43-86-25 ⊷ 7.
♈⊗ **LE RELAIS DE LA HAUTE CHAINE** (N° RR SEPT 27 378) (M.
⌂ Jean Claude **Derouet**) Place Saint-Serge ☎ 41-43-88-99. **Minitel**.
Restaurant: regional cooking. Children's menu. Dinner served
until 1am. Closed Sat, Sun, July. Modern décor. Rest. seats 60.
Hotel ⊷ 10 100F with private WC. Open 6am–1am. Sitting room.
Parking. 24 hour service station nearby.

ANGLES 85750 Vendée **RN 747 Map 11-A1**
♈⊗ **BON ACCUEIL** (N° RR MAR 21 816) (Mme Catherine **Gaborit**) 5,
rue Nationale ☎ 51-97-52-20. Closed 3 weeks in Sept. Rest. seats
160. English spoken. Specialities: seafood, grills, feu de bois,
frogs legs, grilled eel.

ANGLET 64600 Pyrénées-Atlantiques **RN 10 Map 20-A3**
♈⊗ **LES MOUETTES** (N° RR AVR 24 180) (M. Rene **Anneix**) 5,
⌂ avenue de l'Adour ☎ 59-52-46-08 ⊷ 8. Restaurant: closed Sat,
Sun, 15–30 Aug. Evening meals.

ANGLIERS 86330 Vienne **RN 147 Map 12-B2**
♈⊗ **LA GALUCHE** (N° RR NOV 25 729) (M. Claude **Poupard**) ☎
49-98-19-26. Closed Sat evening and some days in Aug. Rest.
seats 76. English spoken. Restaurant: family cooking. Specialities:
salmon and sauce Galuche. Menu 50F. Dinner served until
midnight. Credit cards accepted. Modern décor. Sitting room.
Garden terrace. ⊷ Parking. Showers. Swimming lake and leisure
activities 15km. Sights: Abbey, Chinon, Laires à Monsarault.

ANTONNE ET TRIGONANT 24420 Dordogne **RN 21 Map 15-B3**
♈⊗ **LE RELAIS DE LAURIÈRE** (N° RR MAI 26 899) (M. Jean-Claude
Condaminas) Laurière ☎ 53-06-00-28 ⊷ 4. Closed Sun and 1–15
May. Rest. seats 100. Italian and Spanish spoken. Service station
100m.

ANTONY 92160 Hauts-de-Seine **Map 1-B2**
♈⊗ **LES ROUTIERS** (N° RR OCT 13 147) (Mme Ginette **Laurence**) 86,
avenue de la Division Leclerc ☎ 46-66-02-62. Closed Sun. Home
cooking.

APPEVILLE (ANNEBAULT) 27290 Eure **Map 4-B3**
♈⊗ **LE RELAIS DE LA POSTE** (N° RR AVR 26 503) (M. Eric
Duchumin) route de Pont Audemer ☎ 32-56-11-13. Closed Sun.
Rest. seats 60.

APPOIGNY 89380 Yonne **RN 6 Map 13-A2**
⚑⊗ **Shell Service Station LE RELAIS DE L'AMITIE** (N° RR OCT 55
0000 101) (M. Philippe **Saur**) 21, route d'Auxerre ☎ 86-53-21-76.
Open 24 hours. Closed Sat, Sun and 2 weeks Nov. Evening meals
to midnight. Parking.

APT 84400 Vaucluse **Map 24-B2/3**
♈⊗ **LE RELAIS DU LAC** (N° RR JUL 27 337) (M. Michel **Borde**) Le
Chêne ☎ 90-74-01-10. Closed Sun evening. Evening meals to
11pm. English spoken.

ARBRESLE (L')

ARBRESLE (L') 69210 Rhône **RN 7 Map 2-A1**
♀⊗ **BAR RESTAURANT AUX VOSIGIENS** (N° RR MARS 27 283)
(Mme Évelyne **Péchard**) 49, rue Gabriel-Péri ☎ 74-01-00-13.
Closed July and Sun. Filling station nearby. Dinner served until
8pm.
♀⊗ **LE RELAIS DES ROUTIERS** (N° RR NOV 26 364) (Mme Monique
Giraudier) 27, route de Paris ☎ 74-01-07-59. Closed Sat, Sun, 23
Dec–8 Jan. English, Spanish spoken. Rest. seats 55.
♀⊗ **RELAIS DES ROUTIERS** (N° RR NOV 22 989) (Mme M.-A.
Durix-Michaud) 91, rue Gabriel-Péri ☎ 74-01-05-81. Closed Sun.
Meals served until 8pm from 55F. Direction: Clermont Ferrand.

ARBRET (L') 62158 Pas-de-Calais **RN 25 Map 5-B3**
♀⊗ **LE RELAIS DE LA GARE** (N° RR JUN 17 290) (M. Maurice **Vicart**)
44, Route Nationale ☎ 21-48-24-33. Open 24 hours. Closed Sat,
Sun. Rest. seats 80. Sights: Château de Grand Rullecourt.

ARC-LES-GRAY 70100 Haute-Saône **Map 14-A3**
♀⊗ **LES ROUTIERS** (N° RR SEP 23 928) (Mme Henriette **Demoulin**) 4,
place Aristide-Briand La Croisée ☎ 84-65-37-23. Closed Sun.
Rest. seats 60.

ARCES 89320 Yonne **RD 905 Map 9-B2**
♀⊗ ☆ **NN LE RELAIS DE LA FORET D'OTHE** (N° RR JUN 18 747)
⌂ (Mme Yolande **Misura**) 15, place de l'Eglise ☎ 86-88-10-44. ⇀ 8.
Rest. seats 100.

ARCES SUR ARGENS (LES) 83460 Var **Map 25-A2**
♀⊗ **HOTEL DE L'AVENIR** (N° RR MAI 27 611) (Mme Nadine **Tourou**)
⌂ rue Jean Jaures ☎ 94-73-30-58. **Minitel**. Restaurant: closed Sat out
of season. Hotel ⇀ 9. Open from 7am–10pm.

ARCHES 88380 Vosges **Map 14-B2**
♀⊗ ☆☆ **LA TRUITE RENOMMEE** (N° RR MARS 27 574) (Mme
⌂ Josseline **Hagenauer**) 1, rue d'Epinal ☎ 29-32-79-13. German and
Italian spoken. Restaurant specialities: smoked trout-Vosgien.
Open from 6am–11pm. Closed Sat lunch. Credit cards accepted.
Hotel ⇀ 8. Sights: Print Museum at Epinal.

ARDENTES 36120 Indre **Map 16 A-1**
♀⊗ **CAFÉ DES SPORTS** (N° RR MAI 27 287) (Mme Cécile **Pascaud**)
⌂ 21, avenue de Verdun ☎ 54-36-21-19. Filling station nearby, open
7am–10pm.
♀⊗ **LE RELAIS DE CLAVIERES** (N° RR SEPT 27 377) (Mme Pascale
Portrait) route de Moutluçon Clavières ☎ 54-26-98-46. Restaurant: family cooking. Seats 70. Hotel ⇀ 4 from 75–100F with
showers. Garden terrace. ⊬ Car park. Sights: Château de
Georges Sand.

ARDOISE (L') 30290 Gard **Map 24-A2**
♀⊗ **LE CHALET** (N° RR OCT 26 350) (M. Jacky/Mme Martine
⌂ **Charmasson**) route d'Avignon ☎ 66-50-22-22. **Minitel** ⇀ 7 from
100–170F. Closed Sun, Christmas, New Year. Rest. seats 50.
Restaurant: family cooking. Specialities: croûte morille, poulet au
sang (vin de Bourgogne). À la carte menu. Credit cards
accepted. Open from 7am until midnight. ⊬ Garden terrace.
Parking.

ARGENLIEU 60130 Oise **D916 Map 3-A3**

♈⊗ **LE RELAIS D'ARGENLIEU** (N° RR MARS 26 860) (M. Alain **Meyer**) 45, rue Thierry d'Argenlieu, Avrechy ☎ 44-51-72-18. English spoken. Restaurant: menus from 51–69F. Open from 5.45am–10pm. Dinner served until 9pm. Closed Sat evening and Sun. Garden terrace. Parking.

ARGENT-SUR-SAULDRE 18410 Cher **RD 940 Map 13-A1**

♈⊗ **AUBERGE DES BRUYÈRES** (N° RR JUN 25 959) (M. Jean-Yves **Muelle**) 10, rue Nationale ☎ 48-73-60-20. Closed Sun.

ARGENTAN 61200 Orne **Map 8-A2**

♈⊗ **HOTEL DES GARDES** (N° RR MARS 26 478) (M. Abdel **Kader Aledjikane**) route de Paris. Direction: leave Argentan towards Paris ☎ 33-67-06-68. Restaurant: home cooking. Speciality: couscous. 40 places.

ARGENTAT 19400 Corrèze **RN 120 Map 17-A1/2**

♈⊗ **CHEZ RAYMOND** (N° RR MAI 22 325) (Mme Monique **Pouzaud**)
⌂ Place du 14 Juillet ☎ 55-28-01-97 ⊷ 7. Restaurant: closed Sun and Aug. Rest. seats 110.

ARGENTEUIL-SUR-ARMANÇON 89160 Yonne **CD 118 Map 13-A3**

♈⊗ **CAFÉ DE LA GARE** (N° RR OCT 27 052) (Mme Marie Madeleine **Mestanier**) ☎ 86-75-08-60. Restaurant: regional and family cooking. Specialities: ham in Chablis, coq au vin. Menu 54F. Children's menu. Dinner served until 10pm. Closed Fri afternoon. Traditional décor. ⼊ Parking. Sights: châteaux and picturesque scenery.

ARGENTIÈRE-LA-BESSEE (L') 05120 Hautes-Alpes **Map 19-B3**

♈⊗ **HOTEL DE LA MAIRIE** (N° RR JANV 27 138) (Mme Thérèse
⌂ **Talandier**) 32, avenue Charles de Gaulle ☎ 92-23-10-36 ⊷ 8. Restaurant: closed Sun (low season). Rest. seats 35. Evening meals to 10pm. English spoken. Filling station nearby open 6am–10.30pm.

ARGENTON-SUR-CREUSE 36220 Indre **RN 20 Map 16-A1**

♈⊗ **LE RELAIS DES ROUTIERS** (N° RR NOV 17 413) (Mme Mau-
⌂⊷ ricette **Calmel**) 7, rue de Président, Fruchon Saint-Marcel ☎ 54-24-01-77. Restaurant: closed Sun. Menus 56–100F. Specialities: coq au vin, coquilles de crabes, andouillettes grillées. Children's menu. Lunch 12–2pm. Dinner 7–9pm. Hotel ⊷ 6 85–130F with shower and WC. English, Spanish spoken. Rest. seats 60. Open 7am–10pm. Sitting room. Garden terrace. ⼊ Parking. Sights: the ponds of the Brenne, the Creuse valley, archaeological sites.

ARLES 13200 Bouches-du-Rhône **RN 113 Map 24-A3**

♈⊗ **LE RELAIS DU PASSAGE A NIVEAU** (N° RR AVR 25 893) (M.
⌂ Antoine and Mme Laurence **Pech-Faure**) route de Tarascon 31, avenue de la Libération ☎ 90-96-06-64. Hotel ⊷ 8. Restaurant: closed Sun. Rest. seats 52. English, Italian, German, Spanish spoken.

ARMENTIERES 59280 Nord **RN 42 Map 5-A1**

♈⊗ **AUBERGE DE LA LYS** (N° RR FEV 26 183) (Mme Jacqueline **Leflon**) 110, rue des Résistants ☎ 20-77-21-83. Closed Sun. Rest. seats 150.

ARNAY-LE-DUC

Armentieres continued

♉⊗ **Café-Restaurant LA TERRASSE** (N° RR OCT 27 207) (Mme Jocelyne **Dubar**) 112, rue des Résistants ☎ 20-35-44-80. Situated opposite Customs. Restaurant: family cooking. Menu 37F. Lunch 11.30–3.30pm. Dinner 6–11pm. 80 seats. Garden terrace. ⊨ Parking. Service station 200m. Sights: Près du Hem.

ARNAY-LE-DUC 21250 Côte-d'Or **RN 6 Map 13-B3**

♉⊗ **RELAIS DU ST-PRIX** (N° RR AVR 26 510) (M. Robert **Tonelli**) ☎ 80-84-81-74. Closed Sun. Italian spoken. Parking.

ARRAS 62000 Pas-de-Calais **RN 25 Map 5-B3**

♉⊗ **AU POINT DU JOUR** (N° RR OCT 24 707) (M. Patrick **Renier**) 13, avenue Michonneau ☎ 21-59-96-42. Closed Sat 2pm, Sun. Rest. seats 120. Sights: museum, the belfry, underground passages.

⊗ **RELAIS DE L'ARTOIS** (N° RR 1825) Wancourt service area, access from both sides of the autoroute by pedestrian passageway ☎ 21-55-97-83. English spoken. Restaurant: regional cooking. A reduction of 25% is given to 'chauffeurs routiers'. Children's menu. Self-service. Open 24 hrs. Credit cards accepted. 90 seats. Sitting room. Garden terrace. ⊨ Parking available. Shops. TV. Video games. CB. Telex. Library. Showers.

ARTENAY 45410 Loire **RN 20 Map 9-B1**

♉⊗ ☆☆ **NN LE RELAIS D'ARTENAY** (N° RR SEPT 26 670) (M. Lucian
🏠 **Lichet**) rue de Chartres ☎ 38-80-40-78 ⊨ 30 from 220–240F with bathrooms, TV, telephone. English spoken. Restaurant: family cooking. Menus from 50–88F. Children's menu. À la carte menu. Dinner served until 10pm. Closed Sun Oct–Mar. Credit cards accepted.

ARVERT 17530 Charente-Maritime **RD 14 Map 11-B1**

♉⊗ **LE RELAIS DES 3 CANARDS** (N° RR JUIL 26 938) (Mme Pascale
🏠 **Branco**) rue dos Saunier ☎ 46-36-40-43 ⊨ 5 + 8 bungalows. Closed Fri afternoons, Sat mornings in Nov and 15 days in Feb. English spoken. Rest. seats 160.

ASCOUX 45300 Loiret **RN 721 Map 9-B1**

♉⊗ **AUBERGE SAINT-ELOI** (N° RR MAI 26 543) (SDF **Robillard-Daroux**) 1, rue de Pithiviers ☎ 38-33-00-20 ⊨ 10. Closed Sun. Rest. seats 140 in 2 rooms. Restaurant: dinner served until 9pm.

ASTAFFORT 47200 Lot-et-Garonne **Map 22-A1**

♉⊗ **LES RELAIS DES PYRÉNÉES** (N° RR DEC 27 466) (M. Claude **Parma**) Barbonvièle ☎ 53-67-14-57. Spanish, Italian spoken. Restaurant: regional and family cooking. Speciality: magrets de canard au cêpes. Menu 55F. Lunch 11.30–3pm. Dinner 7–9pm. Closed Sun and last 10 days of Aug. Credit cards accepted. Traditional décor. 33 places. Garden terrace. ⊨ Parking. Service station nearby open 7am–10pm. Sights: château, caves.

ATHÉE-SUR-CHER 37270 Indre-et-Loire **Map 12-B3**

♉⊗ **L'ESCALE** (N° RR NOV 27 444) (M. Gerard **Ramazeilles**) Les Ruelles. Directions: RN 76 towards Vierzon, RN 152 towards Amboise then Bléré ☎ 47-56-67-29. **Minitel**. German, English spoken. Restaurant: family cooking. Speciality: galette de pomme de terre. Children's menu. Dinner served until 9pm.

Closed Sun and 15 Aug–1 Sept. Credit cards accepted. Modern décor. Rest. seats 60. ⌁ Parking. Service station nearby, open 7.30am–9pm. Sights: châteaux, the churches and pagoda of Chanteloupe.

ATTIGNY 08130 Ardennes **Map 6-B2**
♟⊗ **SPORT BAR** (N° RR JANV 26 792) (Mme Nicole **Pienne**) 16, place
⌂ Charlemagne ☎ 24-71-20-69. Hotel ⌁ 3. Restaurant: dinner served until 11pm. 30 seats.

AUBE 61270 Orne **RN 26 Map 8-A2**
♟⊗ **LE PETIT QUEBEC** (N° RR MAI 26 903) (M. Jean-Claude **Rialland**) 47, route de Paris ☎ 33-24-55-34. Closed Sun and Aug. English and Spanish spoken.

AUBERGENVILLE 78410 Yvelines **RN 13 and 190 Map 1-A1**
♟⊗ **RESTAURANT L'AMI RENE** (N° RR DEC 27 123) (M. **Bouchard**
⌂ and **Larbi**) 21, rue Gaston, Jouillerat ☎ 30-95-70-07. Restaurant: closed Sun. Rest. seats 120. Summer terrace. German, English and Arabic spoken. Hotel ⌁ 7 with showers.

AUBERIVES-SUR-VARÈZE 38550 Isère **RN 7 Map 18-B3**
♟⊗ **LE RELAIS DES ROUTIERS** (N° RR AVR 21 498) (Mme Marie-
⌂ Hélène **Graziano**) Route Nationale ☎ 74-84-90-71. Restaurant: closed Sun afternoon, 1–15 Sept. Dinner served until 10pm. Rest. seats 60. Hotel ⌁ 10. Parking.

AUBERVILLIERS 93300 Seine-St-Denis **Porte d'Aubervilliers Map 1-A2**
♟⊗ **LE RELAIS CRÉOL** (N° RR AOUT 26 623) (M. Alain **Mercien**) 119, avenue Victor Hugo ☎ 48-33-68-99.
♟⊗ **AU RENDEZ-VOUS DES CAMIONNEURS** (N° RR SEP 24 330) (M. Akil **Ayadi**) 17, rue de la Haie-Coq ☎ 43-52-09-15.

AUBETERRE 10150 Aube **RN 77 Map 9-B3**
♟⊗ **LES TILLEULS** (N° RR DEC 26 401) (M. Raymond **Mielle**) ☎ 25-37-51-11. Restaurant: family cooking. Menus from 45–54F. Dinner served until 10pm. Credit cards accepted. 33 seats. Parking. Sights: lake, oriental forest, Troyes Cathedral.

AUBEVOYE 27940 Eure **Map 3-B1**
♟⊗ **HOTEL DE LA GARE** (N° RR JUIL 27 326) (Mme Michelle
⌂ **German**) place de la Gare ☎ 32-53-28-88. ⌁ 10. Filling station nearby.

AUBIERS (LES) 79250 Deux-Sèvres **RN 759 Maps 12-B1 and 11-B3**
♟⊗ **HOTEL DU CHEVAL BLANC** (N° RR JUN 11 565) (M. Claude **Sauer**) 9, place St-Melaine ☎ 49-65-60-51 ⌁ 2. Restaurant: closed Sat afternoon, Sun afternoon, Aug.

AUBIGNY-AU-BAC 59265 Nord **RN 17 RN 43 Map 5-B3**
♟⊗ **LE BERTRESIEN** (N° RR JUL 25 990) (M. Didier **Wattelet**) 21,
⌂ Route Nationale ☎ 27-80-96-40. **Minitel** ⌁ 6. Dinner served until 10pm. Rest. seats 140. English spoken.

AUBIGNY-SUR-NÈRE 18700 Cher **RD 940 Map 13-A1**
♟⊗ **LE RELAIS DES ROUTIERS** (N° RR JAN 17 168) (M. Bernard
⌂ **Ollier**) 17, avenue Charles Lefèbvre ☎ 48-58-01-42. Restaurant:

Aubigny-Sur-Nère continued
regional and family cooking. Specialities: hare, wild boar, roe deer in season. Menu 45F. Lunch 12–1.30pm. Dinner 7.30–9.30pm. Closed Sun, bank holidays and Aug. Credit cards accepted. 60 seats in two rooms. Hotel ⊷ 9 from 80–104F. Open 7am–9.30pm. ⊬ Parking.

AUBUSSON 23200 Creuse **Map 16-B2**
♀⊗ **RELAIS DU SPORT-BAR** (N° RR FEV 27 790) (M. Christian **Garnier**) 15, avenue de la République ☎ 55-83-80-60. Restaurant: menus from 50–75F. À la carte. Open 6am–10pm. Closed Sat lunchtime and Sun and for the school holidays. Parking. 24 hr service station.

AUCAMVILLE 31140 Haute-Garonne **Map 22-A2**
♀⊗ **REST LE TOIT** (N° RR JUIN 26 259) (M. Jean-Pierre **Lablanchi**) 50, chaussée des Mazuries ☎ 61-70-46-37. Dinner served until midnight. Rest. seats 250. Spanish spoken.

AUCHY AU BOIS 62190 Pas-de-Calais **Map 5-A2**
♀⊗ **LE VERT DRAGON** (N° RR JAN 27 503) (Mme Marie-France **De Greef**) 3, rue d'Hesdin ☎ 21-26-64-29. Restaurant: regional and family menus from 35–51F. Dinner from 7–10pm. Credit cards accepted. Rest. seats 50. Garden terrace. Parking. Service station nearby.

AUFFERVILLE 77570 Seine-et-Marne **Map 9-B2**
♀⊗ **AUBERGE DE LA DILIGENCE** (N° RR JAN 27 515) (M. Bernard **Vincent**) 9, Route Nationale ☎ 44-28-75-91. Restaurant: family cooking. Specialities: couscous, paella. Menu 53F. Children's menu. Lunch 11–3pm. Dinner 6–9pm. Credit cards accepted. Rest. seats 34 in 2 rooms. ⊬ Parking. Sights: Fontainbleu, Château Landon, Nemours.

AULNAY-SOUS-BOIS 93600 Seine-St-Denis **Autoroute A1 Map 1-A3**
♀⊗ **BISTRONORD** (N° RR AVR 24 923) (M. Jean-Claude **Pradalier**)
⌂ Garonor BP 660 ☎ 48-65-63-41. **Minitel**. Restaurant: closed Sat, Sun. Dinner served until 9pm. English spoken. Coaches welcome. Rest. seats 160. Evening meal. Hotel ⊷ 14.

AUMETZ 57710 Moselle **RN 52 Map 6-B3**
♀⊗ **CAFÉ DE LA POSTE** (N° RR JANV 27 145) (Mme Linda **Cossa**)
⌂ 15, rue Foch ☎ 82-91-91-71. Italian spoken. Restaurant: family cooking. Speciality: Italian dishes. Menu 42F. Lunch 12–3pm. Dinner 7–9pm. Closed afternoons in Mar. Credit cards accepted. Modern décor. Rest. seats 100. Hotel ⊷ 7 from 90–120F. Open from 6am until midnight. ⊬ Parking. Service station nearby open from 8am–8pm.

AUMONE (L') 36170 Indre **Map 16-A1**
♀⊗ **LES ROUTIERS** (N° RR OCT 21 658) (M. Pierre **Bousselly**)
⌂ Directions: at 20km to Argenton turn towards Limoges ☎ 54-47-55-11. Restaurant: family cooking. Menu from 45–70F. À la carte. Lunch 11.30am–4pm. Dinner 7–11pm. Closed Sun. Credit cards accepted. Traditional décor. Rest. seats 70 in 2 rooms. Hotel ⊷ 6 from 80–120F with showers. Open from 6.30am–11pm. ⊬ Parking. Swimming pool. Tennis. Sights: château, lakes, ponds.

AUNEAU 28700 Eure-et-Loir **RD 177 Map 9-B1**

♈⊗ **AUX TROIS MARCHES** (N° RR FEV 27 195) (M. Christian
⌂ **Gasniers Séttaoui**) 2, rue Emile-Labiche ☎ 37-31-70-49. Directions: A11 exit Ablis/A10 exit Allainville. Restaurant: family
cooking. Menu at 46–50F. Children's menu. Lunch from 11.30am–
3pm. Dinner 7.30–10pm. Closed Sun and Aug. Credit cards
accepted. Traditional décor. Rest. seats 35 in 2 rooms. Hotel ⊷ 8
from 100–140F with basin and WC. Open from 6am–10pm. ⊢ Car
parking. Service station nearby. Sights: château.

AURILLAC 15000 Cantal **Map 17-B2**

♈⊗ **BAR DE L'ESCUDILLIER** (N° RR JAN 27 496) (M. Robert **Mon-
tourcy**) place du 8 Mai ☎ 71-63-79-30. Closed Sun. Nearby
service station open 7am–6pm.

♈⊗ **L'ETAPE DU ROUTIER** (N° RR MARS 26 219) (M. Michel **Muller**)
rue des Frères Lumières Zl de Sistrières ☎ 71-64-66-70. Closed
Sun, Sat afternoon. Rest. seats 150.

♈⊗ **RESTAURANT LE SABLIERE** (N° RR 27 777) (Mme Jeanine
Delort) Route Nationale 122 La Sablière ☎ 71-63-53-88. English
and Spanish spoken. Restaurant: menu at 48F. Lunch 11am–3pm.
Dinner from 6.30–9pm. Closed Sat, Sun and the 2nd and 3rd
weeks in Aug. Parking. Service station 500m open 6am–10pm.

AUSSAC 16560 Charente **Map 15-B2**

♈⊗ **LA BELLE CANTINIERE** (N° RR OCT 27 707) (M. Fernand **Judes**)
Directions: 20km north of Angouleme ☎ 45-20-66-89. Restaurant:
family cooking. Speciality: seafood. Menu 50F. Dinner served
until 11pm. Closed Sat and Sun. Credit cards accepted. Traditional décor. Rest. seats 120 in 2 rooms. Garden terrace. ⊢
Parking. Service station 6km.

AUSSILLON MAZAMET 81200 Tarn-et-Garonne **RN 112/118 Map 22-B2**

♈⊗ **CHEZ LOULOU** (N° RR JULY 25 991) (M. Louis **Blavy**) 21, rue
Charles Sabatie ☎ 63-61-26-16. **Minitel**. Spanish spoken. Restaurant: dinner served until 9pm. Closed Sun and Aug. Rest. seats 60
in 2 rooms.

AUTECHAUX 25110 Doubs **Map 10-A3**

♈⊗ **RELAIS DE L'AUTOROUTE** (N° RR DEC 26 112) (Mme Simone
Courtial) Directions: close to the autoroute exit to Beaume-les-
Dames ☎ 81-84-01-14. **Minitel**. Restaurant: family cooking.
Specialities: croûtes aux champignons, fondue with 3 cheeses,
duck with pineapple. Menu 51F. Children's menu. Dinner from
7pm until midnight. Closed Sun and 15 days in Aug. Traditional
décor. Rest. seats 90 in 2 rooms. Hotel: with showers and TV.
Garden terrace. Parking. Sights: ice caves, the depths of
Pouchey.

AUTHEUIL AUTHOUILLET 27490 Eure **RN Map 3-B1**

♈⊗ **LA MARMITE** (N° RR OCT 26 075) (M. André **Person**) 17, rue de
Pacy, La Croix Saint Cefray ☎ 32-34-67-67. Restaurant: closed
Sun afternoon and 10 days in Aug.

AUTHIEUX (LES) 27220 Eure **RD 835 Map 8-A3**

♈⊗ **LE RELAIS DES AUTHIEUX** (N° RR NOV 22 569) (M. Claude
Lecomte) St-André-de-l'Eure ☎ 32-37-31-03. Restaurant: dinner
served until midnight. Closed 22 Dec–3 Jan.

AUTUN

AUTUN 71400 Saône-et-Loire **Map 13-B3**

Y⊗ **LE CLUB** (N° RR NOV 25 169) (Mme Eva **Rizzo**) Pizzeria 13, route de Beaune Pont-l'Evêque ☎ 85-52-27-72. Restaurant: family cooking. Speciality: Italian dishes. Menu from 54–79F. Dinner served until 10pm. Credit cards accepted. Traditional décor. Rest. seats 80 in 2 rooms. Garden terrace. Car parking. Sports centre. Swimming pool. Golf. Equestrian centre. Lakes. Mini-golf. Sights: Gallic Roman town, Roman theatre, temples, Gothic cathedral. Son et Lumière at Roman theatre in the summer.

AUVERSE 49490 Maine-et-Loire **Map 12-A2**

Y⊗ **LES ROUTIERS** (N° RR AOUT 26 030) (M. Michel **Chasseau**) route de Noyant à Beauge ☎ 41-82-20-13. Closed Sat, Sun, 15 days in Oct. Evening meals until 9pm.

AUVILLERS-LES-FORGES 08260 Ardennes **RN 43 Map 6-A2**

Y⊗ **ARRET DES ROUTIERS** (N° RR JAN 23 608) (Mme Nicole
⌂ **Bonnaire**) Mon Idée ☎ 24-36-32-77. Rest. seats 50. Meals served until 10pm ⊷ 6.

AUXERRE 89000 Yonne **RN 6 Map 13-A2**

Y⊗ ☆ **LE SAINTE-NITASSE** (N° RR JUIN 26 916) (Mme Corinne
⌂ **Courault**) rte de Chablis ☎ 86-46-95-07 ⊷ 31 from 95-160F with bathrooms and WC. Restaurant: closed at weekends in winter (permanently May–Sept), 20 Dec–5 Jan. Rest. seats 150. Meals served until 10pm. Menus 51F à la carte. Parking. ⊁ Sights: medieval Auxerre. English spoken. Credit cards accepted.

AUXONNE 21130 Côte-d'Or **RN 4 Map 14-A3**

Y⊗ **LE MICADO** (N° RR OCT 26 696) (Mme Martine **Seurre**) rte de Dôle ☎ 80-31-00-45. Restaurant: family cooking. Speciality: esca-lope of turkey with a mushroom cream sauce. Menu at 38F. Children's menu. À la carte. Lunch 11.30am–1.30pm. Dinner 6pm–2am. Credit cards accepted. Traditional décor. Rest. seats 45. ⊁ Car park. Sights: Château Prost, the Chapel and Museum of Bonaparte at Auxonne, Institute Pasteur.

AUXY 45340 Loiret **RN 375 Map 9-B1**

Y⊗ **AUBERGE DU PUITS** (N° RR JANV 26 419) (Mme Marie-Madeleine **Delteil**) 21, rue Principale ☎ 38-96-70-05. Closed Wed, half of Feb, 8 days in Sept. Rest. seats 50.

AUZITS 12390 Aveyron **RN 140 Map 22-B1**

Y⊗ **IGUE DU MOULIN** (N° RR JUIL 26 957) (Mme Brigitte **Felzines**) Rignac ☎ 65-63-90-90. Open 24 hrs.

AVELIN 59710 Nord **RN 353 Map 5-B1 6-A3**

Y⊗ **A L'EMBUSCADE** (N° RR AOU 14 906) (Mme **Lemoine**) 14, route de Seclin ☎ 20-32-90-33. **Minitel**. Closed Sat, Sun, Fri evening. Meals until 9.30pm. Parking.

AVESNES-SUR-HELPE 59440 Nord **RN 2 Map 6-A1**

Y⊗ **CAFE MARGUERITE** (N° RR JUL 14 444) (Mme Marguerite **Sorriaux**) 22, avenue de la Gare ☎ 20-61-17-88. Closed 1–15 Aug.

AVÈZE 72400 Sarthe **Map 8-B3**

Y⊗ **AUBERGE DU CHEVAL BLANC** (N° RR JANV 27 156) (M. Bernard **Joly**) La Ganche locality ☎ 43-93-17-05 ⊷ 4. Closed Sun evening. Filling station 5km.

AVIGNON 84000 Vaucluse **RN 7 Map 24-A2**

♀⊗ **L'ESCAPADE** (N° RR JUN 27 623) (Sarl **Curnier**) 983, avenue l'Amandier ☎ 90-88-97-31. English and Italian spoken. Parking.

♀⊗ ☆☆**RELAIS D'AVIGNON** (N° RR NOV 22 100) (Sarl **le Relais**
⌂ **d'Avignon**) Quartier la Petite Castelette. Directions: exit Avignon south, opposite the airport ☎ 90-88-18-06. Telex 90-87-79-95. **Minitel**. English and Spanish spoken. Restaurant: regional and family cooking. Speciality: toro à la Gardiane. Menus from 56–100F. Children's menu. À la carte. Lunch 11am–3pm. Dinner 7pm until midnight. Credit cards accepted. Modern décor. Rest. seats 250 in 3 rooms. Hotel ⊶ 19 at 140–280F with showers, toilets, TV and telephone. Sitting room. ⇝ Parking. Shady terrace with 120 seats. Sights: Avignon and Provence.

AVIGNONET DE LAURAGAIS 31290 Haute-Garonne **RN 113 Map 22-A2**

♀⊗ **LA PERGOLA** (N° RR MAI 22 329) (M. Etiénne **Batan**) ☎
⌂ 61-81-63-54. **Minitel** ⊶ 6. Restaurant: closed Sat and Sun evening, Feb. Rest. seats 170 in 2 rooms. Dinner served until 9pm. Spanish spoken. Parking.

⛽ **Total Station Service LE RELAIS DE NAUROUZE** (N° RR JUL 25 060) (Mme Christiane **Fernandez**) Aire du Lauragais ☎ 61-81-68-23. Open 24 hrs. English, Spanish spoken.

AVRANCHES 50300 Manche **RN 176 Map 8-A1**

♀⊗ **LE RELAIS DES ROUTIERS** (N° RR OCT 27 398) (M. George **Hippolyte**) 70, rue de la Constitution ☎ 33-58-01-13. Closed Sun (low season). Evening meals until 8pm.

♀⊗ **LES ROUTIERS Chez Jean-Pierre et Joëlle** (N° RR SEPT 27 030) (M. Jean-Pierre **Lambert**) 107, rue de la Liberté ☎ 33-58-19-30. Closed Sun and 1–20 Aug. Filling station nearby.

AWOINGT près CAMBRAI 59400 Nord **RN 39 Maps 6-A1 and 5-B3**

♀⊗ **AU CHANT DES OISEAUX** (N° RR DEC 22 594) (M. **Plouquet**)
⌂ 3, route du Cateau ☎ 27-81-31-05. **Minitel** ⊶ 12. Restaurant: closed Sat, Sun and Aug. Rest. seats 70.

AYNAC 46120 Lot **RD 940 Map 17-B1**

♀⊗ **LE RELAIS DU QUERCY** (N° RR MARS 27 200) (M. Pierre **Marival**) Grande Rue ☎ 65-38-98-15. German and English spoken. Restaurant. Specialities: tournedos Rossini, poule de volailles à la moutarde ancienne. Menus 75–95F. Dinner served until 10pm. Closed Sun (low season). Parking.

AZAY-LE-FERRON 36290 Indre **Map 12-B3**

♀⊗ **L'UNION** (N° RR JUL 26 971) (M. Thierry **Audoin**) place de l'Eglise ☎ 54-39-20-88. Filling station nearby. Rest. seats 40 in 2 rooms. Evening meals until 9pm.

AZAY-LE-RIDEAU 37190 Indre-et-Loire **RN 751 and RD57 Map 12-B2**

♀⊗ **LE RELAIS DE LA GARE** (N° RR MARS 27 229) (M. Patrick **Vitel**) 59, avenue de la Gare ☎ 47-43-40-60. Closed Sun. English spoken. Rest. seats 140. Filling station nearby open 9am–7pm.

BACCARETS (LES) 31550 Haute-Garonne **RN 20 Map 22-A2**

♀⊗ **LA CHAUMIÈRE** (N° RR JUN 26 933) (M. Daniel **Laroche**) ☎
⌂ 61-08-90-70 ⊶ 12. Restaurant: dinner served until 2am. Closed Sun. Rest. seats 120 in 2 rooms.

BAGNAC-SUR-CELE

BAGNAC-SUR-CELE 46270 Lot **RN 122 Map 12-B2**
♈⊗ **RELAIS ROUTIERS LA PLANQUETTE** (N° RR JUIL 27 340) (Mme
⌂ Micheline **Claudon**) route d'Aurillac ☎ 65-34-93-50 ⊷ 6. Evening
meals served until 10pm. Closed Mon afternoon. Filling station
nearby 7am–10pm. Parking.

BAGNOLS EN FORET 83600 Var **Map 25-B2**
♈⊗ **HOTEL DU COMMERCE** (N° RR AVR 24 901) (M. Serge **Ghigo**)
⌂ Grande rue ☎ 94-40-60-05. Italian spoken. Restaurant: dinner
served until 9pm. Closed Tue (low season). Rest. seats 100. Hotel
⊷ 8.

BAGUER-PICAN 35120 Ille-et-Vilaine **Map 7-A3**
♈⊗ **LE SAINT-MICHEL** (N° RR OCT 27 433) (M. Michel **Robert**)
⌂ Directions: 4km towards Dol-de-Bretagne ☎ 99-48-37-48 ⊷ 2.
Restaurant: family cooking. Menu 45F. À la carte. Meals served
until midnight. Rest. seats 50. ⇝ Parking.

BAIGTS-DE-BÉARN 64650 Pyrénées-Atlantiques **RN 117 Map 20-B2/3**
♈⊗ **LE RELAIS DE BAIGTS** (N° RR MAI 19 349) (Mme Danièle
⌂ **Austruy**) ☎ 59-69-15-05. **Minitel** ⊷ 15. Rest. seats 170 in 2 room.
English, Spanish spoken.

BAIGTS-EN-CHALOSSE 40380 Landes **RD 2 Map 20-B2**
♈⊗ **LE CARREFOUR** (N° RR MAR 24 178) (M. Jean **Bonnot**) ☎
58-98-63-05. Restaurant: dinner served until 10pm. Closed Mon.
Rest. seats 100. Hotel ⊷ 4.

BAILLEUL 59270 Nord **CO 933 Map 5-A1**
♈⊗ ☆ **AUBERGE LE SEAU** (N° RR MAI 23 786) (M. Joël **Dequidt**)
⌂ Chemin Départmental 933 ☎ 20-48-62-00 ⊷ 11 with showers,
bathrooms, toilets, TV, telephone. Restaurant: family cooking.
Speciality: steak de veau de la Mer. Children's menu. À la carte.
Dinner until 10pm. Credit cards accepted. Rest. seats 90 in 3
rooms. Open from 6am–11pm. Garden terrace. Parking. Sights:
museum, Flanders Mount, Mont Noir, Belgium frontier.
♈⊗ **CHEZ ANDRÉ** (N° RR MARS 27 222) (M. André **Nooreberghe**)
Rte Nle 4671 Rte de Lille RD 333 ☎ 28-49-29-14. Filling station
4km.

BAILLEUL-SUR-THERAIN 60930 Oise **RD 12 and RD 620 Map 3-A2**
♈⊗ **L'ALOUETTE** (N° RR MAI 26 902) (Mme Mireille **Lemaire**) 4, rue
de Villers ☎ 44-07-66-26. Closed in Oct.

BAILLEULVAL 62123 Pas-de-Calais **RN 25 Map 5-B3**
♈⊗ **BAC DU SUD** (N° RR JUIL 26 958) (M. Yves **Sanson**) ☎ 21-58-79-
⌂ 12 ⊷ 7. Flemish, Dutch, English spoken. Restaurant: dinner
served until 11pm. Closed Sun. Rest. seats 150.

BAIX 07210 Ardèche **RN 86 Map 24-A1**
♈⊗ **MA CAMPAGNE** (N° RR MAI 19 790) (Mme Nara **Arsac**)
Quartier des Lilas ☎ 75-85-80-26. Closed Sun. Rest. seats 100.

BALIZAC 33730 Gironde **RD 110 and 111 Map 20-B1**
♈⊗ **LE RELAIS BASQUE** (N° RR MAI 22 809) (Mme Jeanne **Desclaux**)
☎ 56-25-36-71. Closed Mon, Oct. Rest. seats 125. Evening meals
until 9pm.

BANNOST 77155 Seine-et-Marne **RN 4 Map 9-A2**
Ⓨⓧ **LE RELAIS DE LA GARE** (N° RR FEV 14 215) (M. George
Fontaine) La Gare RN 4 ☎ 64-01-02-07. Closed Sat, Sun, Aug.

BANYULS DELS ASPRES 66300 Pyrénées-Orientales **RN 9 Map 23-A3**
Ⓨⓧ **L'HOSTAL DE CATALUNYA** Sarl (N° RR JUIN 26 909) (Robert
⌂ **Fanon**) route de Pérthus ☎ 68-21-81-60. Spanish spoken. Restaurant. Speciality: catalan menus at 80–130F. Menu 65–130F. Hotel
◄ 10 from 100–160F. Parking. Service station 4km 6am–11pm.

BAPAUME 62450 Pas-de-Calais **RN 17 Map 5-B3**
Ⓨⓧ **CHEZ BERNADETTE** (N° RR MAR 24 892) (Mme Bernadette
⌂ **Molle**) 45, Faubourg de Péronne ☎ 21-07-12-78. Restaurant:
closed Sat 8pm to Sun 10pm, Christmas to New Year. Rest. seats
50. Hotel ◄ 7.

BARAQUEVILLE 12160 Aveyron **RN 88 and 111 Map 22-B1**
Ⓨⓧ ☆ **NN LE RELAIS PALOUS** (N° RR FEV 21 398) (M. Edmond
⌂ **Palous**) ☎ 65-69-01-89. Restaurant: regional and family cooking.
Speciality: tripe, duck, confit de canard, foie gras. Menu at
45–120F. Children's menu. À la carte. Lunch 11.30am–2.30pm.
Dinner from 5.30–10pm. Closed between Christmas and New
Year. Credit cards accepted. Rest. seats 270 in 2 rooms. Hotel ◄
15 from 100–190F with showers, bathrooms, toilets, TV, tele-
phone. Open from 6.30am until midnight. Sitting room. Garden
terrace. ◄ Parking. Sights: Viaur Viaduct, Paneloup lake,
Congues.

BARBASTE 47230 Lot-et-Garonne **RN 655 Map 21-A1**
Ⓨⓧ **LES PALMIERS** (N° RR AVR 21 891) (Société **Gineste et Fils**)
Lauaseignan ☎ 53-65-55-02. Closed Sat in winter, Mon evening
in summer. Evening meals served until 9pm. Rest. seats 110.
Parking. Garden terrace.

BARBEZIEUX 16360 Charente **Map 15-A2/3**
Ⓨⓧ **LA CAMBROUSSE** (N° RR FEV 26 436) (M. Jean-Claude **Pichan**)
⌂ Le Pont du Noble Le Tatre ☎ 45-78-52-83. **Minitel**. Restaurant:
family cooking. Open 24 hrs. Closed Sat afternoon, Sun, 15
May–15 Jun. Rest. seats 46 in 2 rooms. Parking.

BARBEZIEUX-ST-HILAIRE 16120 Charente **RN 10 Map 15-A2**
Ⓨⓧ **RELAIS DE LA BILLETTE** (N° RR AOU 22 018) (Mme Danielle
Houdusse) RN 10, Châteauneuf ☎ 45-78-57-09. Closed Sun and 1
week Aug. Evening meals. Dinner served until midnight. Menu
from 60–100F. Specialities: confit de canard, escalope à la
charentaise, magret de canard, confit de lapin. Spanish spoken.
◄ Parking. Sights: Château de Barbezieux.

BARNAS 07330 Ardèche **RN 102 Map 24-A1**
Ⓨⓧ **LE RELAIS DES ROUTIERS** (N° RR AVR 16 028) (Mme Marthe
⌂ **Cellier**) ☎ 75-36-40-78 ◄ 12. Restaurant: closed on Sun. Rest.
seats 50.

BARQUE (LA) 13970 Bouches-du-Rhône **RN 96 and RD 6 Map 24-B3**
Ⓨⓧ **LE RELAIS DES QUATRE CHEMINS** (N° RR MAR 26 207) (Mme
Colette **Girardi**) ☎ 42-58-60-03. Italian spoken. Closed Sat, Sun
(low season).

BARRE-EN-OUCHE (LA)

BARRE-EN-OUCHE (LA) 27330 Eure **RN 833 Map 8-A3**

♀⊗ **CHEZ JACKY ET CORINNE** (N° RR OCT 25 144) (M. Jacky **Scipion**) Grande rue ☎ 32-44-35-28. Restaurant: family cooking. Menu 50F. Children's menu. Dinner served until 9pm. Closed Sun afternoon, 8 days in Aug. 20 Dec–1 Jan. Rest. seats 35 in 2 rooms. ⊨ Parking. Sights: Château de Beaunesnil.

BASSE-INDRE 44160 Loire-Atlantique **RD 107 Map 11-A2**

♀⊗ **HOTEL BRETON** (N° RR MAI 25 415) (M. Yannick **Jaheny**) 10,
⌂ quai Langlois ☎ 40–86–01–65 ⊷ 12. Restaurant: closed Sat, Sun, Aug. Rest. seats 80.

BASTIDE-L'EVEQUE (LA) 12200 Aveyron **RD 911 Map 22-B1**

♀⊗ **RELAIS DE L'HERMET** (N° RR FEV 26 810) (M. Yvon **Bourdoncle**) Villefranche-de-Rouergue ☎ 65-65-61-41. Restaurant: dinner served until 9pm. Closed Sun, Mon evenings. Rest. seats 100. Parking.

BAUDRE 50000 Manche **Map 4-B1**

♀⊗ **L'INCOGNITO** (N° RR JUIL 27 317) (M. Lionel et Mme Monique **Maris-Bret**) Le Bourg ☎ 33-57-89-58. **Minitel**. Closed Sun. English spoken. Evening meals. Filling station nearby.

BAUME-LES-DAMES 25110 Doubs **RN 83 Maps 10-A3 and 14-B3**

♀⊗ ☆☆☆ **NN HOTEL ZISS REST LA CREMAILLERE** (N° RR JUL 13
⌂⊷ 903) (M. Alfred **Ziss**) Exit A36 ☎ 81-84-07-88. **Minitel**. Hyèvre-Paroisse ⊷ 21 220–250F, 10 for lorry drivers 60–100F. Closed Sat, Oct. Menus from 55–155F. Regional and family cooking. Menu 60–175F. Children's menu. À la carte. Specialities: coq au vin, canard à l'orange fritures. German, English spoken. Special price for lorry drivers. All facilities including terrace garden. Credit cards accepted.

BAVANS 25550 Doubs **RN 463 Map 10-A3**

♀⊗ **LE RELAIS DES MARRONNIERS** (N° RR AOU 15 757) (M. Louis
⌂ **Garnier**) rue des Cerisiers 10km south west of Montbeliard ☎ 81-96-26-54 ⊷ 5. Closed 2nd/3rd week of Sept. Open all day.

BAVAY 59570 Nord **Map 5-B3**

♀⊗ **ETANG DU PRAY** (N° RR AVR 27 591) (M. Patrick **Delbove**). RN 49 near Valenciennes ☎ 27-39-83-93. Some English spoken. Parking for cars and buses.

BAYEUX 14400 Calvados **RN 13 Map 4-B2**

♀⊗ **LA COLOMBE** (N° RR MAR 22 274) (M. **Hardy**) 13, route de Caen, Saint-Vigor-le-Grand ☎ 31-92-13-65 and 31-21-12-28. **Minitel** ⊷ 3 (furnished). Regional and home cooking. Specialities: fruits de mer. Children's menu. À la carte. Dinner from 7–9pm. Closed Sun evening. Credit cards accepted. Modern décor. Drawing room. Terrace garden. ⊨ Cars and coaches welcome. Sights: plages du débarquement, Avranches, cathedral, museum.

BAZOCHE-GOUET (LA) 28330 Eure-et-Loir **RD 927 Map 8-B3**

♀⊗ **LA BONNE AUBERGE** (N° RR AVR 22 787) (M. Jean-Paul **Thierry**) 54, avenue du Général Leclerc ☎ 37–49–21–61. Closed fortnight in Feb and July. Evening meals for lorry drivers only.

BAZOCHES-EN-DUNOIS 28140 Eure-et-Loir **RN 827 and RD 27 Map 8-B3**

♀⊗ **AU BON ACCUEIL** (N° RR DEC 21 717) (Mme Marie-Claude **Boucher**) 7, rue de l'Eglise ☎ 37-22-08-30. Coaches welcome. Rest. seats 50. Evening meals from 6–10pm. Family cooking. Specialities: truite à l'oignon, potee beaucerronne, rognons au vin rouge, pot au feu sauce Normande. Children's menu. À la carte. Lunch 11am–3pm. Credit cards accepted. Traditional décor. Sitting room. Sights: Loire chateaux, cathedral of Chartres, Orléans.

BAZOUGES SUR LE LOIR 72200 Sarthe **RN 23 Map 12-A2**

♀⊗ **AUBERGE DU SOLEIL LEVANT** (N° RR SEPT 26 996) (M. Denis **Borée**) 79, avenue du Maine ☎ 43-45-33-47. Filling station near. English spoken. Closed Sun. Evening meals to 9pm.

BEAUCE 35133 Ille-et-Vilaine **RN 12 Map 8-B1**

♀⊗ **LES ROUTIERS** (N° RR JAN 26 789) (Mme Nicole **Vandevelde**) 19, rue de Paris 3km before Fougeres ☎ 99-99-08-00. Closed Sun, Aug. Home cooking. Lunch menu 44F from 11.30am–2pm. Dinner 7.30–9pm. Credit cards accepted. Traditional décor. Parking cars and coaches. Sights: Château de Fougeres.

BEAUCHALOT par SAINT-MARTORY 31360 Haute-Garonne **RN 117 Map 21-B3**

♀⊗ **AUX BEARNAIS** (N° RR SEP 20 540) (M. René **Frechou**) 10km
⌂ before St Gaudens ☎ 61-90-23-44 ⊷ 5. Closed Mon, 15–30 Sept. Full-board 100–150F. Coaches welcome. Rest. seats 100. Evening meals to 9pm. English, Spanish, German spoken. Regional cuisine. Specialities: Garbure Bearnaise, foie gras, confit de canard, civret de chevreuil. À la carte menu. Closed Mon, Sept. Sights: Saint Bernard de Commingel.

BEAUCHAMPS 80770 Somme **RN 15 Bis Map 4-A2**

♀⊗ **LES ROUTIERS CHES MICHEL** (N° RR MAI 21 913) (M. Michel
⌂ **Blot**) 44, Grande rue ☎ 22-26-13-12 ⊷ 9. Closed Sun, end Dec. Full-board 120–150F. Coaches welcome. Rest. seats 90. Evening meals to 10pm.

BEAUCROISSANT 38140 Isère **RD 159 Map 24-B1**

♀⊗ **LE RELAIS DU CHAMP DE FOIRE** (N° RR MAR 24 889) (Mme Marie-Thérèse **Blain**) Le Bain – Rive-sur-Fure ☎ 76-91-05-17. Closed Sun, fortnight in May and fortnight in Oct. Coaches welcome. Rest. seats 70.

BEAULIEU SUR DORDOGNE 19120 Corrèze **RD 926 and 951 Map 13-A2**

♀⊗ **CAFES DES VOYAGEURS** (N° RR FEV 27 550) (M. Didier **Maitour**) Place du champ Mars ☎ 55-91-10-04. Lunch menu 45F from 12–2pm. Credit cards accepted. Traditional décor. ⊨ Coaches welcome.

BEAUMONT-SUR-VESLE 51360 Marne **RN 44 Map 6-B2 and 9-A3**

♀⊗ ✰✰ **NN LA MAISON DU CHAMPAGNE** (N° RR MAR 2 227) (M.
⌂ Marc **Boulard**) 2, rue du Port ☎ 26-03-92-45 ⊷ 10 from 100–250F. Closed Sun evening, Mon, 2 weeks in Feb, 2 weeks in Oct. German, English, Luxemburg spoken. Coaches welcome Rest.

BEAUNE

Beaumont-Sur-Vesle continued

seats 170. Evening meals. Menus from 38–130F. Specialities: terrines du chef, rognons de veau au ratafia, canard aux griottes. Parking. Bar. Sights: vineyards, 1st World War battlefields.

BEAUNE 21200 Côte-d'Or **RN 74 Map 14-A3**

♀⊗   **AUBERGE DE LA GARE SARL** (N° RR SEPT 26 655) 11, avenue
⌂   des Lyonnais ☎ 80-22-11-13 ⊢ 6. Closed Sun, public holidays,
      Aug. Coaches welcome. Rest. seats 50. Evening meals to 10pm.
      Open to non residents.

♀⊗   **CAFÉ DE FRANCE** (N° RR NOV 24 023) (M. Jean-Pierre **Le
      Payen**) 13, Faubourg Bretonnière ☎ 80-22-25-44. Coaches wel-
      come. Rest. seats 120. Closed Sun, Aug. Regional and home
      cooking. Specialities: boeuf bourguignon, coq au vin. Menus from
      52F. Lunch 12–2pm. Closed Sun, Aug. Traditional décor. Sights:
      Hospice des Beaune, vineyards.

♀⊗   **LE MALMEDY** (N° RR DEC 21 315) (Mme Yvette **Pecout**) 6, rue
      du Lieutenant-Dupuis ☎ 80-22-14-74. Coaches welcome. Rest.
      seats 90. Closed Sun. Menu 52F. Speciality: boeuf bourguignon.

♀⊗   ☆☆☆ **RELAIS DU BEAUNE** (N° RR 2 030). Not far from motorway.
⌂   Regional cooking. Children's menu. À la carte. Self-service, open
      24 hours. Credit cards accepted. Rest. seats 350. Hotel ⊢ 150
      with full facilities. Terrace garden. ⛨ Situated near the heart of
      Beaune it offers fast food service or a gastronomic restaurant.

♀⊗   **TRUCKSTORE CAFE** (N° RR 1885). Very accessible from motor-
      way. English, Spanish, German spoken. Restaurant: menu from
      58F or à la carte. Open 24 hrs. Credit cards accepted. Modern
      décor. Garden terrace. Sitting room. ⛨ Favoured by truck
      drivers. Every facility for drivers.

BEAUSSET (LE) 83330 Var **RN 8 Map 24-B3, 25-A3**

♀⊗   **TERRASSE OMBRAGÉE SUR L'AERODROME** (N° RR NOV 25
      207) (Mme Marie-France **Gautier**) RN 8 circuit Paul-Ricard Le
      Camp du Castellet ☎ 94-90-71-48. Closed Sat, 22 Dec–8 Jan.
      Coaches welcome. Rest. seats 200. English, Portuguese spoken.
      Evening meals to 8pm.

BEAUVOIR-EN-LYONS 76220 Seine-Maritime **Map 3-B1**

♀⊗   **RELAIS NORMAND** (N° RR JUIL 27 327) (M. Julien **Jué**) Les
⌂   Carreaux ☎ 35-90-17-20. **Minitel**. Closed Sat, Sun and Bank
      holidays. Menus at 50F. Dinner until 9pm. Filling station 5km.
      Parking.

BEAUVOIR-SUR-MER 85230 Vendée **RN 148 Map 11-B2**

♀⊗   **AU RELAIS DU GOIS** (N° RR JUN 14 383) (M. Gilles **Grondin**) ☎
      51-68-70-31. Closed 1–31 Dec. Coaches welcome. Rest. seats 150.
      Evening meals (July, Aug).

BEAUVOIR-SUR-NIORT 79360 Deux-Sèvres **RN 138 Map 15-A1**

♀⊗   **L'ETAPE** (N° RR FEV 27 199) (Mme Annick **Duverne**) 7, place de
      l'Hôtel de Ville ☎ 49-09-70-17. Closed Sun afternoon. Some
      English spoken. Filling station nearby 8am–8pm.

BEDEE 35160 Ille-et-Vilaine **RN 12 Map 7-B3**

♀⊗   ☆ **NN HOTEL DU COMMERCE** (N° RR SEP 13 987) (M.
⌂⛨ Jean-Louis **Rigoreau**) 14, Place de l'Eglise ☎ 99-07-00-37 and
      99-07-00-76. **Minitel** ⊢ 22 94–120F, breakfast 15–18F. Restaurant:

closed Sun, 5–26 Aug. Full-board 170–200F per night. Coaches welcome. Rest. seats 360. Evening meals to 10pm. English spoken. Bar. ⊬ TV room. Parking. Menu 50–95F. Specialities: coquilles Saint-Jacques à la Bretonne, gibelotte au cidre, Magret de canard au vinaigre de jamboises. Hotel closes midnight–7am.

BEDENAC 17210 Charente-Maritime **Map 15-A3**
�wine⊗ **L'ESCALE** (N° RR 27 293) (M. and Mme Arthur **Dandergnier**), Le Bois de Gallois ☎ 46-04-45-42. Restaurant open until midnight. Closed Sun, 10–25 Aug. Coaches welcome.
�wine⊗ **AU PAPILLON ROSE** (N° RR 21 865) (M. Lucien **Hautin**) Route de la Cimentaire ☎ 48-76-50-57. Restaurant: closed Sat, Oct.

BEIGNON 56300 Morbihan **RN 24 Map 7-B3**
�wine⊗ **LE RELAIS DES ROUTIERS** (N° RR MAR 14 268) (M. Pierre
⌂ **Labbe**) 40km from Rennes – 60km from Vannes ☎ 97-75-74-37 ⊬ 6. Closed Sat afternoon. Coaches welcome. Rest. seats 80. Evening meals until 10pm.

BELLAC 87300 Haute-Vienne **Map 16-B1**
�wine⊗ **LE RELAIS** (N° RR AVR 25 906) (M. Henri **Cotte**) 3, rue Fernand Fourreau ☎ 55-68-00-22. Closed Sun, Sept. Evening meals.

BELLANCOURT 80100 Somme **RN 35 Map 5-A3**
�wine⊗ **ALINE ET MICHOU** (N° RR JUL 25 477) (M. Jean-Michel **Hoflack**) RN 2 ☎ 22-24-35-13. **Minitel**. Closed Sun in winter, 15 days in Sept, 15 days in Dec. Coaches welcome. Rest. seats 60.

BELLE INUTILE 72160 Sarthe **Map 8-B2**
�wine⊗ ☆ **LA BICHE DOREE** (N° RR 27 370) (M. Dominique **Herault**) RN
⌂ 23, near Le Mans on the way to Paris ☎ 43-76-70-45. English spoken. Family cooking. Dinner until 10pm. Closed Sat, Sun, except for reservations. Credit cards accepted. Hotel ⊨ 10 rooms from 90–120F with showers. Open 5am–midnight. ⊬ Sights: Le Mans Car Museum, old town.

BELLEGARDE 45270 Loiret **RN 60 Maps 9-B1 and 13-A1**
�wine⊗ ☆ **NN LE CAFÉ DU COMMERCE** (N° RR AOU 9 843) (Mme Nelly
⌂ **Grégoire**) 1, rue de la République ☎ 38-90-10-45 ⊨ 12 (5 with shower) from 85–120F. Hotel open 8am–10pm. Restaurant: closed Fri evening, Sat, the last 2 weeks Aug, 25 Dec–15 Jan. Dinner until 9pm. Coaches welcome. Rest. seats 170 in 3 rooms. Evening meals. Parking. Bar. ⊬ Sights: châteaux, churches.

BELLEME 61130 Orne **RN 155 and RD 938 Map 8-B2**
�wine⊗ **LE CHAMP DE FOIRE** (N° RR MARS 27 236) (Mlle **Baire**) 4,
⌂ place du Général-Leclerc ☎ 33-73-00-38 ⊨ 6. Closed Sun except 1 May–31 Aug. Spanish and English spoken.
�wine⊗ **LE GUÉ ROUTIER** (N° RR DEC 26 762) (M. and Mme Bernard **Herouin**) Le Bourg, Le Gué de la Chaine ☎ 33-73-02-66. Closed Sun. Coaches welcome. Rest. seats 56+. Dinner until 8pm.

BELLENGREVILLE 14370 Calvados **RN 13 Map 4-B2**
♥⊗ **HOTEL DE LA PLACE** (N° RR MAI 26 253) (M. Désiré **Desmeulles**) 16, rue de Paris ☎ 31-23-61-50. Closed Sat afternoon, Sun. Evening meals.

BELLERIVE

BELLERIVE 03700 Allier **Map 16-B3**
♀⊗ **LE BOIS DE BOULOGNE** (N° RR JUIN 26 930) (Mme Edith
⌂ **Moliner**) 130, avenue de Vichy ☎ 70-32-38-11 ⇥ 7. English and
Spanish spoken. Dinner until 1am.

BELLEVILLE 55100 Meuse **Map 6-B3**
♀⊗ **FRANCO BELGE** (N° RR MAI 25 417) (M. **Buffelo**) 164, avenue du
Général-de-Gaulle ☎ 29-84-57-85. Verdun Italian spoken.
Closed Sun and 1st two weeks in Sept. Coaches welcome. Rest.
seats 25–40.

BELLEVILLE 69220 Rhône **Map 18-B1**
♀⊗ **RESTAURANT LE BELLERIVE** (N° RR 27 583) (M. Lucien **Pages**)
6, avenue du Port ☎ 74-66-33-82. Specialities: fritures de Saone,
grenouilles. Menu 52–82F. Dinner until 9pm.

BELLEVILLE-SUR-SAONE 69220 Rhône **Map 18-B2**
⊗ **RELAIS DU BEAUJOLAIS** (N° RR 2 039) ☎ 74-66-19-80. English
spoken. Regional cuisine. Children's menu. À la carte. Self-
service. Open 24 hrs with a varied menu. Credit cards
accepted.

BELLEVUE-COETQUIDAN 56380 Morbihan **Map 7-B3**
♀⊗ **L'UNION** (N° RR MARS 20 131) 3, avenue de Brocéliande ☎
⌂ 97-75-71-46 ⇥ 5. Closed Sun, Aug. Showers, shared bathroom.

BELLEVUE-LA-MONTAGNE 43350 Haute-Loire **RD 906 Map 17-A3**
♀⊗ **HOTEL DES VOYAGEURS** (N° RR MARS 26 217) (Mme Odette
⌂ **Chapon**) ☎ 71-00-60-15 ⇥ 12. Full-board available. Coaches
welcome. Rest. seats 110. Evening meals.

BELLEY 01300 Ain **RN 504 Map 2.A3**
♀⊗ **REST DE LA GARE** (N° RR AOUT 25 614) (Mme Elisabeth **Bavu**)
⌂ avenue de la Gare ☎ 79-81-06-60. 80–130F per night. Coaches
welcome. Rest. seats 80. Evening meals served until 10pm.
Closed Sat, Sun evenings, Dec. Menus 50F including coffee.

BELLIGNAT 01810 Ain **RN 840 Map 19-A1**
♀⊗ **A LA BONNE AUBERGE DES ROUTIERS** (N° RR DEC 18 911)
(M. Michel **Detouillon**) 11, avenue Oyonnax ☎ 74-78-24-18 ⇥ 4.
Closed Aug, Sun. Evening meals to 8pm. Regional and home
cooking. Menus from 53F. Children's menu. Traditional décor.
Hotel ⇥ 4 with showers, WC, telephone. Open 6.30am–10pm.
Coaches welcome.

BELMONT-SUR-RANCE 12370 Aveyron **Map 22-B2**
♀⊗ **LE VAL FLEURI** (N° RR 27 602) (Mme Odette **Moncelon**) ☎
65-99-95-13. English, Italian, German spoken. Restaurant.
Specialities: paella, fondue bourgignon. Menus from 80F.

BENESSE-MAREMNE 40230 Landes **RN 10 Map 20-A2**
♀⊗ ☆ **NN HOTEL DES PINS** (N° RR JUN 25 023) (M. Jean-Claude
⌂ **Bernettes**) ☎ 58-72-56-41 and 72-50-80 ⇥ 5. Closed Sun, 20
Sept–10 Oct. Coaches welcome. Rest. seats 120 in 3 rooms.
Evening meals served until 9pm. Full-board 125–160F.

BERCK-SUR-MER 62600 Pas-de-Calais **Map 5-A2/A3**
♈⊗ **RELAIS D'ARTOIS** (N° RR MARS 26 826) (M. Raoul **Postell**) 20,
⌂ rue Alfred-Lambert ☎ 21-09-29-35. **Minitel** ⌁ 14. Full-board
135–150F. Coaches welcome. Rest. seats 40. Evening meals.

BERNES-SUR-OISE 95340 Val-d'Oise **Map 3-B3**
♈⊗ **CHEZ CLAUDINE** (N° RR DEC 27 124) (Mme Claudine **Diehl**) 1,
rue de Creil ☎ 34-70-04-00 ⌁ 4. Closed Sat, Sun and Aug. Family
cooking. Menus from 49F. Lunch 12–2pm. Dinner 7.30–9pm.
Credit cards accepted. Traditional décor. Hotel ⌁ 4 from 80F.
Open 7.30am–9pm. ⌕ Coaches welcome. Filling station near.

BERRE 13130 Bouches-du-Rhône **Map 24-B3**
♈⊗ **CHEZ MIMI ET DONAT REST DE L'ENTENTE** (N° RR DEC 24
801) (M. Donat **Le Guennec**) Rte du Moulin Vieux ☎ 42-85-37-44.
Closed Sat, Sun, Aug. German, English spoken.

BERSON 33390 Gironde **RN 137 Map 15-A3**
♈⊗ **LA REIGNIERE** (N° RR MAR 18 035) (M. Liliane **Demel**) ☎
57-64-35-36. Closed Sat, Sun, Sept and Oct. Coaches welcome.
Rest. seats 60. Evening meals until 10pm.

BERTHOLENE-par-LAISSAC 12310 Aveyron **RN 88 Map 23-A1**
♈⊗ ☆ **NN HOTEL BANCAREL** (N° RR AVR 21 480) (M. Jean **Brun**)
⌂ Situated on outskirts of Palanges forest ☎ 65-69-62-10. **Minitel** ⌁
13 from 110–190F. Closed 25 Sept–15 Oct. Full-board 170–190F
per night. Coaches welcome. Rest. seats 150. Evening meals.
Parking (individual lockable garages). Bar. ⌕ Grand Terrasse.
Menus 72–100F. Specialities: feuilleté Roquefort, confit de canard
à l'ancienne, tripoux du Rouergue. Sights: Trou de Bozouls,
Gorges du Lot, Montagne de Laves.

BESSAY-SUR-ALLIER 03340 Allier **RN 7 Map 16-A3**
♈⊗ **LE BAR DE LA ROUTE BLEUE** (N° RR JAN 20 633) (M. Francis
Blanche) rue Charles-Louis-Philippe ☎ 70-43-01-59. Closed Sat
afternoon and Sun. Evening meals. Filling station nearby. English
spoken.

BESSE-SUR-BRAYE 72310 Sarthe **RN Map 12-A3**
♈⊗ ☆ **NN LE RELAIS DE LA GARE** (N° RR OCT 13 181) (Mme
⌂ Marguerite **Lenoir**) 19, avenue de la Gare ☎ 43-35-30-22 ⌁ 12.
105–130F. Closed Sun, Aug. ⌕ Coaches welcome. Home
cooking. Dinner 7.30–9pm. Credit cards accepted.

BEURLAY 17250 Charente-Maritime **RN 137 Map 11-B1**
♈⊗ **LE RELAIS D'ARY** (N° RR SEPT 26 631) (M. Yves **Mariaud**)
L'Olivière-Saint-Porchaire ☎ 46-95-01-39. Coaches welcome.
Rest. seats 75 in 3 rooms. Meals served until midnight. Spanish
spoken. Family cooking. Menus 48F or à la carte. Dinner until
midnight. Traditional décor. Hotel rooms with showers. Coaches
welcome. Sights: Château de la Rochecourbon.

BEUZEVILLE 27210 Eure **RN 175 and CD 22 Map 4-B2**
♈⊗ **CAFÉ DE L'ESPÉRANCE** (N° RR DEC 27 125) (Mme Denise
Deguine) 4, rue Pasteur ☎ 32-57-70-60. Closed Sun pm and 2
weeks of Aug. English spoken. Filling station near. Regional and
home cooking. Specialities: couscous, choucroute, escalope
Viennoise, lapin chasseur. Menus from 48F. Lunch 12–2pm. ⌕

BEYNAC-ET-CAZENAC

BEYNAC-ET-CAZENAC 24220 Dordogne **RN 703 Map 15-B2**
♈⊗ ☆☆ **NN SARL HOSTELLERIE MALEVILLE** (N° RR FEV 25 804)
⌂⇥ (M. Jacques **Maleville**) ☎ 53-29-50-06 ⊷ 15. Closed Mon from
Oct to Easter. English spoken. Full-board 195–250F. Coaches
welcome. Rest. seats 150. Evening meals until 10pm.

BEZIERS 34500 Hérault **RN 113 Map 23-A2**
♈⊗ **LE CANTAGAL** (N° RR 27 773) (M. Jean Pierre **Gramay**) ☎
67-31-25-47. Spanish spoken. Restaurant: menus from 55F. Open
7.30am–11pm. Coaches welcome.
♈⊗ **LE KING** (N° RR JUIL 27 350) (M. Hasni **Idrici**) rue quai port
Notre-Dame ☎ 67-28-78-48. Closed Sun (low season). Arabic,
Spanish spoken. Filling station nearby open 24 hrs. Dinner until
11.30pm.

BIARS-SUR-CERE 46130 Lot **RN Map 17-B1**
♈⊗ **CHEZ ALAIN RELAIS ROUTIERS** (N° RR AVR 23 776) (M. Alain
⌂ **Cavalhac**) 16, av. de la République ☎ 65-38-42-30 ⊷ 4. Closed
Sun, Aug. Coaches welcome. Rest. seats 110. Evening meals until
10pm.

BIGAROUX-SAINT-SULPICE-DE-FALEYRENS 33300 Gironde **RN 670
Map 15-A3**
♈⊗ **LE RELAIS CHEZ LA PUCE** (N° RR SEP 10 992) (Mme Renée
⌂ **Forillière**) ☎ 57-24-71-18 ⊷ 5. Closed Sat, Sun. Coaches wel-
come. Rest. seats 70.

BINAS 41240 Loir-et-Cher **RN 157 Map 12-A3**
♈⊗ **LE SAINT CHRISTOPHE** (N° RR AVR 24 930) (M. Philippe
Duvernet) 17, place St-Maurice ☎ 54-82-40-26 ⊷ 5. Closed Sun
afternoon in summer, all day winter. Evening meals.

BIVILLE-LA-BAIGNADE 76890 Seine-Maritime **RN Map 3-A1**
♈⊗ **LA CUILLERE EN BOIS** (N° RR NOV 24 021) (Mme Yvette
Guerillon) ☎ 35-32-88-81. Closed Wed. Evening meals.

BLAGNY 08110 Ardennes **RN 381 Map Map 6-A3**
♈⊗ **LE RELAIS DES CITES** (N° RR FEV 17 463) (M Gérard **Lemaître**)
RN 37 ☎ 24-22-00-23. Closed Sat, Aug. Evening meals. Family
cooking. Children's menus. Lunch 11.30am–3pm. Dinner 7.30–
10pm. Modern décor. ⚑ Coaches welcome. Sights: châteaux,
Vallée de la Meuse, Belgium 15km away.

BLANC-MESNIL (LE) 93150 Seine-St-Denis **RN 2 Map 1-A3**
♈⊗ **LA TRAVESEE DE L'ATLANTIQUE** (N° RR 27 759) (M. Blaidd
Makkeb) 178, boulevard du 8 Mai ☎ 48-67-25-97. English, Italian,
Portuguese spoken. Restaurant: menu 55–78F. Lunch 11.30am–
2.30pm. Dinner 6.30–10pm.
♈⊗ **LE BON ACCUEIL** (N° RR SEP 26 663) (M. André **Seban**) 58,
avenue du 8-Mai-1945 ☎ 48-67-19-88. Open to 9pm. Coaches
welcome. Rest. seats 123 in 3 rooms. English spoken. Credit
cards accepted. ⚑ Modern décor. Sights: aviation museum.

BLANZY 71450 Saône-et-Loire **Map 18-A1**
♈⊗ **BAR RESTAURANT DE LA GARE** (N° RR OCT 27 043) (M.
Bernard **Borowski**) 16, rue de la Gare ☎ 85-68-03-05. English
spoken. Coaches welcome. Rest. seats 60. Evening meal to

10pm. Filling station near. Regional and home cooking. Specialities: boeuf bourgignon, côtes de porc vigneronnes. Dinner to 10pm. Credit cards accepted. Traditional décor. Sights: various caves.

BLAUSASC 06440 Alpes-Maritimes **Map 25-B1**
♈⊗ **LE RELAIS CAMPAGNARD** (N° RR JUIL 27 323) (Mme Marie **Negri**) Pointe de Blausasc ☎ 93-91-13-14. English spoken. Evening meals served until 9pm. Closed Sun.

BLAYE-LES-MINES 81400 Tarn **RN 88 Map 22-B1**
♈⊗ **RELAIS SAINTE MARIE** (N° RR MARS 26 847) (M. Jacky **Lacroix**)
⛫ 53, Bois Redon, Carmaux ☎ 63-76-53-81 ⊷ 7. Closed Sat, Sun. Regional cooking.

BLENOD-LES-PONT-A-MOUSSON 54700 Meurthe-et-Moselle **RN Map 14-B1**
♈⊗ **CHEZ FERNANDE** (N° RR DEC 23 056) (Sarl Chez **Fernande**) 88, avenue Victor-Claude 5 mins off the motorway ☎ 83-81-03-54 ⊷ 2. Closed Sat afternoon, Sun, Aug. English, Portuguese spoken. Restaurant: family cooking. Specialities: couscous, paella, choucroute. Menus 45F. Open 5am–1pm. Traditional décor. Sights: Les Portes d'Or at la place Stanislas de Nancy.

BLERE 37150 Indre-et-Loire **RN 76 Map 12-B3**
♈⊗ **LE RELAIS** (N° RR DEC 17 964) (Mme Paulette **Rossignol**) 48, route de Tours ☎ 47-57-92-31. **Minitel**. Restaurant: family cooking. Menu at 55F. Children's menu. À la carte. Lunch served from 12–2pm. Dinner from 7–10pm. Credit cards accepted. Modern décor. Rest. seats 140. ⊷ Parking. Sights: the Loire châteaux, Pontlevoy Abbey.

BLOIS 41000 Loir-et-Cher **RD 951 Map 12-A3**
♈⊗ **BAR DE LA CITÉ** (N° RR MARS 26 862) (M. Didier **Moreau**) 55, avenue de Vendôme ☎ 54-43-48-54. Closed Sat and Sun. Rest. seats 60.
LA CAFETERIA DE BLOIS (N° RR 2 027) (M. Vincent **Staeleus**), Aire de Blois, Villerbon towards Paris-Bordeaux autoroute ☎ 54-46-84-73.

BLYES 01150 Ain **RN A42 Map 2-A2**
♈⊗ **AUBERGE DE LA PLAINE** (N° RR FEV 27 788) (M. Patrice **Abstier**) ☎ 74-61-50-15. English spoken. Menus from 55–90F. Lunch from 11.30am–2.30pm. Dinner 7–9pm. Closed Sun (low season), and Christmas and the New Year. Parking. Service station nearby open 7am–7pm.

BOEN-SUR-LIGNON 42130 Loire **RN 89 Map 18-A2**
♈⊗ **RELAIS ROUTIERS** (N° RR JUN 26 921) (Mme Laurence **Carton**) 83, rue de Lyon ☎ 77-24-44-76. Closed Sun, 1–15 Oct. Rest. seats 33. Parking.

BOGNY-SUR-MEUSE 08120 Ardennes **Map 6-A2**
♈⊗ **LE RELAIS DE LA GARE CHEZ COCO** (N° RR JUL 24 619) (M. Enrique **Herraiz**) 1, rue de la Vallée ☎ 24-32-03-51. Closed Sun, Aug.

BOIS D'OINGT (LE)

BOIS D'OINGT (LE) 69620 Rhône **Map 2-A1**
♍⊗ **LE RELAIS DU LAC** (N° RR AVR 24 917) (Mme Christiane **Sibourg**) Les Petits Ponts ☎ 74-71-60-01. Closed Tue afternoon, last 2 weeks Aug.

BOISNEY 27300 Eure **RN 13 Map 4-B3**
♍⊗ **CHEZ MARC** (N° RR SEP 25 099) (M. Jean-Pierre **Thomas**) RN 13
⌂ ☎ 32-43-23-43 ◄ 7.

BOISSY-SOUS-ST-YON 91 Essonne **RN 20 Map 9-B1**
♍⊗ **LA RELAIS DE TORFOU** (N° RR FEV 27 181) (M. Mohamed **Toufahi**) RN 20 30, avenue de Paris ☎ 64-91-30-50. English, German and Spanish spoken. Restaurant: dinner served until midnight. Closed Sat and Sun. Rest. seats 120.

BOLBEC 76210 Seine-Maritime **Map 4-B3**
♍⊗ **AUBERGE NORMANDE** (N° RR JUN 27 619) (M. Gérard **Baudribos** RN 15 Trouville – Alliguerville ☎ 35–31–15–21. Restaurant: closed Sat and 15 days in winter. Hotel ◄ 5.

BONLOC 64240 Pyrénées-Atlantiques **RD 21 Map 20-A3**
♍⊗ **RELAIS LILI PEAN** (N° RR NOV 25 190) (M. Gaston **Fouché**) Route Départementale 21. Directions: 3km Hasparren ☎ 59-29-51-48. **Minitel**. Closed Sat (low season) and end Dec. Menus from 50–150F. Children's menu. À la carte. Rest. seats 150. Evening meals to 10pm. English spoken. 200 seats. Garden terrace. Traditional décor. ◄ Parking.

BONNEVILLE 74130 Haute-Savoie **Map 19-A/B2**
♍⊗ **GRILL LA FERME** (N° RR OCT 27 692) (Société Sogertam) Autoroute Blanche Aire de Pouchy. Directions: between Cluses and la Roche sur Foron ☎ 50-97-03-68. English spoken. Restaurant: regional cooking. Specialities: savoyarde, raclette, fondue, brasérade. Menus from 58–98F. Dinner served until 10pm. Credit cards acepted. Traditional décor. Rest. seats 40 in 2 rooms. Garden terrace. ◄ Parking. Showers. TV. 24 hr service station nearby. Winter sports centre. Sights: Chamonix, Mount Blanc.

BONNEVILLE-SUR-ITON (LA) 27190 Eure **RD 129 and RN 830 Maps 3-B1 and 8-A3**
♍⊗ **CAFÉ DES SPORTS** (N° RR NOV 8 068) (M. Roland **Fontaine**) 45, rue Jean-Maréchal ☎ 32-37-10-16 ◄ 4. Restaurant closed Sun, Christmas, New Year. Evening meals to 10pm.

BONSECOURS 12560 Aveyron **Map 23-A1**
♍⊗ **LES ROUTIERS** (N° RR AOU 25 072) (Mme Thérèse **Vayssie**) Campagnac ☎ 65-47-64-77. Closed Sat. Evening meals to 11pm.

BONSON 42160 Loire **RD 82 Map 18–A2**
♍⊗ ☆ **LE RELAIS DES SPORTS** (N° RR FEV 23 679) (Mme Arlette **Pasca**) 14, avenue de la Gare ☎ 77-55-20-12 ◄ 7. Evening meals until 8.30pm. German, Italian spoken. Parking. Bar.

BORDEAUX 33000 Gironde **RN 10 Maps 15-A3, 20-B1 and 21-A1**
♍⊗ **BRIR INTER DES ROUTIERS** (N° RR SEPT 27 657) (M. Orlando **Gonçalves**) 295 Cours Balguerie Stuttenber ☎ 56-43-15-47. Portuguese and Spanish spoken. Restaurant: dinner served until

BOUGUENAIS

11pm. Closed Sat afternoon, Sun and Aug. Service station nearby open 8am–10pm.

♈⊗ **LE BON COIN** (N° RR JAN 27 157) (Mme Sandine **Nouts**) 142, rue Lucien-Faure ☎ 56-39-40-13. Directions: after the bridge, towards the centre of town. Restaurant: family cooking. Menu at 50F. Dinner from 7pm until midnight. Rest. seats 75 in 2 rooms. Closed Sat, Sun, Aug. Filling station 1km open 24 hrs. Traditional décor. ⌁ Parking. 24 hr service station nearby.

♈⊗ ⌂ **LE PORTO** (N° RR DEC 24 771) (Mme Rosa-Maria **Pereira**) 202 bis, quai de Brazza ☎ 56-86-15-93. Directions: Pont-Aquitaine on the Bordeaux-Lormant quay. **Minitel**. Spanish and Portuguese spoken. Restaurant: family cooking. Speciality: Portuguese dishes. Menu 55F. Dinner until midnight. Closed Sat, Sun, bank holidays and Aug. Credit cards accepted. Traditional décor. Rest. seats 68 in 2 rooms. Hotel ⇁ 6 from 100–150F and 95–120F. Open from 6am until midnight. ⌁ Parking. Sights: Bordeaux, cathedral, theatre, Place des Quinconces.

♈⊗ **LE RELAIS CHEZ PIERRETTE** (N° RR AOU 26 973) (M. Alain **Debot**) 186, avenue de Labarde ☎ 56-39-66-70. Closed Sat, July. Some English, German spoken. Filling station near. Evening meals to 10pm.

⊗ **RELAIS DE BORDEAUX** (N° RR 2 036) Aire de Service de Saugon on the Bordeaux-Paris Autoroute ☎ 57-42-52-52. English spoken. Restaurant: regional cooking. A reduction of 25% is given to coach drivers. Children's menus. À la carte. Self-service. Open from 7am–11pm. Credit cards accepted. Rest. seats 100 in 2 rooms. Garden terrace. ⌁ Parking. Boutiques. Nursery. The restaurant offers a varied menu with regional dishes and wine.

♈⊗ **RELAIS DE L'UNION** (N° RR 27 255) (M. Dominique **Depeyns**) 116, rue Lucien Faure ☎ 56-50-05-77. Restaurant: closed Sat afternoon, Sun and Aug. Rest. seats 40 in 2 rooms.

BORDS 17430 Charente-Maritime **Map 11-B1 15-A2**

♈⊗ **CAFÉ DU CENTRE** (N° RR OCT 26 361) (M Martial **Perrocheau**) place de l'Eglise ☎ 46-83-84-31. Family cooking. Menu at 45F. Evening meals served until 9pm. Traditional décor. German spoken. Coaches welcome.

BORT-LES-ORGUES 19110 Corrèze **RN 122 Map 17-A2**

♈⊗ ⌂ **LE RELAIS DES ROUTIERS – CHEZ ANTOINETTE** (N° RR SEP 14 954) (Mme Antoinette **Cheriex**) 9, place du Champ-de-Foire ☎ 55-72-00-42. ⇁ 5.

BOSQUÉRARD DE MARCOUVILLE 27520 Eure **RN 138 Map 4-B3**

♈⊗ ⌂ ☆ **LA TÊTE D'OR** (N° RR MARS 26 844) (M. Gérard **Anquetin**) Route de Lisieux ☎ 35-87-60-24. ⇁ 10, 115–160F.

BOUGE-CHAMBALUD 38150 Isère **Map 18-B3**

♈⊗ **LE VERRE SOT** (N° RR OCT 27 414) (M. Dominique **Duchêne**) ☎ 74-84-05-88. Closed Wed, Nov. Evening meals to 10pm. Parking.

BOUGUENAIS 44340 Loire-Atlantique **RN 751 Map 11-A3**

♈⊗ **A LA FERME** (N° RR JANV 25 786) (M. Yvon **Burlot**) 65, rue de la Pierre facing Zl de Chevire ☎ 40-65-23-58. Closed Sat, Sun. Hotel with showers. Rest. seats 30 in 4 rooms.

BOULAY-LES-BARRES

BOULAY-LES-BARRES 45140 Loiret **RN 155 Map 13-A1**
♡⊗ **L'AUBERGE DE LA ROUTE** (N° RR JUN 22 389) (M. and Mme
⌂ Jacky **Gasnot**) 21, rte d'Orléans ☎ 38-75-34-90 ⊸ 5. Restaurant:
closed Sat, Aug. Evening meals until 10pm.

BOULOGNE-SUR-MER 62200 Pas-de-Calais **RN 1 Map 5-A2**
♡⊗ **LE RELAIS DES DEUX GARAGES** (N° RR OCT 25 673) (M.
⌂ Maurice **Lachère**) 54, avenue John-Kennedy ☎ 21-91-12-96.
English spoken. Restaurant: family cooking. Menu at 55F. Children's menu. À la carte. Dinner served until 9pm. Closed Sat
afternoon and Sun. Credit cards accepted. ⊨ Hotel ⊸ 14 from
76–116F.

BOULOIRE 72440 Sarthe **RN 157 Map 8-B3**
♡⊗ **LE P'TIT MARCHE** (N° RR JUN 26 573) (M. Francis **Hemonnet**),
82, rue Nationale ☎ 43-35-40-04. Closed Thur. Rest. seats 130.

BOUQUEMAISON 80600 Somme **RN 16 Map 5-A3**
♡⊗ **LA CHAUMIÈRE** (N° RR OCT 27 391) (M. Hubert **Payen**) 15,
route de Sainte Pol ☎ 22-77-32-17. Restaurant: family cooking.
Speciality: papillotes de Saint Jacques. Menus 50–80F. À la carte.
Lunch from 11.30am–2pm. Dinner until 10pm. Closed Sat; 8 days
in Feb and 15 days in Sept. Credit cards accepted. Traditional
décor. Rest. seats 30. Garden terrace. ⊨ Parking. Sights: The
village and Chateau of Lucheux, Chateau de Grand Rullecourt.
♡⊗ **LE RELAIS DES ROUTIERS – CHEZ JOSETTE** Tobacconist (N°
RR SEP 14 943) (Mme Josette **Doal**) 60, rue Saint-Pol ☎ 22-77-02-
18. Closed 3 weeks from 10 Aug. Rest. seats 48.

BOURBON-LANCY 71140 Saône-et-Loire **RN 73 Map 16-A3**
♡⊗ **HOTEL DE L'UNION** (N° RR SEPT 26 056) (M. Michel **Fleury**) Le
⌂ Fourneau ☎ 85-89-15-07. Restaurant: family cooking. Menu 45F.
Closed mid Dec. Rest. seats 60. Evening meals to 9pm. Hotel ⊸ 6
from 75–90F. ⊨ Parking.

BOURG BEAUDOUIN 27380 Eure **Map A-1**
♡⊗ **AU PECHE MIGNON** (N° RR JULY 27 641) (M. Gilbert **Watell-
man**, route de Paris ☎ 32-49-05-20.

BOURG-DE-PÉAGE 26300 Drôme **RN 532 Map 18-B3 and 24-A1**
♡⊗ **LE RELAIS DU VERCORS** Sarl (N° RR FEV 23 646) (M. Raphaël
Sanchez) L'Écancière ☎ 75-48-83-44. **Minitel**. English and
Spanish spoken. Restaurant. Regional cooking. Menu 55F. Lunch
from 11.45am–2pm. Dinner from 7.30–10pm. Closed Sun. Credit
cards accepted. Traditional décor. Rest. seats 85 in 2 rooms. ⊨
Parking. Sights: Vercours.

BOURG-ET-COMIN 02160 Aisne **RS 967/925 Map 6-B1**
♡⊗ **L'ESCALE** (N° RR MARS 27 203) (M. Jacques **Pate**) 1, rue de Laon
☎ 23-24-40-44. Closed Sun and Mon pm. Filling station nearby.
Parking.

BOURGANEUF 23400 Creuse **RN 140, 141 and RD 8 Map 16-B1**
♡⊗ **LA COUPOLE** (N° RR FEV 16 891) (M. Gérard **Paquet**) 17,
⌂ avenue Turgot ☎ 55-64-08-99. Closed Sat, 25 Nov–20 Dec.
English spoken. Hotel ⊸ 13.

BOURGES 18000 Cher RN 151 Map 13-B1

LES AILES Sarl (N° RR OCT 27 038) 147, avenue Marcel Haegelen. Directions: Châteauroux ☎ 48-21-57-86. English and German spoken. Restaurant: family cooking. Menu à la carte. Dinner until 10pm. Closed Sat evening and Sun, 15–23 Aug and at Christmas. Credit cards accepted. Rest. seats 86 in 2 rooms. Hotel ⇥ 16 from 90–150F. Open from 6am–11pm. ⊮ Parking. Service station nearby open 6am–midnight. Sights: the old town.

RELAIS DU BERRY (N° RR 2 033) Aire de service de Farges-Allichamps on both sides of the Autoroute. Restaurant: a 25% discount is given to coach drivers. Children's menu. À la carte. Credit cards accepted. Garden terrace. ⊮ Parking.

BOURGET (LE) 93350 Seine-St-Denis.

LE SPOUTNICK (N° RR FEV 27 795) (M. Roger **Brankovic**), 70, rue de Verdun ☎ 48-38-32-97. English and Italian spoken. Restaurant open from 5am–10pm. Closed Sat afternoon, Sun and Aug. Rest. seats 120.

BOURGGNEUF-EN-MAUGES 49290 Maine-et-Loire RN 762 Maps 12-A1 and 11-A3

RELAIS DE LA BOULE D'OR (N° RR OCT 27 683) (M. Thierry **Véron**) 6, rue Notre-Dame ☎ 41-71-03-61. Restaurant: dinner until 8pm. Closed Wed afternoon. Hotel ⇥ 5.

BOURGNEUF-EN-RETZ 44580 Loire-Atlantique Map 11-B3

HÔTEL DES TRADITIONS LE BOIRAT (N° RR OCT 27 429) (M. Noël **Rousselot**) 11, avenue de la gare ☎ 40-21-91-44. Closed Sat. A little English spoken. Evening meals to 9pm. Parking. Hotel ⇥ 6. Service station close by open 8am–9pm.

BOURGOIN-JALLIEU 38920 Isère RN 85 Map 2-B2

RELAIS DE LA MAISON BLANCHE (N° RR AVR 26 493) (M. Andre **Piloz**) RN 85 Nivolas-Vermelle ☎ 74-27-92-86. **Minitel**. Closed Sat, Sun, Aug 3 weeks.

BOURNAN-BAGNEUX 49400 Maine-et-Loire RN 160 Map 12-B2

RELAIS DE BOURNAN (N° RR JUN 16 601) (M. Claude **Sanzay**) 288, rue du Pont-Fouchard ☎ 41-50-18-02. Closed Sun. Rest. seats 48. Evening meals until 9pm.

BOURNEZEAU 85480 Vendée Map 11-A1 and B3

LE RELAIS DU CHEVAL BLANC (N° RR NOV 27 712) (Mme Sylvia **Demesy**) 29, rue Jean Grollean. Directions: La Roche-sur-Yon/Fontenay-le-Comte ☎ 51-40-71-54. Spanish spoken. Restaurant: family cooking. Menu 47F. Children's menu. À la carte. Dinner served until 10pm. Credit cards accepted. Traditional décor. Rest. seats 50. Garden terrace. ⊮ Parking. Service station nearby open 7.30am–7pm. Sights: la Roche-sur-Yon, le Puydu Fou, beaches.

BOURRAS 16200 Charente RN 141 Map 15-A2

LE RELAIS DES VIGNES (N° RR FEV 25 801) (Mme Monique **Delavoie**) RN 141 Commune de Mérignac. Directions: between Cognac and Royan ☎ 45-35-83-16 or 45-35-81-62. **Minitel**. Restaurant: family cooking. Lunch from 11.30am–3pm. Dinner from 7.30–10pm. Closed Sun and Sept. Credit cards accepted. Rest. seats 87 in 3 rooms. Garden terrace. ⊮ Parking. Sights: the distillery.

BOUSSES

BOUSSES 47420 Lot-et-Garonne **RD 665 Map 21-A2**
⚲⊗ **AUBERGE DES RELAIS – CHEZ NICOLE** (N° RR JUL 21 592)
(Mme Nicole **Guillygormar'ch**) Au Bourg. Directions: 50km from
Agen ☎ 53-89-11-62. Restaurant: family and regional cooking.
Specialities: foie gras, confits, duck, game (in season). Menus
from 50–160F. Children's menu. À la carte. Lunch from 11.30am–
3pm. Dinner from 7–9pm. Credit cards accepted. Traditional
décor. Rest. seats 60. Garden terrace. ⚑ Parking. Sights: Château
Henri IV, Barbotan les Thermes, Lac de Casteljoux.

BOUSSOULET 43260 Haute-Loire **RD 15 Map 18-A3**
⚲⊗ ☆ **NN AUBERGE DU MEYCAL** (N° RR FEV 24 840) (M. René
⌂ **Chapuis**) St Julien de Chapteuil. Directions: between Puy and
Valence ☎ 71-08-71-03. Restaurant: family cooking. Specialities:
trout, Norwegian omelette. Menus from 48–75F. À la carte.
Dinner until 9pm. Traditional décor. Rest. seats 180 in 3 rooms.
Hotel ⊨ 12 from 100–130F with showers. Sitting room. Garden
terrace. ⚑ Parking. Bungalows and chalets for weekly hire.
Nature trail, fishing, hunting, cross-country skiing. Sights:
château, lakes.

BOUXWILLER 67330 Bas-Rhin **RD 6 and 7 Map 10-B1**
⚲⊗ ☆☆ **NN LE RELAIS DU SOLEIL PMU** (N° RR AOU 15 750) (M.
⚐ Charles **Jaeger**) 71, Grande Rue ☎ 88-70-70-06 ⊨ 15 85–240F.
Telephone. Restaurant: closed Wed, Sun evening, July, school
holidays. Menus 60–140F. Specialities: choucroute, coq au Rie-
sling, sandre à l'oseille. Coaches welcome Rest. seats 120 in 3
rooms. German, English spoken. Parking. ⚑ Sights: châteaux,
lake, forest.

BOVES 80440 Somme **RN 334 Motorway Amiens-Roye Map 5-B3**
⚲⊗ **LA GRENOUILLERE** (N° RR MAI 25 939) (M. Bouhou **Ouan-
noune**) RN 334. Directions: Expressway Amiens-Roye ☎ 22-09-
31-26. **Minitel**. Closed Sun (except for banquets), 3 weeks Aug.
Coaches welcome. Rest. seats 60. English, Arabic spoken.
Parking.

BOYER 71700 Saône-et-Loire **RN 6 Map 18-B1**
⚲⊗ **RELAIS ROUTIERS DU JONCHET** (N° RR AOÛT 27 359) (M.
Patrick **Bouillin**) RN 6 ☎ 85-57-09-31. Closed Sat pm. Sun. 24 hr
filling station nearby. Parking.

BRAM 11150 Aude **RN 113 Map 22-B2**
⚲⊗ **CHEZ ALAIN** (N° RR DEC 21 332) (M. Alain **Albecq**) RN 113.
⌂ Directions: RN113 between Carcassonne and Toulouse ☎ 68-76-
12-75. Restaurant: regional and family cooking. Specialities:
cassoulet, snails, tripe, white wine sauces. Dinner until 11pm.
Closed Sat, Sun and 3 weeks in Aug. Credit cards accepted.
Traditional décor. Rest. seats 130 in 2 rooms. Hotel ⊨ 10 from
150–200F with showers, WC, telephone. Open from 5am–11pm.
Garden terrace. ⚑ Parking. Sights: Carcassonne, Montréal,
Castelnaudary.

BRANSLES 77620 Seine-et-Maine **RN 219 Map 9-B2**
⚲⊗ **LE LION D'OR** (N° RR OCT 25 156) (M. Philippe **Vercruyssen**) 2,
⌂ av. du Gâtinais ☎ 64-29-55-05. Restaurant: family cooking. Closed
Tue and 15 days in Sept. Rest. seats 30. Hotel ⊨ 7 at 80F.

BRAS-SUR-MEUSE 55100 Meuse **RD 964 Map 6-B3**

♀⊗ **LE RELAIS DE LA PAIX** (N° RR JUN 25 976) (Mme Anne-Marie **Renard**) 8, rue Raymond-Poincaré ☎ 29-83-90-13. Closed Tue. Rest. seats 60.

BRASSAC-LES-MINES 63570 Puy-de-Dôme **RD 34 Map 17-A3**

♀⊗ **LE BRASSAC** (N° RR FEV 27 175) (M. Édouard **Kaluza**) 6, avenue du Château ☎ 73-54-29-23. Restaurant: family cooking. Menu 50F. Lunch from 12–2pm. Dinner 7–9pm. Closed Tues and Sun afternoons. Credit cards accepted. Traditional décor. Rest. seats 60. Garden terrace. ⊨ Parking. Service station nearby open 6am–8pm. Sights: museum of wines, salmon museum.

BRAY 27170 Eure **D 133 Map 4-B3**

♀⊗ **AUX AMIS** (N° RR DEC 26 765) (Mme Margaret **Herils**) Beaumont-Le-Roger ☎ 32-35-05-26. Restaurant: family cooking. Specialities: duck cutlet with peppers, stew, faux filet with mushrooms. Menu 48F. Lunch from 11am–3pm. Closed Sun (except reservations), 15 days in July. Traditional décor. 54 places. ⊨ Parking. Sights: Beaumont, Brionne, Bec Hellouin, Neubourg.

BRECE 53120 Mayenne **Map 8-B1**

♀⊗ **LE DOMINO** (N° RR JAN 26 428) (M. **Carlin**) Le Bourg ☎ 43-08-62-72. **Minitel**. Restaurant: family cooking. Closed Sun.

BRETHENAY 52000 Haute-Marne **RN 67 Map 14-A2**

♀⊗ **BELLEVUE** (N° RR AOUT 7 903) (Mme Micheline **Bourgoin**)
Ⓗ Chaumont ☎ 25-32-51-02. Restaurant: closed Sun and Sept. Rest. seats 60 in 2 rooms. Parking. Filling station nearby open 6am–10pm.

BRETONCELLES 61110 Orne **Map 8-B3**

♀⊗ **HOTEL DE LA GARE** (N° RR OCT 26 335) (M. **Alloteau**) 17, rue
Ⓗ Ernest Sagot ☎ 37-37-20-13. ⊶ 6. Closed Sun.

BRETTEVILLE-L'ORGUEILLEUSE 14740 Calvados **RN 13 Map 4-B2**

♀⊗ **AU GRAND MONARQUE** (N° RR OCT 10 066) (Mme Madeleine
Ⓗ **Laurent**) 37, route de Caen ☎ 31-80-70-35. Restaurant: family cooking. Lunch from 12–3pm. Dinner from 7–10pm. Closed Sat and Sept. Traditional décor. Rest. seats 45 in 2 rooms. Hotel ⊶ 5 from 90–110F. ⊨ Car parking. Sights: the landing beaches, Caen, Bayeux.

BRETTNACH 57320 Moselle **Map 10-A1**

♀⊗ **AU RELAIS LORRAIN** (N° RR SEPT 27 388) (Mme Marie-Madeleine **Geyer**) 95, route de Bouzonville ☎ 87-35-97-36. German spoken.

BRIANÇON 05100 Hautes-Alpes **Map 19-B3**

♀⊗ **LA LANTERNE** (N° RR NOV 24 424) (M. René **Parisot**) Directions: 2km from Sud Briançon RN 80) Chamandrin ☎ 92-21-12-33. Closed 15 –30 Aug. Rest. seats 100. Evening meals until 10pm. English, Spanish spoken. Garden terrace.

BRIARE 45250 Loiret **RN 7 13-A1/2**

♀⊗ **SARL LE RELAIS** (N° RR OCT 26 685) (M. Eric **Bourgouin**) Gare
Ⓗ de Chatillon-sur-Loire ☎ 38-31-44-42. Restaurant: closed Sat

BRIENNE

Briare continued
evening, Sun. German and English spoken. Full-board 180F.
Rest. seats 125 + entertainment room. Hotel ⭲ 10. Parking.

BRIENNE 71290 Saône-et-Loire **Map 18-B1**
♈⊗ **AUX AMIS DE LA ROUTE** (N° RR OCT 27 041) (Mme Elsa **Busca**)
Bas de Brienne ☎ 85-40-04-18. Closed Mon and Aug. Italian and
English spoken. 24 hr filling station, 7km, also local filling station
open 7am–10pm.

BRIENON-SUR-ARMANÇON 89210 Yonne **Map 13-A2**
♈⊗ **LES ROUTIERS** (N° RR MARS 27 239) (M. Christian **Dussart**) 21,
⌂ route de Joigny ☎ 86-43-00-63. Polish, Russian and English
spoken. Hotel ⭲ 8. Filling station nearby open 6am–8pm.

BRIGNOLES 83170 Var **RN 7 and RD 554 Map 25-A2**
⊗ **AUBERGE LA REINETTE** (N° RR NOV 28 081) (Mlle Santina
Sepilesu) RN 7 ☎ 94-59-07-46. Closed Sun and Aug. German,
Italian spoken.
⊗ **RELAIS COTE D'AZUR** (N° RR 2 031) Aire de Service de
Cambarette on both sides of the Autoroute. ☎ 94-69-16-81.
Restaurant: regional cooking. Menu 25% reduction for coach
drivers. Children's menu. Self service. Open from 6.30am–11pm.
Credit cards accepted. Rest. seats 340. Garden terrace. ⌁
Regional shops, information, Bureau de Change, showers.

BRIONNE 27800 Eure **RN Map 4-B3**
♈⊗ ✰✰**HOTEL DU HAVRE** (N° RR DEC 27 748) (M. Jacky **Pavet**) 13,
⌂ rue de la Soie ☎ 32-44-80-28. Restaurant: regional and family
cooking. Specialities: dishes with sauces. Menus from 50–100F.
Children's menu. À la carte. Dinner until midnight. Credit cards
accepted. Rest. seats 100. Hotel ⭲ 32 from 180–240F with
showers, bathrooms, WC, TV. Sitting room. Garden terrace.
Parking. Sights: 12th-century château.

BRIOUDE 43100 Haute-Loire **RN 102 Map 17-A3**
♈⊗ **LES ROUTIERS** (N° RR AVR 16 506) (M. Roger **Devins**) route de
Clermont ☎ 71-50-14-39. ⭲ 4. Closed Sun, 15 Aug–1 Sept. Rest.
seats 52.

BRIOUX-SUR-BOUTONNE 79170 Deux-Sèvres **RN 150 Map 15-A1/2**
♈⊗ **AUBERGE DU CHEVAL BLANC** (N° RR MARS 27 234) (Mme
Catherine **Richard**) place du Champ-de-Foire ☎ 49-07-50-52.
English, German spoken. Restaurant: dinner until 9pm. Closed
Sun afternoon. Rest. seats 66. 24 hr filling station nearby.

BRIOUZE 61220 Orne **RN 24 Bis Map 8-A2**
♈⊗ **LE RELAIS DE LA POSTE** (N° RR FEV 3 369) (Mme **Maupas**) ☎
⌂ 33-66-03-16. ⭲ 10. Evening meals until midnight.

BRIVE-CHARENSAC 43700 Haute-Loire **RN 88 and 535 Map 17-A3**
♈⊗ **LE RELAIS DU COMMERCE** (N° RR DEC 23 561) (Mme **Ferret-**
⌂ **Masson**) 2, route de Lyon (on the banks of the Loire. ☎
71-09-16-16. Directions: Valence. Restaurant: family cooking.
Children's menu. Dinner until 9pm. Credit cards accepted.
Traditional décor. Rest. seats 100 in 2 rooms. Hotel ⭲ 10 from

80–120F with showers. Parking. Sights: the Puy, the Loire châteaux, the source of the Loire.

BRIVE LA GAILLARDE 19100 Corrèze **RN 89 and D Map 17-A1**

Ⓨ⊗ **LE NOUVEL HOTEL** (N° RR JAN 26 159) (M. Patrick **Lomey**) 2, ⌂ rue Desgeuettes ☎ 55-86-01-66. **Minitel**. Directions: Autoroute Paris/Toulouse, West Brive exit. Restaurant: family cooking. Specialities: Quercynoises. Children's menu. Lunch from 12– 1.15pm. Dinner from 6.45–9.30pm. Closed Sat and Sun and 15 days in Aug. Modern décor. Rest. seats 84 in 2 rooms. Hotel ⊷ 11 with showers and WCs. ⌿ Parking. Sights: Les Eyziers de Tayac, grottes de Lascaux, Rocamadour, Padirac.

BROGLIE 27270 Eure **RN 138 Map 8-A2 4-B3**

Ⓨ⊗ **LES TOURISTES ET LES ROUTIERS – RELAIS DE BROGLIE** (N° ⌂ RR JUN 17 824) (Mme Julienne **Vannier**) Côté de Bernay à Broglie, 47, rue Augustin-Fresnel ☎ 32-44-60-38. Closed 10 days Feb. Rest. seats 75. Evening meals to midnight. Hotel ⊷ 5.

BROMONT-LAMOTHE 63230 Puy-de-Dôme **RD 941 Map 16-B2**

⊗ **LE RELAIS DE BOISSY** (N° RR FEV 14 203) (Mme **Boissy**) ☎ 73-88-71-04.

BROSSE MONTCEAUX (LA) 77940 Seine-et-Marne **Map 9-B2**

Ⓨ⊗ **LE PETIT PERICHOIS** (N° RR FEV 27 549) (M. Aimé **Vollereau**) ☎ 60-96-25-75. English spoken. Filling station nearby.

BROU 28160 Eure-et-Loir **RN 155 Map 8-B3**

Ⓨ⊗ **HOTEL DE LA GARE – LE RELAIS DE L'ARC-EN-CIEL** (N° RR ⌂ MAR 16 915) (M. Alain **Duparc**) 76, avenue du Général-de-Gaulle ☎ 37-47-00-81 ⊷ 8. Closed Sun, Aug. Rest. seats 72. Evening meals.

BROUT-VERNET 03110 Allier **RN 9 Map 16-B3**

Ⓨ⊗ **CENTRE ROUTIERS – SARL** (N° RR JANV 24 475) (Mme **Roux**) ⌂ RN 9 ☎ 70-58-24-61. **Minitel**. Closed Sun. Coaches welcome. Rest. seats 70. Hotel ⊷ 14

BRUAILLES 71500 Saône-et-Loire **RD 972 Map 18-B1**

Ⓨ⊗ **REST. DES 4 CHEMINS** (N° RR MARS 27 225) (M. Thierry ⌂ **Rousse**) Les Quatre Chemins, Louhans ☎ 85-75-15-81. ⊷ 5. Closed Tue evening. Filling station nearby open 7am–8pm.

BRUAY LA BUISSIERE 62700 Pas-de-Calais **Map 5-A1**

Ⓨ⊗ ☆ **LA LOVETTE** (N° RR MARS 26 835) (Serge and Dany **Domart**) ⌂ 114, rue Raoult Briquet Place de la Gare ☎ 21-53-42-07. English and German spoken. Rest. seats 250. Hotel ⊷ 15 from 75–135F with TV. ⌿ Parking. Games room (Flipper, fléchettes, billard). Sights: Base d'Olhain, chateaux, the Artois hills.

BUCEY-LES-GY 70700 Haute-Saône **RD 474 Map 14-B3**

Ⓨ⊗ **CAFÉ DE LA GARE PIZZERIA** (N° RR MAI 25 921) (Mme Yvette **Bole-Besancon**) rue de la Gare ☎ 84-32-92-02. Coaches welcome. Rest. seats 50. Evening meals until 10pm.

BUIGNY-ST-MACLOU 80100 Somme **RN 1 Map 5-A3 4-A2**

Ⓨ⊗ **LE RELAIS DES ROUTIERS** (N° RR JUN 16 117) (M. Marc **Caron**) ⌂ ☎ 22-24-20-47 ⊷ 5. Restaurant: closed Sat afternoon.

BUISSE (LA)

BUISSE (LA) 38500 Isère **RN 75 Map 19-B3**

♈⊗ **RELAIS DES ROUTIERS CHEZ ANNIE** (N° RR MARS 27 219) (Mme Annie **Revigliono**) Le Village Voiron ☎ 76-55-00-67. Italian spoken. Filling station nearby open 6am–9pm.

BUNCEY 21400 Côte-d'Or **RN 71 Map 13-A3**

♈⊗ **LE CHARIOT** (N° RR JUN 26 555) (Paulette and Nadine **Lacroix**) Chatillon/Seine ☎ 80-91-09-82. Night bell for drivers. Closed Sun, 15–30 July. English spoken. Dinner served until 10pm.

BUSLOUP 41160 Loir-et-Cher **RN 157 Map 12-A3**

♈⊗ **CAFÉ DU COMMERCE** (N° RR JUIN 26 927) (Mme Marcelle **Flissi**) le Bourg Morée. Directions: between Orléans and Le Mans ☎ 54-23-43-41. Restaurant: family cooking. Menu at 52F. Lunch from 12.45–2.30pm. Closed Sun lunch. Traditional décor. Rest. seats 45. Hotel ⊨ 3 from 90–130F with showers. Open 7am–10pm. Sights: Vendôme, the Loire châteaux.

BUSSIÈRES 77750 Seine-et-Marne **RN 33 Map 9-A2**

♈⊗ **LE RELAIS AU SANS-GENE** (N° RR SEP 19 941) (M. Raymond **Tixier**) 32, route de la Ferté-sous-Jouarre ☎ 60-22-50-18. Closed Tue in Feb, July. Rest. seats 80. German, Polish spoken. Menus from 55-120F. Specialities: andouillette au champagne, filet de canard à l'orange ou aux pruneaux.

BUZANÇAIS 36500 Indre **RN 143 Map 12-B3**

♈⊗ **LE RELAIS DES ROUTIERS** (N° RR NOV 17 676) (M. Serge **Imbert**) 19, rue des Hervaux ☎ 54-84-07-37. Restaurant: dinner until 10pm. Closed Sun, 15 days Aug. Coaches welcome. Rest. seats 120. Hotel ⊨ 8.

♈⊗ **LES ROUTIERS** (N° RR JANV 26 133) (M. Bernard **Souadet**) 48, rue des Hervaux. Directions: on the road to Tours. ☎ 54-84-05-16. Restaurant: family cooking. Menu 50F. Lunch served from 12–3pm. Dinner from 7–9pm. Closed Sun. Modern décor. Rest. seats 14. ⊬ Garden terrace.

CAEN 14000 Calvados **RN 13 Map 4-B2 and 8 A-1**

♈⊗ ☆ **LA RENAISSANCE** (N° RR FEV 20 652) (M. **Lehericey**) Saint-Martin-des-Besaces ☎ 31-68-72-65. Restaurant: dinner served until 10pm. Closed Mon (low season), Feb. Rest. seats 70. English spoken. Hotel ⊨ 8.

CAGNY 14630 Calvados **RN 13 Map 4-B2**

♈⊗ **HOTEL DE LA POSTE** (N° RR JUL 26 602) (M. Dominique **Klaczak**) 32, route de Paris ☎ 31-23-41-26 ⊨ 5. Coaches welcome. Rest. seats 50. Evening meals. Closed Sunday.

♈⊗ ☆ **HOTEL DES ROUTIERS CHEZ JEAN-LOUIS ET MONIQUE** (N° RR FEV 25 806) (M. Louis **Charpentier**) 22, route de Paris ☎ 31-23-41-27 ⊨ 19. Restaurant: dinner served until 9pm. Closed Sat, Sun, Aug.

CAHORS 46000 Lot **RN 20 Map 22-A1 17-B1**

♈⊗ **LE RELAIS DE LA BOURSE** (N° RR MAR 23 721) (M. Jean-Henri **Lebouvier**) 7, place Rousseau ☎ 65-35-17-78 ⊨ 12. Closed Sun, Aug. Rest. seats 90.

CALIGNY 61100 Orne **Map 8 A-1**

♈⊗ **RELAIS DU PONT DE VERE** (N° RR JUN 27 618) (M. Henri **Vivier**) Le Pont de Vère ☎ 33-65-65-60. Restaurant: dinner served until 10pm. Closed Sun (except residental). Parking. 24 hr service station nearby.

CALLAC DE BRETAGNE 22160 Côtes-du-Nord RN 787 Map 7-A2

Ⓨ⊗ **LES ROUTIERS** (N° RR OCT 26 064) (Mme Marie Yvonne
⌂ **Richard**) 21, rue de la Gare. Directions: opposite the station ☎ 96-45-51-10. Restaurant: family cooking. Menu from 42F. Lunch from 12–2pm. Dinner from 7–8.30pm. Closed Sunday and the last two weeks in Aug. Traditional décor. Rest. seats 60 in 2 rooms. Hotel ⊷ 8 from 90–130F. Sights: Callac and the locality, the Coroney Gorges, plan d'eau.

CALMETTE (LA) 30190 Gard RN 6 Map 23-A1

Ⓨ⊗ **RELAIS DE L'ESCALETTE** (N° RR JUIL 27 332) (M. Georges **Apostolakis**) ☎ 66-63-13-63. English spoken. Evening meals to midnight. Filling station.

CAMBRAI 59400 Nord RN 17 Maps 5-B3, 6-A1 and A3

Ⓨ⊗ **AU RELAIS** (N° RR MAI 7 690) (M. Roger **Guisgand**) 1084, avenue
⌂ du Cateau ☎ 27-81-35-82 ⊷ 4. Closed Sun, July and Aug. Rest. seats 30.

Ⓨ⊗ **LA GARGOTE – CHEZ JEAN** (N° RR MAI 25 401) (M. Claude **Bedu**) 136, boulevard Jean-Bart ☎ 27-81-07-18. **Minitel**. Closed Sun. Coaches welcome. Rest. seats 140 in 3 rooms. Dinner served until 10pm.

Ⓨ⊗ **CHEZ ROGER** (N° RR MARS 27 204) (M. Roger **Leprince**) 10, rue
⌂ des Docks ☎ 27-83-26-05. Restaurant: dinner served until 10pm. Closed Sat, Sun and last 2 weeks of Aug. Filling station open 6am–11pm. Hotel ⊷ 6.

CAMBRES 76570 Seine-Maritime Map 3-A1

Ⓨ⊗ **LES AMIS DE LA ROUTE** (N° RR FEV 26 182) (Mme Denise **Ponthieux**) RN 27, Pavilly ☎ 35-32-51-98. Closed Sat, Sun, 1 week Christmas and New Year. Rest. seats 120. Evening meals until 9pm. English spoken.

CAMP DU CASTELLET (LE) 83330 Var RN 8 Map 24-B3

Ⓨ⊗ **LE RELAIS MIMI** (N° RR AVR 25 890) (Mme Francine **Ponche**) Route Nationale 8 ☎ 94-90-70-53. Closed Friday evening, Sat, Sun, between Christmas and New Year. Coaches welcome. Rest. seats 120 and terrace. Evening meals to midnight Sat. English, Italian spoken. Parking.

CAMPSEGRET 24140 Dordogne Nle 21 Map 15-B3

Ⓨ⊗ **LE RELAIS DES TAMARIS** (N° RR JANV 27 766) (M. Alain **Thomas**) Lacroix/Villamblard ☎ 53-24-21-75. Restaurant. Specialities: dishes from the region of Périgord. Menus from 50–125F. Dinner until midnight. Closed Sun night. Parking. Service station nearby open 7am–8.30pm.

CANNES 06400 Alpes-Maritimes Map 25-B2

Ⓨ⊗ ☆**CHALET DE LISÈRE** (N° RR OCT 27 422) (M. Claude **Santoro**)
⌂ 42, avenue de Grassre. Directions: 300m below the Police station ☎ 43-38-50-80. **Minitel**. Italian and a little English and German spoken. Restaurant: regional and family cooking. Menu at 75F. Lunch from 12–2pm. Dinner from 7–9pm. Closed 15 Dec–15 Jan. Traditional décor. Rest. seats 20. Hotel ⊷ 8 at 180F with showers, WC, telephone. Garden terrace. Parking. Service station nearby open 8am–8pm. Sights: the Festival Palace, the beaches.

CANNES-LA-BOCCA

CANNES-LA-BOCCA 06150 Alpes-Maritime **Map 25-B2**

♀⊗ **CAVE DE LA ROUBINE** (N° RR SEPT 26 313) (Mme **Pelletier**) 40, avenue de la Roubine ☎ 93-47-77-10. Restaurant: menu 52F. Open 7am–10pm. Closed Sun. Garden terrace. Parking. Service station nearby. Italian spoken.

♀⊗ **PARIS-PROVENCE** (N° RR AVR 25 903) (M. Joaquim **Roldan**) 68, rue Frances Tonner ☎ 93-47-10-48 ⊷ 15. Closed Sun (low season). Spanish spoken.

CAP-DE-PIN par ESCOURCE 40210 Landes **RN 10 Map 20-B2**

♀⊗ **AU ROUTIER** (N° RR MAR 9 439) (M. Jean-Pierre **Fortinon**)
⌂ Directions: exit 15 Cap de Pin, Sabres-Mimizan ☎ 58-07-20-54. Restaurant: regional cooking. Closed Sat (low season), Christmas holidays. Specialities: salade de foie de canard frais, ris de veau Madère, magret grillé. Menus from 60–190F. Children's menu. À la carte. Dinner served until 10pm. Credit cards accepted. Rest. seats 150 in 4 rooms. Hotel ⊷ 14 from 110–200F with showers. Open from 6am–11pm. Garden terrace. ⊶ Parking. Sights: Museum of Margueze, Mimizan beach, riding, tennis.

CAPENDU 11700 Aude **RN 113 Map 22-B2**

♀⊗ **LA CAVE DES ARTS** (N° RR JANV 26 431) (M. Yves **Peyramayou**) RN 113 ☎ 68-79-09-30. Closed Sun evenings (low season). Rest. seats 60. Evening meals to 9pm. Parking.

CAPPELLE-EN-PEVELE 59242 Nord **RN 393 Map 5-B1**

♀⊗ **LAS VEGAS** (N° RR SEP 26 666) (Mme Eliane **Duquesnoy**) 13, rue de l'Obeau ☎ 20-61-83-10. Closed Sun. Evening meals to 8pm.

CARCAGNY 14740 Calvados **Map 4B-2**

♀⊗ **AUX JOYEUX ROUTIERS** (N° RR SEPT 27 679) (M. Michel **Pacary**) Hameau Saint Léger. Directions: Caen-Bayeux ☎ 31-80-22-01. Italian and English spoken. Restaurant: regional and family cooking. Menu à la carte. Dinner until 11pm. Closed Sun.

CARCASSONNE 11000 Aude **RN 113 Map CO 119 22-B2**

♀⊗ **LE RELAIS DE L'AVENIR** (N° RR MAR 1 824) (Mme Madeleine
⌂ **Pesez**) 93, avenue Franklin-Roosevelt ☎ 68-25-09-39. Hotel ⊷ 12. Restaurant: dinner until 9pm. Closed Sun, public holidays.

♀⊗ **LE XENON** (N° RR JUN 27 626) (**SDF Deblais and Ayward**) route de Mazamet ☎ 68-25-97-62. English and Spanish spoken. Restaurant. Specialities: fillets, meat in sauce, pizza. Menu 30–75F. Dinner until midnight. Parking.

CARENTAN 50500 Manche **RN 13 Map 4-B1**

♀⊗ **LE DERBY** (N° RR SEPT 26 993) (Maurice **Le Guélinet**) 21, rue de la 101 Airborne. Directions: between Cherbourg and Caen ☎ 33-42-04-77. Restaurant: family cooking. Speciality: tripes maison. Dinner until 9pm. Closed Sat afternoon, Sun and last week Sept and first 2 weeks Oct. Filling station nearby. Coaches welcome. Rest. seats 36. Sights: the landing beaches, churches and the Town Hall.

CARHAIX 29270 Finistère **RN 164 Map 7-A/B2**

♀⊗ **AU CHEVAL BRETON** (N° RR SEP 16 715) (M. Louis **Le Mignon**) 2,
⌂ boulevard de la République ☎ 98-93-01-38. Restaurant: closed Sat and Sun. Hotel ⊷ 10. ⊶ Parking.

CARIGNAN 08110 Ardennes **Map 6-A3**

♀⊗ **LE RELAIS D'YVOIS** (N° RR AVR 26 500) (M. Fabrice **Fossani**) 33, route de Sedan ☎ 24-22-08-78. Rest. seats 66.

CARNET DES MAURES (LE) 8340 Var **Map 25 A-2**

♀⊗ **AUX QUATRE VENTS** (N° RR FEV 27 784) (Mme Antonia Sappa) Route Nationale 7 ☎ 94-60-73-05. Italian spoken. Restaurant: menu at 51F. Closed Sun. Lunch. Parking. Service station nearby.

CARNOULES 83600 Var **Map 25-A2**

♀⊗ **CHEZ DOUDOU** (N° RR JUN 25 025) (M. Adrien **Piasco**) 20, rue
⌂ Pierre-Sémard ☎ 94-28-33-15. **Minitel**. Restaurant: closed Sat, 15 days Sept. Rest. seats 150 in 2 rooms. Evening meals until 9.30pm. Italian spoken. Hotel ⊷ 4.

CARPENTRAS 84200 Vaucluse **RN 538 Map 24-A2**

♀⊗ **BAR DU MARCHE GARE** (N° RR AVR 24 922) (M. Bernard **Gil**) Marché Gare ☎ 90-63-19-00. Closed Sun. Coaches welcome. Rest. seats 220. Spanish spoken. Dinner until 9pm.

CARPIQUET 14650 Calvados **Map 4-B2**

♀⊗ **LE POURQUOI PAS?** (N° RR JUIN 27 312) (M. Didier **Prempain**) 33, route de Bayeux Bellevue ☎ 31-73-84-84. Dinner served until 8pm. Closed Sat evening, Sun and Aug. Local filling station.

CARSIX 27300 Eure **RN 13 Map 4-B3**

♀⊗ **L'ESCALE** (N° RR OCT 26 711) (M. Michel **Silliau**) Carrefour de
⌂ Malbrouck Bernay ☎ 32-44-79-99. Restaurant: family cooking. Children's menu. Dinner until 10pm. Closed Sat afternoons and Sun. Credit cards accepted. Rest. seats 54 in 2 rooms. Hotel ⊷ 4 from 95–160F. Open from 7am–9pm. Sights: the Monastery of Bel Hellouin.

CAST 29150 Finistère **RD 7 and 107 Map 7-B1**

♀⊗ ☆ **NN LE RELAIS SAINT GILDAS** (N° RR MAR 22 727) (Mme
⌂ Marie **Philippe** for the hotel and M. Patrice **Philippe** for restaurant). 11 and 13, rue du Kreisker ☎ 98-73-54-76 or 73-55-43. English spoken. **Minitel**. Restaurant: regional and family cooking. Specialities: sea food and couscous maison. Menus from 44–170F. Children's menu. À la carte. Dinner until 9pm. Closed Sat and 15 Oct–15 Nov. Credit cards accepted. Rest. seats 100. Hotel ⊷ 15 from 80–190F with showers, WC. Open from 10am–10pm. Garden terrace. ⊩ Parking. Sights: chapels and roadside crosses, the old town of Locroman, fishing port of Dournenez, beaches.

CASTAIGNOS SOUSLENS 40700 Landes **Map 20 B-2**

♀⊗ **MIAMYS** (N° RR JULY 27 638) (M. Jean-Pierre **Ferrier**) Hagetman ☎ 58-89-06-02. Restaurant. Specialities: heart kebabs, landaise salad, duck filets. Menus from 28–50F. Dinner until 11pm. Closed Mon and Tue evenings.

CASTELNAU-RIVIÈRE-BASSE 65700 Hautes-Pyrénées **Map 21-A2**

♀⊗ **LE MILLEPATTE** (N° RR MAI 27 285) (M. André **Zanardo**) route de Bordeaux ☎ 62-31-97-99. **Minitel**. Local filling station. Restaurant: dinner until midnight. Rest. seats 50. Parking.

CASTELSARRASIN 82100 Tarn-et-Garonne **RN 113 Map 22-A1**

♀⊗ ☆ **CHEZ MAURICE** (N° RR JANV 27 152) (M. Jean-Pierre
⌂ **Boissier**) 35, route de Toulouse. Directions: between Toulouse

CASTETS-DES-LANDES

Castelsarrasin continued
and Bordeaux ☎ 63-32-30-83. Restaurant: regional and family cooking. Specialities: cassoulet, fillet of duck, preserves. Menus from 47–75F. Children's menu. À la carte. Lunch from 12–3pm. Dinner from 7–10.30pm. Closed Sat evening, Sun and Aug. Modern décor. Rest. seats 150 in 2 rooms. Hotel ⇥ 15 with showers. Open from 5.30am–12.30am. Garden terrace. ⊭ Parking. Service station nearby open 7am until midnight. Sights: Moissac, Auvillar, Le canal du Midi, Saint Antonin Noble Val.

CASTETS-DES-LANDES 40260 Landes **RN 10 Map 20-A2**
Ⓨ⊗ **LE STUC** (N° RR SEPT 18 528) (Mme **Calleja**) ☎ 58-89-40-62. Family cooking. Dinner until midnight. Closed Sun, Oct. Spanish spoken. Rest. seats 100 in 3 rooms.
Ⓨ⊗ **LE CARRIOU DE CHANCHON** (N° RR DEC 25 766) (M. Josianne **Lataste**) RN 10 ☎ 58-89-40-63. Restaurant: dinner until 9pm. Closed Mon evening and bank holidays at the end of the year. Rest. seats 145.

CASTRES 81100 Tarn **RN 622 Map 22-B2**
Ⓨ⊗ **AUX AMIS DE LA ROUTE** (N° RR OCT 17 391) (M. Michel
⌂ **Labessouille**) avenue Charles-de-Gaulle ☎ 63-35-54-38. Directions: on the exit to Castres on the road to Béziers. Restaurant: family cooking. Menu 55F. À la carte lunch from 12–3pm. Dinner from 7–9pm. Closed Sun afternoon. Credit cards accepted. Traditional décor. Rest. seats 100 in 2 rooms. Hotel ⇥ 8. Garden terrace. ⊭ Parking. Sights: Le Sidobre, the black mountain.

CATEAU (LE) 59360 Nord **Map 5 B-3**
Ⓨ⊗ **SARL L'ESCALE** (N° RR JUNE 27 012) (Mme Elizabeth **Masson**) 65, route de Bazuel ☎ 27-84-25-50. Restaurant: closed Sun. Parking.

CAUDAN 56850 Morbihan **RD 81 (ZA de Kergoussel) Map 7-B2**
⊗ **LE BOUTON D'OR** (N° RR FEV 27 179) (Mme Joëlle **Le Bail**) ☎ 97-81-16-01. Dinner served until 8pm. Closed Sun. English spoken. Local filling station.

CAUDEBEC-LES-ELBEUF 76320 Seine-Maritime **RN 321 Map 3-B1**
Ⓨ⊗ **LE TIVOLI BAR** (N° RR AVR 25 908) (M. André **Jean**) 43, rue Félix-Faure ☎ 35-77-16-94. **Minitel**. Closed Sun. Dinner served until 9pm.

CAULNES 22350 Côtes-du-Nord **Map 7-B3**
Ⓨ⊗ **LES ROUTIERS** (N° RR MARS 22 726) (Mme **Gaudrel**) 40, rue de la Gare ☎ 96-83-94-14.

CAUNEILLE 40300 Landes **RN 117 Map 20-A2**
Ⓨ⊗ **AU HAOU** (N° RR MARS 26 836) (Mme Henriette **Lalanne**) ☎ 58-73-04-60. Closed 20 Dec–5 Jan. Dinner served until 11pm. Rest. seats 120.

CAUSSADE 82300 Tarn-et-Garonne **RN 20 Map 22-A1**
Ⓨ⊗ **RELAIS D'AUVERGNE** (N° RR JUIL 25 040) (M. Antoine **Noualhac**).
⌂ Directions: between Moutauban and Cahors. ☎ 63-93-03-89. Restaurant: regional cooking. Specialities: grills and cassoulet. Menus from 46–95F. Children's menu. À la carte. Closed Sun. Credit cards accepted. Rest. seats 120 in 2 rooms. Hotel ⇥ 14 from

CERE

88–130F with showers, WC. Open from 6am–11pm. Garden terrace. ⚑ 24 hr service station nearby. Sights: the Tarn Gorges.

CAUVERVILLE-EN-ROUMOIS 27350 Eure RN 175 Map 4-B3
♈⊗ **LE MEDINE** (N° RR NOV 27 462) (M. Jean-Pierre **Ferrette**) Directions: at the Medine crossroads, 450m towards Rouen. ☎ 32-57-01-55. **Minitel**. Restaurant: family cooking. Specialities: sauerkraut, pizza, couscous. Menu at 46F. Dinner until 7pm. Closed Sat, Sun and Aug. Rest. seats 50. ⚑ Parking. Service station nearby. Sights: the Château of Robert le Diable, scrubland of Barneville, the Tancarville Bridge.

CAVAILLON 84300 Vaucluse RN 538/573 Map 24-A3
♈⊗ **LE RELAIS SAINT-JACQUES** (N° RR NOV 24 024) (Mme Jeannine **Raoux**) 649, avenue de la Libération ☎ 90-71-42-02. Closed Sat evening, Sun. Italian spoken.
♈⊗ **LES ROUTIERS** (N° RR OCT 27 440) (M. Claude **Liard**) 21, avenue de Verdun ☎ 90-71-39-41. Closed Sun. Evening meals. 24 hr local filling station.

CAVALERIE (LA) 12230 Aveyron RN 9 Map 23-A1
♈⊗ **RELAIS DES INFRUTS** (N° RR SEPT 27 034) (M. Jeannot 🏠 **Cazabonne**) ☎ 65-62-70-82 ⇌ 7. Spanish spoken.

CAZAN 13116 Bouches-du-Rhône RN 7 Map 24-B3
⊗ **L'ESCALIER CHEZ ALEXANDRE** (N° RR JUL 25 473) (M. Alexandre **Ghigo**) RN 7 Vernègues ☎ 90-59-13-15. Closed Sun.

CEIGNES 01430 Ain Map 18 B-2
⊗ **RELAIS DU BUGEY** (N° RR 2 032) Aire de Service de Ceignes on both carriageways of the autoroute ☎ 74-75-60-06. English spoken. Restaurant: regional cooking. A discount of 25% is given to coach drivers. Menu à la carte. Open from 7am–11pm. Credit cards accepted. Sitting room. Garden terrace. ⚑ Regional exhibition with photos. Regional shops. Tourist information. Nursery. The restaurant offers a variety of local dishes and wines.

CELLE-SAINT-AVANT (LA) 37610 Indre-et-Loire Map 12-B2
♈⊗ **LA CARAVANE** (N° RR DEC 24 440) (M. Serge **Judes**) Descartes 🏠 ☎ 47-65-07-82 ⇌ 7. Meals served until 1am. Closed Sun, 15 days in Aug. Coaches welcome. Rest. seats 92.

CELON 36200 Indre RN 20 Map 16-A1
♈⊗ **LA BROUETTE** (N° RR NOV 22 991) (Mme Yvette **Dufour**) ☎ 54-25-32-08. Closed Sun. Evening meals to 9.30pm.

CENAC-SAINT-JULIEN 24250 Dordogne RN 703 Map 17-B1
♈⊗ **LA PROMENADE** (N° RR OCT 25 153) (M. Pascal **Thomas**) RN 703 ☎ 53-28-36-87. Restaurant: regional cooking. Children's menu. Dinner until 8pm. Credit cards accepted. Rest. seats 65. Hotel ⇌ 4 from 100–150F. Open 7am until midnight. ⚑ Parking. Sights: the heart of Périgord noir.

CERE 400900 Landes Map 20-B2
♈⊗ **RELAIS DE L'ECUREUIL** (N° RR SEPT 26 674) (Mme Martine **Belmonte**) Au Bourg ☎ 58-51-49-33. Closed Wed. Some English, Portuguese, Spanish spoken. Coaches welcome. Rest. seats 110. Closed Wed.

CHAGNY

CHAGNY 71150 Saône-et-Loire **RN 74 Maps 13-B3 and 18-A/B1**
♈⊗ **LE RELAIS TERMINUS** (N° RR JUL 21 575) (M. Jean-Louis
⌂ **Potsimeck**) 1, avenue de la Gare ☎ 85-87-18-13. ⇥ 15. Closed Sun,
Dec. Rest. seats 60. Evening meals to 10pm. English, Polish spoken.

CHAIGNES 27120 Eure **Map 3-B1**
♈⊗ **MA CAMPAGNE** (N° RR AVR 25 920) (M. Gérard **Ducoat**) RN 13
⌂ ☎ 32-36-95-52. Restaurant: closed Sat evening, Sun. English
spoken. Hotel ⇥ 14.

CHAILLE LES MARAIS 85450 Vendée **Map 11 A-1**
♈⊗ **LA FLAMANDRIERE 'Chti-Mi'** (N° RR FEV 27 547) (M. Jean-
Pierre **Tison**) Route Nationale 137. Le Sableau ☎ 51-56-70-87.
Minitel. English spoken. Restaurant: dinner until 9pm. Closed Sat
and 23 Dec–2 Jan. Service station nearby open 9am–9pm.

CHAINTRIX BIERGES 51130 Marne **RN 33 Map 9-A3**
♈⊗ **LE RELAIS DE LA SOUDE** (N° RR DEC 26 113) (SARL Mme
Françoise **Andrieu**) Vertus ☎ 26-66-43-80. Evening meals until
midnight. German spoken. Closed on Mon.

CHALAIS 24800 Dordogne **Map 17 A-1**
♈⊗ **LES JARDINS DE LA TUILIERE** (N° RR JAN 27 491) (Mme Suzette
Deschamps) Mavaleix ☎ 53-52-03-85. English, Spanish spoken.
Restaurant: regional and family cooking. Specialities: preserves
foie gras, local wines available on request. Menu 50F. A la carte.
Lunch from 11.30am–2.30pm. Dinner 7.30–9.30pm. Closed Mon
after 2pm. Modern décor. Rest. seats 70. Garden terrace. ⇥
Parking. Service station nearby open 7am–8pm.

CHALLANS 85300 Vendée **RN 148 Map 11-B2**
♈⊗ **LE RELAIS DE LA NOUE** (N° RR AVR 24 209) (Mme Monique
Menez) Place Victor-Charbonnel ☎ 51-93-20-20. Closed Sat
night, Sun, 3 weeks in Aug.

CHALLUY 58000 Nièvre **RN 7 Map 13-B2**
♈⊗ **LE RELAIS DU PONT CARREAU** (N° RR AVR 22 283) (Mme
Fernande **Taillemitte**) ☎ 86-21-00-02 ⇥ 4.

CHALONS-SUR-MARNE 51000 Marne **RN 3 and 33 Maps 6-B2 and 9-A3**
⊗ **AU MONT SAINT-MICHEL** (N° RR JUN 15 689) (SNC-**Queige,
Mazeau et Cie**) 31, route de Troyes RN 77 ☎ 26-68-05-08. **Minitel**.
Closed Sun evening. Coaches welcome. Rest. seats 160. Evening
meals. English, Spanish spoken. Parking.
♈⊗ **LE DELKO** (N° RR SEP 25 101) (M. Christian **Sinot**) rue de
⌂ Douanes **La Veuve** ☎ 26-67-30-68. **Minitel** ⇥ 8. Closed Sat and
Sun. Dinner until midnight.

CHAMALIERES-SUR-LOIRE 43800 Haute-Loire **Map 18-A3**
♈⊗ **LES ROUTIERS** (N° RR MARS 26 289) (Mme Françoise **Gentes**)
Vorey ☎ 71-03-42-10 ⇥ 4. Filling station 4.5kms. Closed in Oct.

CHAMARANDE 91730 Essonne **RN 20 Map 9-B1**
⊗⌂ ☆ **LE RELAIS DE MONTFORT** (N° RR FEV 17 740) (M. Roland
Cottin) RN 20 ☎ 60-82-20-80. **Minitel**. Closed Sat evening, Sun,
Aug. Coaches welcome. Rest. seats 120. Evening meals until

12pm. English spoken. Hotel ⊷ 30 from 70–180F with showers and WC. Open from 3.30am–11pm. ⚐ Parking.

CHAMBILLY 71100 Saône-et-Loire Map 18-A1

🍽⊗ **LE RELAIS DU COMMERCE ET DES SPORTS** (N° RR MAI 20
⌂ 727) (M. Paul and Monique **Prioris**) rue du Général-de-Gaulle ☎ 85-25-03-62 ⊷ 6. Closed Sat afternoon. Italian spoken. Shaded terrace. 'Boule' played.

CHAMBLY 60230 Oise Map 3-B2

🍽⊗ **LE RELAIS DE CHAMBLY** (N° RR DEC 26 130) (Mme Françoise
⌂ **Violette**) 660, avenue A.-Briand. Directions: On the old RN 1 Paris-Beauvais near to Persan Beaumont sur Oise ☎ 34-70-50-37. **Minitel**. Restaurant: family cooking. Menu 55F. Dinner until 9pm. Closed Sat and Sun, the weeks of 15 Aug, 15 Dec, 15 Jan. Traditional décor. Rest. seats 50. Hotel ⊷ 15 from 120–250F with showers, bathrooms, WC. Garden terrace. ⚐ Parking. Service station nearby. Sights: Chantilly, Seulis, L'Isle Adam, Royaumont Abbey.

CHAMBORET 87140 Haute-Vienne RN 147 Map 16-B1

🍽⊗ **LA BERGERIE** (N° RR AVR 27 241) (M. Francis **Albenque-Moreau**) ☎ 55-75-78-21. Restaurant: dinner until 11pm. Rest. seats 85. Local filling station 7am–8pm.

🍽⊗ **LE COMPOSTEL** (N° RR OCT 27 425) (M. Jacques **Caenon**) La lande ☎ 55-08-50-16 or 53-44-05. English, Spanish, Italian spoken. Evening meals. Local filling station 7am–8pm.

CHAMBOULIVE 19450 Corrèze D 940 Map 17-A1

🍽⊗ **RELAIS DU GOZEE** (N° RR JAN 26 793) (Mme Lina **Mazurier**)
⌂ route de Tulle ☎ 55-21-60-90 ⊷ 5. Closed 24 Aug–8 Sept. Portuguese spoken.

CHAMPAGNE 24650 Dordogne Map 15-B3

🍽⊗ **LE RELAIS DES FOUGERES** (N° RR JUL 26 594) (M. Hubert **Gehan**) RN 157 ☎ 48-89-50-96. Closed Sat night and Sun. Coaches welcome. Rest. seats 50. Meals served until 10pm.

CHAMPAGNE-MOUTON 16350 Charente RN 740 Map 15-B2

🍽⊗ ☆ **RELAIS DE PLAISANCE** (N° RR SEPT 15 354) (Mme Denise
⌂ **Delhoume**) place du Château. Directions: between Ruffec and Confonlens ☎ 45-31-80-52 and 45-31-98-19. Restaurant: regional and family cooking. Specialities: Dublin Bay prawns americaine, fillets of duck. Menu from 120–150F. Children's menu. À la carte. Lunch 12–2pm. Dinner 7–9pm. Credit cards accepted. Rest. seats 100 in 2 rooms. Hotel ⊷ 15 from 150–200F with showers, bathrooms. Sitting room. Garden terrace. ⚐ Parking.

CHAMPAGNEUX 73240 Savoie RN 516 Map 19-A2

🍽⊗ **RELAIS DES TROIS PROVINCES CHEZ NICOLE** (N° RR FEV 26 459) (Mme Nicole **Curtillat**) ☎ 76-31-83-22. Closed Aug.

CHAMPAGNOLE 39300 Jura Map 19-A1

🍽⊗ **LES ROUTIERS** (N° RR AVR 25 873) (M. Georges **Chagre**) La Billaude ☎ 84-52-07-95. Closed Sun. Evening meals.

CHAMPIGNEULLES 54520 Meurthe-et-Moselle RN 4 Maps 10-A2 and 14 B-1

🍽⊗ **AUBERGE FLEURIE** (N° RR MAR 24 891) (Mme Nathalie **Cheikh**)

CHAMPLOST

Champigneulles continued
Fonds de Toul Les Baraques Nancy Ouest ☎ 83-98-27-30. Closed
Sat, Sun, 15 days in Feb, Jul. English, German spoken.

CHAMPLOST 89210 Yonne **Map 9-B2**
♀⊗ **CHEZ MARIE-CLAUDE** (N° RR OCT 26 356) (Mme Marie-
Claude **Lauvin**) 23, route de Paris ☎ 86-43-14-71. Closed Wed, 15
days in Feb and 15 days in Aug. Coaches welcome. Rest. seats
70. Evening meals to 10pm.

CHAMPREPUS 50800 Manche **Map 8-A1**
♀⊗ **LE RELAIS DE CHAMPREPUS** (N° RR AOÛT 27 368) (M. Patrick
Jouaudin) Le Bourg Villedieu-les-Poêles ☎ 33-51-42-32. Closed
Wed, first 8 days in Sept. Dinner served until 9pm. Rest. seats 45.

CHAMPROND-EN-GATINE 28240 Eure-et-Loir **RN 23 Map 8-B3**
♀⊗ **LE RELAIS DE CHAMPROND** (N° RR OCT 23 997) (M. Michel
Jonnier) 5, Grande-Rue ☎ 37-49-82-18. Closed Sun, 15–30 Aug.

CHAMPTOCE-SUR-LOIRE 49170 Maine-et-Loire **Maps 11-A3 and
12-A1**
♀⊗ **HOTEL LES RIVETTES** (N° RR NOV 26 373) (Mme Agnès
Chêne) route de Montjean ☎ 41-39-91-75. Directions: Nantes–
Angers 25kms on the Angers route at Montjean 150m of the RN
23. **Minitel**. Restaurant: regional and family cooking. Specialities:
angevine tripe, duck in a nutmeg sauce. Menu 40F. Self-service.
Closed Sat and Sun; 15 Jul–15 Aug. Rest. seats 40. Hotel ⊷ 4 from
69–145F with shower. Open 7am–9pm. Garden terrace. ⊬ Parking. Sights: the Loire Valley, Angers Château, vineyards.

CHANGÉ 53810 Mayenne **Map 8-A1**
♀⊗ **LE RELAIS DE NIAFLES** (N° RR FEV 27 187) (M. Pierre **Dabet**)
Niafles ☎ 43-53-76-15. Directions: A81 – exit 31 route Laval
Mayenne. Restaurant: family cooking. Menu at 50F. Lunch
11.30am–2pm. Dinner until 10pm. Closed Sat and Sun. Credit
cards accepted. Rest. seats 55 in 3 rooms. Parking.

CHANTENAY-SAINT-IMBERT 58240 Nièvre **RN 7 Map 16-A3**
♀⊗ **AU BON ACCUEIL** (N° RR DEC 9 101) (Mme Lucette **Vacher**)
RN 7, St-Pierre-le-Moutier ☎ 86-38-61-95. Restaurant: family
cooking. Specialities: trout in a Bourbon sauce, omelette bûcher-
onne. Menu 50F. À la carte. Dinner until 10pm. Closed Sun.
Traditional décor. Rest. seats 26. Garden terrace. ⊬ Car parking.
Sights: Saint Augustins Château, animal park, amusement park,
the forest of Tronçais.
♀⊗ **RELAIS SAINT-IMBERT** (N° RR JANV 27 150) (Mlle **Fressie**)
St-Pierre-le-Moutier ☎ 86-36-61-65. Closed Sat afternoon, Sun.
German spoken. Restaurant. Specialities: sauerkraut and potée
(veg cooked with meat and beans). Dinner served until 11pm.
Rest. seats 20. Parking. Local filling station open 8am–12pm.

CHAPELAUDE 03530 Allier **RN 143 Map 16-A2**
♀⊗ **LE RELAIS DES TARTASSES** (N° RR MAR 24 873) (Mme Colette
Boutillon) Huriel ☎ 70-06-45-06. **Minitel**. Coaches welcome. Rest.
seats 50. Evening meals. Hotel ⊷ 4 with showers. Service station
nearby.

CHARENTON-LE-PONT

CHAPELLE-CARO (LA) 56460 Morbihan **RN 166 Map 7-B3**
Ⓨ⊗ HOTEL DE LA GARE (N° RR MAR 23 725) (Mme Marie-Claire
⌂ Boulavais) La Gare ☎ 97-74-93-63. Minitel ⊷ 4. Coaches welcome.
Rest. seats 90. Evening meals until 11pm. Closed 25 Dec–2 Jan.

CHAPELLE D'ANGILLON (LA) 18380 Cher **Map 13 A-1**
Ⓨ⊗ LA SURPRISE (N° RR JANV 27 512) (M. Genon **Ennordres**) ☎
48-58-26-97. English spoken. Restaurant: closed Sat from 3pm
and Sun. Service station nearby.

CHAPELLE D'AUREC (LA) 43120 Haute-Loire **Map 18-A3**
Ⓨ⊗ RELAIS DE LA CHAPELLE (N° RR JUIN 27 295) (M. Gabriel
⌂ Colombet) La Mioulaterre ☎ 71-66-53-55 ⊷ 4. Closed Sun
evening. Evening meals until 10pm. Parking.

CHAPELLE DU BOIS (LA) 72400 Sarthe **Map 8-B2**
Ⓨ⊗ LA CROIX BLANCHE (N° RR MAI 26 886) Directions: Axe
Alençon – Mamers – St Cosmes – La Ferté – Bernard (Mme
Annich **Boudet**) Le Bourg ☎ 43-93-18-01. Closed Aug.

CHAPELLE-LA-REINE (LA) 77760 Seine-et-Marne **RN 152 Map 9-B1/2**
Ⓨ⊗ LE RELAIS DE LA SALAMANDRE (N° RR MAI 27 283) (Mme
⊷ Marie-Claude **Gachet**) 5, rue du Docteur Battesti ☎ 64-24-30-03
⊷ 2. Open 24 hrs. Closed Sat, Sun. Rest. seats 44. Parking.

CHAPELLE-SAINT-LAURENT (LA) 79430 Deux-Sèvres **RN 748 Map 15-A1**
Ⓨ⊗ RELAIS DES SPORTS (N° RR AVR 26 231) (Mme Louisette
Guérin) 6, route de Bressuire ☎ 49-72-05-64. Coaches welcome.
Rest. seats 110. Evening meals.

CHAPELLE-SAINT-SEPULCRE (LA) 45210 Loiret **RN 60 Map 9-B2**
Ⓨ⊗ LA POTENCE (N° RR FEV 25 825) (Mme Liliane **Visier**) RN 60 ☎
38-92-03-10. Minitel. Closed Sat and Sun, 15 days in June.

LA CHAPELLE SOUS DUN 71800 Saône-et-Loire **Map 18-A2**
Ⓨ⊗ RESTAURANT DE LA MINE (N° RR SEPT 26 660) (Mme Ariette
⊷ **Champiaux**) ☎ 85-28-16-15. Closed Sat, 15 days at Christmas and
15 days in Feb. Rest. seats 90. Evening meals to 9.30pm.

CHAPELLE-SUR-LOIRE (LA) 37140 Indre-et-Loire **RN 152 Map 12-B2**
Ⓨ⊗ LE RELAIS DE LA MAIRIE (N° RR AVR 21 509) (M. Jacques
⌂ **Joyeau**) place Albert Ruelle ☎ 47-97-34-07 ⊷ 12. Coaches
welcome. Rest. seats 70.
LE ZEBRE A CARREAUX (N° RR JANV 27 768) (M. Raymond
Noël) Le Bourg ☎ 47-97-45-50. English, German and Flemish
spoken. Restaurant. Menu at 45F. Open from 6am–1am. Parking.
Service station nearby 7am–7.30pm.

CHARENTON-DU-CHER 18210 Cher **RN 151 Bis Maps 13-B2 and 16-A2**
⊗ A LA BONNE TABLE (N° RR NOV 18 554) (Mme Antoinette
Frège) ☎ 48-60-72-73. Family cooking. Closed Aug. ⊷ Evening
meals to 10pm. Parking.

CHARENTON-LE-PONT 94220 Val-de-Marne Porte de Charenton
Map 1-B3
Ⓨ⊗ L'ALLIANCE (N° RR AOU 19 120) (M. Albert **Series**) 121, rue de
Paris ☎ 43-68-03-71. Closed Wed, Aug. Meals served until 9pm.

CHARMES-SUR-L'HERBASSE

Charenton-Le-Pont continued

☠⊗ **PARIS-LISBONNE** (N° RR MAI 24 229) (SARL **Le Paris-Lisbonne-Durarte**) 195, rue de Paris ☎ 43-68-32-29. Closed Aug. Evening meals until 10pm. Portuguese, Spanish spoken.

CHARMES-SUR-L'HERBASSE 26260 Drôme **Map 18-B3**

☠⊗ **LE CABARET NEUF** (N° RR AVR 27 253) (M. Michel **Deveton**) ☎ 75-45-65-65. Closed Tue and 15 Sept–1 Oct. Local filling station 6am–8pm.

CHARSONVILLE 45130 Loiret **RN 157 Map 12-A3**

☠⊗ **LE RELAIS DES ROUTIERS** (N° RR DEC 27 120) (M. Patrick **Biliard**) 15, rue de la Libération ☎ 38-74-23-00. Restaurant: regional and family cooking. Menu 41–50F. Closed Sun, Mon afternoon and Aug. Credit cards accepted. Rest. seats 50. Garden terrace. Parking. Local filling station (petrol only) 7.30am–9pm. Sights: the Loire châteaux.

CHARTRE SUR LE LOIR (LA) 72340 Sarthe **Map 12 A-2**

☠⊗ **RESTAURANT JEANNE D'ARC** (N° RR SEPT 27 662) (M. Jacques **Olivier**) 23 Place Carnot ☎ 43-44-41-14. Restaurant: closed Sun. Hotel ⊨ 5.

CHARTRES 28000 Eure-et-Loir **RN 10 Map 8-B3**

☠⊗ ✰✰ **LE RELAIS BEAUCERON** (N° RR AVR 19 743) (M. **Lichet**) Mignières. This hotel, in the centre of Beauce, is 200m from the A11–Thivars exit, and near RN 10: 10km from Chartres, 100km from Paris ☎ 37-26-46-21. English and Spanish spoken. **Minitel**. Hotel ⊨ 30 from 190–210F bath, shower, own WC, colour TV. Restaurant: regional and family cooking. Specialities: oeufs à la Chartres, côte de boeuf au gris meunier, escargots de Voves à la fondue de poireaux, filet mignon à l'orléanaise. Menu from 67–120F. Children's menu, à la carte. Open 5am until midnight. Closed Sat (low season) and Sun. Rest. seats 60. Garden terrace. ↳ Parking. Sights: the valleys of the Eure and Loire, Beauce windmill, Chartres Cathedral, Châteaudun château.

☠⊗ **LE RELAIS DES BEAUMONTS** (N° RR MAI 25 392) (M. Patrick **Petit**) avenue François Arago, Rocade sur de Chartres ☎ 37-28-22-00. Closed Sat, Sun, Aug. Evening meals until 10pm. Rest. seats 70 in 2 rooms. Parking. 24 hr service station nearby.

☠⊗ **RESTAURANT LE PALMIER** (N° RR FEV 26 803) (M. Boussad **Naar**) 20, Le Saint-Maurice ☎ 37-21-13-89. Restaurant: regional and family cooking. Specialities: couscous, paella, grills. Menus from 45–98F. Lunch from 11.30am–2.30pm. Dinner from 7–11pm. Sights: Chartres Cathedral.

CHARVIEU 38230 Isère **RD 98 Map 2-A2**

☠⊗ **LES ROUTIERS** (N° RR NOV 27 454) (Mme Pierrette **Dubour-guais**) route de Lyon – La Léchère – Pont de Cheruy ☎ 78-32-23-27. Local filling station.

CHASSE-SUR-RHONE 38670 Isère **CD 12 Map 2-B1**

☠⊗ **LE CENTRAL BAR** (N° RR AOU 20 804) (M. Jean-Luc **Merandat**) 5, rue Pasteur. Directions: first exit on the Chasse sur Rhône ☎ 72-24-00-88. Spanish, English spoken. Restaurant: family cooking. Specialities: couscous, paella, cassoulet, choucroute (on Fri). Menu 50F. Children's menu. À la carte. Lunch from 11.30am–1.30pm. Dinner from 7–10pm. Closed Sat night, Sun and bank holidays. Modern décor. Rest. seats 140 in 2 rooms. ↳ Parking. Service station 200m.

CHASSILLE 72910 Sarthe **RN 157 Map 8-B2**

♟⊗ **LE PETIT ROBINSON** (N° RR NOV 26 740) (M. **Fournigault**) ☎
🏠 43-88-92-01. Restaurant: family cooking. Specialities: tête de veau
sauce ravigote, tarte tatin. Menu at 45F. Dinner from 7–8.30pm.
Closed Fri evenings, Sat, Sun and the beginning of Aug. Credit
cards accepted. Rest. seats 180 in 2 rooms. Hotel ⊣ 4. Parking.
Sights: Grottes de Saulze (20km).

CHATEAU-GAILLARD-SANTILLY 28310 Eure-et-Loir **RN 20 Map 9-B1**

♟⊗ **LE RELAIS 20** (N° RR JUIN 27 304) (M. Dahmani **Frères**) RN 20 ☎
37-90-07-33. **Minitel**. Closed Sat pm, Sun. Evening meals. English,
German, Arabic, Yugoslav spoken. Service station opposite.

♟⊗ **AU ROUTIER GAILLARD CHEZ LILI** (N° RR DEC 21 750) (Mme
Liliane **Kieffer**) ☎ 37-90-07-03. Closed Sat night and Sun. Evening
meals to midnight. Rest. seats 70.

CHATEAU-GONTIER 53200 Mayenne **Map 12-A1**

♟⊗ **L'ÉTOILE** (N° RR JUN 27 313) (M. Norbert **Corvé**) 43, rue Garnier
☎ 43-07-20-80. Closed Sun, 1 week at Christmas and Aug.
Evening meals to 9pm. Local filling station.

CHATEAU-L'HERMITAGE 72510 Sarthe **RD 307 Map 12-A2**

♟⊗ **LA BELLE CROIX** (N° RR NOV 26 742) (M. Bruno **David**)
Beauregard-Mansigné ☎ 43-46-35-73. Closed Sun. Coaches welcome. Rest. seats 160. Evening meal.

CHATEAUBERNARD 38650 Isère **Map 15-A2**

♟⊗ **PENSION DU CAMP** (N° RR NOV 25 726) (M. Jean-Louis **Bruno**)
Rte de Barbezieux La Pointe A Rullaud. Directions: Cognac
direction Bordeaux ☎ 45-82-09-47. Restaurant: family cooking.
Specialities: couscous, cassoulet, choucroute (Thur only). Menu
at 50F. Children's menu. Lunch from mid-day. Dinner from
7–11pm. Closed Fri night, Sat and Sun. Credit cards accepted.
Modern décor. Rest. seats 90 in 3 rooms. Hotel ⊣ 3 at 50F. Open
6am–11pm. Parking. Sights: Cognac.

CHATEAUBRIANT 44110 Loire-Atlantique **Map 7 B-3**

♟⊗ **PARIS-OCEAN** (N° RR FEV 27 548) (M. Patrick **Gelée**) 25 à 29
🏠 rue Ancenis ☎ 40-81-21-79. **Minitel**. English and Spanish spoken.
Hotel ⊣ 7 from 85–100F. Service station nearby.

CHATEAUDUN 28000 Eure-et-Loir **RD 955 Map 8-B3**

♟⊗ **LE SAINT JEAN** (N° RR MAI 27 276) (M. Pierre **Thomas**) 1, route
de Brou ☎ 37-45-56-75. Closed Sat and Sun. Rest. seats 550. Local
filling station.

CHATEAUNEUF 35430 Ille-et-Vilaine **RN 137 Map 7-A3**

♟⊗ **HOTEL DU LION D'OR** (N° RR NOV 25 167) (Mme Ginette
🏠 **Brodbecker**) 137, rue Principale. Directions: Rennes/St Malo road
10km from St Malo ☎ 99-58-40-11. **Minitel** ⊣ 10. Closed Mon.
Restaurant: family cooking. Specialities: sea food. Menus from
42–80F. Children's menu. À la carte. Lunch from 12–2pm. Dinner
from 7–10pm. Closed Wed from 2–5pm (except bank holidays).
Credit cards accepted. Traditional décor. Rest. seats 60. Hotel ⊣
11 at 110–220F (one ground floor room for wheelchairs) with
showers, bathrooms, WCs. Open from 7am–1am. Sitting room.
Garden terrace. ⊬ Parking. Hunting, fishing, tennis. Sights: Dinan,
Saint Malo, Saint Suliac, the area of La Rance.

CHATEAUNEUF-LE-ROUGE

CHATEAUNEUF-LE-ROUGE 13790 Bouches-du-Rhône **RN 7 Map 24-B3**
♀⊗ **LA CARDELINE** (N° RR MAI 25 425) (M. Michel **Bernard**) RN 7
☎ 42-58-62-30. Closed first fortnight in Jan and All Saints Day.
Evening meals until 11pm. English, German spoken. Rest. seats
130. Parking.

CHATEAUNEUF-LES-MARTIGUES 13220 Bouches-du-Rhône **RN 568
Map 24-B3**
♀⊗ **L'OASIS** (N° RR NOV 27 456) (Ste Poasis Thierry et Père) route
de Marseille ☎ 42-79-88-35. **Minitel**. Closed Sat evening, Sun.
Evening meals to 10pm. Parking. Local filling station.

CHATEAUNEUF-SUR-LOIRE 45110 Loiret **Map 13 A-1**
♀⊗ **HOTEL DE LA PLACE** (N° RR JAN 25 250) (M. Jacky **Maillard**) Le
⌂⇆ Bourg Germiny des Près. Directions: Orléans, direction of Mon-
targis, exit: Chateauneuf-sur-Loire ☎ 38-58-20-14. Restaurant:
family cooking. Speciality: fricasse of guinea fowl. Menu 50–110F.
Children's menu. Lunch from 12–2pm. Dinner from 8–9.30pm.
Closed Fri and 15 Jan–15 Feb. Credit cards accepted. Traditional
décor. Rest. seats 70 in 2 rooms. Hotel ⇤ 12 from 100–170F with
showers, bathrooms. Open from 7am–10pm. Garden terrace. ⊨
Parking. Fishing. Hunting. Mopeds. Walking. Riding. Sights:
Valley of the Kings, St Benoit's Monastery, Château of Sully, Gien.

CHATEAUROUX 05360 Hautes-Alpes **RN 94 Map 25-A1**
♀⊗ **BAR DE L'AVENUE** (N° RR OCT 25 147) (M. Laurent **Guillot**), 1,
avenue de la Manufacture ☎ 54-34-09-27. Closed Sun. English
spoken.
♀⊗ **RESTAURANT L'ESCALE** (N° RR FEV 23 681) (Gérant M.D. **Noiret**)
Opposite the airport ☎ 54-22-03-77. **Minitel**. Open 24 hrs. Coaches
welcome. Rest. seats 300. Credit cards accepted. ⊨ Parking.
♀⊗ ☆ **LE RALLYE** (N° RR JANV 26 433) (Mme Françoise **Jasmin**) 9,
⌂ rue Bourdillon ☎ 54-34-37-41 ⇤ 8 from 59–100F. ⊨ Closed Sun
and bank holidays.

CHATEAUTHEBAUD 44690 Loire-Atlantique **RN 137 Map 11-B3**
♀⊗ **LA SAUCISSE VOLANTE** (N° RR FEV 25 820) (M. Serge **Violeau**)
⌂ Le Butay Route de La Rochelle. Directions: 15 miles from Nantes
on the south side of the Loire ☎ 40-06-63-55. Restaurant: family
cooking. Specialities: grills. Menu at 52.50F. Lunch from 12–
2.30pm. Dinner from 7–8.30pm. Closed Sat evening, Sun, 3 weeks
in July and Aug. Credit cards accepted. Traditional décor. Rest.
seats 84 in 2 rooms. Hotel ⇤ 5 from 78F. Open from 5am until
midnight. Garden terrace. Parking. Sights: Nantes, route de vin.

CHATELUS 03120 Allier **Map 16-B3**
♀⊗ **LES CHEVREAUX** (N° RR MARS 27 209) (M. Joseph **Bernard**) RN
7 Arfeuilles ☎ 70-55-00-79. Spanish and English spoken. Filling
station 10km.

CHATELUS-MALVALEIX 23270 Creuse **RN 690 Map 16-A2**
♀⊗ **LE RELAIS DES VOYAGEURS** (N° RR AOU 23 409) (M. Claude
⌂ **Brunet**) Route de La Châtre ☎ 55-80-78-11 ⇤ 5. Closed 15 Aug–4
Sept and 23 Dec–4 Jan. English spoken. Evening meal to 9pm.

CHATILLON-EN-BAZOIS 58110 Nièvre **RD 978 Map 13-B2**
♀⊗ **HOTEL DU RELAIS** (N° RR MAR 22 737) (M. Jean-Jacques
⌂ **Charprenet**) ☎ 86-84-13-79 ⇤ 7. Closed Sun, public holidays.

CHATILLON-LE-ROI 45480 Loiret **RD 927 Map 9-B1**
🍸⊗ **LE RELAIS DU FIN GOURMET** (N° RR FEV 26 812) (M. and Mme Joël and Jeanne **Lenglet**) 41, rue du Château ☎ 38-39-97-12. **Minitel**. Closed Tue afternoon, Sun (except in hunting season), 15 days in June, 15 days in Sept. Coaches welcome. Rest. seats 100. Evening meals until 8pm.

CHATILLON-SUR-INDRE 36700 Indre **RN 143 Map 12-B3**
🍸⊗ **LE RELAIS DU MAIL** (N° RR OCT 22 980) (M. **Duluard**) Boulevard du Général-Leclerc ☎ 54-38-71-21 and 38-80-25. Restaurant: family cooking. Menu at 48F. Lunch from noon. Dinner from 7–9pm. Closed 10 days at All Saints. Traditional décor. Rest. seats 50. Hotel 🛏 4 at 70–190F. Parking. Sights: The Château of Azay le Ferron.

CHATRES-SUR-CHER 41320 Loir-et-Cher **RN 76 Map 13-B1**
🍸⊗ **LES ROUTIERS** (N° RR MARS 25 857) (M. Gérard **Coutaud**) 60, rue du 11-Novembre ☎ 54-98-01-93. Restaurant: family cooking. Menu at 52F. Open from 7am–9pm. Closed Sun and the last 15 days in Aug. Credit cards accepted. Traditional décor. Rest. seats 40. Car parking.

CHATTE 38160 Isère **RN 92 Map 18-B3**
🍸⊗ **LE SIROCCO** (N° RR AVR 26 227) (M. Maurice **Moyroud**) Quartier St Ferreol ☎ 76-64-43-41. Closed Sat afternoon, Sun, 1–15 Aug. Rest. seats 110. Parking.

CHAUFFOUR-LES-BONNIERES 78270 Yvelines **RN 13 Maps 3-B1 and 8-A3**
🍸⊗ ☆ **AU BON ACCUEIL** (N° RR DEC 6 601) (M. Gérard **Magne**) ☎ 34-76-11-29. **Minitel**. Restaurant: family cooking. Children's menu. À la carte. Lunch from 11am–2.30pm. Dinner from 7–9pm. Closed Sat and 15 July–15 Aug. Credit cards accepted. Traditional décor. Rest. seats 150 in 3 rooms. Hotel 🛏 13 from 90–200F with showers, WC. Garden terrace. Parking.

CHAUMONT 52000 Haute-Marne **RN 19 Map 14-A2**
🍸⊗ **CHEZ JEAN** (N° RR MAI 14 804) (M. Jean **Corroy**) 29, avenue Carnot ☎ 25-03-06-57.

CHAUMONT EN VEXIN 60240 Oise **Map 3 B2**
🍸⊗ **LA TABLE DE FLEURY** (N° RR JAN 26 797) (M. Ivan **Marie**) Grande rue Fleury ☎ 44-49-04-60. Restaurant: family cooking. Menu from 38–80F. Children's menu. À la carte. Lunch from 11.30am–2.30pm. Credit cards accepted. Traditional décor. Rest. seats 24 in 2 rooms. Parking.

CHAUNY 02300 Aisne **Map 6-A/B1**
🍸⊗ **LE CASAMANCE** (N° RR DEC 27 114) (M. Gilles **Claisse**) 92, rue de la Chaussée ☎ 23-52-16-33. Closed Sun. English spoken 🛏 6. Coaches welcome. Rest. seats 30. Evening meals to 10pm. Local filling station open 6am–10pm.

CHAUVIGNY 86300 Vienne **RN 151 Map 15-B1**
🍸⊗ **RELAIS DU MARCHE** (N° RR JUL 25 048) (M. Joël **Torsat**) 8, place du Marché ☎ 49-46-32-34. Closed Thur, 15 Sept–15 Oct. Coaches welcome. Rest. seats 70. Evening meals until 9pm.

CHAZEUIL

CHAZEUIL 03500 Allier **CD 146 Map 16-A3**
♀⊗ **LE RELAIS DU PONT DE CHAZEUIL** (N° RR NOV 26 094) (M. Maurice **Chaduc**) Pont Chazeuil Paray Sous Briailles. Directions: between Varennes-sur-Allier and St-Pourcain-sur-Sioule ☎ 70-45-08-11. Restaurant: family cooking. Speciality: friture de L'allier. Children's menu. À la carte. Dinner until 10pm. Closed Sat (low season). Credit cards accepted. Traditional décor. Rest. seats 55. Parking. Sights: châteaux, Roman churches, zoo, St-Pourcain-sur-Sioule, wine producing centre.

CHELLES 77500 Seine-et-Marne **RN 34 Map 1-A3**
♀⊗ **HOTEL DE LA PETITE VITESSE** (N° RR AVR 26 875) (M. Michel
⌂ **Chea**) 32, avenue du Marais ☎ 64-21-09-47 ⊷ 7. Restaurant: closed Sun.

CHELSEY 21430 Cote-d'Or **RN 6 Map 13-B3**
♀⊗ **LE ROUTIERS** (N° RR JAN 23 630) (M. Bernard **Sentein**) Liernais. Directions: halfway between Saulieu and Arnay le Duc ☎ 80-84-40-42. Restaurant: family cooking. Menu at 58F. Closed Sun, 15–25 Aug. Coaches welcome. Rest. seats 100/50/45. Open from 7am–1am. German spoken. Hotel ⊷ 5 from 90–210F with shower. ⌿ Parking.

CHEMAUDIN 25320 Doubs **RN 73 Map 14-B3**
♀⊗ **RELAIS DES ROUTIERS – CHEZ COCOTTE** (N° RR FEV 20 663) (Mme **Grosperrin**) La Cocotte ☎ 81-59-51-92.

CHEMERY-LES-DEUX 57320 Moselle **RD 918 Map 10-A1**
♀⊗ **RELAIS MATHIS** (N° RR DEC 19 601) (Mme Marie **Koch**) ☎
⌂ 87-64-91-73 ⊷ 6. Closed Wed, 15 Aug–30 Sept. German spoken.

CHENEVIERES 54120 Meurthe-et-Moselle **RN 59 Maps 10-A2 and 14-B1**
♀⊗ **CHEZ JEAN-LOU ET AGNÈS** (N° RR JAN 23 629) (M. Jean-Louis **Rémy**) 10, Route Nationale ☎ 83-72-62-75. Closed Sun, Sept. Rest. seats 50.

CHENOVE 21300 Cote-d'Or **RN 74 Map 14-A3**
♀⊗ ☆ **AU BON COIN** (N° RR OCT 23 957) (M. Marcel **Marin**) 54, route
⌂ de Dijon ☎ 80-52-58-17 ⊷ 13. Restaurant: closed Sat, Sun, Aug.

CHERBOURG 50100 Manche **RN 13 Map 4-A1**
♀⊗ **LES ROUTIERS** (N° RR JUN 26 258) (Mme Viviane **Couvrie**) 10,
⌂ rue de l'Onglet ☎ 33-53-08-15 ⊷ 11. Closed Fri evening, Sun evening. English, Spanish spoken.

CHESNAY 27160 Eure **Map 8-A3**
♀⊗ **CHEZ CLAUDE** (N° RR MAI 26 244) (M. Claude **Blanfune**) Condé sur Iton ☎ 32-29-89-27. Closed Sun, Aug.

CHEVILLY-LARUE 94150 Val-de-Marne **RN 7 Map 1-B2**
♀⊗ **LE RELAIS D'AUVERGNE** (N° RR JAN 17 729) (M. **Carayol**) 4, place de la Libération ☎ 46-86-55-32. Closed Sat, Sun, Aug. Coaches welcome. Rest. seats 120.

CHICHE 79350 Deux-Sevres **RN 149 Bis Map 12-B2**
♀⊗ **LE RELAIS CHEZ JACQUES** (N° RR DEC 24 434) (M. Jacques **Vincent**) 27, place St-Martin ☎ 49-72-40-51. **Minitel**. Closed Wed evening, Christmas to 1 Jan. Coaches welcome. Rest. seats 55.

CHIERZAC par BEDENAC 17210 Charente-Maritime **RN 10 Map 15-A3**
♈⊗ **AU RENDEZ-VOUS DES ROUTIERS** (N° RR JUN 1 922) (M. Robert **Laville**) ☎ 46-04-44-24. Closed Sat evening, Sun evening. Evening meals until 11pm.

CHINON 37500 Indre-et-Loire **Map 12 B-2**
♈⊗ **LE RELAIS DE LA FORET** (N° RR MARS 27 572) (M. Marco **Millet**) Route de Tours Les Plaines de Vaux. Directions: between Tours and Saumur. Restaurant: family cooking. Menu at 50F. Lunch from 11am–3pm. Dinner 6–8pm. Closed Sat and Sun, 3 weeks in Aug, 15 days at Christmas. Traditional décor. Rest. seats 90. Garden terrace. ⋔ Parking. Sights: châteaux.

CHIRENS 38850 Isère **Map 19 A-2**
♈⊗ **LE RELAIS SAINT-HONORE** (N° RR OCT 27 691) (Mme Georgette **Luque**) Le Gayet. Directions: on the road to Bourg-en-Bresse, near Voiron ☎ 76-35-25-86. Spanish spoken. Restaurant: family cooking. Menus from 55–78F. Children's menu. À la carte. Lunch from 12–2pm. Dinner from 7–9pm. Credit cards accepted. Traditional décor. Rest. seats 90 in 2 rooms. Garden terrace. ⋔ Parking. Service station nearby open 8am–9pm. Sights: Chirens Priory, Chartreuse caves, tour of Montclair and Clermont Tonnerre.

CHOISY-LE-ROI 94600 Val-de-Marne **RN 186 Map 1-B3**
♈⊗ **LE STADE** (N° RR DEC 26 750) (M. J-Claude **Villechenoux**) 134,
⌂ avenue de Villeneuve-Saint-Georges ☎ 48-90-90-55 ⌿ 6. Closed Sat, Sun.

CHOLET 49300 Meurthe-et-Moselle **RN 160 Maps 11-B3 and 12-B1**
♈⊗ **CHEZ DÉDÉ** (N° RR FEVR 25 809) (M. André **Bourgey**) 66, boulevard de Strasbourg ☎ 41-62-27-79. **Minitel**. Restaurant: family cooking. Menu at 42.50F. Lunch from 11.45am–2.15pm. Dinner from 7.15–9.30pm. Closed Sat, Sun and Aug. Credit cards accepted. Traditional décor. Rest. seats 64 in 2 rooms. ⋔ Parking. Showers available for drivers.
♈⊗ **LE RELAIS DES PRAIRIES** (N° RR SEPT 26 318) (Mme **Albert**) Parc des Prairies, boulevard du Pont de Pierre. Directions: opposite the airport. English and German spoken. Restaurant: family cooking. Specialities: eel with onion, côte de boeuf, tête de veau. Children's menu. À la carte. Dinner until 9pm. Closed Sat evening, 25 Dec–2 Jan. Credit cards accepted. Rest. seats 250 in 3 rooms. Sitting room. Garden terrace. ⋔ Parking. Sights: Ribou Lake, Verdon Lake, Puy du Fou.
♈⊗ **LE RELAIS DES ROUTIERS** (N° RR JUL 12 347) (M. Michel **Dubillot**)
⌂ 13, place de la République ☎ 41-62-11-09 ⌿ 19. Closed Sun, 13 Jul–13 Aug. Evening meals. Coaches welcome. Rest. seats 180.

CHONAS-L'AMBALLAN 38121 Isère **RN 7 Map 2-B1**
♈⊗ **L'ETAPE** (N° RR OCT 26 359) (M. Guy **Ailloud**) Grand-Champ. Directions: north exit Chanas, south exit Vienne ☎ 74-58-87-50. **Minitel**. Restaurant: family cooking. Menu 50F. À la carte. Traditional décor. ⋔ Garden terrace. Closed Sun, 1–15 Aug. Rest. seats 60. Evening meals to 12pm. Parking.

CHORGES 05230 Hautes-Alpes **RN 94 Map 25-A1**
♈⊗ ☆ **NN HOTEL DES ALPES** (N° RR NOV 19 996) (M. Roger
⌂ **Mauduech**) Route Nationale 94. Directions: 17km from Gap,

CHUISNES

Chorges continued

direction Briançon. ☎ 92-50-60-08. Restaurant: regional and family cooking. Specialities: salade caturgie, gratin Dauphinois, gigot pré-Alpes. Children's menu. À la carte. Dinner until 9pm. Closed 1 Oct–11 Nov. Credit cards (carte Bleu) accepted. Rest. seats 90. Hotel ⇌ 16 from 120–230F with WC, TV. Sitting room. Garden terrace. ⛟ Parking. Sights: Serre Pouçon Lake, Parc de Ecrias, mountains, dam, Saint Appolinaire Lake, Réallon.

CHUISNES 28190 Courville-sur-Eure – Eure-et-Loir **RN 23 Map 8-B3**
♟⊗ **L'ESCALE ROUTIÈRE** (N° RR JUIN 27 305) (M. Gerard **Brulé**) lieu-dit Les Chatelets ☎ 37-23-21-75. Open 24 hrs. Closed Sun. Rest. seats 60. Parking. Filling station 2km.

CIVRAY 86400 Vienne **Map 15-B1/2**
♟⊗ **RELAIS DES USINES** (N° RR DEC 27 120) (M. Patric **Martel**) 19, route de Saint-Pierre. Directions: Nioret/Limoges axis ☎ 49–87–04–33. Restaurant: family cooking. Menu at 45F. Children's menu. Open 6am–9pm. Dinner until 9pm. Closed Sat and Sun afternoon. Traditional décor. Rest. seats 40 in 2 rooms. ⛟ Parking. Service station nearby open 7am–8pm. Sights: Civray church, Saint Nicolas, Charroux.

CIVRAY DE TOURAINE 37150 Indre-et-Loire **Map 12 A3**
♟⊗ **LE MARCECHAL** (N° RR DEC 24 479) (M. Jean **Jabvenean**) 1, rue de Bléré ☎ 47-23-92-16. Restaurant: regional menu. Menu 50F. À la carte. Closed Sat afternoon, Sun, Sept. Evening meals until 10pm. Credit cards accepted. Rest. seats 75 in 3 rooms. Garden terrace. ⛟ Parking. Showers. Nearby service station open 8am–8pm.

CLAIRVAUX-LES-LACS 39130 Jura **RN 78 et 83 Map 19-A1**
♟⊗ **LES ROUTIERS** (N° RR SEPT 27 024) (M. Denis **Perrin**) 4, route de Lons-le-Saunier ☎ 84-25-85-57. Closed Sun (low season), 1–15 Sept. English and Italian spoken. Evening meals to 10pm. Open 24 hrs.

CLAYE-SOUILLY 77410 Seine-et-Marne **CD 212 Map 1-A3**
♟⊗♟**RESTAURANT DE LA ROSEE** (N° RR AVR 25 367) (M. Jean-Claude **Castel**) ☎ 60-26-17-74. **Minitel**. Closed Sun. Evening meals. German spoken. Hotel rooms with showers. Service station with HGV garage.

CLERAC 17270 Charente-Maritime **CD 158/134 Map 15-A3**
♟⊗ **LES BANANIERS** (N° RR SEPT 26 651) (Mme Danielle **Arcay**)
⌂ Montguyon ☎ 46-04-13-17. **Minitel**. Closed Sat. Evening meals to 9pm. Hotel ⇌ 5. Service station nearby.

CLERMONT-FERRAND 63000 Puy-de-Dôme **RN 9 Map 16-B3**
♟⊗ ☆ **NN AUVERGNE PYRÉNÉES – LES ROUTIERS** (N° RR AVR 22
⌂ 778) (Mme **Laborde**) 12 bis, place des Carme ☎ 73-92-35-73. Night bell. English spoken. Restaurant: regional and family cooking. Speciality: coq au vin. Dinner until 9pm. Rest. seats 100 in 2 rooms. Hotel ⇌ 15 from 130–250F with showers, WC, telephone. Open from 7am–11pm. Sitting room. Garden terrace. ⛟ Parking. Sights: Puy de Dome, Chaunalières, Montferrand.
⊗ **RELAIS DES VOLCANS D'AUVERGNE** (N° RR 2 034) Aire de Service des Volcans on both sides of the autoroute. Restaurant. Regional cooking. 25% discount for coach drivers. Children's menu. À la carte. Self-service. Garden terrace. ⛟

CLERY-EN-VEXIN 95420 Val-d'Oise **Map 3-B2**

♀⊗ **AUBERGE DE CLERY-EN-VEXIN** (N° RR FEV 27 174) (M. Jean-Guy **Degoul**) 4 RN 14 ☎ 34-67-44-15. Closed Sat and Sun. Parking.

CLICHY 92100 Hauts-de-Seine **Map 1-A2**

♀⊗ **AU SOLEIL** (N° RR SEPT 26 989) (M. Roger **Queyraud**) 105, bld Victor Hugo ☎ 47-37-15-45. Closed Sun and Aug.

CLION-SUR-INDRE 36700 Indre **Map 12-B3**

♀⊗ **AUBERGE DU PIE DE BOURGES** (N° RR AOU 24 652) (Mme
⌂ Nicole **Chamton**) 31, rue Nationale ☎ 54-38-60-90. Hotel ⊷ 7. Coaches welcome. Rest. seats 120. Lunch 11am–1.30pm. Evening meals from 7–9.30pm. Closed Aug.

CLUNY 71250 Saône-et-Loire **RN 80 Map 18-A1**

♀⊗ **AUBERGE DU CHEVAL BLANC** (N° RR FEV 21 785) (SARL **Bouillin/Papion**) 1, rue Porte-de-Mâcon ☎ 85-59-01-13. Closed Sat and Nov. Rest. seats 120. Evening meals until 9pm.

♀⊗ **AU PETIT BAR** (N° RR JUL 17 022) (M. Jean **Dufour**) 1, rue du Lyonnais ☎ 74-76-03-57. Closed Sun, Aug. Coaches welcome. Rest. seats 40.

CLUSES 74300 Haute-Savoie **Map 19-B2**

♀⊗ ☆ **LE RESTOPORT DU MONT BLANC** (N° RR OCT 27 411) (M.
⌂ Anastase **Savridis-Legana** SA) Autoport du Mont Blanc La Maladiere. Directions: Cluses exit. ☎ 50-96-01-08. **Minitel**, English, Greek and Italian spoken. Restaurant: family cooking. À la carte. Self-service. Dinner until midnight. Closed Sat at 4pm, Sun. Credit cards accepted. Hotel ⊷ 18 from 95–160F with showers. Open from 7am to midnight. ⊭ Parking. 24 hr service station close by.

COARRAZE-NAY 64800 Pyrénées-Atlantiques **Map 20-B3**

♀⊗ **LE TERMINUS** (N° RR JUIL 27 353) (Mme Josette **Kohnen**) 3, avenue de Berrejacq ☎ 54-61-02-60. Spanish spoken. Restaurant: dinner from 8pm until midnight. Rest. seats 40. Parking in front of the station.

COEMONT-VOUVRAY 72500 Sarthe **RN 158 Map 12-A2**

♀⊗ **LE BON COIN** (N° RR SEP 19 886) (Mme **Jouanneau**) ☎ 43-44-04-17. Restaurant: family cooking. Children's menu. Open from 7am–9pm. Lunch from 11.30am–3pm. Closed Sun and in Aug. Traditional décor. Rest. seats 35. Garden terrace. ⊭ Parking. Fishing. Forests. Sights: Loire Valley.

COGOLIN 83310 Var **RN 98 Map 25-A3**

♀⊗ **LE GISLET** (N° RR JUL 26 954) (M. Robert **Vialenc**) ☎ 94-56-40-39. Italian, Spanish, English spoken. Restaurant: closed Sun (low season). Coaches welcome. Rest. seats 40 plus terrace.

COLIGNY 51130 Marne **Map 6-B2**

♀⊗ **LE VAL DES MARAIS** (N° RR FEV 27 551) (M. Michel **Lagnié**) 61 rue Saint Gond ☎ 26-52-23-15. **Minitel**. Restaurant: family restaurant. Menu 50F. Lunch from 12–2pm. Dinner from 7–10pm. Credit cards accepted. Traditional décor. Rest. seats 38 in 2 rooms. ⊭ Service station nearby open 6.30am–6.30pm. Sights: the caves of Epernay.

COLLONGES-LES-PREMIERES 21110 Côte-d'Or **RN 5 and RD 116 Map 14-A3**

♀⊗ **LA BONNE AUBERGE** (N° RR AVR 26 521) (M. Pierre **Colot**)

COLLONGES-SOUS-SALEVE

Collonges-Les-Premieres continued
8, avenue de la Gare ☎ 80-31-32-01. Restaurant: dinner until 9pm.
Closed Sun and Aug.

COLLONGES-SOUS-SALEVE 74610 Haute-Savoie **RN 206 and 201 Map 19-A2**
♀⊗ **LE RELAIS DU COMMERCE** (N° RR AOUT 27 361) (Mme
Marianne **Gougne**) Bas de Collonges St-Julien-en-Genevois ☎
50-43-60-29. Closed Sat. Rest. seats 170 in 2 rooms. Local filling
station 7am–8pm. Parking.

COLOMBELLES 14460 Calvados **RD 513 Map 4-B2**
♀⊗ **HÔTEL DU COMMERCE** (N° RR AVR 26 221) (M. Jean-Claude
⌂ **Musson**) 3, route de Cabourg ☎ 31-72-18-89 ⊷ 27. Closed Sun.
Aug. Coaches welcome. Rest. seats 80. Evening meals to 11pm.

COLOMBEY-LES-BELLES 54170 Meurthe-et-Moselle **RN 74 Map 14-B1**
♀⊗ **AUBERGE LORRAINE** (N° RR AVR 26 234) (M. Claude **Arnould**)
71, rue Carnot ☎ 83-52-00-23. Rest. seats 70. Evening meals until
10pm. Closed from Christmas to New Year.

COLOMBY 50700 Manche **RD 2 (Valognes/Avranche) Map 4-B1**
♀⊗ **CHEZ MÉMÈNE** (N° RR JUN 26 572) (Mme Germaine **Delacotte**)
Le Bourg-Valognes. Directions: Valognes/Avranche ☎ 33-40-10-
59. Closed Mon. Rest. seats 28. Dinner until 7pm.

COLPO 56390 Morbihan **Map 7-B2**
♀⊗ **AUX DÉLICES DE L'OCÉAN** (N° RR AVR 25 385) (M. Jean-
⌂ Claude **Le Guillan**) 1, avenue de la Princesse ☎ 97-66-82-21.
Hotel ⊷ 13. Restaurant: closed Sat, 15 June–19 Jul. Coaches
welcome. Rest. seats 180. Large parking area for overnight stops.

COMBLANCHIEN 21700 Côte-d'Or **RN 74 Map 14-A3**
♀⊗ **AUBERGE DU GUIDON** (N° RR FEV 24 121) (M. André **Vauchez**)
⌂ Route Nationale 74 ☎ 80-62-94-39 ⊷ 8. Closed Sat, Sun, Aug.
Meals served until 10pm.

COMBRES 28480 Eure-et-Loir **Map 8-B3**
♀⊗ **HOTEL DE LA CROIX BLANCHE** (N° RR OCT 27 045) (Mme
⌂ Christiane **Vaux**) Place de l'Église ☎ 37-29-59-54 ⊷ 7. Full-board
160–180F. Coaches welcome. Rest. seats 44. Evening meals to
10pm. English spoken.

COMINES 59560 Nord **Map 5-B1**
♀⊗ **RESTAURANT DE LA GARE** (N° RR FEV 27 792) (Mme Yvette
⌂ **Desiéter**) 81–83 Avenue du Général Leclerc ☎ 20-39-45-78 or
20-39-45-83. **Minitel**. English, German and Spanish spoken. Res-
taurant. Menus from 55–95F. Children's menu. À la carte. Open
7am until midnight. Lunch 12–3pm. Dinner 6pm until midnight.
Rest. seats 160 in 2 rooms. Hotel ⊷ 10 at 119F with showers.
Garden terrace. ⊬ Parking.

COMMODITE (LA) par SOLTERRE 45700 Loiret **RN 7 Map 13-A1/2**
♀⊗ **AUBERGE DE LA ROUTE BLEUE** (N° RR MAR 2 687) (SNC
⊷ Charles et Albert **Rocco**) ☎ 38-94-90-04. Restaurant: family
cooking. Closed Tue evening, Wed, Aug. Restaurant has two
dining areas seating 60 and 32. Menu 55–120F. Specialities: ris de
veau Normand, escalope cordon bleu, escargots Roquefort.
Credit cards accepted. Garden terrace. ⊬ Parking.

COMPIEGNE 60200 Oise **RN 31–32–35 Map 3-A3**

�Ⓧ **BAR DE LA MARINE** (N° RR JUL 25 993) (M. Bernard **Piat**) 17, rue de l'Estacade ☎ 44-40-15-14. Closed Sat afternoon, Sun. Coaches welcome. Rest. seats 44. Service station nearby.

CONCOURSON-SUR-LAYON 49700 Maine-et-Loire **RN 960 Map 12-B2**

�Ⓧ **AUBERGE DU HAUT LAYON** (N° RR DEC 26 746) (M. Bernard **Battais**) Route Nationale ☎ 41-59-27-60. English spoken. Restaurant: family cooking. Specialities: sauce dishes. Children's menu. À la carte. Lunch from 12–3pm. Dinner from 7–9.30pm. Closed Sun night. Traditional décor. Rest. seats 50. ⊨ Parking. Sights: zoo, rose garden, village of cave dwellers.

CONDÉ-SUR-NOIREAU 14110 Calvados **RN 162 Map 8-A12**

☐Ⓧ **HOTEL LES DES PROMENADES** (N° RR JAN 18 594) (M. Michel
⌂ **Jomat**) 2, rue Motte-de-Lutre Angle rue St-Martin. Directions: Caen-Flers ☎ 31-69-03-36. **Minitel**. Restaurant: family cooking. Specialities: veal kidneys with calvados. Menus from 45–105F. Lunch from 12–1.30pm. Dinner from 7.30–9pm. Closed Sun and Aug. Rest. seats 25. Hotel ⊶ 6.

CONDE-SUR-VIRE 50890 Manche **Map 4-B1**

☐Ⓧ **HOTEL DES ROCHES** (N° RR MAI 26 546) (M. Achour **Mohabed-**
⌂ **dine**) 12, rue Alfred Duros ☎ 33-55-20-82 ⊶ 7. Closed Sun. Aug. English spoken. Rest. seats 27. Dinner served until 8pm.

CONNANTRAY 51230 Marne **RN 4 Map 9-A3**

☐Ⓧ **LA ROUTIÈRE** (N° RR OCT 27 415) (M. Michel **Villain**) ☎
⌂ 26-42-42-03 ⊶ 8. Open 7 days. 24 hr local filling station.
☐Ⓧ **LA GRAPPE D'OR** (N° RR MARS 26 472) (M. Claude **Longatte**) 1,
⌂ rue de la Gare ☎ 26-81-04-62. **Minitel** ⊶ 6. Closed Sun. Dinner until 9pm. Service station nearby open 6am–11pm.

CONNERRE 72160 Sarthe **RN 23 Map 8-B2/3**

☐Ⓧ **LE RELAIS DU COMMERCE** (N° RR AVR 11 404) (M. Daniel **Charpentier**) 14, rue de Paris ☎ 43-89-00-55. Closed Sun, Aug. Coaches welcome. Rest. seats 120.

CONSENVOYE 55110 Meuse **RD 964 Map 6-B3**

☐Ⓧ **AUBERGE LORRAINE** (N° RR MAR 26 854) (Mme Denise
⌂ **Poussant**) Grand Rue ☎ 29-85-80-19. Hotel ⊶ 6. Closed Sat, 2nd fortnight Feb and Sept. English spoken. Coaches welcome. Rest. seats 60 + 150. Dinner served until 9pm.

CORAY 29145 Finistère **CD 15 and 36 Map 7-B1**

☐Ⓧ **LE BREIZH RELAIS** (N° RR NOV 27 089) (M. Albin **Le Roux**) Place de l'Église ☎ 98-59-36-26. Closed Mon pm. Local filling station.

CORBEIL-ESSONNES 91100 Essonne **RN 7 Map 1-B3**

☐Ⓧ ☆ **NN L'ERMITAGE** (N° RR OCT 27 037) (Mme Suzanne **Ger-**
⌂ **lache**) 137, boulevard de Fontainebleau ☎ 64-96-29-42. Hotel ⊶ 19. Restaurant: closed Sun.

CORBENAY 70800 Haute-Savoie **Map 10-A3**

☐Ⓧ ☆ **AU P'TIT CHARIOT** (N° RR OCT 27 427) (M. Thierry
⌂ **Mougenot**) 1, rue des Cannes Route de Fougerolles ☎ 84-94-13-60. Hotel ⊶ 10 at 95–110F. Restaurant: closed Sun night, Aug. German, English spoken. Evening meals to 10pm. Local filling station 7.45am–8.30pm. Showers available to drivers.

CORBIGNY

CORBIGNY 58800 Nièvre **Map 13-B2**

♀⊗ **LES AMIS DES ROUTIERS** (N° RR DEC 24 777) (Mme Colette **Perini**) Route de Clamecy ☎ 86-20-19-77. Restaurant: family cooking. Menu at 48F. Lunch from 12–3pm. Dinner from 7.30–9.30pm. Closed Sat afternoon, Sun and 15 Aug–8 Sept. Credit cards accepted. Traditional décor. Rest. seats 34. ⊨ Parking. Sights: regional park of Morvan, museum of Septennet at the Château Chinon.

CORMEIL-EN-PARISIS 95240 Val-d'Oise **Map 1-A2**

♀⊗ **LE BON ACCUEIL** (No RR OCT 27 436) (M. **Granday** and Mme **Richard**) 26 boulevard du Maréchal Juin ☎ 39-78-83-24. Russian, Polish spoken. Restaurant: family cooking. Menu at 49–50F. À la carte. Lunch 11.30am–4pm. Dinner from 7.30–9pm. Closed Sat and Sun. Traditional décor. Rest. seats 60 in 2 rooms.

CORMEILLES-EN-VEXIN 95830 Val-d'Oise **Map 3-B2**

⊗♀ **LE MONTMATRE** (N° RR JANV 26 427) (M. Jean-Claude **Lorre**) SNC Le Relaxe 4, rue Jean Jaurès ☎ 34-66-61-18. **Minitel**. Closed Mon. Coaches welcome. Rest. seats 40.

CORMORANCHE-SUR-SAONE 01290 Ain **Map 18-B1**

♀⊗ ✩✩ **AUBERGE CHEZ LA MÈRE MARTINET** (N° RR JUL 23 864)
⌂⊷ (Mme Geneviève **Martinet**) ☎ 85-36-20-40. Directions: at Crèche-sur-Saone at the first traffic lights turn left. **Minitel**. English and German spoken. Restaurant: regional and family cooking. Specialities: hot sausage with Beaujolais, suprême de volaille. Menus from 62–170F. Lunch from 12–1.30pm. Dinner from 7.15–8.30pm. Closed Wed, Sun night and from 15 Aug–10 Sept. Credit cards accepted. Traditional décor. Rest. seats 35. Hotel ⊨ 7 from 142–152F with showers and bathrooms, WC, TV, telephone. Open from 8am–9pm. Garden terrace. ⊨ Parking. Pétanque played. Mini-golf. Water pastimes. Sights: Bey church, Beaujolais mount, Solutré rock, Lamartine circuit.

CORNÉ 49250 Maine-et-Loire **RN 147 Map 12-A2**

♀⊗ **LE RELAIS DE LA CROIX BLANCHE** (N° RR JUL 25 479) (M. Jean-Noël **Pignard**) La Croix Blanche RN 147 ☎ 41-45-01-82. Closed Sat evening, Sun, Christmas to New Year, 1 week from 15 Aug. Evening meals to 10pm. Parking.

CORPS 38970 Isère **RN 85 Map 19-A3**

♀⊗ **LE RELAIS DU TILLEUL** (N° RR JUL 25 979) (M. Claude **Jourdan**)
⌂ Rue des Fossés ☎ 76-30-00-43. Restaurant: regional and family cooking. Specialities: gratin dauphinois, civet de porcelet, poulet aux écrevisses. Menus from 60–125F. Closed Nov and 1–15 Dec. Credit cards accepted. Rest. seats 60. Hotel ⊨ 10 from 170–270F with showers and bathrooms, WC, TV, telephone. ⊨ Parking.

CORPS-NUDS 35150 Ille-et-Vilaine **RN 163 Map 7-B3**

♀⊗ **LES ROUTIERS** (N° RR FEV 22 676) (Mme Solange **Piel**) Place de l'Eglise. Directions: Rennes/Angers road ☎ 99-44-00-25. Restaurant: family cooking. Closed Sat and Aug. Credit cards accepted.

COSNE D'ALLIER 03430 Allier **Map 16-A2**

♀⊗ **L'ESCALE** (N° RR NOV 27 457) (Mme Marie-Josephe **Sauvat**) 2,
⊷ place de la Liberté ☎ 70-07-21-10. English, Spanish spoken. Evening meals. 24 hr local filling station.

COSNE-SUR-LOIRE 58200 Nièvre **RN 7 Map 13-A/B2**

Y⊗ ☆ **LE RELAIS DES TROIS COULEURS** (N° RR MAR 6 751) (MM.
Jean and Pierre **Morfaux**) 21, rue St-Agnan ☎ 86-28-23-50.
Restaurant: regional and family cooking. Specialities: coq au vin,
cuisses de grenouilles à la provençale. Menus from 46–90F.
Children's menu. Dinner until 9pm. Closed last week in Dec and
first week in Jan. Credit cards accepted. Rest. seats 120 in 3
rooms. Hotel ⊷ 13 from 100–180F with showers. Sitting room. ⊬
Parking.

Y⊗ **LE RELAIS DE LA TASSE** (N° RR NOV 24 409) (M. Claude
Maurice **Chet**) RN 7 Maltaverne ☎ 86-26-11-76. Closed Sun
(open for coach bookings), public holidays, Aug. English spoken.
Coaches welcome. Rest. seats 70.

COSTAROS 43490 Haute-Loire **RN 88 Map 17-B3**

Y⊗ **RELAIS ROUTIERS** (N° RR JUN 21 957) (Mme Marie-Thérèse
Rossello) Rue Principale ☎ 71-57-16-04. Hotel ⊷ 17. Restaurant:
closed Sat afternoon in winter. Coaches welcome. Rest. seats 60.
Spanish spoken. Parking in the village centre.

COTEAU (LE) 42120 Loire **RN 7 exit south de Roanne Map 18-A2**

Y⊗ **LE PARIGNY** (N° RR OCT 24 397) Sarl Le Parigny (Mme Jeanine
Pamurie) Les Bas de Rhins. Directions: Roanne, south exit ☎
77-62-06-18. Restaurant: dinner until 9pm. Closed on Sun and
15–30 Aug. Hotel ⊷ 9.

COUCOURDE (LA) 26740 Drôme **Map 24-A2**

Y⊗ **LE RELAIS DES ROCHES** (N° RR NOV 27 730) (Mme Denise
Tranchat) Route Nationale 7 ☎ 75-53-70-02. Restaurant: menu at
55F. Open from 5am to midnight. Lunch from 11.30am–2.30pm.
Dinner from 6.30–11pm. Parking. Service station nearby.

COUCY-LE-CHATEAU 02380 Aisne **Map 6-B1**

Y⊗ **LE LION ROUGE** (N° RR NOV 27 450) (M. Patrick **Clavet**) 62,
avenue Altenkessel ☎ 23-52-70-13 ⊷ 13. Closed 2 weeks at
Christmas. German, English spoken. Evening meals to 9.30pm.
Filling station 2km open 7am–9pm.

COULLONS 45720 Loiret **RD 51 Map 13-A1**

Y⊗ **LA BARBE GRISE** (N° RR OCT 25 681) (M. Jean **Poirirer**) route
Jacques Coeur CD 940 ☎ 38-36-11-27. Closed Mon (except bank
holidays), early Sept and Feb. English spoken.

Y⊗ **LE PECHEUR** (N° RR JAN 27 511) (Mme Eileen **Burrows**) 45, rue
du Sergent-Lelievre ☎ 38-29-22-22. Hotel ⊷ 8. English spoken.

COULMIER-LE-SEC 21400 Côte-d'Or RD 980 **Map 13-A3**

Y⊗ **LE RELAIS DE LA POSTE** (N° RR DEC 27 736) (M. Jean-Lois
Divel) ☎ 80-93-13-09. English spoken. Restaurant. Specialities:
poule au pot. Menus from 45–75F. Open 6am–10pm. Dinner until
10pm. Closed Sat evening and Sun. Parking. Service station close
by open until 10pm.

COULOMBIERS 86600 Vienne **RN 11 Map 15-B1**

Y⊗ **LE RELAIS DE LA PAZIOTERIE** (N° RR JUL 25 050) (Mme
Yvonne **Barrusseau**) Lusignan ☎ 49-60-90-59. **Minitel**. Coaches
welcome. Rest. seats 67.

COURCELLES-LES-GISORS

COURCELLES-LES-GISORS 60240 Oise **RD 981 Map 3-B2**

♈⊗ **AUBERGE DU CARREFOUR** (N° RR DEC 21 716) (M. Daniel **Hillion**) Route Départmentale 981 ☎ 32-55-03-16. Restaurant: family cooking. Menu at 44F. Dinner until 11pm. Closed Sat evening to Sun evening, 1–15 Sept. Credit cards accepted. Traditional décor. Rest. seats 110 in 3 rooms. ⋔ Parking. Sights: museum of Claude Monet, Boury Château, feudal château of Gisors.

COURGAINS 72260 Sarthe **Map 8-B2**

♈⊗ **LA PETITE MARMITE** (N° RR MAI 27 598) (Mme Marie-Pierre **Vincelet**) Le Bourg Marolles-les-Braults ☎ 43-33-69-44. Restaurant: closed Thur, 15 days in Feb.

COURGIVAUX 51310 Marne **RN 4 Map 9 B-2**

♈⊗ ☆ **AUBERGE DE CHAPERON ROUGE** (N° RR JAN 27 501) (M.
⌂ Bernard **Moreau**) ☎ 26-81-57-09. Restaurant: dinner served until 10pm. Closed Sat. Hotel ⊨ 14 from 60–130F. Parking.

COURNEUVE (LA) 93120 Seine-St-Denis **Porte de la Villette Map 1 A2/3**

♈⊗ **L'ESCALE DES ROUTIERS** (N° RR JAN 26 786) (M. and Mme **Khaled**) 27, avenue Jean-Jaurès ☎ 48-36-43-78. Arabic, English, Italian spoken. Family cooking. Specialities include couscous Tunisian style. Menus from 35–65F or à la carte. Lunch 12–3pm. Dinner 7–11pm. Closed Sun. Credit cards accepted. Traditional décor. Sitting room.

♈⊗ **CAFE DU L'AVENIR** (N° RR SEP 26 662) (M. Sadid **Hadj-Arab**) 98, avenue P.V. Couturier ☎ 48-36-37-53. Closed Sun, Aug. Coaches welcome. Rest. seats 42.

COURSON LES CARRIERES 89560 Yonne **Map 13 B-A2**

♈⊗ **LE RELAIS DE COURSON** (N° RR OCT 27 686) (M. Jose **Carvalho**) Route Nationale 151 ☎ 86-41-52-58. Portuguese and Spanish spoken. Family cooking. À la carte menu. Lunch 11am–3pm. Dinner 6.30pm until midnight. Credit cards accepted. Modern décor. Rest. seats 70. Garden terrace. ⋔ Parking for coaches. Filling station on site. Sights: Abbey de la Vezelay (30m), Array Grotto (25km), Avallon (35km).

COURTENAY 45320 Loiret **RN 60 Map 9-B2**

♈⊗ **LE RELAIS DES SPORTS** (N° RR MAI 7 681) (M. Armand **Martin**)
⌂ 38, rue de Villeneuve ☎ 38-97-32-37 ⊨ 9. Closed Sun, 15–30 Mar, 15–30 Aug. Coaches welcome. Rest. seats 60. Evening meals.

COURTHEZON 84350 Vaucluse **RN 7 Map 24-A2**

♈⊗ **LE RELAIS DU SOLEIL** (N° RR MAI 27 292) (Mme Marie Ange **Meilloret**) RN 7 ☎ 90-70-74-36. Closed Sat, Sun. Italian, English, German spoken. Evening meals. Local filling station 7am–10pm.

COURTINE (LA) 23100 Creuse. **Map 16-B3**

♈⊗ **LA BONNE AUBERGE** (N° RR AVR 27 581) (M. Manuel **Ival**) ☎ 55-66-74-49. Peregourdine regional specialities. English and Spanish spoken.

COUTANCES 50200 Manche **RN 171 Maps 8-A1 and 4-B1**

♈⊗ ☆ **NN LE RELAIS DU VIADUC** (N° RR JUN 16 098) (Mme
⌂⋔ Georgette **Hossin**) 25, avenue de Verdun ☎ 33-45-02-68. **Minitel**

— 10 from 70–150F, breakfast 17–20F. Telephone in room. Closed Fri evening, Sun evening (out of season), all Sep. Full-board 170–250F per night. Coaches welcome Rest. seats 70+40. Evening meals to 9pm. English, German spoken. Menus from 38–230F. Specialities: langouste gratinée, tripes maison, gigot d'agneau. Sights: cathedral.

SARL CLOSERIE DES LILAS (N° RR JUN 27 631) (M. Gilles **Letourner**) 1, rue des Abattoirs ☎ 33-45-53-23. Portuguese, Spanish, English spoken. Restaurant: regional cooking. Open 5.30am–1.00am. Hotel — 14 from 90–103F per night.

COUVILLE 50690 Manche **Map 4A-2**

LE BOURG NEUF (N° RR EV 27 527) (M. Yves **Anquetil**) Le Bourg Neuf ☎ 33-52-01-76. Restaurant: family cooking. Set menu 48F. Children's menu. À la carte. Lunch from 12–4pm. Dinner from 7–10pm. Closed Tue afternoon and Aug. Credit cards accepted. Traditional décor. Rest. seats 26. Local filling station 100m.

COUX (LE) 24220 Dordogne **RD 703 Map 17-B1**

LA COTTE DE MAILLES (N° RR NOV 27 078) (Mme Michelle **Mandler**) place de l'Église ☎ 53-31-61-04. Closed 15 Dec to 15 Jan. English and German spoken. Local filling station close by 7am–8pm.

COZES 17120 Charente-Maritime **Map 15-A2**

Shell Service Station BEL AIR (N° RR AVR 550 000 8) (M. Jacques **Gadiou**) Rte de Royan, Grezac ☎ 46-90-84-12.

CRAVANT 89460 Yonne **RN 6 Map 13-A2**

LE RELAIS DES DEUX PONTS (N° RR JAN 17 724) (Mme Isabelle **Nogueria**) 17, route de Paris ☎ 86-42-24-01 — 10. Portuguese spoken.

CREIL 60100 Oise **RN 16 Map 3-B3**

CHEZ PIERROT (N° RR JUL 25 489) (M. Abdel **Kader Aceval**) 36, rue des Usines ☎ 44-25-37-22 — 11. Closed Sun. Dinner until 9pm.

CREMIEU 38460 Isère **RN 157 Map 2-A2**

LE RELAIS DE L'HOTEL DE VILLE (N° RR MAI 24 579) (M. Jean **L'Hopital**) 1, place de la Nation ☎ 74-94-76-09. Closed Aug.

CRENEY PRES TROYES 10150 Aube **RD 960 Map 9-B3**

LE RELAIS DU CENTRE (N° RR DEC 26 128) (M. Jacques **Jeandon**) 29, route de Brienne ☎ 25-81-39-79. Evening meals to 9pm. Rest. seats 50.

CRESANCEY 70100 Haute-Saône **RD 7 Map 14-A3**

AUBERGE DE LA PETITE FRINGALE (N° RR JUIL 27 349) (M. Jean-Paul **Loisel**) ☎ 84-31-56-08. Closed Mon am, Wed pm and Thur am. English spoken. Evening meal to 9pm. Local filling station. Parking.

CRESPIERES 78121 Yvelines **RN 307 Map 1-A1**

AUBERGE DES ROUTIERS (N° RR DEC 9 124) (Mme Magdeleine **Glatigny**) ☎ 30-54-44-28. Closed Sat. Evening meals to 8pm.

CREST

CREST 26400 Drôme **Map 24-A1**
♀⊗ **LE CHAMPS DE MARS** (N° RR AVR 27 259) (M. Bernard
Genthon) 8, place de la Liberté ☎ 75-40-61-06. German spoken.
Filling station 2km. Restaurant: 3 rooms with 135 places.

CRETEIL 94000 Val-de-Marne
⊗♪ **Le MIRABELLIER** (N° RR 2049) Aire de Service de Pompadour
☎ 48-99-77-00. Showers. Shops. Newsagent. TV. Message facilities. Rest rooms. Business centre (fax, **Minitel**, etc).

CREUSOT (LE) 71200 Saône-et-Loire **RN 80 Map 18-A1 13-B3**
♀⊗ **LE RELAIS DE ROUTIERS** (N° RR SEPT 22 041) (M. Guy
⌂ **Beauclair**) 26, rue de l'Yser ☎ 85-55-03-34. Showers. Restaurant:
family cooking. À la carte. Dinner until 9pm. Closed Sat afternoon
and Sun evening. 1 dining room, 50 places. Hotel ⊨ 14 from
68–125F. Parking for cars and lorries.

CREUTZWALD 57150 Moselle **Map 10-A1**
♀⊗ **AU TROCADERO** (N° RR DEC 27 740) (M. Martin **Balow**) 2, rue
de Merten. Directions: Creutzwald exit going towards Falch and
Merten. Turn left at the crossroads. ☎ 87-82-61-46. Restaurant:
regional and family cooking. Specialities: couscous. Set menu
45F. Children's menu. Dinner until 1am. Closed Mon and Aug.
Modern décor. Rest. seats 40. Terrace garden. Parking for cars
and lorries. Sights: Creutzwald Lake (3km).

CREUZIER-LE-VIEUX 03300 Allier **Map 16-B3**
♀⊗ **CHEZ LA MÈRE RIBOULIN SARL** (N° RR AVR 27 247) (M. Marcel
⌂ **Joly**) 10, rue des Ailes ☎ 70-98-44-88 ⊨ 13. Rest. seats 120.

CREVANT-MONTIERCHAUME 36130 Indre **Map 13-B1**
♀⊗ **CHEZ YVONNE** (N° RR DEC 11 180) (Mme **Belouin-Ferre**) ☎
54-36-00-19. Closed Sun.

CREVECOEUR LE GRAND 60360 Oise **RN 30 and RD 93 Map 3-A2**
♀⊗ **LE RELAX** (N° RR JUIL 26 969) (M. Michel **Dubois**) 12, rue de
Breteuil ☎ 44-46-87-65. Closed Sun. Filling station nearby.

CROISEE-ROUVRAY (LA) 21530 Côte-d'Or **RN 6 and 13 Map B-2**
♀⊗ **RELAIS DE LA CROISEE** (N° RR DEC 27 464) (M. Belaïd **Ammar
Khodja**) ☎ 80-64-70-44. Restaurant: closed Sun. Local filling
station nearby open 5.30am–midnight.

CROISIÈRE (LA) 23300 Creuse **RN 145 and 20 Map 16-B1**
♀⊗ **LES ROUTIERS** (N° RR JUIL 26 596) (M. Raymond **Boutet**) La
⌂ Croisière St-Maurice ☎ 55-63-77-55 and 55-63-30-36 ⊨ 15.
Closed Sun, 24 Dec–2 Jan. Coaches welcome. Rest. seats 230.
Evening meals to 11pm.

CROISY-SUR-ANDELLE 76780 Seine-Maritime **RN 31 Map 3-A1**
♀⊗ **LE RELAIS DU COMMERCE** (N° RR OCT 23 975) (Mme Colette
Belière) ☎ 35-23-61-82. **Minitel**. Closed Sun, 15 Dec–10 Jan.
Coaches welcome. Rest. seats 80. Evening meals to 11pm. Parking.

CROIX 59170 Nord **RD 14 Map 5-B1**
♀⊗ **LE RELAIS DE L'HOTEL DE VILLE** (N° RR MAR 21 837) (Mme
Lucette **Streleki**) 211, rue Jean-Jaurès ☎ 20-70-50-92. Closed Mon
afternoon, Jul.

CULAN

♟⊗ **LE RELAIS CHEZ HENRI** (N° RR DEC 24 051) (M. Henri
⌂ **Vandesompele**) 53, avenue Georges-Hannart ☎ 20-72-59-08.
Minitel. Restaurant: regional and family cooking. Specialities:
flemish stews. Menu 60F. Lunch 11am–4pm. Dinner: 6–8.30pm.
Closed Sat, Sun and Aug. Modern décor. 2 dining rooms, 60
places. Hotel ⇥ 9, from 100–150F with showers, own WC, TV and
telephone. Open 3.30am–9pm. Rest rooms. Parking for cars and
lorries. Sights: Lille, Roubaix, Tourcoing.

CROIX-CHAPEAU 17220 Charente-Maritime **Map 11-B1**
♟⊗ **CAFE-DE-PARIS** (N° RR JAN 27 494) (EURL DM PB – Daniel
Mineur) 60, rue de la Libération ☎ 46-35-81-20. Evening meals.
English, Spanish spoken.
♟⊗ **RELAIS DE PARIS** (N° RR DEC 26 412) (M. Jean-Paul **Thabault**)
60, avenue de la Libération ☎ 46-35-81-20. Closed Wed.

CROIX-VALMER (LA) 83420 Var **RN 559 Map 25-A3**
♟⊗ **LA CIGALE** (N° RR MAI 24 966) (M. Eric **Korhel**) ☎ 94-79-60-41
⌂ ⇥ 7. Coaches welcome. Rest. seats 50. Dinner until 9pm. Closed
Sat.

CROLLES 38190 Isère **RN 90 Map 19-A3**
♟⊗ ☆ **NN HOTEL DU PETIT PONT** (N° RR JUN 25 946) (M. André
⌂ **Legallais**) ☎ 76-08-03-92. Montfort ⇥ 13 from 85–230F. Closed
Mon, Nov. Full-board 160–280F per night, Coaches welcome.
Rest. seats 60. Evening meals to 8pm. Parking. Bar. ⚐ Some
German spoken.

CRUAS 07350 Ardèche **RN 86 Map 24-A1/2**
♟⊗ **AUX AMIS DES ROUTIERS** (N° RR JUL 17 322) (Mme Sylvie
Madeira) ☎ 75-51-41-12. Rest. seats 120. Menu 50F. Parking.

CUIGY-EN-BRAY 60850 Oise **RN 3 Map 3-A2**
♟⊗ **RELAIS DE ST-LEU** (N° RR NOV 26 365) (M. Jacques **Delaruelle**)
☎ 44-82-53-17. **Minitel**. Closed Sat afternoon, Sun, Aug. Coaches
welcome. Rest. seats 100. Evening meals to 9pm. Menu at 48F.
Sights: the Abbey of St Germer le Fly and Gerbevoy.

CUISE-LA-MOTTE 60350 Oise **RN 31 Map 6-B1**
♟⊗ **AUX AS DU VOLANT** (N° RR MAI 26 547) (M. Dominique **Bignet**)
⌂ 23, rue du Dr Moussaud ☎ 44-85-70-51. ⇥ 6. Closed Sat, Sun, 2
Dec–2 Jan. Coaches welcome. Rest. seats 64. Evening meals to
9pm.

CUISEAUX 71480 Saône-et-Loire **Map 18-B1**
♟⊗ **RELAIS FRANC COMTOIS** (N° RR JUL 27 341) (M. Jean-Marc
Girona) Joudes ☎ 85-72-79-79. Evening meals to 10pm. Closed
Sun. Local filling station 7am–8pm.

CUISERY 71290 Saône-et-Loire **18-B1**
♟⊗ **LE RELAIS DE BRUÈRE** (N° RR MARS 27 557) (M. Jean-Pierre
⌂ **Guillot**) ☎ 85-40-04-51. **Minitel**. English and German spoken.
Hotel ⇥ 6. Filling station nearby.

CULAN 18270 Cher **RD 943 Map 16-A2**
♟⊗ **HOTEL DU BERRY** (N° RR MAR 27 224) (Mme Chantal **Gallurt**)
place du Champ ☎ 48-56-65-93. Closed Sun. English spoken.
Sights: château, church, museum, dam at Sidiailles.

CUON

CUON 49150 Maine-et-Loire **RN 938 Map 12-A2**
♀⊗ **LA POMM'DE PIN** (N° RR AVR 25 904) (Mme Yvette **Pécot**) Le
Bourg ☎ 41-82-75-74. Closed Mon afternoon, Aug. Coaches
welcome. Rest. seats 60. Evening meals until 10pm. Hotel ⇌ 4.

CUQ-TOULZA 81470 Tarn **RD 621 Map 22-A2**
♀⊗ ☆ **CHEZ ALAIN** – "La Bombardière" (N° RR MAR 22 271) (M.
⌂ Alain **Pratviel**) ☎ 63-75-70-36. ⇌ 10 at 160F. Coaches welcome.
Rest. seats 400. Parking. Bar. ⌕ TV room. Walks. English spoken.
Sights: Lake Saint Ferréol, Cordes, Sidobre.

CUSSAC 87150 Haute-Vienne **RD 699 Map 15-B2**
♀⊗ **LA BARRIÈRE** (N° RR AVR 27 240) (Mme Denise **Barrière**) ☎
⌂ 55-70-94-84 ⇌ 9. Rest. seats 150. Local filling station 7am–8pm.

CUSSET 03300 Allier **Map 16-B3**
♀⊗ **HOTEL DE LA GARE LES ROUTIERS** (N° RR JAN 26 421) (M.
Jean **Laroque**) 1, route de Paris ☎ 70-98-26-10. ⇌ 3 80F. Closed
Sun, Jul. Lunch midday to 1.30pm.
♀⊗ **LES MONTAGNARDS** (N° RR JUL 26 960) (M. Roger **Pol**) 20, rue
Général Raynal ☎ 70-98-38-60. Closed Sun, Aug. Filling station
nearby. Coaches welcome. Rest. seats 40. ⌕ Lunch 11.30am–
2pm. Menu 50F.

CUSSY-LES-FORGES 89420 Yonne **RN 6 Map 13-A3**
♀⊗ **LE RELAIS 6** (N° RR FEV 26 805) (M. Hamid **Adjaoud**) ☎
86-33-10-14. Closed Sun. Coaches welcome. Rest. seats 130.

CUVILLY 60490 Oise **RN 17 Map 3-A3**
♀⊗ **LA CAMPAGNARDE** (N° RR JUN 26 922) (M. Daniel **Hillion**)
⌂ 5, route de Flandres ☎ 44-85-00-30 ⇌ 9. Closed Sun, 1–15 Sept.

CUZIEU 42330 Loire **RN 82 Map 18-A2**
♀⊗ **RESTAURANT DE LA MAIRIE** (N° RR AVR 26 225) (Mme Janine
⌂ **Dard**) Le Bourg ☎ 77-54-88-21. **Minitel** ⇌ 12 110–170F with TV.
Closed Sat pm, Sun, Aug. Evening meals. Credit cards accepted.
Modern décor. Rest. seats 80. Open 5am to midnight. Rest rooms.
⌕ Parking. Sights: Museum of Modern Art at St Etienne, the
plains and Mount Forez, the barrages of Villerest and Grangent.

DAGNEUX 01120 Ain **RN 84 Map 2-A2**
♀⊗ **RELAIS DE LA PLACE** (N° RR OCT 26 336) (Colin and Aliu) 96,
route de Genève ☎ 78-06-43-70. Spanish, Italian spoken.

DANGÉ-ST-ROMAIN 86220 Vienne **Map 12-B2**
♀⊗ **LE NATIONAL** (N° RR JUIN 27 296) (M. Bernard **Peronneau**) 120,
⌂ RN 10 ☎ 49-86-40-14 ⇌ 5. Closed Sun. Evening meals until
midnight. Coaches welcome.

DANGERS 28190 Eure-et-Loir **CD 939 Map 8-A/B3**
♀⊗ **LE RELAIS** (N° RR DEC 27 124) (M. Patrick **Ollier**) rue de
Chartres ☎ 37-22-90-30. Closed Sun and two weeks in Aug. Local
filling station open 7.15am–8.30pm.

DANNEMOINE 89700 Yonne **RD 905 Map 13-A3**
♀⊗ **A LA BONNE AUBERGE** – **LES ROUTIERS** (N° RR MAI 21 096)
(Mme Nicole **Verdin**) ☎ 86-55-54-22. Coaches welcome. Rest.
seats 70 ⇌ 12.

DARDILLY 69570 Rhône **RD 67 and RD 73 Map 2-A1**

¶⊗ **LE CHENE ROND** (N° RR FEV 23 144) (M. Emile **Lagoutte**) 87,
⌂ route Nationale 7 ☎ 78-87-15-48 ⌿ 6. Closed Sat midday, Sun,
Aug. and public holidays. Evening meals for drivers. Lunch 47F.
Midday to 1.30pm. Rest. seats 32.

¶⊗ **RELAIS DE LA RADIO** (N° RR JAN 27 137) (M. Pierre **Caputo**) 22
⌂ RN 7. Lieu-dit "Moncourant" ☎ 78-48-01-89. English and Italian
spoken. Restaurant: family cooking. Specialities: lasagne, couscous, choucroute. Menu 50F. Closed Sat, Sun and Aug. Rest.
seats 50. Hotel ⌿ 8 from 100–130F. Open 6.30am–9pm. Terraced
garden. Parking. Local filling station 1.5km, open 7am–8pm.
Sights: Fourvière (12km), Le Port de la Truite d'Or, vieux Saint
Jean (10km).

RELAIS DE LA BASCULE (N° RR NOV 27 7718) (M. Roger
Martins) Porte de Lyon ☎ 78-35-56-30. Portuguese and Italian
spoken. Restaurant: dinner 60F menu until 10pm. Closed Sat, Sun
and Aug. Parking. Local filling station open 6am–midnight.

DARVOY 45150 Loiret **RN 751 Map 13-A1**

LES ROUTIERS (N° RR FEV 27 785) (Mme Julie **Vingerder**) 4,
route d'Orléans. Lieu dit "La Place" ☎ 38-59-71-00. Restaurant:
family cooking. Menu 50F. Lunch midday to 2pm. Closed Sat
afternoon, Sun and Aug. Traditional décor. Rest. seats 42. ⌿
Parking. Tobacconist. Newsagent. Local filling station 150m.
7.30am–7pm. Sights: La Sologne (10km), châteaux of the Loire,
Orléans Cathedral, flower gardens.

DAX 40100 Landes **RN 647 and 124 Map 20-A2**

¶⊗ **AUBERGE DE LA CHALOSSE** (N° RR OCT 22 956) (M. **Richaud**)
157, avenue Georges Clémenceau ☎ 58-74-23-08 ⌿ 6. Closed
Sun, Aug. Evening meals to 10pm. Parking.

DECAZEVILLE 12300 Aveyron **RN 140 (axe Brive Mediterranée) Map
22-B1 and 17-B2**

¶⊗ **REST. DES USINES** (N° RR OCT 25 132) (Mme Régine **Forsse**) 23,
⌿ faubourg Desseligny Fontvergnes ☎ 65-43-15-88 Closed Sun.
Evening meals. Menus 40–105F. Specialities: écrevisses améri-
caines, cuisses de grenouilles. Rest. seats 76. Hotel with showers.
Terraced garden. ⌿ Parking.

DECINES 69150 Rhône **RN 517 Map 2-A2**

¶⊗ ☆☆ **NN – HOTEL DE LA POSTE – Chez Simone** (N° RR JUL 18
⌂ 783) (Mme Marcelle **Buisson**) 11, rue d'Alsace ☎ 78-49-19-03.
Minitel ⌿ 34 from 100–180F, breakfast to 20F. Restaurant: closed
Sun (hotel open). Car park (area 2000sq.m.) locked at night.
Evening meals. English, Spanish, Italian spoken. Bar. ⌿ Boule
played. Track and pool near. Coaches welcome. Rest. seats 20.

DECIZE 58300 Nièvre **Map 16-A3**

¶⊗ **LE RELAIS BEL-AIR** (N° RR MARS 27 213) (M. André **Demery**)
164, avenue de Verdun ☎ 86-25-01-86. Closed Sun, Aug.

DENEE 49190 Maine-et-Loire **12 A-1**

¶⊗ **LE PENALTY** (N° RR FEV 27 523) (M. Alain **Saulgrain**) Place
Muller ☎ 41-78-72-03. **Minitel**. German spoken. Restaurant:
dinner 60F until 10pm. Restaurant closed Sunday afternoon and
over Christmas and New Year. Filling station nearby. Open
7am–9pm.

DENGUIN

DENGUIN 64230 Pyrénées-Atlantiques **RN 177 Map 20-B3**
☆ **NN LES ROUTIERS DE DENGUIN** (N° RR MARS 26 846) (**Sarl Pyrénées Montagne Océan**) ☎ 59-68-85-15 ⊷ 14. English, Spanish, German spoken. Closed Sat. Evening meals until 11pm. Parking. Rest. seats 140.

DÉOLS 36130 **see CHATEAUROUX**

DESVRES 62240 Pas-de-Calais **RN 341 Map 5-A2**
LE RELAIS DE LA BELLE CROIX (N° RR SEP 23 462) (M. Jean-Claude **Grumelart-Mielot**) 1, rue du Bidet Longfosse. ☎ 21-91-65-81 or 21-87-46-93. English spoken. Restaurant: regional and family cooking. Menu à la carte. Dinner until 11pm. Closed Sun. Rest. seats 60. Hotel ⊷ 5 60F with shower.

DETRIER 73110 Savoie **RD 925 Map 19-A2**
LES SMOUTANS (N° RR MARS 19 217) (M. Alain **Sigrand**) La Rochette ☎ 79-25-52-59. Closed Sun. English spoken. Filling station 1km 6.30am–10pm. Exhibition of paintings by Mme Sigrand.

DEUIL-LA-BARRE 95170 Val-d'Oise **RN 428 Map 1-A2**
LE RELAIS DU COQ HARDI (N° RR SEP 19 940) (M. and Mme **Lantinier**) 61, bis, avenue de la Division Leclerc ☎ 39-64-16-81. Closed Sat, Sun, Aug.

DEULEMONT 59890 Nord
LA BOULE D'OR (N° RR JAN 27 508) (M. Guy **Catteau**) 16, rue du Maréchal Foch, Le Bel Arbre ☎ 20-39-24-38. Closed Wed. Evening meals. Filling station nearby.

DEUX-CHAISES 03240 Allier **Map 16-A3**
LE RELAIS DE L'AMITIÉ (N° RR AVR 24 904) (M. Louis **Douge**) RN 145 ☎ 70-47-15-64. **Le Montet**.

DEVAY 58300 Nièvre **Map 16-A3**
L'ETRIER (N° RR MARS 26 842) (M. Jean-Marc **Boutet**) route Nationale ☎ 86-25-15-65. German spoken. Coaches welome. Rest. seats 80. Evening meals until 10pm.

DIEPPE 76200 Seine-Maritime **RN 15 Map 4-A2**
CAFE DE L'AVENIR (N° RR JUN 23 856) (M. Benoît **Pan**) 10, Cours de Dakar Port de Commerce ☎ 35-84-18-10. Closed Sun, Aug. Evening meals until 8pm.

DIEPPEDALLE 76380 Seine-Maritime
LE RELAIS DE LA FORÊT (N° RR MAI 27 600) (M. Pierre **Goupil**) 97, Quai du Danemark ☎ 35-36-25-70. English and Spanish spoken. Restaurant: dinner until 10pm. Closed Sun afternoon. Hotel ⊷ 7 at 80–100F. Parking.

DIJON 21490 Côte-d'Or **14 Map A3**.
⊗ **RELAIS DE DIJON CÔTE D'OR** (N° RR 2035) Aire de Service de Dijon Brognon – both directions (motorway) ☎ 80-23-30-30. German and English spoken. Restaurant: menu 25% discount for lorry drivers. Children's menu. À la carte. Self service. Open 7am–11pm. Credit cards accepted. Rest. seats 120. Rest room. Terraced garden. ⊷ Parking. Business centre. Shops. Tourist information office. Hotel reservations. Nursery.

DINAN 22100 Côtes-du-Nord **RN 166 and 176 Map 7-A3**

Ψ⊗   **LA MARMITE** (N° RR AOU 23 904) (M. **Bouillet**) 91, rue de Brest
⌂◄   ☎ 96-39-04-42. ◄ 5 with shower 90–150F. Closed Sat evening, Sun. Coaches welcome. Rest. seats 36. English, German spoken. Open 7am–10pm. ◄ Sights: Mont Saint Michel, Cap Fréhal, Dinan old town.

DISSAY-SUR-COURCILLON 72500 Sarthe **RN 138 Map 12-A2**

Ψ⊗   **RELAIS MAINE-TOURAINE** (N° RR MAI 21 918) (Mme Colette **Petit**) Route Nationale 138 ☎ 43-44-09-08.

DIVES-SUR-MER 14360 Calvados **Map 4-B2**

Ψ⊗   **LE CAFE DU PARKING** (N° RR SEP 26 047) (M. Daniel **Constant**) 2, rue des Frères-Le-Paule ☎ 31-91-24-25. Closed Sun, Aug.
LE BON GITE (N° RR NOV 27 734) (M. Alain **Belkacemi**) 71, rue du Général de Gaulle ☎ 91-91-24-39. Restaurant. Specialities: couscous, paella. Menu 45–120F. Open 6.30am–11pm. Lunch midday to 2.30pm. Dinner 7–10.30pm. Closed Sun afternoon and from 25–31 Dec. Parking. Local filling station 500m.

DIZY-LE-GROS 02150 Aisne **RD 336 Map 6-A2**

Ψ⊗   **LE RELAIS FRANCE-EUROPE** (N° RR AOU 19 454) (M. Claude **Gantier**) Route de Reims ☎ 23-21-23-15. **Minitel** ◄ 3. Closed Sun, 15 to 31 Aug. Evening meals until 9pm. Rest. seats 160. Terraced garden.

DOL-DE-BRETAGNE 35120 Ille-et-Vilaine **RN 12 Map 7-A3**

Ψ⊗   **LE RELAIS DE BELLE LANDE** (N° RR OCT 23 999) (M. Jean-
⌂   Yves **Beubry**) 23 bis, rue de Rennes ☎ 99-48-06-14. **Minitel** ◄ 2. Coaches welcome. Rest. seats 50. Evening meals to 9pm. Menu 43–65F. À la carte. Specialities: moules marinières, bouchots de la baie.

DOMANCY 74700 Haute-Savoie **Map 19-B2**

Ψ⊗   **AUBERGE DE L'ETRAZ** (N° RR FEV 27 787) (Mme Viviane **Fivel-Demoret**) RN 205 L'Etraz ☎ 50-93-90-86. **Minitel**. English spoken. Restaurant: specialities from Savoy and Normandy. Menu from 55–90F. À la carte. Open 9am–3pm. Closed Sun, from Chistmas to the New Year. Parking. Filling station nearby.

DOMFRONT 61700 Orne **RN 12 and CD 908 Map 8-A1**

Ψ⊗   ☆ **LE RELAIS SAINT MICHEL** (N° RR JAN 10 298) (M. Michel
⌂◄   **Prod'homme**) 5, route du Mont Saint Michel ☎ 33-38-64-99. **Minitel**. English spoken. Restaurant: regional family cooking. Specialities: andouillette aux poires, truite flambées aux calvados. Menu 50–140F. Children's menu. À la carte. Lunch 12–2pm. Dinner 7.30–9pm. Closed Fri evening, Sun evening (low season), 24 Dec–15 Jan. Credit cards accepted. Rest seats 52. Hotel ◄ 13 singles 110–210F; double 140–250F with shower, bathroom, private WC, TV, telephone. Open 7.30am–10pm. ◄ Cars only – free garaging. Sights: 11th century church, medieval city.

Ψ⊗   **LA CROIX DES LANDES** (N° RR NOV 27 093) (M. Claude
⌂   **Leveau**) La Croix des Landes ☎ 33-38-51-35. **Minitel**. English and Spanish spoken. Restaurant: regional and family cooking. Children's menu. À la carte. Dinner until 11pm. Closed Sun (low season). Credit cards accepted. Traditional décor. Rest. seats 120. Hotel ◄ 8 from 80–150F with shower, bathroom, private WC,

Domfront continued

TV, telephone. ⌁ Parking. Filling station nearby, open 7.30am–9pm. Sights: Swiss Normandy (60km), Mont Saint Michel (80km), St Frainbault (20km) Forest of Andaine (5km), leisure centre at Ferté-Macé (20km).

DOMONT 95330 Val-d'Oise **RN 1 Maps 1-A2 and 3-B3**
♀⊗ **LA VIELLE AUBERGE** (N° RR JAN 24 085) (M. Roger **Badair**) 7, RN 1 ☎ 39-91-01-66 ⊷ 7. Closed Sat, Sun, Aug. Spanish spoken. Evening meals until 9pm.

DOMPIERRE-SUR-BESBRE 03290 Allier **RN 79 Map 16-A3**
♀⊗ **LE RELAIS DE LA BESBRE** (N° RR JUN 25 453) (M. Jean-Pierre **Marossa**) 207, avenue de la Gare ☎ 70-34-53-69. Closed Sun, half Sept. Lunch 12–2pm. Evening meals 7–9pm. Rest. seats 20.

DONZENAC 19270 Corrèze **RN 20 Map 17-A1**
♀⊗ **RELAIS DE LA POÊLE D'OR** (N° RR SEPT 26 987) (M. Daniel **Vermand**) Avenue de Paris ☎ 55-85-72-20. Filling station nearby.

DONZÈRE 26290 Drôme **RN 7 Map 24-A2**
♀⊗ ☆ **NN AU BON ACCUEIL** (N° RR OCT 26 701) (M. Jacky **Paunon**)
🏠 RN 7 ☎ 75-51-64-58 ⊷ 11. Dutch, Spanish spoken.
♀⊗ ☆ **LE BOLO** (N° RR NOV 27 724) (M. Merciano **Dafonsec**) RN 7.
🏠 ☎ 75-51-61-48. English, Portuguese and Spanish spoken. Restaurant: family cooking. Set menu 59F. Children's menu. À la carte. Open 24 hours. Credit cards accepted. Traditional décor. Rest seats 150. Hotel ⊷ 24 from 80–180F with shower, bathroom, private WC. Terraced garden. ⌁ Parking. Covered swimming pool. Sights: grottos in Ardeche, Tricastin.

DORLISHEIM 67120 Bas-Rhin **RN 392 Map 10-B2**
♀⊗ **LE RELAIS DE LA GARE** (N° RR NOV 9 059) (M. René **Jost**) 4,
🏠 avenue de la Gare ☎ 88-38-14-28 ⊷ 7 70–90F. Closed Sat, Sun afternoon, from 28 Aug to 15 Sep, 10 days in Oct. Coaches welcome. Rest. seats 70. Evening meals to 9pm.

DOUAI 59500 Nord **RN 17 and 34 Map 5-B3**
♀⊗ **A L'EPI D'OR** (N° RR FEV 22 663) (M. Michel **Barjou**) 38, faubourg
🏠 d'Arras Lambres ☎ 27-87-04-56 ⊷ 7. Closed Sat after 3pm and Sun. Open 4.30am to midnight. Full-board (150F). Coaches welcome. Rest. seats 55.

♀⊗ **LE RELAIS** (N° RR MARS 25 844) (Mme Jeannine **Deyreck**) 370,
🏠 rue d'Aniche ☎ 27-88-12-06 ⊷ 8.

DOUÉ-LA-FONTAINE 49700 Maine-et-Loire **Map 12-B2**
♀⊗ **CHEZ PAUL** (N° RR 27 118) (M. Paul and Mme Josette **Type-Bassant**). Zone industrielle route de Montreuil ☎ 41-59-03-33. **Minitel**. English and Spanish spoken. Restaurant: family cooking. Children's menu. Self service. Open 4am to midnight. Dinner until 9pm. Closed Sun (low season), fortnight in Aug. Credit cards accepted. Modern décor. Rest. seats 100. Hotel rooms with telephone. Terraced garden. ⌁ Parking.

DOUSSARD 74210 Haute-Savoie **Map 19-A2**
♀⊗ ☆ (N° RR OCT 26 677) (Mme Lucette **Faure-Bonvin** SARL
🏠 Scherfa) La Tour du Lac ☎ 50-44-30-37. Restaurant: family and

regional cooking. Specialities: fondues Savoyarde and bourguig-none, grenouilles. Menu 57–95F. Children's menu. À la carte. Lunch 12–2pm. Dinner 7–9.30pm. Closed Sun. Credit cards accepted. Traditional décor. Rest. seats 60. Hotel ⌒ 8 100–165F. Open 6.30am–11pm. Terraced garden. ⊬ Parking. Sights: Col de la Forclaz.

DOZENS 11700 Ande **Map 22-B2**

Ⴘⓧ **LES ROUTIERS** (N° RR AOUT 27 651) (Mme Monique **Hulin**) ☎
⌂ 68-79-19-99. Hotel ⌒ 8.

DOZULE 14430 Calvados **RN 175 Map 4-B2**

Ⴘⓧ **LES CHARMETTES** (N° RR FEV 26 804) (M. Patrice **Tanguy**)
⌂ 1, route de Rouen ☎ 31-79-21-87 ⌒ 4. Closed Sun evening, Oct. German spoken.

DRAGUIGNAN 83300 Var **Map 25-A2**

Ⴘⓧ **LE PENALTY** (N° RR FEV 26 427) (M. Guy **Chabrand**) 1, avenue de la 1ʳᵉ Armée Quartier St Léger ☎ 94-68-11-28. **Minitel**. Closed Sun.

DREUIL-LES-AMIENS 80730 Somme **RN 235 Map 5-A3**

Ⴘⓧ **CHEZ JEAN-MARIE ET CHRISTIANE** (N° RR FEV 23 645) (M. Jean-Marie **Dumeige**) 285, avenue Pasteur ☎ 22-43-12-95. **Minitel**. Closed Sun, Aug. Lunch 11.45–2pm. Dinner until 9pm. Rest. seats 53. ⊬ Parking.

DREUX 28100 Eure-et-Loir **RN 12 and RN 154 Map 8-A3**

Ⴘⓧ **LE RELAIS DE LA POSTE** (N° RR SEP 19 506) (Mme **Sedaine**) 2, rue du Général-de-Gaulle ☎ 37-42-12-00. Closed Sun.

Ⴘⓧ **LE MARCEAU** (N° RR SEPT 26 998) (M. Jean-Pierre **Parent**) 40/42, avenue du Général Marceau ☎ 37-46-05-57. Closed Sun, Aug. Menu à la carte. Credit cards accepted. Rest. seats 30. Terraced garden. ⊬ Parking.

DROCOURT 78440 Yvelines **Map 1-A2**

Ⴘⓧ **AU RELAIS DU NORD** (N° RR OCT 27 413) (M. Daniel **Tirouard**) 15, rue Nationale ☎ 34-76-71-23. Menu from 50–70F. Children's menu. Lunch 11.30–2pm. Dinner 7–8.30pm. Closed Sat. Credit cards accepted. Traditional décor. Rest. seats 50. ⊬ Parking. Sights: Château de la Roche Guyon (8km), Claude Monet's garden at Giverny (20km), Collegiale de Martes la Jolie (9km).

DUNKIRK 59140 Nord **RN 16 Map 5-A2**

Ⴘⓧ **AU PANIER FLEURI** (N° RR DEC 23 073) (Mme **Playe**) 15–17, rue
⌂ du Ponceau ☎ 28-66-76-19 ⌒ 8. Closed Sat from 2pm. Coaches welcome. Rest. seats 40. Evening meals to 11pm. English spoken.

DURANVILLE 27230 Eure **Map 4-B3**

Ⴘⓧ **LES ARCADES** (N° RR DEC 27 742) (Mme Genevieve **Boga**) RN 15 ☎ 32-46-83-019. Restaurant: menu from 47–55F. Closed Sat afternoon to Sun. Filling station nearby.

DURAVEL 46700 Lot **Map 21-B1**

Ⴘⓧ **LE PIED DE MOUTON** (N° RR DEC 26 417) (M. John **Duberley**)
☎ 65-36-50-39. Closed Mon (low season). Evening meals to 9pm. English spoken. Menu 58–85F. Children's menu. À la carte. Traditional décor. Rest. seats 70. ⊬ Parking.

DURFORT

DURFORT 30170 Gard **Map 23-B1**

ᵀ⊗ **LE MAMOUTH** (N° RR JUIL 27 637) (Mr Alain **Issert**) Rond-point
du Mamouth. Saint Hippolyte ☎ 66-77-55-33. Spanish spoken.
Restaurant: closed Sun.

ECALLES-ALIX 76190 Seine-Maritime **RN 15 Bis Map 4-A3**

ᵀ⊗ **AUBERGE DE LA FOURCHE** (N° RR AVR 25 867) (M. Serbe
🏠 **Vannier**) Tobacconist Hameau de Loumare ☎ 35-95-45-01. **Minitel** ⊷ 5. Closed Sun. Coaches welcome. Rest. seats 32. Evening
meals.

ECARDENVILLE-LA-CAMPAGNE 27170 Eure **RN 13 Map 4-B3**

ᵀ⊗ **AUBERGE DU RELAIS** (N° RR JUN 26 928) (M. Phillippe **Le-
🏠 lièvre**) ☎ 32-35-05-32 ⊷ 10. Closed Sun, 2nd fortnight Aug.
English, German spoken. Coaches welcome. Rest. seats 100.
Evening meals to 11pm.

ÉCHELLES (LES) 73360 Savoie **RN 6 Map 2-B3**

ᵀ⊗ **L'ESCAPADE** (N° RR JUL 25 997) (M. Jean-Françoise **Daude**)
Route Nationale 6 ☎ 79-36-55-99. Closed Sun, last week Aug, 1st
week Sept.

ECLAIBES 59330 Nord **RN 2 Map 6-A3**

ᵀ⊗ **LE ROBINSON** (N° RR JUN 26 270) (M. Elhadi **Manseur**) Route
Nationale 2 ☎ 27-61-14-63. Coaches welcome. Rest. seats 240.
Evening meals.

ECULLY 69130 Rhône **RN 7 Map 2-A1**

ᵀ⊗ **LES ROUTIERS** (N° RR JUIN 26 906) (Mme Sylvie **Taillandier**) 30,
route de Paris ☎ 78-34-01-40. Closed Sat, Sun and last fortnight
Aug. Coaches welcome. Rest. seats 30.

ÉGLISES-D'ARGENTEUIL (LES) 17400 Charente-Maritime. **CD 950
Map 15-A2**

ᵀ⊗ **CHEZ VEVETTE** (N° RR SEP 27 023) (M. Joël **Pilot**) Saint-Jean-
🏠 d'Angély ☎ 46-59-94-21. Closed Fri and Sat night, Sun pm.
Coaches welcome. Rest. seats 110. Evening meals to 8pm.

ELVEN 56250 Morbihan **RN 166 Map 7-B2 11-A2**

ᵀ⊗ ☆ **NN LE RELAIS DE L'ARGOUET** (N° RR AOU 16 177) (M. and
🏠⊷ Mme André **Le Douarin**) 36, avenue de l'Argouët ☎ 97-53-32-98.
WC, bidets. English spoken. Restaurant: regional cooking.
Specialities: fruits de mer and poissons. Menu 45–120F. Children's menu. À la carte. Dinner until 10pm. Closed Sat (low
season), last 2 weeks in Sept. Credit cards accepted. Rest.
seats 180. Hotel ⊷ 12 100F with showers, private WC. Open 7am–
midnight. Terraced garden. ⊢ Parking.

EMONDEVILLE 50310 Manche **RN 13 Map 4-B1**

ᵀ⊗ **AU COUP DE FREIN** (N° RR MARS 26 825) (Mme Thérèse **Jean**)
Montebourg ☎ 33-41-22-74. Closed Sat, Sun and July. **Minitel.**
Rest. seats 44.

ENNORDRES 18380 Cher **RD 30 Map 13-A1**

ᵀ⊗ **LE RELAIS DES ROUTIERS** (N° RR JAN 19 620) (Mme Georgette
Champion) Route Départementale 30 ☎ 48-58-06-36. Closed Sat.

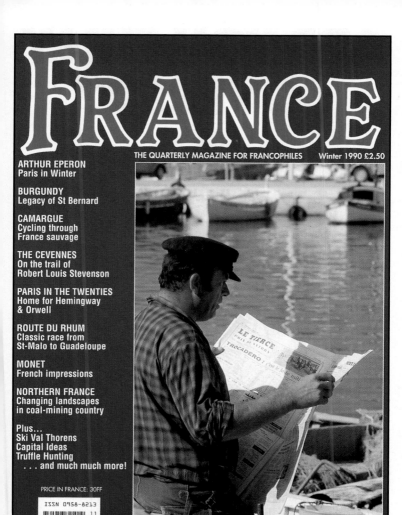

ARE YOU FULLY COVERED?

With over 20 million cars in its care, Mondial Assistance is one of Europe's largest assistance organisations.

That's how we can offer you complete holiday motoring cover including breakdown, recovery, medical and travel – all in one value-for-money policy.

There's even a special deal for frequent travellers that covers you for the whole year.

Just pick up the phone for full details (immediate cover available with any major credit card).

FRANCE A LA CARTE

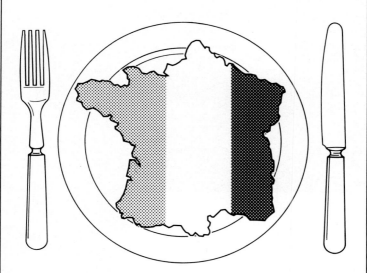

Pick up the phone to whet your appetite.

There's a wide choice on the VFB menu. Try regional cooking and local specialities in comfortable surroundings, in hand-picked, friendly auberges or country cottages. Travel by car or fly-drive to some of France's loveliest regions, including Corsica. Or by air to Paris or any of five fascinating provincial cities, or even the French Caribbean. Or sample the outdoor life with an activity or canal holiday.

Phone now for a brochure, letting us know the type of holiday you'd like to select from our menu.

 0242 580187 (24hr)   **VFB**

VFB Holidays (RG), Cheltenham GL50 3HW **SERVICE COMPRIS**

It's
your
Lifestyle

When powder hounds look for snow, they go to Val d'Isère. When sun worshippers look for sun, they go the the Cote d'Azur. If it's fashion, it must be Parisienne Haute Couture. When gourmets think about good food, they think of Cordon Bleu. When groupies think about film stars, they think about the Cannes Film Festival. When connoisseurs think about good wine, they think of Bordeaux. When the jet set think of fast cars, they think of Le Mans or Monaco. When greens imagine rural bliss they think of the Dordogne or Provence. When lovers look for romance, it's Paris again.

That's why, when people think about Lifestyle, people think about France

Switch
it
On

MODERN VILLAS

CHARACTER FARMHOUSES

BEACHFRONT PROPERTIES

CHIC TOWN HOUSES

HISTORIC CHATEAUX

THATCHED COTTAGES

ELEGANT MANORHOUSES

SFV specializes in self-catering villa holidays for the independent traveller to France, Spain and Italy.

Offering a choice of self-drive, fly/drive, or property only options, SFV has something to suit all requirements and tastes.

Choose from a wide selection of over 400 properties. Traditional or modern, coastal or rural, peaceful or lively. Many properties have private pools and are available all year round.

Now in its tenth succesful year, SFV takes pride in providing a professional, reliable, and most importantly a personal service to all its clients.

SFV
holidays

18/24 Middle Way, Summertown, Oxford OX2 7LG.
Tel 0865 311331 Fax 0865 310682

Classic French Authors For Your Holiday

Short stories – ideal for your holiday

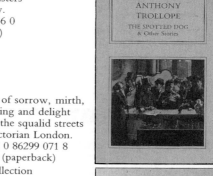

Dear traveller, although this guide is more concerned with good food, good overnight accommodation and good value for money than with your final holiday destination, there is no doubt that each should complement the other for a happy visit to France. We at Vacances en Campagne hope to introduce all our clients to a new enjoyment of the French countryside in all its variety. We believe that your holiday is a precious opportunity to make new friends and, above all, to know France better.

Chris Eyre
Managing Director

Our images of Gascony

A land of lakes and misty blue flaxfields. A countryside dotted with unspoilt villages and on the horizon, the shimmering Pyrenees.

It's the perfect place for a peaceful holiday. Rich in fine food and fragrant soft fruits and the home of two memorable spirits – d'Artagnan and Armagnac. This traditional house in Masseube, which was once a thriving sheep farm, is surrounded by woodland, with beautiful mountain views.

There are many more propertie in the Vacances en Campagn brochure, from a farmhouse i Provence to a villa in Corsica.

Send for your free copy an turn our images into reality.

FREE COLOUR BROCHURE
RING 0533 460033 QUOTE REF F26

Or post to: Vacances en Campagne, Dept F263, P.O. Box 201, Leicester LE4 7WL.

Name

Address/P'code

Vacances en Campagne
FRANCE PAR EXCELLENCE

ENTRAYGNES SUR TRUYERE 12140 Aveyron **Map 22-B1**
♈⊗ **RELAIS DE LA CAMBUSE** (N° RR JUN 27 624) (M. José **Decaix**)
⌂ Route Départmentale 920, La Cambuse ☎ 65-44-53-71. Hotel ⇥ 5
100F. Parking.

EPANNES 79270 Deux-Sèvres **RN 11 Map 15-A1**
♈⊗ **LE RELAIS SUISSE-OCÉAN** (N° RR MAI 8 479) (M. Jacky
⌂ **Guilloteau**) On edge of the Poitevin Marais, 10km from A23 exit.
☎ 49-04-80-01 ⇥ 10. Closed Sun (low season). Coaches welcome. Rest. seats 125. Evening meals to 10pm.

EPERNAY 51200 Marne **RN 3 Map 9-A4 6-B2**
♈⊗ **LES ROUTIERS** (N° RR JAN 16 390) (Mme Marie-Louise **Prejent**)
⌂ 13, avenue J.-J. Rousseau ☎ 26-55-23-29. **Minitel** ⇥ 15 100–150F
with shower, private WC. Closed Sat evening and Sun, Jan.
Coaches welcome. Rest. seats 78. Evening meals until 10pm–
midnight. Hotel open until midnight. ⌁

EPERRAIS 61400 Orne **RD 938 Map 8-B2**
♈⊗ **LA PETITE VALLÉE** (N° RR SEPT 26 053) (M. Gérard **Didier**) 63,
rue de Nancy ☎ 29-82-32-13. Closed Sun. Evening meals until
midnight. Credit cards accepted. Rest. seats 60. Sights: Musée
de l'imagerie.

EPINAY-SUR-SEINE 93800 Seine-St-Denis **RN 14 Map 1-A2**
♈⊗ **AU RENDEZ-VOUS DES COCHERS LIVREURS** (N° RR JUIN 26
924) (M. Jean-Francois **Fremont**) 32, bld Foch ☎ 48-26-80-03.
Closed Sun, public holidays. Evening meals to 10pm.
LE ROUTIER (N° RR JANU 27 759) (M. Khider **Legai**) 42, avenue
du Marechal Joffre ☎ 48-41-89-17. English spoken. Restaurant:
menu 48F. Open 5.30am–10pm.

EPINEAU-LES-VOVES 89400 Yonne **RN 6 Map 13-A2**
♈⊗ **LE RELAIS DES 6 BOULES** (N° RR JUL 22 864) (M. Ahmed
⌂ **Betroune**) 2, route de Chambéry ☎ 86-91-20-45 and 86-91-20-54.
Arabic, German spoken.

EPINEUIL-LE-FLEURIEL 18360 Cher **Map 16-A2**
♈⊗ **LES ROUTIERS** (N° RR JAN 26 154) (Mme Hélène **Bergerat**)
Saulzais-le-Potier ☎ 48-63-02-81. **Minitel**. Closed Mon afternoon.
Coaches welcome. Rest. seats 80. Evening meals until 9pm.

EPONE 78680 Yvelines **RN 13 Map 1-A1**
♈⊗ **LE REST' AU VERT** (N° RR MAI 26 891) (**Sarl Restauvert**) route
de Gargenville Rangiport ☎ 30-95-60-20. **Minitel**. Italian spoken.
Closed Sat and Sun. Hotel ⇥ 12.

EPREVILLE-près-LE-NEUFBOURG 27110 Eure **RD 133 Maps 3-B1 and
4-B3**
♈⊗ **LE BRABANT** (N° RR AVR 27 248) (M. Jean-Paul **Goblin**)
Départmentale 133 ☎ 32-35-04-40. Closed Sun night.

EQUEURDREVILLE 50120 Manche **RD 901 Map 4-A1**
♈⊗ **RESTAURANT DE LA HAGUE** (N° RR JUN 22 835) (M. Claude
⌂ **Lamy**) 120, rue de la Paix ☎ 33-53-14-87. Specialities: boeuf
bourguignon. Menu 42F. Lunch 12–2.30pm. Dinner 7.30–8.45pm.
Closed Sat, Sun, two weeks in Aug. Hotel ⇥ 20 from 100–220F.

ERBRAY

ERBRAY 44110 Loire-Atlantique **Map 7-B3**
♈⊗ **LE SAINT HUBERT** (N° RR MAI 27 616) (M. Bernard **Bellanger**) 1, place du Calvaire ☎ 40-55-08-37. Restaurant: dinner until 11pm. Closed Fri evening. Tobacconist.

ERVY-LE-CHATEL 10130 Aube **D 374 Map 9-B3**
♈⊗ **RESTAURANT DE LA GARE** (N° RR FEVR 26 811) (M. Dany **BORDIER**) place de la Gare ☎ 25-70-66-36. Closed Tue at 2pm, 1–15 Aug. Evening meals. Coaches welcome. Rest. seats 60.

ESLETTES (LES) 76710 Seine-Maritime **RN 27 Map 3-A1**
♈⊗ **LE RELAX** (N° RR MAI 21 091) (M. Jean **Sorel**) Route de Dieppe Côte de Malaunay ☎ 35-75-11-70. Closed Sun. Coaches welcome. Rest. seats 30.

ESNON 89210 Yonne **RN 443 Maps 9-B2 13-A2**
♈⊗ **LE RELAIS DES AMIS** (N° RR FEV 26 806) (Mme Danièle **Ollivon**) RN 20 ☎ 86-56-13-26. **Minitel.** Closed Mon and Sept. Coaches welcome. Rest. seats 70. Filling station 3.5km.

ESPALION 12500 Aveyron **RN 120 Map 23-A1**
♈⊗ **LE RELAIS DES QUATRE ROUTES** (N° RR MARS 27 563) (M. Guy **Chabanon**) RD 920 Quatre Routes ☎ 65-44-01-69 ⊷ 7. Closed Sun, last week in December. Evening meals until 9pm. Parking. Filling station nearby, open 7am–8pm.

ESSARTS (LES) 85140 Vendée **RN 160 Map 11-B3**
♈⊗ **LE PINIER** (N° RR MAR 20 423) (Mme Jacqueline **Dupont**) ☎ 51-62-81-69. Closed Sat and Sun (low season). Coaches welcome. Rest. seats 35.

ESSARTS-LE ROI (LES) 78690 Yvelines **RN 10 Maps 1-B1 and 9-A1**
♈⊗ **LE RELAIS DE L'ARCOAT** (N° RR JAN 25 793) (SARL **ARCOAT**) 39, route Nle 10 ☎ 30-41-60-53. Closed Sat, Sun. English spoken.
♈⊗ **A LA GRACE DE DIEU** (N° RR JUL 25 055) (M. Daniel **Bigot**) RN 10 ☎ 30-41-60-04. Closed Sat, Sun, Aug. Coaches welcome. Rest. seats 120. Evening meals to 10pm. Parking.

ESTRABLIN 38780 Isère **Map 2-B2**
♈⊗ **LA TABOURETTE** (N° RR FEV 27 531) (Mme Yvette **Ouled**) ☎ 74-85-97-98. **Minitel.** Restaurant: dinner until 9pm. Closed Sun, one week during early Aug. Filling station nearby, open 6am–8pm.

ESTREÉS-DENIECOURT 80660 Somme **RN 336 Maps 5-B3 and 6A1**
♈⊗ **L'AUBERGE DE LA MAIRIE** (N° RR AVR 21 466) (Mme Claudette
⌂ **Demuynck-Dehenry**) Péronne exit Autoroute A1 to Amiens ☎ 22-85-20-16 ⊷ 4. Closed Sat, Sun, Aug. Coaches welcome. Rest. seats 120. Evening meals.

ESTREES-MONS-EN-CHAUSSEE 80200 Somme **RN 29 Maps 5-B3 and 6-A1**
♈⊗ **A LA POMME D'API** (N° RR FEV 14 686) (M. Albert **Gras**) 28, Route Nationale ☎ 22-85-60-04. **Minitel.** Restaurant: family cooking. Menu 54F. Lunch 12–2.30pm. Dinner 7–9.30pm. Closed Sun, Aug. Traditional décor. Rest. seats 40. Terraced garden. ⊷ Parking.

ETAGNAC 16150 Charente **RN 141/948 Map 15-B2**

♈⊗ **RELAIS D'ETAGNAC** (N° RR AVR 25 376) (M. Christian **Labrousse ☎** 45-89-21-38 ⊷ 10. Coaches welcome. 4 dining rooms. Filling station, tobacconist, newsagent. English spoken. Evening meal.

ETAIS-LE-SAUVIN 89840 Yonne **Map 13-A2**

♈⊗ **CAFÉ DE LA PLACE** (N° RR NOV 27 441) (M. Bérard **Dupuis**) rue de la Gare **☎** 86-47-21-56. Evening meals to 10pm. Closed Tue, Sept. Local filling station, open 7am–7pm. Terraced garden. ⇥ Parking.

ETALONDES 76260 Seine-Maritime **RD 925 Map 4-A3**

♈⊗ **LA BAHUTIÈRE** (N° RR JUIN 27 298) (M. Alain **Savelon**) ☎ 35-50-21-10. Closed Sun, end Aug, beginning Sept. Evening meals until 8pm. Rest. seats 36.

ETAMPES 91150 Essonne **RN 20 Map 9-B1**

GARAGE DES ROUTIERS (N° RR JAN 15 508) (M. Roger **David**) RN 20 South of Etampes **☎** 64-94-56-18. Unic Agent and Westinghouse brake-fitters.

ETANG SUR ARROUX 71190 Saône-et-Loire **Map 13-B3**

♈⊗ **RESTAURANT DE LA GARE** (N° RR MARS 27 558) (M. Pierre ⌂ **Bouteloup**) rue de la République **☎** 85-82-23-76. Restaurant: dinner until 9pm. Closed Sun. Hotel ⊷ 8. Parking. Filling station nearby, open 7am–8pm.

ETERVILLE 14930 Calvados **Map 4-B2**

♈⊗ **L'INTENDANCE** (N° RR OCT 27 703) (Mme Michele **Laurent**) 15, route d'Annay **☎** 31-73-17-06. Restaurant: family cooking. Menu 45F. Open 7am–8pm. Lunch 11.30–2pm. Closed Sun, Aug. Rest. seats 60. Terraced garden. ⇥ Sights: Caen (4km), WWII landing beaches, the Memorial (4km).

ETOGES 51270 Marne **Map 9-A3**

♈⊗ **LE CAVEAU DE L'ANCIENNE FORGE** (N° RR AUG 27 357) (SARL **La Forge**) Grand Rue **☎** 26-59-32-79. Local filling station 8am–8pm. Dinner until 8pm. Closed Wed. Rest. seats 65.

ETOUVELLES 02000 Aisne **RN 2 Map 6-B1**

♈⊗ **CHEZ JEANNOT** (N° RR MAR 16 908) (M.J.-M. **Serre**) 30, rue de Paris **☎** 23-20-63-26 ⊷ 7. Closed Aug. Evening meals until 11pm. Coaches welcome. Rest. seats 120.

EU 76260 Seine-Maritime **RN 15 Bis Map 4-A2**

♈⊗ **LE CAFE DE L'ETOILE** (N° RR JUN 16 132) (M. Maurice **Pajot**) ⌂ 37, boulevard Thiers **☎** 35-86-14-89 ⊷ 12.

EVANS 39700 Jura **Map 14-B3**

⊗ **SARL RELAIS 73** (N° RR FEV 27 536) (Mme Françoise **Barra**) RN 73 **☎** 84-71-15-97. **Minitel**. English spoken. Restaurant: family cooking. Open 24 hours. Closed for Christmas and New Year. Credit cards accepted. Traditional décor. Rest. seats 50. ⇥ Parking. Filling station nearby.

EXMES

EXMES 61310 Orne **RD 14, 26 Map 8-A2**
♈⊗ **LE RELAIS DU COMMERCE** (N° RR JUN 21 556) (Mme Fernande **Simon**) Grand-Rue ☎ 33-39-93-04 ◄ 4. Coaches welcome. Rest. seats 200.

EYGUIANS 05300 Hautes-Alpes **RN 75 Maps 24-B2 and 25-A1**
♈⊗ ☆ **NN LE RELAIS DE LA GARE** (N° RR NOV 15 439) (Mme Michelle **Robert**) ☎ 92-66-20-08. **Minitel**. Restaurant: family cooking. Specialities: gigot d'agneau de pays, pieds paquets, daube. Children's menu. À la carte. Dinner until 9pm. Closed Sat (low season), Jan. Credit cards accepted. Rest. seats 100. Hotel ◄ 15 from 90–210F with showers, bathroom, private WC, TV. Open 6am–10pm. Terraced garden. ⊬ Parking. Sights: Georges de la Méouge, citadelle de Sistéron, Orpière village (7km).

EYGURANDE 19340 Corrèze **Map 16-B2**
♈⊗ **RELAIS DU VIEUX CHENE** (N° RR AVR 27 582) (Mme Monique **Blancheton**). Merline L'Abeille ☎ 55-94-41-13. Restaurant: dinner until 9pm. Closed Sat midday until Mon 5pm.

EZY-SUR-EURE 27530 Eure **RD 143 Map 8-A3**
♈⊗ **HOTEL TERMINUS** (N° RR AVR 17 514) (Mme Madeleine **Veisen**) 16, boulevard Ulysse-Lavertu – place de la Gare ☎ 37-64-73-24 ◄ 10. Closed Fri 2pm, Sat, Aug.

FABREGUES 34690 Hérault **RN 113 Map 23-B2**
♈⊗ **BAR LE 113** (N° RR AOU 24 303) (Mme Josette **Avignon**) 36, avenue Georges-Clémenceau ☎ 67-85-12-86. Closed Sun, Oct. Coaches welcome. Rest. seats 50. Evening meals to 9pm.

FALAISE 14700 Calvados **RN 158 Map 8-A2**
♈⊗ **LE RELAIS DES ROUTIERS** (N° RR OCT 21 674) (M. Christian **Durand**) 33, avenue d'Hastings ☎ 31-90-04-67. **Minitel**. Restaurant: family cooking. Menu 42F. Children's menu. À la carte. Lunch 12–1.30pm. Dinner 7.30–8.30pm. Closed Sun, July. Credit cards accepted. Traditional décor. Rest. seats 35. Hotel ◄ 5 from 65–90F. Open 6.30am–10pm. ⊬ Parking. Sights: Falaise (tourist town)

FALLERON 85670 Vendée **11-B2**
♈⊗ **CHEZ MARLÈNE** (N° RR MARS 27 555) (Mme Marlène **Poterlot**) 54, rue Nationale ☎ 51-35-50-22. Restaurant: dinner until 8pm. Closed Sat after midday and Sun (low season), one week in Feb. Filling station nearby, open 7am–8.30pm.

FAOUET (LE) 56320 Morbihan **RN 782 Map 7-B2**
♈⊗ **LE RELAIS DES HALLES** (N° RR MAR 4 067) (M. Armel **Le Puil**) 19, rue du Soleil ☎ 97-23-07-66 ◄ 8. Closed Sun, Sept. Evening meals. English spoken.

FARGUES-SUR-OURBIZE 47700 Lot-et-Garonne **RN 655 Map 21-A1**
♈⊗ **LE RELAIS DES ROUTIERS** (N° RR FEB 22 218) (Mme Michèle **Riffart**) ☎ 53-93-04-54 ◄ 4. Closed Wed from 2–7pm. Coaches welcome. 3 dining rooms 220 seats. Evening meals. Spanish spoken.

FARGUETTES (LES) 81190 Tarn **RN 88 Map 22-B1**
Ⓨ⊗ **RELAIS DE LA PLAINE** (N° RR OCT 27 049) (Mme Marie-Ange
Feral) ☎ 63-76-65-89. **Minitel**. Closed Sat to 5pm and the last two
weeks of Aug. Evening meals to 9pm. ⊷ Rest. seats 220. Parking.
Local filling station open 6.30am–10.30pm.

FECAMP 76400 Seine-Maritime **RD 925 Map 4-A3**
Ⓨ⊗ **AU CHEMIN DE FER** (N° RR AVR 25 899) (M. Jean-Marie
Lefèbvre) 29/31, quai-Bérigny ☎ 35-28-06-17. Closed Sat night
and Sun (evening only in season) and 22 Dec–15 Jan. Evening
meals until 9pm.

FEISSONS-SUR-ISERE 73260 Savoie **RN 90 Map 19-B2**
Ⓨ⊗ **LE RELAIS DES ROUTIERS** (N° RR OCT 24 699) (M. Michel
Ruffier) between Albertville and Moutiers (take 1st right after
Cevins) ☎ 79-22-50-97. **Minitel**. Closed Sat pm, Sun. Some
English and German spoken. Coaches welcome. Rest. seats 50.
Credit cards accepted. Terraced garden. ⊷ Parking.

FELINES 07340 Ardèche **RN 82 Maps 24-A1, 18-A/B3**
Ⓨ⊗ ☆ **NN LE RELAIS DE LA REMISE** (N° RR JUN 25 032) (M. Jacky
⌂ **Laurencin**) RN 82 ☎ 75-34-82-22. **Minitel** ⊶ 4. Closed Sat, Sun
(low season) and public holidays. Full-board 135–155F per night.
Coaches welcome. Rest. seats 130 + 80 on terrace. Evening
meals until 10pm.

FENOUILLET (LE) 85800 Vendée **RD 754 Map 11-B2**
Ⓨ⊗ **LA MADELON** (N° RR JAN 26 137) (Mme Madeleine **Pouvreau**)
⌂ 64, rue du Centre, St-Gilles-Croix-de-Vie ☎ 51-55-05-35. ⊶ 20.
Coaches welcome. Rest. seats 135. Evening meals until 9pm.
English spoken. Closed Sat, Sun (low season rest. only).

FERRIÈRE (LA) 79390 Deux-Sèvres **RN 148 bis Map 15-A1**
Ⓨ⊗ **AU BON ACCUEIL** (N° RR JUN 25 469) (Mmes **Bilheu-Berger**) La
Ferrière Route Poitiers/Nantes ☎ 49-63-03-01. **Minitel**. Closed
Thur evening, last 2 weeks Jan, end Aug. Coaches welcome.
Rest. seats 65. Evening meals to 9pm.

FERRIÈRES-EN-BRAY 76220 Seine-Maritime **RN 31 Map 3-A2**
Ⓨ⊗ **HOTEL DU CHEMIN DE FER** (N° RR MAI 24 573) (M. Jean **Feret**)
⌂ 26, avenue de la Gare ☎ 35-90-01-61 ⊶ 10. Closed Sat, Sun, Bank
holiday. Coaches welcome. Rest. seats 90. Evening meals until
10pm.

FERTE-BERNARD (LA) 74400 Haute-Savoie **Map 18-B1**
Ⓨ⊗ **L'ARCHE DE LA FERTE BERNARD** (M.G. **Bisson**) Autoroute A11
Aire de la Ferté Bernard direction Paris/Nantes ☎ 43-93-41-02.

FERTE-GAUCHER (LA) 77320 Seine-et-Marne **RN 34 Map 9-A2**
LE CONTRE-TEMPS (N° RR FEV 27 786) (M. Hervé **Langle**) 4,
avenue de la Gare. Directions: opposite the station ☎ 64-04-01-
90. English spoken. Restaurant: family cooking. Menu à la carte.
Lunch from 12–2.30pm. Dinner 7–10pm. Closed Sun. Credit cards
accepted. Traditional décor. Rest. seats 40. Terraced garden. ⊷
Parking.

FIANCEY-PAR-LIVRON

FIANCEY-PAR-LIVRON 26250 Drôme **RN 7 Maps 18-B3 and 24-A1**

♥⊗ **RELAIS DU SUD-EST** (N° RR MAI 26 552) (M. André **Courbier**)
⌂ RN 7 ☎ 75-61-61-19 ⤙ 9. English and German spoken. Closed
Sun. Evening meals served until 11pm. Coaches welcome. Rest.
seats 52.

♥⊗ **AUBERGE MACAMP** (N° RR JUIL 27 316) (Mme Josian **Vo-
canson**) RN7 ☎ 75-61-73-91. **Minitel**. Hotel ⤙ 17. Filling station
500m.

♥⊗ **ROUVEYROL** (N° RR JANU 26 134) (M. Roland **Rouveyro**) RN7 ☎
75-61-62-06. English and German spoken. Restaurant: family
cooking. Menu 51F. Children's menu. Lunch 12–2.30pm. Dinner
7.30–11pm. Closed Sun and last two weeks in Aug. Credit cards
accepted. Rest. seats 80. Hotel ⤙ 13 from 80–110F (with toilet
facilities). Rest room. Terraced garden. ⊮ Parking.

FIENVILLERS PAR CANDAS 80500 Somme **Map 5-A3**

♥⊗ **LE RELAIS FLEURI** (N° RR MARS 27 569) (M. Francis **Peltier**)
RN 66, ☎ 22-32-51-78. German spoken. Restaurant: closed Tue.

FIGEAC 46100 Lot **Map 17-B2**

♥⊗ **RELAIS DES CHASSEURS** (N° RR DEC 27 478) (Mme Veronique
⌂ **Noyez**) route de Capdenac La Vayssière. Directions: exit Figeac
in the direction of Rodez ☎ 65-34-12-33. English spoken. Restaurant: regional and family cooking. Menu 50F. Dinner until 10pm.
Closed Sun. Credit cards accepted. Traditional décor. Rest.
seats 50. Hotel ⤙ 8 100F. Terraced garden. ⊮ Parking. Filling
station nearby, open 9am–9pm.

FINS (LES) 25500 Doubs **Map 14 B-3**

♥⊗ **HOTEL DU COMMERCE** (N° RR MARS 27 565) (M. Alban
Legrand) 2, route de Besançon ☎ 81-67-12-29. **Minitel**. Restau-
rant. Specialities: gibiers, entrecôte forestière. Menu 49–78F.
Open 6.30am–10pm. Hotel ⤙ 10 from 80–143F. Parking.

FIRBEIX 24450 Dordogne **RN 21 Map 17-A1**

♥⊗ **LE RELAIS DES SPORTS** (N° RR JUN 21 548) (M. René **Beaubatit**)
RN 21 ☎ 53-52-82-53. Closed Oct. Coaches welcome. Rest. seats
100. Evening meals.

FIRMINY 42600 Loire **Map 18-A3**

♥⊗ **AU PETIT BONHEUR** (N° RR SEPT 27 379) (M. Hervé **Salleron**) 9,
rue du Prof Calmette ☎ 77-61-29-73. Italian, Spanish spoken.
Local filling station 6.30am–10pm.

FISMES 51170 Marne **RN 31 Map 6-B2**

♥⊗ **LE LION ROUGE** (N° RR AVR 24 200) (M. Michel **Sohier**) 6, route
⌂ de Soissons ☎ 26-78-12-63 ⤙ 5. Closed Sun. Evening meals until
10pm.

FITOU 11510 Aude **RN 9 Map 23-A3**

♥⊗ ☆ **RELAIS LE PARADOR** (N° RR MAI 27 273) (M. Robert
⌂ **Morhain**) Cabanne de Fitou ☎ 68-45-79-11 ⤙ 50 70–170F.
German, Spanish and Italian spoken. Filling station 7am–11pm.

FIX-SAINT-GENEYS 43320 Haute-Loire **RN 102 Map 17-A3**

♥⊗ **RELAIS DU COL** (N° RR OCT 18 858) (Mme **Gallien**) ☎ 71-57-02-
67. Closed Sun.

FLASSANS-SUR-ISSOLE 83340 Var **RN 7 Map 25-A2**
♈⊗ **LE BIEN ÊTRE** (N° RR OCT 27 438) (M. Robert **Mourrat**) Les
Quatre Chemins ☎ 94-59-67-65. Italian spoken. Showers for
drivers. Restaurant: family cooking. Specialities: paella, patis-
serie maison. Menu à la carte. Credit cards accepted. Rest. seats
80. Terraced garden. ⊬ Parking. Filling station 100m, open
7am–8pm. Sights: Gorges du Verdon (40km), Lac de Carces
(20km).

FLAVIAC 07000 Ardèche **Map 24-A1**
♈⊗ **LES ROUTIERS** (N° RR DEC 26 407) (M. Didier **Garrayt**) Place
Emile-Crémière ☎ 75-65-77-57. Restaurant: family cooking. Chil-
dren's menu. À la carte. Dinner until 9pm. Closed Sun and 15
Sept–15 Oct. Credit cards accepted. Rest. seats 60. Hotel ⊶ 8
from 100–180F with showers, bathroom. ⊬ Parking. Sights:
Gorges de L'Ardeche (55km), Vallée Eryenne (20km).

FLAVY-LE-MARTEL 02520 Aisne **Maps 5-B3 and 6-A1**
♈⊗ **LE RELAIS DES ROUTIERS** (N° RR FEV 26 178) (M. Jean-Paul
Brière) 17, rue André-Brûlé ☎ 23-52-51-31. **Minitel**. Closed Sat.
Coaches welcome. Rest. seats 40. Evening meals to 9pm.

FLERS 61100 Orne **RD 924 and RD 18 Map 8-A1/2**
♈⊗ **HÔTEL DES TOURISTES** (N° RR DEC 26 758) (M. Maurice
⌂ **Dupont**) 80, rue de Paris ☎ 33-65-25-57 ⊶ 12. Closed Sun.
Evening meal until 10pm. Rest. seats 40. Coaches welcome.

FLERS-EN-ESCREBIEUX 59128 Nord **RN 43 Map 51-B2/3**
♈⊗ **AU BON CASSE-CROÛTE** (N° RR OCT 27 050) (M. Raymond
Dufour) 59, RN 43 ☎ 27-86-69-41. Closed Sat and Sun. Coaches
welcome. Rest. seats 40. Evening meals to midnight. Parking.
Filling station 3km.

FLEURANCE 32500 Gers **RN 21 Map 21-B2**
♈⊗ **REST. DU STADE** (N° RR MAR 22 261) (M. Alphonse **Pujade**)
place de l'Eglise ☎ 62-06-02-23. Closed Sat, 15 June–15 July.
Coaches welcome. Rest. seats 60. Evening meals until 9pm.

FLEURE 86340 Vienne **RN 147 Map 15-B1**
♈⊗ **AUX AMIS DE LA ROUTE** (N° RR JUIN 26931) (Mme Michèle
Guionnet) route de Poitiers ☎ 49-42-60-25. Coaches welcome.
Rest. seats 60. Evening meals to 10pm.

FLEURIEU-SUR-SAÔNE 69250 Rhône **CD 433 Map 2-A1**
♈⊗ **LA CABANE** (N° RR AVR 26 492) (M. Jean-Robert **Richard**) 54,
route de Lyon ☎ 78-91-40-60. **Minitel**. Closed Sat, Sun, Aug.
Coaches welcome. Rest. seats 40. English and Italian spoken.

FLEURY-SUR-ORNE 14000 Calvados **RN 162 Map 4-B2**
♈⊗ **RELAIS DE LA POMME D'OR** (N° RR OCT 21 680) (Mme
Emilienne **François**) 20, route d'Harcourt ☎ 31-82-36-87. Closed
Sun, public holidays, Aug. Menu 43F (exclusive of drinks). Lunch
12–3pm. Rest. seats 28. Parking. Lorries.

FLIREY 54470 Meurthe-et-Moselle **RN 958 Map 14-B1**
♈⊗ **WARIN LES ROUTIERS** (N° RR MAI 12 261) (M. Jacques **Warin**)
☎ 83-84-31-14.

FLIXECOURT

FLIXECOURT 80420 Somme **30 m RN 1 Map 5-A3**
♀⊗ **LES FLONFLONS DU BAL** (N° RR DEC 26 768) (M. Jean-Marc **Rohaut**), 16, rue Georges-Clémenceau ☎ 22-51-36-34. English spoken. Restaurant: regional and family cooking. Specialities: canard aux navets, viandes grillées, couscous. Menu from 45–100F. Children's menu. À la carte. Open 6am–1am. Credit cards accepted. Traditional décor. Rest. seats 50. Terraced garden. ⌖ Parking. Sights: Camp galois "Samara" (5km), prehistoric grotto at Naours (20km), Drugy Farm (Joan of Arc's prison) 15km, Amiens Cathedral (20km).

FOIX 09000 Ariège **RN 20 Map 22-A3**
♀⊗ **LE RELAIS DU SOLEIL D'OR** (N° RR AOU 20 527) (M. Jean
⌂ **Coumes**) 57, avenue du Général-Leclerc ☎ 61-65-01-33 ⊷ 6. Closed Sat evening and Sun. Dinner until 10pm. Rest. seats 60.

FONDETTES 37230 Indre-et-Loire **RN 152 Map 12-A2**
♀⊗ **LE BEAU MANOIR** (N° RR MAR 27 230) (Mme Edith **Bourreau**) 6, quai de la Guignière ☎ 47-42-01-02. Closed Sat evening, Sun, 1–15 May. Rest. seats 30. Filling station 1km.

FONTAINE-LE-COMTE 86240 Vienne **RN 11 near to RN 10 Map 15-B1**
♀⊗ **AUBERGE DE LA GARENNE** (N° RR AVR 25 386) (Mme Michelle **Guerin**) ☎ 49-57-01-22. **Minitel**. Closed Sun, Aug. Coaches welcome. Rest. seats 70. Evening meals until 11pm. Parking.

FONTAINE-SAINT-MARTIN (LA) 72330 Sarthe **RN 23 Map 12-A2**
♀⊗ **LE RELAIS DU CHENE VERT** (N° RR FEV 16 890) (Mme **Flameych**) ☎ 43-87-80-84. Closed Sun, Aug. Evening meals. Rest. seats 70. Coaches welcome.

FONTAINE-SIMON 28240 Eure-et-Loir **RD 2 and 25 Map 8-A/B9**
♀⊗ **AU BON COIN** (N° RR JAN 23 108) (M. **Durand**) rue de la Mairie
⌂ La Loupe ☎ 37-81-84-98 ⊷ 10. Closed Fri, Aug. Evening meals until 9pm.

FONTENAY-SUR-LOING 45210 Loiret **RN 7 Map 9-B2**
♀⊗ **LES CENT BORNES** (N° RR DEC 21 722) (M. Guy **Martin**) RN 7 ☎ 38-95-82-06. Open 24 hours. Closed 9–24 Aug. Coaches welcome. Rest. seats 140. Evening meals.

FONTVANNES 10190 Aube **Map 9-B3**
♀⊗ **AUBERGE DE LA VANNE** (N° RR JAN 26 425) (M. Michel
⌂ **Dubrulle**) 1, rue Léandre-Denis ☎ 25-70-37-60. **Minitel** ⊷ 8. Closed Sun, Feb. Coaches welcome. Rest. seats 35. Menu 52F. Lunch 12–2pm. Dinner 7–8pm. Parking. ⌖

FORMERIE 60220 Oise **Map 3-A2**
♀⊗ **CAFE DE LA PAIX** (N° RR MAI 24 576) (Mme Françoise **Merlin**)
⌂ 8, rue Dornat ☎ 44-46-17-08. **Minitel** ⊷ 6. Closed Sun afternoon. Coaches welcome. Rest. seats 60.

FOS-SUR-MER 13270 Bouches-du-Rhône **Map 24-A3**
♀⊗ **LE MOULIN** (N° RR OCT 25 135) (M. Jean-Bernard **Lefèbvre**) place du Cavaou ☎ 42-05-48-38. **Minitel**. Coaches welcome. Rest. seats 71. Evening meals to 10pm. English spoken.

Y⊗ RELAIS DE LA FOSSETTE – CHEZ ANNIE ET GUY (N° RR MAR 25 317) (M. Guy **Hologne**) quartier de la Fossette ☎ 42-05-30-01. Closed Sat, Sun, Aug. Coaches welcome. Rest. seats 80. Evening meals to 10pm. Credit cards accepted. ⊶ Parking.

FOUCARMONT 76340 Seine-Maritime **RN 28 Map 4-A2**
Y⊗ LE RELAIS ROUTIERS (N° RR JAN 25 275) (Mme **Bénard**) RN 28 ☎ 35-93-91-50. **Minitel**. Closed Sun. Evening meals.
Y CHEZ FRANÇOISE (N° RR JUN 25 458) (Mme Françoise **Maubert**) 35, rue Douce ☎ 35-93-70-37. Closed Sat. Evening meals to 8pm.

FOUGERES 35300 Ille-et-Vilaine **RN 12 Map 8-B1**
Y⊗ ☆ NN AUX AMIS DE LA ROUTE (N° RR SEP 23 992) (M. Michel
⌂ **Bastien**) 6, boulevard St-Germain ☎ 99-99-07-62 ⊷ 12 from 100–120F. Coaches welcome. Rest. seats 90. Evening meals. English, German spoken. Parking for 1,000 vehicles. Bar. ⊶ Recreation: fishing, watersports. Sights: Saint-Mâlo, Mont St Michel, countryside and châteaux.

FOUILLOUSE (LA) 42480 Loire **RN 82 Map 2-B1**
Y⊗ LE RELAIS (N° RR JAN 24 830) (Mme Louise **Bonnet**) locally 'Les Molineaux' ☎ 77-30-13-51. Closed Sat, Sun, 14 July–15 Aug. Evening meals.

FRAISSE-HAUT 15300 Cantal **Map 17-A2**
Y⊗ ☆ NN HOTEL DES CIMES (N° RR SEPT 26 656) (M. Christophe
⌂ **Cros**) RN 122 Laveissière ☎ 71-20-07-42. **Minitel**. Toilet facilities. Restaurant: regional and family cooking. Specialities: gibiers. Menu from 45–100F. Children's menu. À la carte. Dinner until 9pm. Closed Sun, Oct/Nov. Rest. seats 90. Hotel ⊷ 20 from 74–135F with showers. Rest rooms. Terraced garden. Parking. TV. Sights: Parc des Volcans d'Auvergne, Salers (25km), Station de Super Lioran (4km).

FRANCUEIL 37150 Indre-et-Loire **Map 12 B-3**
Y⊗ RELAIS DES CHATEAUX (N° RR MAI 27 603) (M. Jean-Claude **Lemarie**) RN 76 Les Perrières. ☎ 47-23-96-30. Spanish spoken. Restaurant: closed Sun evening, 24 Dec–2 Jan. Parking.

FRASNE 25560 Doubs **RD 471/49 Map 14-B3**
Y⊗ L'ARC-EN-CIEL (N° RR MARS 26 477) (M. Claude **Guyon**) 98, Grande-du-Rue ☎ 81-49-83-68. Closed Tue, July. Evening meals until 8pm.

FRÉJUS 83600 Var **RN 7 Map 25-B2**
Y⊗ ☆ NN LES TROIS CHÊNES (N° RR AVR 16 518) (Mme Monique
⌂ **Laurent**) route de Cannes ☎ 94-53-20-08. **Minitel** ⊷ 18 all with showers (5 with own WC) from 140–210F. Credit cards accepted. Access for disabled. Coaches welcome. Rest. seats 100. Evening meals. English, German, Italian spoken. Open 7am–10pm. Parking. Bar. Boules played. Recreation: swimming pool, tennis courts nearby. Sights: Gorges du Verdon, lakes of Saint Cassien.

FRÉJUS (Tunnel) 73500 Savoir **see MODANE**

FRESNES-EN-TARDENOIS 02130 Aisne **Autoroute A4 Map 6-B1**

♀⊗ **RELAIS DU TARDENOIS** (Mme **Pongnan**) Aire de Service du Tardenois – both directions of the motorway. Access by pedestrian walkway. ☎ 23-70-23-16. English and German spoken. Restaurant: regional cooking. 25% discount given to lorry drivers. Children's menu. Self-service. Open 6.30am–11pm. Credit cards accepted. Rest. seats 180. Rest room. Terraced garden. ⊯ Parking. Shops, TV, showers.

FRESNES-MAZANCOURT 80320 Somme **RN 17 Maps 5-B3**

♀⊗ **L'ESCALE DES ROUTIERS** (N° RR SEPT 27 010) (M. Jean-Claude **Guerquin**) ☎ 22-85-28-50. Closed Sat, Sun, Aug. Coaches welcome. Rest. seats 32. Evening meals to midnight. Sights: Château de Peronne.

FRETEVAL 41160 Loir-et-Cher **RN 10 Map 12-A3 and 8-B3**

♀⊗ **SARL LE PLESSIS** (N° RR OCT 27 404) (Mme Isabelle **Thébault**) ☎ 54-82-64-28. Closed Sat from 10am. English, German, Spanish spoken. Evening meals to 12pm. Filling station 1km 6.30am–10pm.

FROISSY 60480 Oise **RN 1 Map 3-A2**

♀⊗ **LE BEAUVAIS BRETEUIL** (N° RR JUIL 26 962) (M. Raymond
⌂ **Julen**) Bois Saint-Martin ☎ 44-79-13-09 = 5. Closed Sun and three weeks in Aug. Evening meals served to 10pm. Rest. seats 90.

FROMENTEL par PUTANGES 61210 Orne **RN 24 Bis and 809 Map 8-A2**

♀⊗ **LE RELAIS DE L'AIGLE D'OR** (N° RR SEPT 27 664) (M. Christophe **Huard**) ☎ 33-96-21-00. **Minitel**. English spoken. Parking. Filling station nearby.

FROUARD 54390 Meurthe-et-Moselle **RN 57 Maps 10-A1/2 and 14-B1**

♀⊗ **AU RELAIS DES SPORTIFS CHEZ RAPH** (N° RR JAN 14 656) (M. Raphaël **Capezzali**) 1, rue de la Salle ☎ 83-59-03-52. Closed Mon, Sept.

♀⊗ **LA GRANDE CHOPE** (N° RR JUL 21 168) (Mme Christiane **Pallagi**) 4, rue de la Gare ☎ 93-49-05-64. Closed Sat, Sun, Aug. **SARL LA CHAUERTAISE** (N° RR JANU 27 663) (Mme Pierrette **Motignon**) 29, rue de l'Embarie ☎ 83-24-36-08. Restaurant. Specialities: couscous (every 2 weeks). Menu 50F. Lunch 11.30am–3pm. Dinner from 7–10pm. Closed Sun. Parking. Filling station nearby.

FUILET (LE) 49270 Maine-et-Loire **Map 12-B1**

♀⊗ **CHEZ ALPHONSE ET MONIQUE** (N° RR DEC 26 394) (Mme Monique **Bodo**) 1, rue de la Blandinière ☎ 41-70-52-58. Closed Aug. Evening meals until 9pm.

FUMAY 08170 Ardennes **RN 51 Map 6-A2**

♀⊗ ☆ **NN LE RELAIS DU LION** (N° RR AVR 21 465) (Mme Édith
⌂ **Potier**) 41, rue de la Gare ☎ 24-41-10-27. Bidets. Restaurant: family cooking. Specialities: couscous. Children's menu. À la carte. Dinner until 9pm. Closed Sun afternoon, Sept. Rest. seats 35. Hotel = 7 55–120F, with showers, bathroom. Open 7am–10pm. ⊯ Sights: Musée de l'ardoise.

FUMEL 47500 Lot-et-Garonne **Maps 17-Al and B1**

♀⊗ **BAR DE LA SOIERIE** (N° RR NOV 27 098) (Mme Liliane **Lafon**) 88, avenue de l'Usine ☎ 53-71-34-22. Menu 45F. Closed Sat, Sun. Coaches welcome. Rest. seats 35. Evening meals until 9pm. Parking. Sights: Château de Bonaguil, le Périgord.

GAËL 35290 Ille-et-Vilaine **Map 7-B3**

♀⊗ **LE RELAIS DES SPORTS – REST. CHEZ ANNICK** (N° RR MAI 24 970) (Mme Annick **Rebillard**) place des Tilleuls ☎ 99-07-72-39 ⊷ 4. Closed Fri evening. Coaches welcome. Rest. seats 150. Evening meals until 10pm.

GAGES 12630 Aveyron **RN 88 Map 22-B1 10 km from Rodez**

♀⊗ ☆ **NN LE RELAIS DE LA PLAINE** (N° RR DEC 20 920) (Mme
⌂ Yvonne **Dallo**) ☎ 65-42-29-03. Restaurant: regional and family cooking. Specialities: tripous, confit de canard, gésiers. Children's menu. Dinner until 9pm. Closed Fri evening until Mon morning (low season), end Oct/beginning Nov and end Dec. Modern décor. Rest. seats 195. Hotel ⊷ 22 from 92–200F with shower, bathroom, private WC. Open 6am–11pm. Rest rooms. ⌐ Parking. Sights: the Lot Valley, Gorges du Tarn, lakes of Anblac.

GAILLAN LESPARRE 33340 Gironde **Map 20 A-1**

♀⊗ **MARIE-FRANCE** (N° RR SEPT 27 656) (Mme Marie-France **Duprey**) place des Ecoles ☎ 56-41-20-53. Restaurant: dinner until 10pm. Closed Sun (low season), Easter, 15–31 Aug, one week at Christmas. Parking.

GAMACHES 80220 Somme **Map 4-B2**

♀⊗ **LES ROUTIERS** (N° RR FEVR 26 817) (M. Claude **Feffay**) 20, place du Général Leclerc ☎ 22-26-16-33. Closed Sun afternoon.

GAN 64290 Pyrénées-Atlantiques **RN 134 Maps 20-B3 and 21-A3**

♀⊗ ☆ **NN HOTEL MODERNE** (N° RR DEC 23 568) (M. Patrick **Piette**)
⌂ 41–43, place de la Mairie ☎ 59-21-54-98. Restaurant: family cooking. Specialities: garbure, confits de canard. Menu 50–100F. Children's menu. À la carte. Dinner until 9pm. Closed Sun. Rest. seats 215. Hotel ⊷ 15 from 70–140F with shower. Open 6.30am–8.30pm. ⌐ Parking. Sights: Château de Pau (8km), Lourdes (50km), Artouste (30km) Pictat and Asson Zoo, caves.

GANNAT 03800 Allier **16-B3**

♀⊗ **HOTEL DU CHATEAU** (N° RR JANU 24 814) (M. Marcel **Busson**)
⌂ 9, place Raintain. ☎ 70-90-00-88. Restaurant: closed Jan. Hotel ⊷ 12.

GAP 05000 Hautes Alpes **Map 25-A1**

♀⊗ **AUX AMIS DE LA ROUTE** (N° RR AUG 27 373) (M. Marcel **Bary**)
⌂ La Plaine de Lachaup ☎ 92-52-36-94. Closed Sun (low season). Evening meals to 11pm. Local filling station. Parking.

GARGES-LES-GONESSES 95140 Val-d'Oise **Map 1-A2**

♀⊗ **AUX VIEUX GARGES** (N° RR DEC 27 485) (Mme Paulette **Aubre**) 37, rue Marcel-Bourgogne ☎ 39-86-30-31. Closed Sat afternoon and Sun.

♀⊗ **CHEZ RENE** (N° RR OCT 27 698) (M. Rene **Dubuisson**) 49, rue Ambroise Croizat ☎ 39-86-25-60. English spoken. Restaurant: menu 54–65F. À la carte. Closed Sat, Sun and 3 weeks in Aug.

GASVILLE

GASVILLE see MAINVILLIERS

GAVRELLE 62580 Pas-de-Calais **Map 5-B3**
♀⊗ **RELAIS DE LA CHAUMIÈRE** (N° RR SEPT 27 013) (M. Franck **Courcelle**) RN 21, ☎ 21-58-16-99. English spoken. **Minitel**. Local filling station. Restaurant: family cooking. Menu à la carte. Dinner until 9pm. Credit cards accepted. Rest. seat 30. ⌁ Parking.

GENNEVILLIERS 92230 Hauts-de-Seine **Map 1-A2**
♀⊗ **LES ROUTIERS** (N° RR SEPT 26 664) (Mme Anne-Maria **Vidalenc**) 39, avenue Marcel-Paul ☎ 47-92-11-70. Closed Fri evening, Sat, Sun. Evening meals served until 9pm. Menu 48F. Credit cards accepted. Parking for coaches.

GER 64550 Pyrénées-Atlantiques **RN 117 Map 21-A3**
♀⊗ **A LA CLÉ D'OR** (N° RR AVR 20 706) (M. Robert **Coudert**) ☎
⌂ 62-31-50-56 ⊨ 4. Closed Sat, Sun, Aug.

GERMIGNY-SUR-YONNE 89600 Yonne **RN 5 Maps 9-B2 and 13-A2**
♀⊗ **SARL LE RELAIS DES ROUTIERS** (N° RR MAI 23 806) (M. **Cornu**)
⌂ route de Genève ☎ 86-35-06-39. **Minitel** ⊨ 9. Closed Sun.

GERTWILLER 67140 Bas-Rhin **Map 10-B2**
♀⊗ **RELAIS DES GOURMETS** (N° RR JUIL 27 324) (M. Hubert **Klein**) 154, route de Strasbourg ☎ 88-08-92-69. Closed Tue and mid-Feb to mid-Mar. English and German spoken. Evening meals served until 9pm. Local filling station 8am–7pm.

GHYVELDE 59254 Nord **Map 5-B2**
♀⊗ **CAFE ST-SÉBASTIEN** (N° RR OCT 26 712) (Mme Edith **Marie Rubben**) 161, rue Nationale ☎ 28-26-61-95. Closed Tue, Aug. Dutch spoken. Coaches welcome. Rest. seats 180. Regional and family cooking. Specialities: Flemish dishes. Menu 40–180F. Children's menu. À la carte. Lunch 11.45am–5pm. Credit cards accepted. Terraced garden. ⌁ Parking. Sights: Bergues, Dunkirk, Belgium.

GIBERVILLE 14730 Calvados **RN 175 Map 4-B2**
♀⊗ **AU VERT GALANT** (N° RR MAI 26 892) (M. Jean-Luc **Outrequin**)
⌂ 19, route de Rouen ☎ 31-72-36-52. Closed Sun. English spoken. Coaches welcome. Rest. seats 60. Evening meals to 9pm. Hotel ⊨ 14.

GIDY 45520 Loiret **Map 13-A1**
LA PORTE DU VAL DE LOIRE (N° RR 1818) (M. Philippe **Kaiser**)
☎ 38-73-31-02.

GIEN 45500 Loiret **RN 140 Map 13-A1**
♀⊗ **CAFÉ DU NORD** (N° RR OCT 27 054) (Mme Suzanne **Botineau**) 51, place de la Victoire ☎ 38-67-32-98. Closed Sun and first 2 weeks of Aug. English spoken. Local filling station 7am–8pm.
♀⊗ **SARL AU RELAIS NORMAND** (N° RR OCT 27 055) (M. Pierre
⌂ **Montceau**) 64, place de la Victoire ☎ 38-67-28-56. **Minitel**. Restaurant: family cooking. Menu 47F. Children's menu. Lunch 12–2pm. Dinner 7.30–9.30pm. Closed Sat, Sun, 3 weeks in July. Rest. seats 100. Hotel ⊨ 12 from 150–180F with showers. Terraced garden. Parking. Filling station nearby, open 7am–8pm. ⌁ Sights: pottery museum, hunting museum, château.

GIÈVRES 41130 Loir-et-Cher **RN 76 Map 12-B3**
♀⊗ **LA BALANCELLE** (N° RR JUL 26 946) (Mme Francine **Brialy**), 1, route de Romorantin ☎ 54-98-64-76. Evening meals to 11pm. Closed Sun.

GISORS 27140 Eure **RN 15 Map 3-B2**
♀⊗ **BAR DE L'AVENUE** (N° RR JUN 26 564) (M. **Roussel**) Sarl Tina, 95, route de Dieppe ☎ 32-27-19-45. Closed Sun, 15–30 Aug. Evening meals served until 9pm. English spoken.

GLACERIE (LA) 50470 Manche **RN 13 Map 4-A1**
♀⊗ **LE RELAIS DE LA GLACERIE** (N° RR SEPT 26 034) (M. Paul **Roupsard**) near Conforama ☎ 33-44-13-54. **Minitel**. Closed Sun. Coaches welcome. Rest. seats 80. Evening meals until 9pm. Parking. Sights: World War II landing beaches, Cherbourg, The Hague.

GLOS-SUR-RISLE 27290 Eure **Map 4-B3**
♀⊗ **RELAIS DE LA FORGE** (N° RR DEC 27 487) (M. Serge **Langlois**) La Forge. Directions: between Montfort-sur-Risk and Brionne by the old route. ☎ 32-56-16-34. Restaurant: family cooking. Menu 50F. Dinner until 10pm. Closed Sun afternoon. Credit cards accepted. Traditional décor. Rest seats 25. ⊨ Parking. Filling station opposite. Sights: the Abbey of Bec Hellouin (6km), Risle Valley.

GODEWAERSVELDE 59270 Nord **RN 348 Map 5-A1**
♀⊗ **LE CUSTOM** (N° RR JUIL 26 961) (M. Antoine **Trassaert**) "Callicanes" ☎ 28-43-33-87. Service station opposite. Dutch spoken.

GOLBEY 88190 Vosges **RN 66 460 Maps 14-B1 and 10-A2**
♀⊗ **RELAIS DU PETIT CERF** (N° RR MAI 26 888) (M. Christian **Kuntz**) 63, rue du Général-Leclerc ☎ 29-34-23-25. Restaurant: open 7am–11pm. Closed Sun, public holidays. Evening meals until 8pm. Credit cards accepted. 2 rest. seating 50. Snacks served.

GONNEVILLE-SUR-HONFLEUR 14600 Calvados **Map 4-B2**
♀⊗ **LE MERLE BLANC** (N° RR DEC 24 775) (M. **Renault**) Honfleur ☎ 31-89-11-98. Closed Sat, Aug, 20–31 Dec. Coaches welcome. Rest. seats 58. Evening meals until midnight. English spoken.

GOUESNIÈRE (LA) 35350 Ille-et-Vilaine **RD 4 Map 7-A3**
♀⊗ **LE RELAIS DES ROUTIERS** (N° RR JUL 21 599) (Mme M.-T. **Bourgalais**) Le Bourg ☎ 99-58-80-57 ⊨ 16 with showers. Closed Sun, 15–30 Aug. Coaches welcome. Rest. seats 180. Evening meals until 10pm.

GOURDON 46300 Lot **RN 704 Map 17-B1**
♀⊗ **HOTEL DE LA MADELEINE** (N° RR JUL 18 770) (M. Jean **Barbes**)
⌂ boulevard de la Madeleine ☎ 61-41-02-63. **Minitel** ⊨ 16. Closed Sun (low season), Oct. Coaches welcome. Rest. seats 55 + covered terrace.

GOURIN 56110 Morbihan **RD 1/769 Map 7-B2**
♀⊗ **AUBERGE DE TOUL-AN-CHY** (N° RR MAI 26 541) (M. Joseph
⌂ **Hillion**), 20, rue de la Libération ☎ 97-23-43-77. ⊨ 9. Closed Sat. English spoken.

GOUSSAINVILLE

GOUSSAINVILLE 95190 Val-d'Oise **Map 1-A3**
♀⊗ **AUX SPORTS** (N° RR MAR 24 885) (M. Marcel **Dufros**) 22, avenue Albert Sarrault ☎ 39-88-10-84. Closed Sat.

GOUSTRAINVILLE par DOZULE 14430 Calvados **RN 815 Map 4-B2**
♀⊗ **LE RELAIS DES ROUTIERS** (N° RR DEC 11 933) (M. Daniel **Duval**) ☎ 31-79-21-90. Closed Sun, Aug.

GRAINVILLE 27380 Eure **RN 14 Map 3-A1**
♀⊗ **LE RELAIS DE GRAINVILLE** (N° RR JUN 26 563) (Mme Edwige **Legatt**) RN 40, ☎ 32-48-06-28. Closed Sat afternoon, Sun, end Dec. Coaches welcome. Rest. seats 45. Evening meals 6–8pm.

GRAMAT 46500 Lot **RN 140 and D 677 Map 17-B1**
♀⊗ ☆☆ **NN HOTEL DU CENTRE** (N° RR FEV 13 419) (M. André
🏠⊷ **Grimal**) place de la Republique ☎ 65-38-73-37. **Minitel** ⊷ 14 170–300F with showers, bathroom, private WC, telephone, TV in room. Access for disabled. Closed Sat (low season), Feb. Coaches welcome. Rest. seated 150. Evening meals to 9pm. English spoken. Parking. Bar. ⊬ Rest room. Terrace. Menus 60–80F. Specialities: foie gras, confit de canard, cassoulet maison, cèpes, tripos, gésiers. Sights: Rocamadour, Gouffre de Padirac (10km).

GRAND-BREUIL (LE) par ROUILLÉ 86480 Vienne **RN 150 Map 15-A1**
♀⊗ **CHEZ MARYSE** (N° RR JUN 19 800) (Mme Maryse **Tellier**) ☎ 49-43-90-62 ⊷ 6. Closed Sun, 22 Dec–2 Jan. Evening meals to 9pm. Parking.

GRAND-FOUGERAY (LE) 35390 Ille-et-Vilaine **RN 137 Map 11-A2**
♀⊗ ☆ **NN RELAIS DE LA BELLE ÉTOILE** (N° RR MAI 25 407) (M.
🏠 Roland **Pirot**) La Belle Étoile ☎ 99-08-42-59. Closed Sun. English spoken.

GRAND QUEVILLY 76120 Seine-Maritime **Map 3-A1**
♀⊗ **HÔTEL DU CADRAN** (N° RR JUIN 27 301) (M. Phillippe
🏠 **Delafenestre**) 1, rue Pierre-Corneille ☎ 35-69-69-34 ⊷ 7. English spoken. Rest. seats 40.

GRANDE-VALÉE (LA) 37110 Ille-et-Vilaine **see VILLEDOMER**

GRAVELINES 59820 Nord **RN 40 Map 5-A1**
♀⊗ **CAFÉ DE L'AGRICULTURE** (N° RR 24 414) (M. Jean **Devilland**) 52, avenue Jean-Jouhaux ☎ 28-23-05-50. Closed Oct. Menu 47–50F. Parking for coaches.

GRAVIGNY 27930 Eure **RN 154 Maps 3-B1 and 4-B3**
♀⊗ **HOTEL DES SPORTS** (N° RR OCT 23 513) (M. Tarik **Senonci**) 109,
🏠 avenue A.-Briand ☎ 32-33-16-19 ⊷ 7. English, Spanish, Arabic spoken.

GREMONVILLE 76790 Seine-Maritime **RD 20 Map 4-A3**
♀⊗ **LA CHAUMIERE** (N° RR JAN 26 776) (M. Christian **Le Masurier**) place de l'Eglise, Motteville ☎ 35-56-45-65. English spoken. Restaurant: family cooking. Specialities: lapin au cidre, langue à la sauce piquate, entrecote à l'echalote. Menu 45F. Children's menu. Dinner until 9pm. Closed Tue afternoon and Wed after-

noon. Credit cards accepted. Traditional décor. Rest. seats 30. Terraced garden. ⚐ Parking. Sights: Yvetot church, the beach at Saint Valery (25km), the oak trees at Allouille Bellefosse.

GRENOBLE 38100 Isère **Maps 19-A3 and 24-B1**

Ⓧ **LE CATALPA** (N° RR JUL 27 334) (Mme Denise **Brisset**) 8, boulevard de l'Esplanade ☎ 76-47-38-03. Closed Sun. Italian spoken. Evening meals to midnight. Rest. seats 40. Local filling station 6.30am–8.30pm.

GRIGNY 69250 Rhône **Map 2-B1**

Ⓧ **LE PHOENIX** (N° RR JUIL 27 320) (M. Michel **Lelarge**) 80, rue de Bouteiller ☎ 78-73-03-72. Closed Sat afternoon, Sun and 7 July–15 Aug. English, Spanish and Italian spoken. Evening meals. Local filling station nearby.

GRIMAUD 83360 Var **Map 25-A2**

Ⓧ **LE RESTAUROUTE** (N° RR JAN 24 815) (M. Bernard **Gentile**) RN
ⓗ 98 St Pons-les-Murs ☎ 94-56-03-75. **Minitel** ⚐ 10. Closed Sun, Dec. Rest. seats 80. Evening meals. English, German, Dutch, Italian spoken. Parking. Restaurant: family cooking. Menu 60F. Children's menu. À la carte. Lunch 12–1.45pm. Dinner 7.30–9.45pm. Credit cards accepted. Terraced garden. ⚐ Sights: Port Grimaud (1km), St Tropez (6km).

GRISOLLES 82170 Tarn-et-Garonne **RN 20 and 113 Map 22-A2**

Ⓧ **LE RELAIS DE LA GARE** (N° RR FEV 25 807) (M. Pierre **Dupuis**) RN 20 ☎ 63-67-31-83. **Minitel**. Coaches welcome. Rest. seats 40. Closed Sat and Sun night, 5–19 Feb. Dinner until 10pm.

GUEMAR 68970 Haut-Rhin **RN 83 Map 10-B2**

Ⓧ **A L'ANGE** (N° RR MAR 24 173) (M. Claude **Meinrad**) 16, route de
ⓗ Sélestat ☎ 89-71-83-03 ⚐ 14. Closed Sat, 15 Dec–15 Jan. German, English, Italian spoken.

GUENIN 56150 Morbihan **7 B-2**

Ⓧ **LE RELAIS DE BON VALLON** (N° RR OCT 27 687) (M. Joël Le **Hazif**) ZI de Bon Vallon ☎ 97-39-10-41. English spoken. Parking. Filling station nearby, open 7am–midnight.

GUER 56380 Morbihan **7-B3**

Ⓧ **LE LION D'OR** (N° RR JANU 27167) (M. Pierre **Poirier**) 7, place
ⓗ de la Gare ☎ 97-22-00-26. Restaurant: closed Sun. Hotel ⚐ 5. Filling station nearby, open 8am–8pm.

Ⓧ **LE RELAIS DE L'UNION** (N° RR MARS 20 131) (M. Olivier **Guerin**) 3, avenue Broceliande ☎ 97-75-71-46. Restaurant: closed Sun, Aug. Hotel ⚐ 5.

GUERCHE-DE-BRETAGNE (LA) 35130 Ille-et-Vilaine **RN 178 Map 8-B1**

Ⓧ **LE RELAIS DU PONT D'ANJOU** (N° RR JUN 19 813) (M. **Moussu**)
ⓗ 11, faubourg d'Anjou ☎ 99-96-23-10. **Minitel** ⚐ 12. Closed Sat evening. Rest. seats 70. Menus 40.50–82.50F. Specialities: fruits de mer, couscous, paella. Dinner until 11pm.

GUERCHE-SUR-L'AUBOIS (LA) 18150 Cher **Map 13-B2**

Ⓧ **LE REFUGE** (N° RR OCT 27 409) (M. Dominique **Letin**) La Chapelle Hugon ☎ 48-74-05-25. Closed Tue, Feb. Local filling station nearby.

GUEREINS

GUEREINS 01090 Ain **RN 17 Map 18-B2**

♈⊗ **LA CROISÉE** (N° RR MAI 26 551) (M. Michel **Manains**) La
Croisée de Guereins ☎ 74-66-14-93. Closed Tue from 4pm, 3
weeks in Aug. Parking.

GUÉRIGNY 58130 Nièvre **RD 977 Map 13-B2**

♈⊗ **HOTEL DU COMMERCE** (N° RR NOV 26 095) (M. Gerard **Page**)
⌂ 2, Grande rue. Directions: opposite the post office and beside the
Credit Agricole. ☎ 86-37-32-77. German spoken. Restaurant:
regional and family cooking. Menu 50–62F. Dinner until 9pm.
Closed Sat and Sun (low season), Sun during summer, 20 Dec–5
Jan. Credit cards accepted. Traditional décor. Rest. seats 50.
Hotel ⊷ 8 from 100–150F. ⚐ Parking. Sights: Old Guérigny, the
museum at Château Chinon.

GUILBERVILLE 50160 Manche **RN 175 Maps 4-B1 and 8-A1**

♈⊗ **RESTAURANT LE POTEAU** (N° RR MAI 15 941) (M. Fredy
Menant) Le Poteau 33-56-73-10. **Minitel**. Closed Sat, Sun,
Christmas holiday. Evening meals until midnight. English, Ger-
man spoken. Coaches welcome. Rest. seats 45.

GUIPAVAS 29215 Finistère **CD 712 Map 7-A1**

♈⊗ **LE RELAIS DU LION D'OR** (N° RR NOV 8 075) (Mme **Troadsec**)
⌂ 52, rue de Paris ☎ 98-28-00-33.

GUMBRECHTSHOFFEN 67110 Bas-Rhin 500m from **RN 62 RD 242 Map
10-B1**

♈⊗ **AU SOLEIL – CHEZ BERNARD ET LILI** (N° RR AOU 22 020)
(Mme Liliane **Peifer**) 30, rue Principale ☎ 88-72-90-77 ⊷ 3.
Closed Sun afternoon, Aug. Coaches welcome. Rest. seats 200.
Evening meals to midnight. German spoken.

GUMERY 10400 Aube **RD 439 Map 9-A/B2**

♈⊗ **AU RELAIS** (N° RR FEV 27 194) (Mmes Évelyne and Jacqueline
⌂ **Visse**) 3, route de Sens ☎ 25-39-16-01. Closed Sun, 3 weeks in July.
English spoken. Restaurant: family cooking. Menu 50F. Lunch
11.30am–2pm. Dinner 7–9pm. Traditional décor. Rest. seats 40. Hotel
⊷ 5 from 70–110F. ⚐ Parking. Sights: Château de la Motte Tilly.

GURUNHUEL 22390 Côtes-du-Nord **RN 787 Map 7-A2**

♈ **AU RENDEZ-VOUS DES CHASSEURS ET DES PECHEURS –
CHEZ GILBERTE** (N° RR JUL 19 429) (M. Yves **Georgelin**)
Kérambellec ☎ 96-21-81-00. **Minitel**. Closed Jul. Coaches wel-
come Rest. seats 50.

HABSHEIM 68440 Haut-Rhin **RN 66 Map 10-B3**

♈⊗ **A LA VILLE DE MULHOUSE** (N° RR OCT 21 676) (Mme
Gabrielle **Lehmann**) 76, rue du Général-de-Gaulle ☎ 89-44-31-
33. Coaches welcome. Rest. seats 245. German, English spoken.

HAGONDANGE 57300 Moselle **RN 53 Maps 10-A1 and 6-B3**

♈⊗ **LE RELAIS DES AMIS** (N° RR JAN 16 412) Mme Martine
⌂ **Bognolo**) 36, rue de Metz ☎ 87-71-46-63. German and Italian
spoken. Dinner until 10pm. Closed Sun and two weeks in Aug.
Hotel ⊷ 9.

HAVRE (LE)

HALLEMES-LEZ-HAUBOURDIN 59320 Nord **RD 941 Map 5-B1**
♀⊗ **AUX AMIS DE LA ROUTE** (N° RR SEPT 27 668) (M. Dominque **Delecluse**) 329, rue du Général de Gaulle ☎ 20-07-14-24. **Minitel**. Restaurant: closed Sat and Sun, Aug.

HALLUIN 59250 Nord **RN 17 Map 5-B1**
♀⊗ **AU ROUTIER** (N° RR OCT 26 687) (M. Richard **Kozior**) 196, rue de la Lys ☎ 20-23-88-20. Closed Sat afternoon, Sun, Aug. Polish, Serbo-Croat, Dutch spoken. Evening meals to 10pm. Rest. seats 80. Parking.

HARDRICOURT 78250 Yvelines **RN 190 Map 1-A1**
♀⊗ **LE DEVINETTE** (N° RR NOV 26 367) (M. Michel **Lemoine**) 30, boulevard Michelet ☎ 34-74-06-32. Closed Sat, Sun, Aug.

HARNES 62440 Pas-de-Calais **Map 5-B2**
♀⊗ **CHEZ FREDINE** (N° RR DEC 27 745) (Mme Fredine **Turner**) 17, route de Lille ☎ 21-42-30-90. Restaurant. Menu 60–120F. Parking. Filling station 2km.

HASNON 59173 Nord **Map 5-B1**
♀⊗ **LE RELAIS DE LA FORET** (N° RR MARS 27 568) (Mme Thérèse **Draux**) RN 1 ☎ 27-26-62-11. Parking. English spoken.

HAVRE (LE) 7660 Seine-Maritime **RN 13 Bis Map 4-A/B2**
♀⊗ **LE RELAIS DES ROUTIERS** (N° RR NOV 23 550) (Mme Marie-Pierre **Priser**) 57, rue Marceau ☎ 34-74-06-32. Restaurant: family cooking. Speciality: fruits de mer. Menu 50F, children's menu. Self service. Open 7am–1am. Lunch 11.30am–4pm. Dinner 7–11pm. Closed Friday evening and 23 Dec–7 Jan. Traditional décor. Rest. seats 55. Parking. TV room. Sights: the port, seaside.

♀⊗ **LE RELAIS** (N° RR OCT 24 367) (M. Didier **Eudes**) 128, boulevard de Graville ☎ 35-24-54-48. Closed Sun, 15 days in Sept. Coaches welcome. Rest. seats 100. English spoken. Restaurant: regional cooking. Specialities: magrets, saumon frais, viandes rôtis et grillées. Menu à la carte. Lunch 11.45am–2.30pm. Dinner 6.45–10.30pm. Credit cards accepted. Rest room. ⊮ Parking. Sights: the port

♀⊗ **LE P'TIT COMPTOIR** (N° RR JUN 26 558) (M. Bernard **Rondel**) 31, rue du Général Faidherbe ☎ 35-42-78-72. Closed Sun, 20 Dec–20 Jan. Rest. seats 60. Evening meals to 11pm. English spoken.

♀⊗ **AU TÉLÉPHONE** (N° RR AVR 27 258) (M. Jean-Claude **Bouillon**) 173, boulevard Amiral Mouchez ☎ 35-53-24-73. Closed Sat and Sun. English spoken.

♀⊗ **LE WELCOME** (N° RR OCT 27 048) (Mme Marie-Pierre **Priser**)
⌂ Quai de Southampton ☎ 35-43-17-84. Restaurant: regional cooking. Specialities: huitres, fruits de mer. Menu à la carte. Self-service. Lunch 12–3pm. Dinner 7pm–1am. Credit cards accepted. Modern décor. Rest. seats 40. Hotel ⇥ 8 from 90–180F open 8.30am–2am. Parking. Filling station in the town. Sights: the port, seaside.

♀⊗ **AU PETIT MOUSSE** (N° RR FEV 27 178) (M. Patrice **Munster**) 19, rue Amiral Courbet ☎ 35-25-13-43. Closed Sat afternoon and Aug. Restaurant: family cooking. Specialities: couscous, paella. Menu 50F, children's menu. Open 8.30am–2am. Lunch 11.30am–3.30pm. Dinner 7.30–9pm. Traditional décor. Rest. seats 34. ⊮ Parking. Sights: the port

HAYE-DU-PUITS (LA)

Havre (Le) continued

LE MARCEAU (N° RR OCT 27 704) (M. Jean-Claude **Beaurain**) 27, rue Marceau ☎ 35-26-68-28. English spoken. Restaurant. Menu 47F. Closed Sun. Filling station 300m, open 24 hours.

HAYE-DU-PUITS (LA) 50250 Manche **RN 800 Map 4-B1**

♈⊗ **LE RELAIS DES AMIS** (N° RR MAI 24 572) (M. Louis **Le Filliastre**) 16, rue du Château ☎ 33-46-03-42. Closed Sun in winter. Rest. seats 150.

HAYE PESNEL 50320 Manche **RD 7 Map 8-A1**

♈⊗ **LE RELAIS CHEZ ARMELLE** (N° RR AOUT 15 766) (Mme Armelle **Jacquette**) rue de la Libération ☎ 33-61-50-83. Closed Sat, Sun (low season), Dec. Full-board guest rooms. Coaches welcome. Rest. seats 120. Evening meals to 10pm. English spoken.

HAYONS-ESCLAVELLES par NEUFCHATEL-EN-BRAY (LES) 76270 Seine-Maritime **RN 28 and 29 Map 3-A1**

♈⊗ **RELAIS DES HAYONS** (N° RR SEPT 27 680) (M. Jean-Claude **Riednoël**) RN 28. Directions: Paris–Dieppe crossroads ☎ 35-93-13-15. Restaurant: family cooking. Menu 43F. Children's menu. Lunch 11am–2pm. Dinner 6–10.30pm. Closed Sun. Credit cards accepted. Traditional décor. Rest. seats 140. Rest room. Terraced garden. ⚑ Parking. Shower available. Filling station 500m.

HENDAYE 64700 Pyrénées-Atlantiques **RN 10 Map 20-A3**

♈⊗ **LE RELAIS DES ROUTIERS CHEZ MARCEL** (N° RR MAI 18 415) (M. **Mongobert**) 11, avenue d'Espagne Pont International ☎ 59-20-78-95. Closed Sun, Aug. Evening meals to 10pm. German spoken.

♈⊗ **RESTAURANT DE PONT** (N° RR OCT 27 071) (M. Richard **Mas**) 17, avenue d'Espagne ☎ 59-20-73-96. Closed Sun and 15–30 Aug. Spanish spoken. Filling station nearby.

HERBERGEMENT (L') 85260 Vendée **Map 11-B3 and 12-B1)**

♈⊗ **LE RELAIS DES ROUTIERS** (N° RR NOV 24408) (M. Michel **Bretin**) 17, rue Georges Clémenceau. Directions: Nantes, la Roche-sur-Yon via Montaigu ☎ 51-42-80-71. Restaurant: family cooking. Menu 45F. Children's menu. Dinner until 9pm. Closed Thur afternoon, Sun afternoon, Aug. Credit cards accepted. Parking.

HERBIERS (LES) 85500 Vendée **RN 160 Map 11-B3**

♈⊗ ☆ **NN L'ORÉE DES BOIS VERTS** (N° RR OCT 27 044) (M. René
⌂ **Joulin**) route des Sables ☎ 51-91-00-18. Restaurant: family cooking. Dinner until 9pm. Closed Sun, All Saint's Day, Easter. Credit cards accepted. Rest. seats 80. Hotel ⇥ 11 from 65–180F with shower, bathroom, private WC. Rest room. Terraced garden. ⚑ Parking. Sights: Puy du Fou, Tricherie Pond, Grainetière Abbey.

♈⊗ ☆☆ **CHEZ CAMILLE** (N° RR JANU 20 079) (M. Camille **Massé**) 2,
⌂ rue Monseigneur Massé. Direction: Montchamps, Les Herbiers-Sud ☎ 51-91-07-57. **Minitel**. Restaurant: family cooking. Menu 55–100F. À la carte. Modern décor. Rest. seats 200. Hotel ⇥ 13 from 180–245F with shower, bathroom, private WC, TV, telephone. Open 7am–11pm. Rest room. Terraced garden. ⚑ Parking. Sights: Puy du Fou (9 km) the sea (80km)

HERMITAGE (L') 35590 Ille-et-Vilaine **RD 125 Map 7-B3**
♀⊗ **LE VILLAGE** (N° RR MAI 27 604) (M. Michel **Boissel**) 23, rue de Rennes ☎ 99-64-03-31. Closed Sun, Aug.

HERMITAGE-LORGE (L') 22150 Côtes-du Nord **RD 168 Map 7-A2**
♀⊗ **LE SOLEIL D'OR** (N° RR SEPT 26 031) (Mme Huguette **Maillard**)
⌂ Le Paly ☎ 96-42-11-39. Restaurant: family cooking. Dinner until 8pm. Closed Sun evening. Credit cards accepted. Rest. seats 125. Hotel ⇥ 7 from 65–80F. Parking.

HEUDEBOUVILLE 27400 Eure **RN 15 Map 3-B1**
♀⊗ **LE TROU NORMAND** (N° RR AVR 25 387) (M. Guy **Fort**)
⌂ Louviers ☎ 32-40-18-00. ⇥ 5. Closed Sun, Aug.

HINGLE (LE) 22100 Côtes-du-Nord **RN 166 Map 7-A3**
♀⊗ **LE RELAIS DE LA GARE** (N° RR JUL 24 633) (M. Rémy **Pessel**)
⌂ place de la Gare Les Granits ☎ 96-83-58-45 ⇥ 6. Closed Sat, Sun. Rest. seats 80. Evening meals to 9pm. English spoken.

HIRSON 02500 Aisne **RN 43 Map 6-A2**
♀⊗ **CHEZ JULIANO** (N° RR SEP 26 644) (**Corsini-Lonnoy**) 151, avenue Joffre ☎ 23-58-14-03. Closed Sun, Aug. Coaches welcome. Rest. seats 50. Evening meals to 10pm.

HOPITAL-CAMFROUT (L') 29224 Finistère **RN 170 Map 7-A1**
♀⊗ **LE RELAIS DES ROUTIERS** (N° RR DEC 21 301) (M. Bernard **Hamery**) 68, rue Emile Salaun Le Bourg. Directions: 20km from Brest, 50km from Quimper ☎ 98-20-01-21. Restaurant: family and regional cooking. Speciality: fruits de mer. Menu à la carte. Self-service. Closed Mon afternoon, 15 Aug–1 Sept. Credit cards accepted. Traditional décor. Rest. seats 245. ⊨ Parking. Sights: Daoulas Abbey (2km), Amorique Park, beaches.

HOPITAL SOUS ROCHEFORT (L') 42130 Loire **Map 16-B3**
♀⊗ **CHEZ SYLVIANNE ET JEANNOT** (N° RR JUN 27 633) (M. Jean **Devanne**) RN 89 Boen-sur-Lignon. ☎ 77-24-55-52. English spoken. Parking.

HOPITAL-SUR-RHINS (L') par ST-CYR-DE-FAVIERES 42132 Loire **RN 7 Map 18-A2**
♀⊗ **LE RELAIS DES ROUTIERS** (N° RR MARS 9 420) (M. Jean **Lagoutte**) ☎ 77-64-80-13 ⇥ 7. Closed Sat, Aug. Credit cards accepted. Rest. seats 35. Open 5.30am–10pm. Evening meals until 9pm. Parking for lorries.

HOSPITALET DU LARZAC (L') 12230 Aveyron **RN 9 Map 23-A1**
♀⊗ ✩✩ **RELAIS ESPACE** (N° RR AVR 27 243) (Mme Ginette **Gineste**)
⌂ RN 9 Aérodrome Millau-Larzac ☎ 65-62-76-22. English and Spanish spoken. Restaurant. Children's menu. À la carte. Self-service. Rest. seats 250. Hotel ⇥ 10 200F with bathroom, private WC, TV. Parking. Filling station 2km, open 6am–11pm. Sights: Gorges du Tarn, Navacelle circle, la Convertenade, Roquefort.

HOSTENS 33125 Gironde **RN 657 Map 20-B1**
♀⊗ **AU BON ACCUEIL** (N° RR SEPT 27 670) (SARL Au Bon Accueil)
☎ 56-88-50-63. Restaurant: closed Sat and Sun, Aug. Parking. Filling station 500m, open 6.45am–12.30pm.

HOTTOT LES BAGUES

HOTTOT LES BAGUES 14250 Calvados **CD 9 Map 4-B2**
♀⊗ **LE RELAIS DE LA MANCHE** (N° RR JANV 26 794) (M. Roland **Jeanne**) Grande Rue ☎ 31-80-81-72. Closed Sat, June. Credit cards accepted. Traditional décor. Rest. seats 46. Terraced garden.

HOUCHES (LES) 74310 Haute-Savoie **RN 205 Map 19-B2**
♀⊗⚑**RELAIS DU CHATELARD** (N° RR JUL 26 593) (M. Bernard **Chibaudel**) Passy Le Chatelard ☎ 50-47-21-62. Closed Sun. Spanish spoken.

HOURTIN 33990 Gironde **Map 20-A1**
♀⊗ **LE NOUVEAU NICE** (N° RR NOV 27 100) (M. Phillippe **Roberel**) 6, rue du Médoc ☎ 56-07-40-75. English and Spanish spoken. Local filling station nearby.

HOUSSAYE-EN-BRIE (LA) 77610 Seine-et-Marne **RN 36 Map 9-A1**
♀⊗ **AUBERGE DU COUCOU** (N° RR JUL 26 607) (M. Christian **Broust**)
⌂ La haute-Gonière ☎ 64-07-40-75. English spoken. 1 shower for drivers.

HOUSSOYE (LA) 60390 Oise **RN 181 Map 3-B2**
♀⊗ **LE CHEVAL BLANC** (N° RR SEP 15 790) (Mme **Juttier**) 5, rue de
⌂ Gisors ☎ 44-81-40-23 ⊷ 6. Closed Sun, Sat, Dec.

HUISSEAU-EN-BEAUCE 41310 Loir-et-Cher **RN 10 Map 12-A3**
♀⊗ **LES PLATANES** (N° RR SEPT 27 001) (M. Hubert **Breton**)
☎ 54-82-81-46. Closed Sat evening, Sun. Rest. seats 54. Evening meals to 11pm. Filling station nearby.

HUMIERES 62130 Pas-de-Calais **Map 5-A3**
♀⊗ **LA SEMEUSE Fina Station** (N° RR MAR 24 537) (Mme Berthe **Ternisien**) RN 39 ☎ 21-41-85-77. **Minitel**. Rest. seats 50.

HUSSEREN WESSERLING 68470 Haut-Rhin **RN 66 Map 10-B3**
⊗ **RELAIS DU PONT ROUGE** (N° RR JANV 26 783) (Mme Juliana **Menzione**) RN 36 ☎ 89-82-14-81. Closed Sun. Italian spoken. Parking for lorries.

HUTTENHEIM 67230 Bas-Rhin **RN 83 Map 10-B2**
♀⊗ **AU JARDIN DES ROSES** (N° RR SEPT 27 027) (M. Maurice **Schneider**) Près Benfeld ☎ 88-74-41-44. **Minitel**. Closed Sat and mid-Aug. Rest. seats 60. Evening meals to 9pm. German spoken. Local filling station nearby.

HYENVILLE 50660 Manche **RD 971 Map 8-A1**
♀⊗ **LE RELAIS DE LA SIENNE** (N° RR MARS 26 481) (Mme Éliane
⌂ **Mayor**) Le Pont Hyenville-Quettreville-sur-Sienne ☎ 33-07-56-03. **Minitel** ⊷ 7. Closed Sun (in winter). English spoken.

HYERES-PAROISSE 25110 Doubs **RN 73 Maps 10-A3 and 14-B3 see BAUME-LES-DAMES**

IMLING SARREBOURG 57400 Moselle **RN 4 Map 10-B2**
♀⊗ **RELAIS DE LA FERME** (N° RR DEC 25 757) (M. Jean-Luc **Steiner**) route de Sarrebourg ☎ 87-23-68-72. Closed 15 days beginning Aug, 15 days end Dec/Jan. Rest. seats 50. German spoken.

INTVILLE-LE-GUETARD 45300 Loiret **see PITHIVIERS**

IRIGNY 69540 Rhône **Map 2-B1**

☼⊗ **LE RELAIS DE LOISIRS** (N° RR FEV 27 529) (M. Patrice **Pelourson**) 31, rue de Vieux Port ☎ 78-51-23-47. Restaurant: dinner until 9pm. Closed Sat and Sun, Aug. Filling station nearby.

IS SUR TILLE 21120 Côte-d'Or **Map 14-A3**

☼⊗ **CAFE DU MIDI** (N° RR JUIL 17 848) (M. Philippe **Chalopet**) 2, place Villeneuve ☎ 80-95-07-51. Rest. seats 60.

ISDES 45620 Loiret **Map 13-A1**

☼⊗ **LE DAUPHIN** (N° RR DEC 27 463) (M. Lucien **Laurent**) 11,
⌂ Grande-Rue ☎ 38-29-10-29. Restaurant: family and regional cooking. Menu 48F. À la carte. Lunch 11.30am–2pm. Dinner 7–8.30pm. Closed Mon afternoon. Traditional décor. Rest. seats 80. Hotel ◢ 11 from 60–100F. Open 6am–10pm. Terraced garden. ◤ Parking. Filling station nearby. Sights: Château du Sully, Gien, Pontanal, Brionne, Orléans, Château de Chambord.

ISLE-ADAM (L') 95290 Val-d'Oise **RN 322 Map 3-B2**

☼⊗ **AU RALLYE** (N° RR FEV 18 325) (Mme Paulette **Combes**) 71, rue de Pontoise ☎ 34-69-08-24. Closed Sat evening, Sun evening, Aug.

ISLE-D'ABEAU (L') par BOURGOIN-JALLIEU 38300 Isère **Autoroute A 43 Map 2-B2**

☼⊗ **L'ARCHE** Autoroute A3, Bourgoin-Jallieu ☎ 74-27-27-91. Parking. Shop.

ISLE-JOURDAIN (L') 32600 Gers **RN 124 Map 22-A2**

☼⊗ **L'OLYMPIA–LES ROUTIERS** (N° RR SEP 19 912) (M. Michel **Amour**) 5, rue de la République ☎ 62-07-01-35. Closed Sun, Aug. Evening meals to 10pm. Menu from 44–70F. Rest seats 90. Rest room. ◤ Parking. Sights: ancient town of Auch, including the cathedral. Numerous châteaux and lakes.

ISLES-SUR-LA-SORQUE 84800 Vaucluse **Map 24-A/B2**

☼⊗ **CHEZ L'ANCHOIS** (N° RR OCT 27 439) (M. Jean-Marc **Baudet**) Velorgues ☎ 90-38-01-38. Closed Sun. Evening Meals to 9pm. Terraced garden. Parking.

ISSANKA 34540 Hérault **RN 113 23-B2**

☼⊗ ✩✩ **LE GARRIGOU** (N° RR DEC 27 471) (Mme Danyelle **Hohmann**)
⌂ ☎ 67-78-71-30. Restaurant: family and regional cooking. Specialities: seiche à la rouille, poisson. Menu 57–110F, children's menu. Dinner until 10pm. Hotel ◢ 8 from 100–140F with bathroom, telephone. Parking. Filling station nearby, open 7am–8pm.

ISSOIRE 63500 Puy-de-Dôme **RN 9 Map 17-A3**

☼⊗ **AU REPOS DES ROUTIERS** (N° RR NOV 25 746) (Mme Ginette
⌂ **Clauzin**) Veneix ☎ 73-96-62-01 ◢ 7.

ISSOUDUN 36100 Indre **RN 151 Map 13-B1**

☼⊗ **LE RELAIS DE LA CROIX-ROUGE** (N° RR AOU 22 432) (M.
⌂ Claude **Grosyeux**) 14, faubourg de la Croix-Rouge ☎ 54-21-04-91. **Minitel** ◢ 5. Closed Sat and Sun, mid-Aug. Rest. seats 90. Evening meals to 9pm. English, German, Italian, Turkish spoken.

JALLAIS

JALLAIS 49510 Maine-et-Loire **RN 756/RD 15 Maps 11-B3 and 12-B1**

♈⊗ ☆☆ **NN LE RELAIS DE LA CROIX VERTE Son Restaurant Le**
⌂⇆ **Vert Galant** (N° RR MARS 18 345) (M. **Gaillard**) place de la
Mairie ☎ 41-64-20-22. **Minitel** ⊷ 20 from 120 to 240F, with
shower, bathroom, private WC, telephone, TV. Closed Fri
evening (low season). Rest. seats 150. English, German spoken.
Car park. Bar. ⊷ Menu from 63–135F. À la carte. Lunch 12–2pm.
Dinner 7–10pm. Credit cards accepted. Traditional décor.
Specialities: salade de rillauds d'Anjou chauds, pavé de boeuf au
chinon. Sights: vineyards of Muscadet and Anjou, museum of
Cholet.

JANZE 35150 Ille-et-Vilaine **RN 777 Maps 7-B3 and 8-B1**

♈⊗ **HOTEL RESTAURANT BAR METAYER** (N° RR JANV 20 967) (M.
Michel **Metayer**) 5, rue Jean-Marie Lacire ☎ 99-47-05-10. Restaurant: family cooking. Lunch 12–2pm. Dinner 7–8.30pm. Modern
décor. Rest. seats 150. Hotel ⊷ 7 from 140–160F with showers,
private WC, TV, telephone. Open 8am–10pm. Terraced garden.
Parking for coaches.

JARNAC 16200 Charente **RN 141 Map 15-A2**

♈⊗ **CHEZ MARYSE ET DEDE** (N° RR AOU 22 910) (Mme Maryse
Bouffinie) 77, rue Pasteur ☎ 45-81-02-40. Closed Sun. Rest. seats
55. Evening meals to 10pm.

JARRIE 38560 Isère **RN 85 Maps 19-A3 and 24-B1**

♈⊗ **LE RELAIS DU PETIT PONT** (N° RR MAI 27 599) (M. André
Nucci) Champ sur Drac ☎ 76-68-85-30. Italian spoken. Dinner
until 9pm. Closed Sat evening and Sun evening.

JARS 18420 Cher **RN 723 Map 13-B1**

♈⊗ **LE RELAIS DES ROUTIERS** (N° RR JUL 11 601) (M. **Castagnie**) ☎
48-58-70-44.

JARZE 49140 Maine-et-Loire **Map 12-A2**

♈⊗ **LE MOULINET** (N° RR DEC 27 735) (M. Daniel **Domas**) RN 766.
☎ 41-95-37-52. Restaurant. Speciality: fruits de mer. Menu 46F
and 70–120F. Lunch 11.30am–2.30pm. Dinner 6.30–9pm. Closed
Sun evening. Parking. Filling station nearby.

JOSSELIN 56120 Morbihan **RN 24 Map 7-B3**

♈⊗ **LA ROCHETTE DES ROUTIERS** (N° RR AOUT 22 002) (Mme
Annie **Le Corre**) 128, rue Glatinier ☎ 97-22-27-29. Closed Sat,
Sun (low season). Rest. seats 110. English spoken.

JOUE-EN-CHARNIE 72540 Sarthe **RN 157 Map 8-B2**

♈⊗ ☆ **RESTAURANT DU CHEVAL BLANC** (N° RR JUIL 23 400) (M.
⌂ **Lalande**) ☎ 43-88-42-13. Closed Fri night, 15 days in Feb. Rest.
seats 160. Hotel ⊷ 11.

JUGON-LES-LACS 22270 Côtes-du-Nord **N12 near Dolo exit Map 7-A3**

♈⊗ **LES VALLÉES** (N° RR SEPT 26 645) (Mme Paulette **Hervé**) Les
Vallées-Dolo ☎ 96-31-64-62. **Minitel**. English spoken. Children's
menu. Credit cards accepted. Terraced garden. ⊷ Parking. TV
available to drivers. Sights: Jugen-les-Lacs, Boquen-Foret Abbey
(10km).

JUMELLIERE (LA) 49120 Maine-et-Loire **RD 961 Map 11-A3**

♈⊗ **LA BOULE D'OR** (N° RR JAN 12 009) (Mme **Sécher**) 2, rue du Val de Loire ☎ 41-64-33-23. Restaurant: family cooking. Specialities: Merlu au beurre blanc, coq d'Anjou rouge. Menu 45–160F. Lunch 11.30am–1.45pm. Dinner 7–8.15pm. Closed Sun. Rest. seats 75. Hotel ⊨ 4 at 80–125F with shower, private WC. Open 7am–9pm. ⊨ Parking. Sights: industrial museum, wine museum, botanical garden (6km).

JURANVILLE 45340 Loire **RN 375 and RD 31 Map 9-B1**

♈⊗ **L'AUBERGE DES ROUTIERS** (N° RR JUN 24 611) (M. Maryse **Rocher**) Pavé de Juranville ☎ 38-33-24-61. Closed Mon evening. Evening meals to 9pm. Coaches welcome. Rest. seats 60.

JURQUES 14260 Calvados **RN 117 Maps 4-B2 and 8-A1**

♈⊗ **AU BON ACCUEIL** (N° RR MARS 27 211) (M. Christian **Lesage**) route de Vire ☎ 31-77-81-17. Restaurant: regional and family cooking. Menu 45F. Lunch 11.45am–2pm. Dinner 7–9.30pm. Closed Sun between 3–5pm. Credit cards accepted. Rest. seats 36. Parking. Sights: Jurques Zoo (3km), Bungy (10km), Gorges de la Vire.

JUVISY-SUR-ORGE 91260 Essonne **RN 7 Map 1-B2**

♈⊗ **LE JOFFREY** (N° RR JANV 27 147) (M. Patrick **Thierry**) 45, avenue de la Cour-de-France ☎ 69-21-27-50. Closed Sun.

JUZANVIGNY 10500 Aube **RD 400 Map 9-B3**

♈⊗ **CHEZ JACKY ET ROSE** (N° RR FEV 21 789) (M. Jacques **Deflin**) Brienne le Chateau ☎ 25-92-80-57 ⊨ 3. Closed Sat, Sun, Aug. Evening meals to midnight.

KERGONAN-LANGUIDIC 56440 Morbihan **RN 24 Map 7-B2**

♈⊗ **LE RELAIS DES ROUTIERS** (N° RR JUL 20 785) (M. **Le Garrec**) 9, rue du Commerce ☎ 97-65-90-69. Closed Sat, end Dec. Rest. seats 100.

KERHOSTIN 56510 Morbihan D 768 Map 11-A1 see SAINT-PIERRE-QUIBERON

KINGERSHEIM 68470 Haut-Rhin **Map 10-B3**

♈⊗ **AU CHASSEUR VERT** (N° RR JUIN 26 561) (Mme Kheria **Ma-**
⌂ **brouk**) 5, rue de Guebwiller ☎ 89-52-36-47. English, German spoken. Rest. seats 150. Evening meals until midnight.

KOGENHEIM 67230 Bas-Rhin **RN 83 Map 10-B2**

♈⊗ ☆ **A L'ÉTOILE** (N° RR AOUT 26 624) (M. Robert **Rapp**) 36, route
⌂ de Strasbourg ☎ 88-74-70-02. **Minitel**. Closed Mon (except hotel), Jan. Rest. seats 110. Evening meals served until midnight. German spoken.

KRUTH 68820 Haut-Rhin **Map 10-B3**

♈⊗ ☆☆ **NN AUBERGE DE FRANCE** (N° RR OCT 22 987) (M.
⌂ **Ruffenach**) 20, Grand-Rue ☎ 89-82-28-02. English and German spoken. Restaurant: family and regional cooking. Menu à la carte. Dinner until 9pm. Closed Thur, Nov. Credit cards accepted. Rest. seats 130. Hotel ⊨ 16 from 115–170F. with shower, bathroom, private WC, TV, telephone. Open 8am–midnight. Terraced garden. ⊨ Parking.

LABATUT

LABATUT 40300 Landes **RN 177 Map 20-A/B2**

♈⊗ **LA GUINGUETTE** (N° RR JUL 26 968) (M. Christian **Begu**) ☎
⌂ 58-98-18-82. **Minitel** ⊷ 5. Spanish spoken. Evening meals to 9pm.
Closed Sun night. Rest. seats 90. Local filling station.

LABEGUDE 07200 Ardèche **RN 102 Maps 23-B1 and 24-A2**

♈⊗ **LE RELAIS DE LA POSTE** (N° RR AVR 8 426) (M. Maurice
⌂ **Teyssier**) Route Nationale 64 ☎ 75-37-40-25 ⊷ 12. Closed Sun in
winter, Sept. Rest. seats 50.

LABENNE 40530 Landes **RN 10 Map 20-A2**

♈⊗ **HÔTEL BOUDIGAU** (N° RR DEC 25 221) (M. Francis **Begards**)
⌂ Route Nationale 10 ☎ 59-45-40-18 ⊷ 6. Closed Sat, Sun, public
holidays.

LABROYE par HESDIN 62140 Pas-de-Calais **RD 928 Map 5-A3**

♈⊗ **CHEZ GEORGETTE** (N° RR AOU 19 459) (M. Paul **Flicourt**) route
du Val d'Authie ☎ 21-86-83-10. **Minitel**. Closed last 2 weeks Sept.
Rest. seats 95.

LABRUGUIERE 81290 Tarn **RN 621 Map 22-B2**

♈⊗ **LA MARMITTE** (N° RR JAN 24 073) (M. René **Ozanne**) 35, avenue
⌂ Henri-Simon ☎ 63-50-221-19 ⊷ 16. Closed Sat, Sun. Rest. seats
120. Evening meals served until 9pm.

LACAPELLE MARIVAL 46320 Lot **CD 940 Map 17-B1/2**

♈⊗ **LE RELAIS DU SEGALA** (N° RR JAN 26 788) (M. Jean **Cagnac**)
⌂ route de Leyme ☎ 65-40-81-91 or 65-40-88-19. English, Spanish
spoken. Restaurant: regional and family cooking. Specialities:
fondue auvergnate. Children's menu. À la carte. Lunch 12–2pm.
Dinner 7–9pm. Credit cards accepted. Traditional décor. Rest.
seats 140. Hotel ⊷ 4 at 120F with showers, private WC, telephone. Open 8am–10pm. Terraced garden. ⊬ Parking. Sights:
Rocamador, Paiirac (30km), Saint Céré, Figeac (20km), Conques,
Saint Cirq, Lapopie (30km), Lascaux grottos.

LACAUNE 81230 Tarn **RD 622 Map 22-B2**

♈⊗ **LE CHALET** (N° RR NOV 26 736) (M. Joseph **Delpino**) 14, rue
⌂ André Théron ☎ 63-37-08-91. English and Spanish spoken.
Restaurant: family cooking. Specialities: paella, couscous, cass-
oulet. Menu 60F (drinks included). Children's menu. À la carte.
Dinner until 9pm. Closed Sun (low season). Modern décor. Rest
seats 45. Hotel ⊷ 10 from 120–160F. Terraced garden. ⊬
Parking.

LACHAPELLE AUZAC 46200 Tarn **RN 20 Map 17-B1**

♈⊗ **LE RELAIS DE MAURE** (N° RR JAN 26 140) (M. Patrick **Cam-**
⌂ **broux**) Souillac ☎ 63-37-82-32. **Minitel**. English and Spanish
spoken. Restaurant: regional cooking. Menu 50–90F. Children's
menu. À la carte. Dinner 8–10pm. Closed Sun. Credit cards
accepted. Modern décor. Rest. seats 60. Hotel ⊷ 6 from 90–150F
with showers, private WC. Open 6am–11pm. Terraced garden.
⊬ Parking. Sights: Souillac, Martel, Gignac (golf)

LADON 45270 Loiret **RN Maps 9-B1 and 13-A1**

♈⊗ **LE RELAIS DE LADON** (N° RR FEVR 25 829) (M. Pierre
⌂ **Guillaumin**) 400, avenue du 24 Novembre ☎ 38-95-51-32 ⊷ 7.
Closed Sun, 24 Jun–14 Jul. Rest. seats 35. Evening meals until 10pm.

LAMBALLE

LAFITTE-LOT 47320 Lot-et-Garonne **RN D 666 Map 21-B1**

ΨⓍ **LES AMIS DE LA ROUTE** (N° RR NOV 26 085) (M. Max **Briot**) route de Villeneuve ☎ 53-84-08-98. **Minitel**. Closed Sat, Aug. English, Spanish spoken. Lunch 12–2pm. Dinner 7–10pm. Parking.

LAFOX 47270 Lot-et-Garonne **RN 113 Map 21-B1/2**

ΨⓍ ☆ **NN LE RELAIS TOULOUSAIN** (N° RR JAN 22 155) (M. and Mme
⌂ **André**) 113, route de Toulouse ☎ 53-68-54-83. **Minitel** ⊷ 27.
Closed Sun, 15 Aug–18 Sept and 24 Dec–2 Jan. Rest. seats 220.
Evening meals until 1.30am. Spanish, Italian spoken.

LAILLE 72220 Sarthe **RN 138 Map 12-A2**

ΨⓍ **LA LISIÉRE DE BERGE** (N° RR AOUT 27 367) (Anne and Robert
⌂ **Giscos**) Marugné ☎ 43-42-12-11. English spoken. Restaurant:
family and regional cooking. Specialities: fish. Menu 50F. Children's menu. À la carte. Lunch 12–2pm. Dinner 7–11pm. Credit
cards accepted. Traditional décor. Rest. seats 160. Hotel ⊷ 10 at
120F with showers. Open 7am–11pm. Terraced garden. ⊷
Parking. Filling station 200m. Sights: Loire Valley, Loire châteaux.

ΨⓍ **AUBERGE DU BON ACCUEIL** (N° RR OCT 27 401) (M. Jean-Louis
Londiere) RN 138 Ecommoy ☎ 43-42-12-01. Restaurant: menu à la
carte. Open 7am–10pm. Dinner until 10pm. Closed Wed afternoon. Credit cards accepted. Rest. seats 300. Parking. Filling
station nearby, open 6am–9pm.

LAISSAC 12310 Aveyron **RN 88 Map 23-A1**

ΨⓍ ☆ **AUBERGE DU ROVERGUE** (N° RR DEC 27 467) (SARL **Jancla**)
⌂ route de Rodez ☎ 65-69-60-38 ⊷ 17 at 95–120F. Filling station
nearby, open 6am–9pm.

LALOUBERE 65310 Hautes-Pyrénées **RD 135 Map 21-A3**

ΨⓍ ☆ **NN HÔTEL DES PYRENEES** (N° RR AOUT 16 207) (Mme
⌂ Michelle **Cazamayou**) 13, rue du Ml-Foch ☎ 62-93-19-62 ⊷ 9 from
90–110F. Closed Sun, Aug. Evening meals until 9pm. Car park. Bar.
⊷ English, Spanish, Italian spoken. Rest. seats 40. Sights: Lourdes
(17kms), Pic du Midi, Pyrenees.

LAMAGISTERE 82360 Tarn-et-Garonne **RN 113 Map 21-B2**

ΨⓍ **CHEZ BOMPA** (N° RR AVR 23 774) (M. Gilbert **Bompa**) 86, avenue
Saint-Michel ☎ 63-39-91-56. **Minitel**. Closed Sat, 15 days in Aug.
Rest. seats 100. Evening meals until midnight. Spanish, Italian
spoken

LAMBALLE 22400 Côtes-du-Nord **RD 12 Map 7-A3**

ΨⓍ ☆☆ **NN LA TOUR D'ARGENT** (N° RR JAN 3 713) (M. Claude
⌂ **Mounier**) 2, rue du Docteur Lavergne ☎ 96-31-03-37. Restaurant:
family cooking. Specialities: crevettes grillées, canard à l'orange,
blancs de seiches. Menu 65–150F. Children's menu. À la carte.
Lunch 12–2pm. Dinner 7–9pm. Closed Sat, Nov. Credit cards
accepted. Traditional décor. Rest. seats 80. Hotel ⊷ 30 from
110–280F, with showers, bathroom, private WC, TV, telephone.
Open 7am–11pm. Rest room. Terraced garden. ⊷ Games,
billiards, table tennis. Sights: Saint Malo, Mont St Michel (80km),
Dinan (40km), the coast (15km).

LAMBESC

LAMBESC 13410 Bouches-du-Rhône **RN 7 Map 24-B3**

♉⊗ **RELAIS DE LA GARE** (N° RR AVR 26 044) (Mme Germaine **Lansac**) boulevard des Coopèratives ☎ 42-92-97-60. Closed Sun. Rest. seats 70. Italian spoken.

♉⊗ **LE RELAIS DES CIGALES** (N° RR JUN 27 625) (Mme Daniel **Biermann**) RN 7, La Marchorne ☎ 42-92-88-72. Restaurant. Specialities: Normandy dishes. Closed Sun, Oct. Hotel ⊶ 4 from 80–105F. Parking.

LAMONZIE-ST-MARTIN 24130 Dordogne **RD 936 Maps 15-B3 and 21-B1**

♉⊗ **RELAIS LA POMME D'OR** (N° RR AVR 27 246) (Mme Micheline **Gonthier**) ☎ 53-24-04-00. Closed Sat, Aug. Spanish, English spoken. Parking. Filling station nearby, open 7am–10pm.

LAMOTTE-DU-RHONE 84500 Vaucluse **RN 994 Map 24-A2**

♉⊗ **LE RELAIS DU RHONE** (N° RR JANV 27 160) (Mme Elise **Ruat**)
⌂ RN 994. Direction: exit from motorway at Bollère, towards Port St Esprit ☎ 90-30-41-89. Restaurant: family cooking. Menu 50F. Lunch 11.30am–2.30pm. Dinner 6.30–9.30pm. Closed from Sat at 3pm to Mon at 6am. Credit cards accepted. Traditional décor. Rest. seats 74. Hotel ⊶ 7 from 50–70F. ⊢ Parking. Filling station nearby. Sights: Ardèche Gorges (13km)

LANCON-DE-PROVENCE 13680 Bouches-du-Rhône **RN 113 Map 24-B3**

♉⊗ **RELAIS DES FOURCHES** (SARL) (N° RR NOV 27 084) (M. Guy **Kokos**) Ferrages quarter RN 113. Direction: A7 toll, Salon-de-Provence ☎ 90-42-71-21. Italian spoken. Restaurant: family cooking. Specialities: paella, couscous. Menu 50F. Closed Sun. Credit cards accepted. Traditional décor. Rest. seats 120. Hotel ⊶ 3 100F with shower and private WC. Open 7am–10pm. Rest room. Terraced garden. ⊢ Parking. Filling station nearby. Sights: Salon de Provence (7km), Aix en Provence (22km), Arles (45km).

♉⊗ **LE RELAIS DE PROVENCE** (N° RR 18 10) (M. Marcel **Prioul**) Aire de Lançon. Direction: Autoroute A7, Lyon/Marseille ☎ 90-42-88-88.

LANDE-SUR-EURE (LA) 61290 Orne **Map 8-A3**

♉⊗ **RELAIS DE LA TOUR** (N° RR FEV 26 408) (Mme Denise **Leprince**) Le Bourg ☎ 33-73-65-00.

LANDES 17380 Charente-Maritime **RN 139 Map 15-A2**

♉⊗ **AUX AMIS DE LA ROUTE** (N° RR MARS 26 218) (M. Robert
⌂ **Picard**) Tonnay Boutonne ☎ 46-59-73-12 ⊶ 4. Evening meals until 9pm. Rest. seats 30.

LANDEVANT 56690 Morbihan **RN 165 Map 7-B2**

♉⊗ **LE RELAIS DU PELICAN** (N° RR JUL 6 281) (M. **Bourn**) 14, RN ☎ 97-56-93-12. Closed Mon evening, Tue, Oct.

LANDIVISIAU 29230 Finistère **RN 12 Map 7-A1**

♉⊗ **LE TERMINUS** (N° RR JUN 17 822) (M. Raymond **Floch**) 94,
⌂⊷ avenue Foch ☎ 98-68-02-00. Restaurant: family cooking. Specialities: fruits de mer. Menu 90F. Children's menu. À la carte. Closed Sat, Aug. Rest. seats 150. Hotel ⊶ 16 from 90–110F with showers, TV. Open 7am–11pm. Rest room. Parking. Sights: Brest (35km), the coast (25km)

LANISCAT

LANDRECIES 59550 Nord **RN 45 Map 6-A1**

Y⊗ **LE SAMBRETON** (N° RR AOUT 23 896) (Mme Monique **Lacoche**) Guise Road ☎ 27-84-81-58. Closed Sat afternoon, Sun afternoon, 15–30 Aug.

LANDRETHUN-LE-NORD 62250 Pas-de-Calais **RD 234 and 231 Map 5-A2**

Y⊗ **A LA DESCENTE DES VOYAGEURS** (N° RR JUN 24 244) (Mme Nelly **Brisbout**) Le Village ☎ 21-92-85-55 ➞ 3. Rest. seats 60.

LANESTER 56600 Morbihan **RN 24 Map 7-B2**

Y⊗ ☆ **NN LA ROTONDE** (N° RR NOV 15 440) (Mme **Mercier**) 120,
⌂ rue Jean-Jaurès ☎ 97-76-06-37. Restaurant: family cooking. Menu 40–60F. À la carte. Lunch 12–2pm. Dinner 7–9pm. Closed Sat afternoon, Sun, 15 days at the end of Aug and 15 days at Christmas. Credit cards accepted. Rest. seats 35. Hotel ➞ 13 from 80–120F with showers, bathroom. ⊭ Parking. TV. Sights: the beaches.

Y⊗ **LE RELAIS DU PONT-DU-BONHOMME** (N° RR OCT 23 963) (M. Lucien **Phillippe**) avenue du Pont-du-Bonhomme ☎ 97-76-51-23. Closed Aug. Menu à la carte. Lunch 12–2.30pm. Rest seats 60.

LANGOGNE 48300 Lozère **RN 102 Map 17-B3**

Y⊗ ☆ **NN HOTEL DU LUXEMBOURG** (N° RR AVR 22 750) (Mme
⌂ Adrienne **Chabalier**) place de la Gare ☎ 66-69-00-11. **Minitel** ➞ 14. Closed Jan. Rest. seats 60.

LANGON 33210 Gironde **RN 113 and RN 132 Autoroute A61 Maps 20-B1 and 21-A1**

Y⊗ **RESTAURANT DARLOT** (N° RR MAR 14 293) (M. Jean-Paul
⌂➞ **Darlot**) 10, rue Dotézac ☎ 56-63-01-36. English and Spanish spoken. Restaurant: family cooking. Specialities: civet de lièvre, cèpes à la bordelaise, salmis de palombe. Menu 50F. Lunch 11.30am–3pm. Dinner 7–9pm. Closed Sun, 15–31 Aug, 1st week Sept. Traditional décor. Rest. seats 40. Hotel ➞ 11 from 100–150F with showers, private WC, TV, telephone. Open 7am–10pm. Terraced garden. ⊭ Parking for coaches. Sights: Bazas Cathedral, Château Roquetaillade (5km), Sauternes (5km), Sainte Croix du Mont (5km).

LANGRES 52200 Haute-Marne **RN 19 Map 14-A2**

Y⊗ **RELAIS DE LA COLLINIÈRE** (N° RR JUL 26 601) (Mme Élisabeth
⌂ **Guerra**) Faubourg de la Collinière ☎ 25-87-03-27. Portuguese spoken. Restaurant: family cooking. Speciality: couscous. Menu 53F. Dinner until 10pm. Closed Sun, end Dec. Rest. seats 60. Hotel ➞ 8 from 85–150F. Open 5am–10pm. Sights: Roman town.

Y⊗ **A LA BONNE AUBERGE** (N° RR AVR 16 016) (SNC **Beaumann/**
⌂ **Olivier**) Faubourg de la Collinière ☎ 25-87-09-18 ➞ 6. Closed Sun, Christmas, 15 days in May. Rest. seats 70.

LANISCAT 22 570 Côtes-du-Nord **Map 7-B2**

Y⊗ **LE CHALET DES ROUTIERS** Chez José (N° RR JANV 27 761) (M. Joseph **Le Bihan**) ☎ 96-24-81-78. Restaurant: menu 48F. Open 6am–1am. Closed Sun, end Dec. Parking for lorries. Filling station 200m.

LANNION

LANNION 22300 Côtes-du-Nord **Map 7-A2**
♀⊗ **LA CROIX ROUGE** (N° RR DEC 23 571) (Mme **Pasquiou**) Croix
⌂ Rouge Ploumilliau route de Morlaix ☎ 96-35-45-08. Restaurant:
family cooking. Lunch 11.30am–2pm. Dinner 7–9pm. Closed last 2
weeks in Aug. Rest. seats 183. Hotel ⊷ 14. ⊷ Parking.

LAONS 28270 Eure-et-Loir **RD 4 Map 8-A3**
♀⊗ **L'EOLE** (N° RR NOV 27 725) (Mme Christine Emilie **Jendon**) 2,
place du Carrefour ☎ 37-38-10-21. Restaurant: menu 45F. Closed
Sun. Filling station 200m.

LAPALISSE 03120 Allier **RN 7 and RD 3 Map 16-A3**
♀⊗ ☆ **NN LE CHAPON DORÉ** (N° RR FEV 26 814) (M. Jean-Luc
⌂ **Lalauze**) 2, avenue du 8 Mai 1945 ☎ 70-99-09-51. Restaurant:
family cooking. Menu 48F. Lunch 12–2.30pm. Dinner 7–9.30pm.
Rest. seats 90. Hotel ⊷ 8 from 65–130F with showers. Open
6.30am–10pm. Terraced garden. ⊷ Parking. Games: petanque.
Sights: zoo, châteaux.

LAPALME 11480 Aude **RN 9 Map 23-A3**
♀⊗ **LE CHANTECLAIR** (N° RR AVR 26 867) (M. Maurice **Preignan**)
⌂ ☎ 68-48-15-03 ⊷ 7. Evening meals until 10pm. Closed Sat
evening and Sun.

LAPANOUSE-SERVERAC 12150 Aveyron **RN 595 Map 23-A1**
♀⊗ **LE RELAIS DES ROUTIERS** (N° RR DEC 21 736) M. Roger **Arnal**)
route de Rodez ☎ 65-71-60-44. **Minitel**. Restaurant: family
cooking. Dinner until midnight. Closed Sun. Rest. seats 120.
Sights: the Levezou lakes (40km), Gorges du Tarn (20km),
Mediaeval Château de Séverac (3km), Laguiole-Bramelong ski
runs (40km).

LAPEYRADE 40240 Landes **RD 933 Map 21-A2**
♀⊗ **LE RELAIS DES BRUYÈRES** (N° RR JANV 27 161) (Mme Aline
⌂ **Lallemant**) Labastide d'Armagnac ☎ 58-93-61-16 ⊷ 11. Closed
Sun evening to Tues morning (low season) and mid-Nov to
mid-Dec. English and Spanish spoken.

LAROUILLIES 59219 Nord **RN 2 Map 6-A1/2**
♀⊗ **L'AVESNOIS** (N° RR AVR 27 264) (Mme Annie **Parr**) 61 RN2 ☎
27-59-22-88. Restaurant: dinner until midnight. Rest. seats 50.
Filling station nearby, open 7am–7pm.

LARRAZET 82500 Tarn-et-Garonne **RD 928 Map 22-A1**
♀⊗ **AUBERGE DE LA BARBACANE** (N° RR JANV 26 798) (M. Roland
Cancel) route d'Auch ☎ 63-20-71-29 ⊷ 5. Closed Mon afternoon.

LAVAL 53000 Mayenne **RN 162 and RD 53 Map 8-B1**
♀ **BAR DE LA GARE** (N° RR JUL 25 493) (Mme Claudia **Helbert**)
107, avenue Robert Buron ☎ 43-53-94-88. Dinner until 10pm.
Closed Mon. Rest. seats 27. Terraced gardens. ⊷

LAVANS-LES-DOLE 39700 Jura **RN 73 Map 14-A3**
♀⊗ **LE PANORAMIC** (N° RR MAI 26 238) (Mme Nadège **Hardy**)
⌂ Orchamps ☎ 84-81-21-41 ⊷ 10. Dinner until midnight. Closed
Sun. Rest. seats 50. Parking.

LEZINNES

LAVERSINES 60510 Oise **RN 31 Map 3-A2**
♈⊗ **LE RELAIS ROUTIERS** (N° RR DEC 27 130) (Mme Nadine **Fontaine**) 90, rue St-Germain ☎ 44-07-75-80. Closed Sat and Sun. Filling station nearby.

LEDENON 30210 Gard **RN 86 Map 24-A2**
♈⊗ **RELAIS DE LEDENON** (N° RR MAI 27 613) (Mme Monique
⌂ **Braud**) Route Nationale 86 ☎ 66-37-12-83. Spanish spoken. Restaurant: closed Sat evening, Sunday and last 2 weeks in Aug. Hotel ⇁ 7 from 100–120F. Open 6am–11pm. Parking.

LEGE 44650 Loire-Atlantique **Map 11-B2**
♈⊗ **L'ATHÉMA** (N° RR OCT 27 430) (M. Jacky **Michon**) Centre Commercial Super U ☎ 40-04-93-98. Filling station 800m.
♈⊗ **LE PARADIS** (N° RR MARS 27 575) (M. Michel **Clochard**) 27, rue de l'Atlantique, route de Chalans ☎ 40-04-99-66. Restaurant: open 7am–11pm. Closed Mon afternoon, 8 days in Apr, 3 weeks in Dec. Parking.

LENCLOITRE 86140 Vienne **RD 725 Maps 15-B1 and 12-B2**
♈⊗ **AU 14** (N° RR JUIL 26 934) (M. André **Pernelle**) 2, place du Champ de Foire ☎ 49-90-71-29. Closed Sun. Filling station opposite and at 200m. Dinner until 11pm. Parking.

LESCHELLES 02170 Aisne **RN 30 Map 6-A1**
♈⊗ **LE RELAIS DES QUATRE CHEMINS** (N° RR OCT 13 164) (M. Pierre **Rousseaux**) ☎ 23-97-04-88 ⇁ 2. Closed Aug. Rest seats 50. Evening meals until 10pm.

LESMONT 10500 Aube **RN 60 Map 9-B3**
♈⊗ **LE RELAIS DE L'AUBE** (N° RR APR 11 402) (M. Pierre **Ternard**)
⌂ Route Nationale 60 ☎ 25-92-45-08 ⇁ 5. Closed Sat, Sun, 8 days at Easter and 15 days of Aug. Dinner until 10pm.

LEUE (LA) 85210 Vendée **RN 137 Map 11-B3**
♈⊗ **LE RELAIS DES ROUTIERS** (N° RR AVR 20 714) (SARL **Carbon-**
⌂ **neau Dariet**) RN 137 ☎ 51-94-41-46. **Minitel** ⇁ 7. Closed Sat, Sun, Jul, Christmas and New Year. Rest. seats 56. Evening meals until 10pm.

LEVIGNEN 60800 Oise **3 B-3**
♈⊗ **RELAIS DE LA 11** (N° RR SEPT 27 676) (M. Jacques **Carrier**) RN 2 ☎ 44-87-63-70. English spoken. Filling station nearby.

LEYMENT 01150 Ain **RN 84 Map 2-A2**
♈⊗ **LE RELAIS DE LA GARE** (N° RR FEV 27 190) (M. Marcel
⌂ **Bessière**) 34, rue de la Gare ☎ 74-34-94-30 ⇁ 7. Closed Tue afternoon and Wed afternoon, 22 Dec–2 Jan. Filling station 2km, open 5am–midnight.

LEZINNES 89160 Yonne **RD 905 Map 13-A3**
♈⊗ **LE RELAIS DES VOYAGEURS** (N° RR OCT 25 701) (M. Eric
⌂ **Vermeulen**) 41, Route Nationale 905 ☎ 86-75-61-49. Restaurant: family cooking. Menu 49F. Children's menu. Dinner until 9pm. Credit cards accepted. Rest. seats 50. Hotel ⇁ 8 from 80–130F. Open 6am–9pm. Terraced garden. ⛾ Parking.

LIBOURNE

LIBOURNE 33500 Gironde **RN 89 Map 15-A3**

♈⊗ ☆ **MOULIN BLANC** (N° RR JANV 27 171) (Mme Geneviève
Fernandez) 132, avenue Georges-Clemenceau ☎ 57-25-01-61.
German, Spanish and Italian spoken. Restaurant: family cooking.
Specialilty: couscous. Menu 60F. Children's menu. À la carte.
Lunch 12–3pm. Dinner 7.30–11pm. Traditional décor. Rest. seats
160. Hotel ━ 10 from 100–200F with showers. Rest room. Terrace
garden. ✔ Parking. Filling station nearby, open 24 hrs. Sights:
Bordeaux wine region: Saint Emilion (8km) Pomerol (3km),
Fronsac (3km), Castillon.

LIEVIN 62800 Pas-de-Calais **Map 5-B2**

♈⊗ **LE ZOLA** (N° RR FEV 27 794) (M. André **Clément**) 215, rue Emile
Zola ☎ 21-29-29-72. Restaurant: regional and family cooking.
Specialities: tripes à l'ancienne, moules. Menu 50–75F. Children's
menu. Open 6am–midnight. Closed Mon. Rest. seats 100. Sights:
Notre Dame de Lorette, Canadian Memorial.

LIGARDES 32650 Gers **RN 131 and RD 36 Map 21-B2**

♈⊗ **LE RELAIS CHEZ DUDULE** (N° RR MAR 21 820) (M. Francis
Dulong) route d'Agen ☎ 62-28-85-76.

LIGNANE 13540 Bouches-du-Rhône **RN 7 Map 24-B3**

♈⊗ **LE RELAIS DE LIGNANE** (N° RR MAR 21 453) (M. Christian
Mondin) Route Nationale 7 ☎ 42-92-51-15. Coaches welcome.
Rest. seats 50. Dinner until 10pm. Closed Sun, Aug. Parking for
lorries.

LIGNOL 56150 Morbihan **RD 782 Map 7-B2**

♈⊗ **RELAIS DES VOYAGEURS** (N° RR DEC 26 126) (M. Bernard **Le**
🏠 **Solliec**) 4, rue de la Marie ☎ 97-27-03-48. **Minitel**. Restaurant:
family cooking. Menu 42.50F. Lunch 12–2pm. Dinner 7–9pm.
Closed Mon evening. Credit cards accepted. Rest. seats 80.
Hotel ━ 7 from 72–85F. Open 7am–9pm. ✔ Parking for coaches.
Sights: Kernascleden Church (5km), Priziac Pond, Harlay Zoo
(20km).

LIGNY-EN-BARROIS 55500 Meuse **Map 14-A1**

♈⊗ **RELAIS DE L'EUROP** (N° RR FEV 27 780) (M. Hervé **Leseur**) rue
des Etats Unis ☎ 29-78-00-83. English spoken. Restaurant: menu
50F. Dinner until 12.30am. Closed Sat and Sun (except reservations). Parking. Shower available. Filling station nearby.

LIMAY 78520 Yvelines **Map 3-B2**

♈⊗ **LA MARMITE** (N° RR AOUT 25 617) (M. Claude **Pesta**) 1, route
de Meulan ☎ 34-78-65-52. **Minitel**. Closed Sun. Polish, English,
Spanish spoken.

LIMOGES 87000 Haute-Vienne **RN 20 Map 16-B1**

♈⊗ **CHEZ BICHON** (N° RR DEC 23 057) (M. **Houard**) 68, avenue de
Lattre-de-Tassigny ☎ 55-30-68-83. English and Spanish spoken.
Restaurant: family cooking. Menu 55F (children under 10 half
price). Children's menu. Dinner until 9pm. Closed Sat. Traditional décor. Rest. seats 30. ✔ Sights: cathedral, porcelain factory
and museum, Oradour sur Glane (20km).

♈⊗ **LES LILAS** (N° RR OCT 27 709) (Mme Gilbert **Broussas**) 233,
avenue Bandin. Direction: come into Limoges from the direction

of Perigueux ☎ 55-34-35-67. Toilet facilities for drivers. Restaurant: family cooking. Specialities: lotte, beignet de gambas, potée Limousine. Menu 50–68F. Children's menu. À la carte. Dinner until midnight. Credit cards accepted. Traditional décor. Rest. seats 50. Terraced garden. Parking for coaches. Filling station nearby, open 24 hrs.

LINAS-MONTLHÉRY 93310 Essonne RN 20 Map 1-B2

♈⊗ LE JUBILÉ (N° RR SEPT 25 096) (M. Jacques Boissier) Route Nationale 20 ☎ 69-01-40-76 or 69-80-60-66. Minitel. Restaurant: family cooking. Menu 59F. Open 6.30am–midnight. Closed Sat and Sun. Traditional décor. Rest. seats 90. ⊢ Parking.

LIPOSTHEY 40410 Landes RN 10 Map 20-B1

♈⊗ CHEZ ALINE (N° RR MAR 10 433) (Mme Aline Gros) ☎
⌂ 58-82-30-30 ⊸ 10. Closed Sat in winter, Christmas holidays. Rest. seats 80. Evening meals until 9pm.

LISIEUX 14100 Calvados RN 13 and CD 579 Map 4-B2

♈⊗ RELAIS PARIS-CHERBOURG (N° RR MAI 21 902) (Mme Pestel)
⌂ 113, avenue du Six-Juin ☎ 31-62-06-38 ⊸ 6. Closed Sun evening, 15 days in Sept. Coaches welcome. Rest. seats 70. Evening meals until midnight.

LISSAY LOCHY 18340 Cher RD 28/73 Map 13-B1

♈⊗ AUBERGE DES MAISONS ROUGES (N° RR MARS 26 473) (M. Robert Leger) Levet ☎ 68-64-76-07. Minitel. Closed 15 Dec–15 Jan. Parking.

LIVRON-SUR-DROME 26250 Drôme Map 24-A1

♈⊗ BAR DE LA PETANQUE CHEZ SYLVIE (N° RR DEC 27 482) (Mme Sylvie Perez) 23, avenue J. Combier ☎ 75-85-62-85. Closed Wed. Spanish spoken. Filling station nearby, open 24 hrs.

LOCMARIA 56390 Morbihan Map 7 A-1

♈⊗ RELAIS DE COLLEC (N° RR AOUT 27 366) (Mme Huguette Jouland) Collec Grand Champs ☎ 97-66-66-80. Restaurant: dinner until 11pm. Closed Wed afternoon, mid Aug. Rest. seats 30.

LODEVE 34700 Hérault RN 9 Map 23-A2

♈⊗ LE RELAIS DE LA FONTAINE D'AMOUR (N° RR JUN 21 149) (Mme Renée Granier) Route Nationale 9 ☎ 67-44-02-77. Closed Tue. Evening meals until 9pm.

♈⊗ RELAIS DE LA CROIX (N° RR JUN 26 910) (M. Jean-Dennis Roig) Cartels ☎ 67-44-00-72 ⊸ 6. Closed Sun. Filling station 5kms. Rest. seats 70. Parking.

♈⊗ LE RELAIS DE L'ESCALETTE (N° RR MAI 27 275) (M. Gilbert Cavalier) RN 9 ☎ 67-44-01-14. English, German and Italian spoken. Restaurant: dinner until 10pm. Rest. seats 140. Hotel ⊸ 21.

LOGE (LA) par THEILLAY 41390 Loir-et-Cher RN 20 Map 13-B1

♈⊗ ☆ NN LE RELAIS DE LA LOGE (N° RR JAN 25 249) (M. Guy
⌂ Paillaud) RN 20. Direction: approximately 13km from Vierzon ☎ 54-83-37-20. Minitel. English spoken. Restaurant: family cooking. Speciality: game (when in season). Credit cards accepted. Rest. seats 150. Hotel ⊸ 30 from 75–120F, with showers, private WC. ⊢ Parking.

LOGRON

LOGRON 28200 Eure-et-Loir **Map 8-B3**
♀⊗ **AUBERGE SAINT NICHOLAS** (N° RR OCT 27 400) (M. Bruno **Hubert**) 2, rue des Buissonnets. Direction: route Orléans/Alençon ☎ 37-98-98-02. Restaurant: family cooking. Menu 48-85F. Children's menu. Lunch 11.30am–2pm. Dinner 7–10pm. Closed Sun and 15 days at Christmas. Filling station 500m.

LOIGNE-SUR-MAYENNE 53200 Mayenne **Map 12-A1**
♀⊗ **AUBERGE DE LA ROCHE** (N° RR JUIN 23 314) (M. José **Atlan**) 2, rue de la Roche-du-Maine ☎ 43-07-19-10. Closed Mon afternoon and first 2 weeks of Aug. Evening meals until 9pm. Parking.

LOIRE 49480 Maine-et-Loire **Map 11-A3**
♀⊗ **AU RENDEZ-VOUS DES ROUTIERS** (N° RR AVR 24 551) (M. Philippe **Andouin**) 24, rue de la Libération ☎ 41-94-10-83. Rest. seats 100.

LOISON-SOUS-LENS 62218 Pas-de-Calais **Map 5-B3**
♀⊗ **LE PRESIDENT** (N° RR MARS 27 221) (M. Noël **Fauer**) 7/9, rue de
⌂ Lille ☎ 21-78-51-95 ← 5. Closed Sun. Filling station nearby.

LOISY 54700 Meurthe-et-Moselle **Autoroute A-31 Maps 10-A1 and 14-B1**
♀⊗ **RESTAURANT DU RELAIS DE L'OBRION** (N° RR 1 821) Aire de Service de l'Obrion ☎ 83-81-18-89. **Minitel**. Restaurant: menu routier (served at all times). Self service. Open 6am–11pm. Rest. seats 140. Terraced garden. Shop. Newsagent. Photocopying. TV. Message facility. Showers.

LONDE DES MAURES (LA) 83250 Var **Map 25 A-3**
♀⊗ **LE PETIT BOIS** (N° RR JANV 27 755) (Mme Yvette **Bouvier**) route de Maramar ☎ 94-66-80-12. Restaurant: menu 55F. Open 7am–10.30pm. Parking for lorries. Filling station 600m.

LONGEAU-LE-VALLINOT 52600 Haute-Marne **RN 67 Map 14-A2**
♀⊗ **L'AUBERGE ROUTIERE – CHEZ PATRICIA** (N° RR MARS 27 576)
⌂ (Mme Patricia **Godart**) RN 74. Direction: Autoroute A-31, exit Langres Sud ☎ 25-88-42-16. German spoken. Restaurant: family cooking. Menu 45-90F. Children's menu. A la carte. Dinner 6–10.30pm. Closed Sun evening (low season). Credit cards accepted. Traditional décor. Rest. seats 50. Hotel ← 10 from 80–120F, with showers. Open 6am–11pm. Terraced garden. ⊢ Parking at beginning of village – 400m. Sights: Langres (10km), excavations at Andilly (30km), numerous lakes.
♀⊗ **LE CAFÉ DES ROUTIERS** (N° RR JUL 21 994) (Mme Edwige
⌂ **Denis**) Route Nationale 67 ☎ 25-88-40-51. **Minitel** ← 7. Closed Fri evening. Rest. seats 80. Evening meals until 10pm.

LONGUE 49160 Maine-et-Loire **RN 138 Map 12-A2**
♀⊗ **LE RELAIS DES SOUVENETS** (N° RR SEP 25 623) (Mme Réjane **Taugourdeau**) RN 147 ☎ 41-52-13-86. Closed Sat afternoon, Sun, end Aug.
♀⊗ **LE RELAX** (N° RR AVR 26 499) (M. Pascal **Desert**) 22, rue Michel-Couet ☎ 41-52-10-37. Dinner until midnight. Rest. seats 95.

LOUPLANDE

LONGUEAU 80330 Somme **RN 35 Map 5-A3**

�ⓧ **LE REALIS DE L'HOTEL DE VILLE** (N° RR SEP 23 944) (M.
⌂ Konider **Bellaredj**) 105, avenue Henri-Barbusse ☎ 22-46-16-14 ⇥
10. Closed Sun. English, Arabic spoken.

LORRIS 45260 Loiret **RD 961 Map 13-A1**

�ⓧ **LE RELAIS DES ROUTIERS** (N° RR OCT 27 039) (Société
Mathieu et Fils) 21, Grande Rue ☎ 38-92-40-64. Filling station
nearby, open 7am–8pm.

�ⓧ **AUBERGE DE LA CROIX ROUGE** (N° RR MAI 27 269) (Mme
⌂ Lisiane **Berlin**) 28, rue Guillaume de Lorris ☎ 38-92-87-03. Filling
station 700m.

�ⓧ **LA CHAUMIERE** (N° RR MAI 27 614) (Mme Huguette **Smethurst**)
97, Grande Rue ☎ 38-92-30-67. Restaurant: closed 15 days in Mar
and Sept. Parking.

LOUDEAC 22600 Côtes-du-Nord **Map 7-B2**

�ⓧ **LE STOP** (N° RR NOV 27 103) (M. Yves **Gicquel**) Le Haut-Breuil
☎ 96-28-01-76. English spoken. Restaurant: closed Sun. Filling
station nearby.

�ⓧ **☆☆ RESTAURANT LES ROUTIERS** (N° RR JANV 26 426) (M.
⌂ Dominique **Le Cozannet**) 7, rue Lavergne ☎ 96-28-01-44. Restaurant: regional and family cooking. Speciality: fruits de mer. Menu
40–50F. A la carte. Lunch 12–2.30pm. Dinner 7–9pm. Closed Sun,
Aug. Credit cards accepted. Rest. seats 240. Hotel ⇥ 40 from
68–120F with showers, bathroom, private WC, telephone. ⛏

LOUHANS 71500 Saône-et-Loire **RN 78 Map 18-B1**

�ⓧ **LES ROUTIERS** (N° RR MAR 18 031) (M. Michel **Alexandre**) 19, rue
Lucien Guillemot ☎ 85-75-11-75. Closed Sun, Aug. Rest. seats 65.

�ⓧ **L'AMI DES ROUTIERS** (N° RR JUIL 27 331) (M. Jean Marc
Levexier) 90, rue du Guidon ☎ 85-76-44-13. German spoken.
Restaurant: dinner until 11pm. Closed every other Fri (low
season), end Oct. Filling station on site, open 6am–midnight.

LOULAY 17300 Charente-Maritime **RN 150 Map 15-A2**

�ⓧ **CHEZ JO** (N° RR NOV 27 714) (M. Georges **Mandid**) 10, place du
⌂ General de Gaulle. Direction: Saint Jean d'Argély niort ☎
46-33-80-59. Shower and toilet facilities. Restaurant: family
cooking. Menu 45 and 50F (for tourists). Children's menu. Lunch
12–3pm. Dinner 7–9pm. Closed Sat. Traditional décor. Rest. seats
140. Hotel ⇥ 5 from 80–150F. Open 7am–9pm. Terraced garden.
Parking. Filling station nearby, open 8am–9pm. Sights: La Rochelle (40km)

�ⓧ **LE COUCOU** (N° RR MAI 26 536) (Mme Antoinette **Couturier**)
Tout-y-Faut Vergne ☎ 46-33-90-16. Closed Sat evening (low
season).

LOUPE (LA) 28240 Eure-et-Loir **RN 23 Map 8-B3**

�ⓧ **CHEZ BEATRICE – LA HURIE** (N° RR OCT 26 069) (Mme
Béatrice **Collin**) 23, La Hurie ☎ 37-81-30-38. Closed Sun. Evening
meals until 10.30pm. English spoken. Credit cards accepted.
Rest. seats 78. ⛏ Parking.

LOUPLANDE 72780 Sarthe **RN 768 Map 8-B2**

�ⓧ **LE RELAIS DE L'HOTEL DE FRANCE – LES ROUTIERS** (N° RR
⌂ MARS 11 344) (M. **Fretault**) 1, route de Sablé ☎ 43-88-52-18 ⇥ 5.
Closed Fri 1pm, Aug. Rest. seats 160.

LOUVIERS

LOUVIERS 27400 Eure **RN 154 Map 3-B1**
☿⊗ **LE RELAIS DES ROUTIERS** (N° RR MAR 23 714) (Mme **Quesney**)
13, rue de Paris ☎ 32-40-29-22. **Minitel**. Rest. seats 80. Evening
meals until 1am.

LUANT 36350 Indre **Map 16-A1**
☿⊗ **LE RELAIS DES ROUTIERS** (N° RR SEPT 27 376) (M. Jacky
Michaud) Lothiers ☎ 54-36-76-43. Filling station nearby.

LUBBON 40240 Landes **RD 933 Map 21-A2**
☿⊗ **CHEZ MAMY** (N° RR FEV 20 116) (M. Louis **Nicoletto**) ☎
⌂ 58-91-60-47. Italian spoken. Restaurant: regional and family
cooking. Specialities: confit et foie de canard, cèpes, poule
farcie. Menu 55F. Children's menu. À la carte. Lunch 12–3pm.
Dinner 7–9pm. Closed Sat evening, Oct. Credit cards accepted.
Traditional décor. Rest. seats 180. Hotel ⊷ 9 with shower. Open
5am–10pm. ⊮ Parking. Sights: thermal station at Barbotan, the
chocolate factory at Nérac.

LUCEAU 72500 Sarthe **RN 138 Map 12-A2**
☿⊗ **LA CROIX DE PAILLE** (N° RR OCT 24 744) (M. **Moreau**) route du
Mans Château du Loir ☎ 43-44-05-50. **Minitel**. Closed Sun except
for banquets, Aug. Meals served until 1am.

LUDE (LE) 72800 Sarthe **Map 12-A2**
☿⊗ **LE RELAIS DES PECHEURS** (N° RR DEC 23 061) (M. **Moire**) 14,
boulevard de l'Hospice ☎ 43-94-61-03. Closed Sun in winter.
Rest. seats 60. Evening meals until 8pm.

LUGNY 71260 Saône-et-Loire **Map 18-B1**
☿⊗ **LE PORTE DE BOURGOGNE** (N° RR 1827) (M. Loïc **Brasseur**
Aire de Saint Aubain La Salle. Direction: Paris/Lyon ☎ 85-33-19-
80.

LUMBRES 62380 Pas-de-Calais **Map 5-A2**
☿⊗ **HOTEL MODERNE** (N° RR SEPT 26 671) (M. Pierre **Fichaux**) 18,
rue Francois-Cousin opposite the station ☎ 21-39-62-87. Closed
Sun, Aug. Rest. seats 70. Evening meals until 9pm.

LUSIGNY-SUR-BARSE 10270 Aube **RN 19 Map 9-B3**
☿⊗ **AUBERGE DES PRAIRIES** (N° RR NOV 25 173) (Mme Monique
⌂ **Mireaux**) ☎ 25-41-20-32. **Minitel**. Restaurant: family cooking.
Menu 55F. À la carte. Dinner until 10pm. Credit cards accepted.
Rest. seats 50. Hotel ⊷ 5. Full-board 180F, half-board 140F. ⊮
Parking for lorries. Sights: Lake of La forêt d'Orient, the 9
churches at Troyes.

LUSSAC-LES-CHATEAUX 86320 Vienne **RN 147 Map 15-B1**
☿⊗ **LE CHENE VERT** (N° RR AVR 26 874) (Mme Alexandrine **Dos
Reis Martins**) 14, avenue Léon-Pineau ☎ 49-48-40-30. Closed
Sun. English, Italian, Spanish spoken. Rest. seats 60. Parking.
Filling station nearby, open 7am–midnight.

LUSSANT 17680 Charente-Maritime **CD 739 Map 11-B1**
☿⊗ **CHEZ MOI** (N° RR AOUT 26 983) (SARL **Guerin and Fils**) Le
⌂ Bourg ☎ 46-83-42-44 ⊷ 10. English spoken. Rest. seats 50.
Evening meals until 10pm.

LUTZ-EN-DUNOIS 28200 Eure-et-Loir **Map 8-B3**
♈⊗ **LA RENCONTRE** (N° RR JUIN 27 299) (M. Francis **Berrier**)
⌂ ☎ 37-45-18-08. Closed Sun, Feb. Filling station on site, open 5am–10pm.

LUZENAC-GARANOU 09250 Ariège **RN 20 Map 22-A3**
♈⊗ **LE RELAIS DES ROUTIERS** (N° RR DEC 24 041) (Mme Marie
⌂ **Pires**) avenue de la Gare. Direction: between Toulouse and Andorra ☎ 61-64-47-13. Spanish and Portuguese spoken. Restaurant: family cooking. Menu 53F. Lunch 12–2pm. Dinner until midnight. Closed Sat, Aug. Traditional décor. Rest seats 60. Hotel ⇥ 9 from 90–110F with showers, TV. Open 7am–midnight. ⊨ Parking for coaches.

LYON 69002 Rhône **RN 6 and 7 Maps 2-A2 and 18-B2**
♈⊗ **LES ROUTIERS** (N° RR JUL 21 983) (M. Pierre **Sala**) 21, quai Perrache ☎ 78-37-75-86. Closed Sat, Sun, Aug. Evening meals until 1am. Rest. seats 40.

MACHECOUL 44270 Loire-Atlantique **RN 11-B2**
♈⊗ **LA BICYCLETTE D'ARGENT** (N° RR JAN 27 504) (Mme. Marie-
⌂ Josephe **Baudry**) 6, place du Pont ☎ 40-78-50-48 ⇥ 9. Closed Sat afternoon, Sun afternoon, 18–25 Feb, 22 Dec–1 Jan. Evening meals until 9pm. Specialities: cuisses de poulet "bonne femme", roti à la saumuroise, omelette, "Arc en Ciel". Parking. English spoken. Tourist sites. Coaches welcome.

MAGNAC-BOURG 87380 Haute-Vienne **RN 20 Map 17-A1**
♈⊗ **LE RELAIS PARIS-TOULOUSE** (N° RR JUL 24 629) (M. **Meriadec**) ☎ 55-00-81-53. Closed Wed (except July, Aug). Coaches welcome. Rest. seats 35. Evening meals until 1am.

MAGNANAC par VILLEMUR-SUR-TARN 31340 Haute-Garonne **RN 630 Map 22-A2**
♈⊗ **CHEZ FRANÇOISE** (N° RR SEPT 26 331) (Mme **Rossi**) ☎
⌂ 61-09-01-87 or 61-09-32-72 ⇥ 4. Closed Fri, Sat evening, Sun, 1st 2 weeks Aug. Evening meals until 8pm. Coaches welcome. Rest. seats 85. Parking.

MAGNY-EN-VEXIN 95420 Val-d'Oise **Map 3-B2**
♈⊗ **HOTEL DE LA GARE** (N° RR OCT 24 737) 150 (Mme **Degoul Alves**) 65, rue de Beauvais ☎ 34-67-20-70. Full-board 150–160F per night with shower. Coaches welcome. Rest. seats 50. Evening meals until 10pm. Home cooking speciality: couscous. Menu à la carte ⇥ 10. Closed Sun. 23 Dec–1 Jan. Credit cards accepted. ⊨ Parking. Open 6am–10pm.

MAGNY-LA-CAMPAGNE 14270 Calvados **RD 40 Map 4-B2**
♈⊗ **A LA VALLÉE D'AUGE** – **Tobacconist** (N° RR AVR 21 502) (Mme Marie-Thérèse **Sevin**) ☎ 31-20-04-20. Restaurant closed Mar and Sept. Rest. seats 75.

MAINVILLIERS 28300 Eure-et-Loir **Map 8-B3**
♈⊗ **"L'ARCHE DE CHARTRES NORD"** Autoroute A11 (M. Thierry **Bart**) Aire de Chartres Gasville Sens Paris/Nantes direction ☎ 37-31-62-42.
♈⊗ **"L'ARCHE DE CHARTRES SUD"** RR 1814 (M. Christian **Sigler**) Aire de Chartres Bois-Paris Sens Nantes/Paris autoroute ☎ 37-31-62-41.

MAISON-NEUVE

MAISON-NEUVE Commune QUENOCHE-par-RIOZ 70190 Haute-Saône
RN 57 Maps 10-A3 and 14-B2/3
☿⊗ **LES ROUTIERS MAISON NEUVE** (N° RR MAY 27 596) (Mme
⌂ Chantal **Cartier-Villemin**) ☎ 84-91-80-54 ⚊ 7 60–120F. Closed Sat
and Christmas holidays. Full-board 135–160F per night. Evening
meals. Open 7am–9pm. Parking. Filling station 300m. Coaches
welcome.

MAISONS-LAFITTE 78600 Yvelines **Porte Maillot Map 1-A1**
☿⊗ **LE RALLYE** (N° RR FEV 23 650) (M. Jacques **Lalanne**) 17, rue des
Plantes ☎ 39-62-44-28. Closed Sun, Aug.

MAIZIERES LA GRANDE PAROISSE 10510 Aube **Map 9-B3**
☿⊗ **LE RELAIS DE POUSSEY** (N° RR FEV 27 522) (Mme Sylvaine
Gaillard) Z.1. La Glacière ☎ 25-24-27-96. **Minitel**. English speak-
ing. Restaurant: closed Sun. Open 5am–midnight. Services close.

MALAKOFF 92240 Hauts-de-Seine **RN 306 Map 1-B2**
☿⊗ **BAR LE DÉPART** (N° RR OCT 24 399) (M. Armand **Alle**) 64, avenue
Pierre Brossolette ☎ 46-57-76-05.

MALE 61260 Orne **RN 23 Map 8-B3**
☿⊗ **HOTEL DE LA BELLE RENCONTRE** (N° RR OCT 25 129) (M.
⌂ André **Carle**) **Le Gibet** between Nogent-Le-Rotrou and La
Ferté-Bernard ☎ 37-49-68-85. **Minitel** ⚊ 6 at 60–85F with TV.
Closed Sun (except for coaches, banquets) and August. Coaches
welcome. Rest. seats 130. Evening meals until 10pm. Open
6am–10pm. Home cooking. Menu 48F. Sights: château, Vallée du
Perche.

MALEMORT 19360 Corrèze **RN 89 Map 17-A1**
☿⊗ **CHEZ PAULETTE** (N° RR JAN 23 604) (Mme Paulette **Vegne**) 2,
avenue Pierre et Marie Curie ☎ 55-98-28-14. Closed Sun, Aug.
Coaches welcome. Rest. seats 90. ⌐ Regional home cooking. Menu
52F. Lunch 12–2.30pm. Dinner 7–8.30pm. Specialities: mique petit
salé, choux farci, paté de pomme de terre. Sights: Collonge la
Rouge, Tour de Brenige Malemont.

MALTAVERNE Commune de TRACY-LOIRE 58150 Nièvre **RN 7 Map
13-B2**
☿⊗ **LE RELAIS DES ROUTIERS** (N° RR OCT 24 007) (M. **Robillot**) ☎
58-28-15-34. Closed Sat afternoon, Sun, 10–31 Aug. Evening meals.

MANS (LE) 72100 Sarthe **RN 23 Map 8-B2**
☿⊗ **CHEZ GABY** (N° RR MARS 27 235) (Mme Marie-Thérèse **Cou-
table**) 8, rue du Pied-Sec ☎ 43-84-24-48. Closed Sat pm, Sun and
Aug. Home cooking. Dinner to midnight. Modern décor. Rest. seats
44. ⌐ Parking. Coaches welcome. Service station nearby.

☿⊗ **L'AUTO-CLUB** (N° RR JUN 23 340) (M. Rémy **Adet**) 239 bis, avenue
Bollée ☎ 43-84-70-73. Closed Sun and the week of Aug 15. Coaches
welcome. Rest. seats 60. Evening meals served until 9.30pm.

☿⊗ **LA BRISE** (N° RR JUIL 27 330) (Mme Marie-Madeleine **Boustouler**)
10, place de l'Eperon ☎ 43-28-20-52. Closed Sat. Service station
nearby.

164

MANTES-LA-JOLIE 78200 Yvelines **RN 13 Map 1-A1**
♈⊗ **LE NOVELTY** (N° RR AVR 27 586) (M. Joakim **Estevao**) 47, rue de la Papeterie ☎ 30-94-64-65. English, Spanish and Portuguese spoken.
♈⊗ **RESTAURANT DES AMIS** (N° RR AVR 27 585) (M. Jacques **Bression**) 48–50, rue Pierre Sémard ☎ 30-94-55-15.

MANTES-LA-VILLE 78200 Yvelines **RN 13 Map 1-A1**
♈⊗ **LA DEMI-LUNE** (N° RR DEC 26 129) (Mme Nicolas **Petitpas**) 51, boulevard Roger Salengro ☎ 34-77-03-66. Closed Sun. Dinner to 10.30pm.
♈⊗ **LE HOUDAN BAR** (N° RR AVR 23 747) (M. Mohamed **Benariba**) 43, route de Houdan ☎ 34-77-06-11. **Minitel**. Closed Sun. Meals served until 9pm.

MANTHELAN 37240 Indre-et-Loire **Map 12-B3**
♈⊗ **LE RELAIS DE LA CROIX-VERTE** (N° RR SEP 21 626) (Mme Christiane **Martin**) 25, rue Nationale ☎ 47-92-80-16. English spoken. Parking. Coaches welcome.

MARAIS (AUX) 60000 Oise **RN 181 Map 3-A2**
♈⊗ **AU GRAND "R"** (N° RR NOV 26 369) (M. Marcel **Boutoille**) 12, route de Gisors ☎ 44-48-18-66. **Minitel**. Closed Sat. evening Sun, Aug. Rest. seats 70. Evening meals until 9.30pm. Parking. Coaches welcome.

MARANS 17230 Charente-Maritime **Map 11-A1**
♈⊗ **LE POINT DU JOUR** Chez Sylviane et Joël (N° RR SEPT 27 675)
⌂ (Mme Sylviane **Gérard**) 2, rue des Moulins ☎ 46-01-10-38 ⊷ 5 Open 10pm. Services nearby.

MARBACHE 54820 Meurthe-et-Moselle **Map 14 B-1**
♈⊗ **LA MARMITE** (N° RR FEV 27 781) (Jean-Pierre and Laurence **Repiquet**) 136, rue Jean Jaurès ☎ 83-24-90-04. **Minitel**. English and Spanish spoken. Menu to 48F. Lunch 12–2.30pm. Dinner 7–9pm. Closed on Sun. Credit cards accepted. Parking. Coaches welcome. Service station 200m. Open 6.30am–8pm.

MARCHELEPOT 80200 Somme **Map 5-B3**
♈⊗ **HOTEL DU PARC** (N° RR MAR 24 531) (M. Dahmane **Houady**)
⌂ Route Nationale 17 ☎ 22-83-90-85 ⊷ 6.

MARCILY-LA-CAMPAGNE 27320 Eure **Map 8-A3**
♈⊗ **LE RELAIS EUROPEAN** (N° RR SEPT 27 382) (SNC Mme Sylvie **Fieneder**) Tivoly ☎ 32-58-31-75. Point phone 32-58-37. Closed Sat pm, Sun, Aug. English, German spoken. Home cooking. Rest. seats 100. Credit cards accepted. ⊶ Parking.

MARES (LES) 27160 Eure **RD 840 Map 8-A3**
♈⊗ **LE RELAIS DES MARES** (N° RR NOV 26 743) (M. **Guiot**) Le Chesne-Breteuil-sur-Iton ☎ 32-29-85-09. **Minitel**. Closed Sat pm, Sun. Coaches welcome. Rest. seats 30. Evening meals until midnight. Children's meals. Antique décor. ⊶ Parking. Coaches welcome.

MAREUIL SUR OURCQ 60890 Oise **Map 3-B3**
♈⊗ **LES ROUTIERS** (N° RR SEPT 22 927) (Mme Huguelte **Picard**) 7, rue de Meaux. Direction Soissons ☎ 23-96-72-11. **Minitel**. Home cooking. Dinner to 8pm. Rest. seats 20. ⊶ Parking.

MARGON

MARGON 28400 Eure-et-Loir **Map 8-B3**
♈⊗ **L'ESPÉRANCE** (N° RR OCT 26 360) (M. Marc **Robinet**) 20,
avenue de Paris, Nogent-le-Rotrou ☎ 37-52-19-03. **Minitel**. Evening meals served until 8.30pm. Closed Sun and Christmas.

MAROLLES par BROUE 28260 Eure-et-Loir **RN 12 Map 8-A3**
♈⊗ **AU RELAIS DE MAROLLES** (N° RR SEP 18 193) (Mme Viviane
⊶ **Beauvais**) 44, rue Georges-Bréant ☎ 37-43-20-50. Closed Sat, Sun
(except for banquets), 1st fortnight Aug. Coaches welcome. 3
dining rooms, 200 seats. Evening meals until midnight. Specialities: escalope Normande, omelette aux pleurotte, grills. Menu
55–85F.

MAROLLES-SUR-SEINE 77130 Seine-et-Marne **RN 51 Map 9-B2**
♈⊗ **AU RENDEZ-VOUS DES PECHEURS ET DES CHASSEURS** (N°
RR NOV 19 566) (Mme **Bodic**) 70, Grande Rue ☎ 64-31-32-20.
Closed Sun. Evening meals to 8.30pm.

MAROLLETTE 72600 Sarthe **Map 8-B2**
♈⊗ **LE RENDEZ-VOUS DES CHASSEURS** (N° RR SEPT 26 038) (M.
Norbert and Colette **Vaidie**) Le Bourg ☎ 43-97-67-00. Closed
Tue pm, Aug. Coaches welcome. Rest. seats 80. Evening meals
until 10pm.

MARQUEFAVE 31390 Haute-Garonne **RN 117 Map 22-A2**
♈⊗ ☆ **NN LE RELAIS CHEZ ROGER** (N° RR JUL 13 851) (M. Roger
⌂ **Descuns**) Route Nationale 117 ☎ 61-87-85-07 ⚊ 10 from 60–80F.
Access for disabled. Closed Sun, Oct. Evening meals. Car park.
Bar. ⊨ Recreations: fishing, shooting. Sports: pétanque.

MARSAN 32270 Gers **RN 124 Map 21-B2**
♈⊗ **RELAIS 124** (N° RR SEPT 26 990) (M. Fernand **Castaing**) Aubiet
☎ 62-65-63-43. **Minitel**. Closed Sat, Sun, 1 week in Aug and Dec.
English spoken. Evening meals served until 11pm. Filling station
nearby. Regional home cooking. Children's menu. Credit cards
accepted. Rest. seats 80. Terrace. ⊨ Parking.

MARSAS 33620 Gironde **Map 15-A3**
♈⊗ **LE TOURIN** (N° RR SEPT 27 659) (M. Daniel **Leclerc**) rte de
Libourne ☎ 57-68-08-04. Closed Sun. Parking. Filling station
nearby, open 24hrs.

MARSEILLAN PLAGE 35340 Hérault **Map 23-B2**
♈⊗ **LE CREOLE** (N° RR OCT 27 695) (M. Gilles **Lepinette**) 5, avenue
de la Méditerranée (from the square take the road to the sea
500m on right) ☎ 67-21-98-25. Showers (for drivers). English
spoken. Regional home cooking. Menu 50–120F. Children's
menu. Dinner to 10pm. Closed Wed from Nov to March. Credit
cards accepted. Rest. seats 30. ⊨ Phone point. Filling station
nearby, open from 7am–10pm. Sights: Ville grecque (6km),
Minerve – medieval town (45km), Pézenas (20km).

MARSEILLE 13016 Bouches-du-Rhône **RN 8 Map 24-B3**
♈⊗ **LE RELAIS DE L'INDEPENDANCE** (N° RR JAN 27 754) (M. René
Cataldo) 234, boulevard de Paris ☎ 91-91-21-89. Closed Sun.
Spanish/Italian spoken. Open 5.30am–11pm. Menu 48F. Coaches.
Parking.

♈⊗ **LE RELAIS DES AMIS** (N° RR JUN 15 693) (M. Raymond **Servière**) 188, boulevard de Paris ☎ 91-62-60-76. **Minitel.** Closed Sun, public holidays (without res.), Aug. Coaches welcome. Rest. seats 60. Evening meals to 9.30pm. Menu 32F. Choice of 8 dishes.

♈⊗ **AUX DELICES DE MOUREPIANE** (N° RR OCT 25 136) (M. Daniel **Barnabon**) 578, chemin du Littoral ☎ 91-46-08-11. Closed Sun. Coaches welcome. Rest. seats 100. Evening meals served until 11pm. Italian spoken.

♈⊗ **LE RELAIS** (N° RR OCT 26 342) (Mlle **Commeau**) 40, quai du Lazaret ☎ 91-90-93-02. Closed Sat, Sun, last 2 weeks in Aug. Coaches welcome. Rest. seats 80. Evening meals served until 11pm. Home cooking.

♈⊗ ☆ **NN BEAULIEU-GLARIS** (N° RR NOV 27 085) (M. Yvon **Garros**)
⌂ 1/3 place des Marseillaises ☎ 91-90-70-59. **Minitel** ⊷ 36 100–230F with showers, private WC, tel. Closed Sat and Sun (hotel always open). English and Arabic spoken. Home cooking. Menu 39–65F. Lunch 11.30–2pm. Dinner 7–9pm. Credit cards accepted. Rest. seats 48. ⊬

MARTIGNE-FERCHAUD 35640 Ille-et-Vilaine **RN 178 Maps 8-B1 and 12-A1**

♈⊗ **LE POT D'ETAIN** (N° RR JAN 10 229) (Mme Yvonne **Bouteiller**)
⌂ 10, Grand Rue ☎ 99-47-90-1. ⊷ 8. Rest. seats 25. Home cooking. Antique décor.

MARTINCAMP 76270 Seine-Maritime **RD 915 Map 3-A1**

♈⊗ **RELAIS DE LA FORET D'EAWY** (N° RR DEC 26 404) (M. Michel **Yon**) Neufchâtel-en-Bray ☎ 35-93-07-03. Closed Wed, end Aug. Coaches welcome. Rest. seats 50. English spoken.

MARVEJOLS 48100 Lozère **RN 9 Map 17-B3**

♈⊗ **NN REST DE LA PAIX** (N° RR NOV 26 735) (M. Jean-Jacques
⌂ **Bourguignon**) 2, avenue Brazza ☎ 66-32-10-17 ⊷ 19. English, Spanish spoken. Rest. seats 70. Evening meals served until 9pm.

MARZAN 56130 Morbihan **Map 11-A2**

♈⊗ **LES RIVES DE VILAINE** (N° RR OCT 27 393) (M. Gilles **Jouan**) 13, rue de la Fontaine ☎ 99-90-63-22. **Minitel.** Evening meals served 6.45–8.30pm. Specialities: fruits de mer, poisson (on request). Menu 38–57F. Children's menu. Lunch 11.45–2.30pm. Credit cards accepted. Rest. seats 100. Terraced garden. ⊬ Parking. Coaches welcome. Filling station nearby. Sights: Zoo de Branféré (18km), Darzal dam (6km), La Roche Bernarnd (2km).

MASSERET 19510 Corrèze **RN 20 Map 17-A1**

♈⊗ **LE RELAIS DES VOYAGEURS** (N° RR NOV 27 460) (M. Michel
⌂ **Pons**) Route Nationale 20 towards Brivie, 1st right entering town ☎ 55-73-40-11. **Minitel.** Closed Mon. Evening meals. Credit cards accepted. Antique décor. Rest. seats 80 ⊷ 6 at 90–170F with shower. Regional home cooking. Speciality: corrèziennes. Menu 50–180F. Children's menu. À la carte. Lunch 12–3pm. Dinner 7–11pm. Filling station 250m. Sights: Plan d'eau (2km).

MASSEUBE 32140 Gers **RN 129 Map 21-B2/3**

♈⊗ **CHEZ YVETTE** (N° RR JUN 12 898) (Mme Yvette **Beyries**) Route Nationale 129 ☎ 62-66-02-14. Closed Sun and Aug. Dinner to 8pm.

MATHIEU

MATHIEU 14920 Calvados **RD 7 Map 4-B2**
♈⊗ **RELAIS LA COTE DE NACRE** (N° RR OCT 26 068) (M. Marc
Bedeau de l'Ecochère) 4, rue Auguste-Fresnel ☎ 31-44-10-17 ⊷
2. Closed Sun and 15 days in Dec. Home cooking. Menu 45–55F.
Evening meals to 9pm. Antique décor. Coaches welcome. Rest.
seats 38.

MAUBEUGE 59600 Nord **RN 2 Map 6-A3**
♈⊗ **AUX ARCADES Chez Ginette** (N° RR AVR 26 522) (M. Claude
⌂ **Spittel**) 260, route de Mons ☎ 27-64-60-97 ⊷ 8. Closed Sun
afternoon. Rest. seats 45. Evening meals until 2am.

MAUBOURGUET 65700 Hautes-Pyrénées **Map 21-A2**
♈⊗ **RELAIS DES AUTOBUS** (N° RR FEV 26 185) (Mme Nicole **Dauba**)
67, place de la Libération ☎ 62-96-38-78. **Minitel**. Bar open every
day. Restaurant closed Sat evening, Sun.

MAURIAC 15200 Cantal **RD 678 Map 17-B2**
♈⊗ ☆ **LES ROUTIERS** (N° RR NOV 26 744) (**SARL Laroche Rongier**)
⌂ 27, rue St-Mary ☎ 71-68-00-79 ⊷ 10. Closed Fri evening. English
spoken. Rest. seats 60. Evening meals served until 10pm.

MAY-SUR-ORNE 14320 Calvados **RD 562 Map 4-B2**
♈⊗ **L'AMMONITE** (N° RR DEC 26 119) (M. Jean-Claude **Horel**) 2, rue
⌂ du Canada. Direction: main road to Caen/Flers. ☎ 31-79-80-27.
Minitel ⊷ 8. 100–145 F. Rest. seats 106. Regional home cooking.
Menu 48–109F. Children's menu. À la carte. Lunch 11.45–2pm.
Dinner 7.30–11.30pm. Closed Sun in winter, 17 Aug–8 Sept, 2nd
week Aug. Credit cards accepted. Antique décor. Terraced
garden. ⌁ Parking. Coaches welcome. Sights: Vallée de L'Orne,
Suisse Normande, landing beach, routes des fromage.

MAYENNE 53100 Mayenne **RN 162 and 823-12 Map 8-B1**
♈⊗ **LE RELAIS L'ESCALE** (N° RR JUN 20 742) (Dominique **Fortin**)
⌂ route du Mans 2, rue Colbert ☎ 43-04-19-14 ⊷ 13. Closed Sat
afternoon, Sun. Evening meals until 8.30pm. Rest. seats 142.

MAZERES 33210 Gironde **RD 932 Map 20-B1 & 21-A1**
♈⊗ **LE PASSAGER** (N° RR AVR 18 665) (M. Serge **Garrigues**) route
de Pau ☎ 56-63-15-22. Closed Sat, Sun, 2 weeks Aug. Evening
meals to 11pm. Some English, German, Spanish spoken. Parking.
Coaches welcome.

MAZINGARBE 62670 Pas-de-Calais **RN 43 Map 5-A1**
♈⊗ **AU RELAIS DES ROUTIERS** (N° RR AVR 20 444) (Mme Gene-
viève **Marcinkowski**) 85, Route Nationale 43 ☎ 21-72-00-09.
Closed Sun, Aug. Rest. seats 50. Polish, German spoken.

MEDE (LA) 13220 Bouches-du-Rhône **RN 568 Map 24-A/B3**
♈⊗ **L'ARC EN CIEL** (N° RR JUL 26 949) (Mme Marie **Courevellis**) 5A,
⌂ avenue Mirabeau ☎ 42-07-04-38 ⊷ 5. Spanish, Greek spoken.

MEES 40180 Landes **RN 124 Map 20-A2**
♈⊗ **L'OREE DU BOIS** (N° RR OCT 26 067) (M. Jean-Paul **Gueffier**)
Route de Bayonne ☎ 58-97-57-77. Closed Sun.

MEGEVE 74120 Haute-Savoie **RN 212 Map 19-B2**

♀⊗ ☆☆ **NN LE CHALET DES FLEURS** (N° RR JAN 17 730) (M.
⌂⇆ Georges **Roussel**) route de Sallanches au Pont d'Arbon. 1st
building on left entering town ☎ 50-21-21-46 ⇥ 26 with showers,
baths, WC, tel, from 135–260F. Breakfast 25F. Open 7am–11pm.
Closed 15 Sept–20 Dec, 15 Apr–15 June. Credit cards accepted.
Antique décor. Coaches welcome. Rest. seats 105. Evening meals.
English spoken. Car park. Bar. ⚲ Recreations: miniature golf,
playground. Menus 80–150F. Home cooking. Specialities: truite à
la creme et aux amande. Children's menu. À la carte. Lunch
12–2pm. Dinner 7.30–11.30pm. Sights: lakes, Mont Blanc, Annecy.

MELGVEN 29140 Finistère **Map 7-B1**

♀⊗ **KERAMPAOU** (N° RR AVR 23 771) (**SARL Mevellec**) ☎ 98-97-90-
18. Closed Sun morning. Video. Coaches welcome. HGV parking. Cable TV.

MELLAC 29300 Finistère **Map 7-B2**

♀⊗ **LE MARLI** (N° RR AVR 27 267) (M. Rodolphe **Dupart**) Z.A. de
Keringant ☎ 98-39-31-97. **Minitel**. Closed Sun am. Meals served
until 10pm. Filling station nearby.

MENIL-BROUT (LE) par DAMIGNI 61250 Orne **RN 12 Map 8-A/B2**

♀⊗ **LE RELAIS A LA BONNE FRANQUETTE** (N° RR AVR 14 764)
(Mme **Castelier**) ☎ 33-27-10-03. Auberge rurale. Closed Sat, Sun,
Aug. Coaches welcome. Parking.

MENTON 06500 Alpes-Maritimes **Map 25-B2**

♀⊗ **RAPID BAR** (N° RR FEV 27 783) (M. Alexandrie **Pérucchini**) 63,
avenue Cernuschi ☎ 93-35-93-69. Menu from 60F. Lunch 11.30–
2.30pm. Dinner 7.30–11.30pm. Closed Sun (restaurant only).
English and Italian spoken. Parking. Coaches welcome. Filling
station 1km.

MERCUREY 71640 Saône-et-Loire **RD 978 Map 18-A1**

♀⊗ ☆ **LE MERCUREY** (N° RR AUG 27 372) (Mme Roseline **Goy**)
⌂ Grande Rue ☎ 85-45-13-56. ⇥ 8 from 90–130F. German and
English spoken. Evening meals served until 11pm. Rest. seats 50.
Filling station opposite. Open 8am–7pm.

MERY-SUR-CHER 18100 Cher **RN 76 Map 13-B1**

♀⊗ **LE RELAIS BERRY-SOLOGNE** (N° RR NOV 16 762) (M. Claude
⌂ **Carré**) route de Tours ☎ 48-75-20-34 ⇥ 10 with showers and
baths. Closed Sat, Sun. Restaurant: home cooking. Credit cards
accepted. Terraced garden. Parking. Coaches welcome. Sights:
châteaux de la Loire.

MESGRIGNY 10170 Aube **RN 19 and CD 373 Map 9-B2/3**

♀⊗ **LA BELLE ÉTOILE** (N° RR FEB 27 196) (Mme Sylvie **Schmutz**)
Méry-sur-Seine ☎ 25-21-15-70. **Minitel**. English and German
spoken. Dinner to 11pm. Rest. seats 30. Parking. Coaches
welcome. Filling station 3km, open 7am–11pm.

MESNIL-DURAND 14140 Calvados **RD 579 Map 4-B2**

♀⊗ **LE RELAIS DE LA FORCE** (N° RR JUL 23 881) (M. Roger
Cardonnel) Les Forges Mézières ☎ 31-63-52-79. **Minitel**. Closed
Sun, Aug. German spoken. Coaches welcome. Rest. seats 120.
Evening meals served until 10pm.

MESSIA-SUR-SORNE

MESSIA-SUR-SORNE 39570 Jura **RN 83 Map 19-A1**

♍⊗ **LA CHARMILLE** (N° RR JANV 22 618) (M. Patrick **Vaucher**) 570, route de Lyon Lons-le-Saunier ☎ 84-24-65-92. Closed Sun. English spoken. Home cooking. Menu 50F. Lunch 12–2pm. Rest. seats 41. Terraced garden. ⊨ Parking for cars. Antique décor. Sights: Les Grottes de Baume, les Cascades de Hérisson, le pont de la Pyle.

MEYLIEU 42210 Loire **RN 82 Map 18-B2**

♍⊗ **LES OMBRELLES** (N° RR SEPT 26 661) (M. Christian **Chadrin**) Montrond-Les-Bains ☎ 77-54-52-44. Closed Sat, Sun and 1st 2 weeks in Aug. English spoken. Coaches welcome. Rest. seats 32. Evening meals served until 10pm.

MEYTHET 74960 Haute-Savoie **Map 19-A2**

♍⊗ **NN LES ROUTIERS** (N° RR OCT 27 693) (M. Claude Gallay
⌂ **Garachan**) 22, route de Frangy ☎ 50-22-02-93. Closed Sun, Christmas to New Year and in May. English and German spoken. Coaches welcome. Rest. seats 65. Evening meals served until 10pm ⊷ 17 at 120–150F. Filling station nearby.

MEYZIEU 69330 Rhône **2 A-2**

♍⊗ **BRASSERIE DE L'INDUSTRIE** (N° RR OCT 27 694) (M. Gérard **Dumont**) 104, rue de la République ☎ 78-31-78-31. Restaurant: dinner to 9pm. Closed Aug. Parking. Coaches welcome. Filling station nearby.

MEZE 34140 Hérault **RN 113 Map 23 A/B2**

♍⊗ **LE MARSEILLAIS** (N° RR NOV 26 109) (M. Willie **Rennie**) 8, avenue de Montpellier ☎ 67-43-81-29. Closed Sun (out of season). Rest. seats 160. Evening meals. English spoken.

♍⊗ **LA VITARELLE II** (N° RR AUT 27 261) (M. Daniel **Garcia**) Route Nationale 113. Directions towards Beziers 2km after exit ☎ 67-43-95-70 and 67-43-53-89 ⊷ 3. Closed Sun evening. English, Spanish and Italian spoken. Evening meals served until midnight. Regional family cooking. Specialities: fruits de mer (on request) bouillabaisse. Menu 60–110F. Children's menu. À la carte. Credit cards accepted. Rest. seats 200. Open 6am–12pm. Rest room. Garden terrace. ⊨ Parking. Coaches welcome. Filling station 3km. Sights: Mèze (2km), Sète (15km), Cap d'Agde (18km).

MEZEL 04270 Alpes-de-Haute-Provence **RD 207 Map 25-A2**

♍⊗ ☆ **NN LE RELAIS DE LA PLACE** (N° RR JUL 22 884) (Mme
⌂ Christiane **Sarracanie**) Place Victor-Arnaux ☎ 92-35-51-05. **Minitel** ⊷ 11 110–150F. Open 7am–12pm. Closed Mon (except July, Aug, Sept), Dec. Full-board. Regional home cooking. Menu 55–70F. Children's menu. À la carte. Coaches welcome. Rest. seats 80. Evening meals served until 9pm. Credit cards accepted. Rest room. Garden terrace. ⊨ Parking. Sights: Gorge de Verdun, Col d'Allos, Lac de Sainte Croix.

MÉZÉRIAT 01660 Ain **RN 79 Map 18-B1**

♍⊗ **RELAIS DE MÉZÉRIAT** (N° RR NOV 27 111) (M. Alain **Darbon**) Les Pigots ☎ 74-30-25-87. Closed Sat and Sun evenings, 15 days in Aug, 1 week Dec. Coaches welcome. Rest. seats 60. Evening meals served until 10pm. Regional cooking. Speciality: grenouilles, poulet à la crème. Menu 60–135F. Children's menu. À la carte. Antique décor. Garden terrace. Parking. Filling station 2km.

MEZIERES EN BRENNE 36290 Indre **Map 12-B3**

⚓⊗ **RESTAURANT DES SPORT** (N° RR JUL 27 643) (M. Christian
⌂ **Charpentier**) 11, rue de l'Ouest ☎ 54-38-11-62 ⊷ 6 with showers.
Filling station nearby.

MEZIERES-SUR-ISSOIRE 87330 Haute-Vienne **RN 151 Bis Maps 15-B2
and 16-B1**

⚓⊗ **HOTEL DES VOYAGEURS** (N° RR MARS 25 341) (Mme Odette
⌂ **Daganaud**) ☎ 55-68-34-47 ⊷ 5. Closed Sun, Oct. Coaches
welcome. Rest. seats 180.

MILLAU 12100 Aveyron **RN 9 Map 23-A1**

⚓⊗ **LES TILLEULS** (N° RR DEC 26 406) (M. Jean **Vernhet**) 17, avenue
Martel ☎ 65-60-43-98. Closed Sun, last 2 weeks Sept.

MILLIÈRES 50190 Manche **Map 4-B1**

⚓⊗ **LE RELAIS DES TOURISTES** (N° RR SEPT 27 381) (M. Gérard
Lunel) La Bézenterie. Direction, between Perriers and Lensay.
☎ 33-46-71-12. Closed Sun. English spoken. Evening meals
served until 9pm. Home cooking. Specialities: coq à la bière ou
au vin. Children's menu. Credit cards accepted. Garden terrace.
⊷ Parking. Coaches welcome. Filling station nearby. Sights: St
Lo (20km), Lessaye (4km), cheese making (3km), ham smoking
factory (tasting).

MIMIZAN 40200 Landes **RN 626 Map 20-A2**

⚓⊗ **AUBERGE LE GRAIN DE SEL** (N° RR DEC 27 741) (Mme Jeanine
⌂ **Mansiet**) 28, avenue de la Plage Bel Air ☎ 58-09-17-20. Restaurant.
Specialities: confit de canard (48F), brochette de coeur canard
(50F). Menu 50F (menu routiers) and 65F (menu à la carte). Dinner
to 9pm. Closed Sun. Hotel ⊷ 2 50–60F per person. Parking.
Coaches welcome. Filling station nearby, open 8am–10pm.

⚓⊗ **RELAIS DUCOURT** (N° RR MARS 26 475) (Mme Françoise
⌂ **Bricard**) 20, avenue de la Plage ☎ 58-82-42-37. **Minitel** ⊷ 35.
Closed Sun off season. Rest. seats 80. Evening meals.

MINIAC MORVAN 35540 Ille-et-Vilaine **Map A-3**

⚓⊗ **RELAIS DE LA GARE** (N° RR MARS 27 571) (Mme Marie-
⌂ Thérèse **Termet**) La Costardais ☎ 99-58-58-14 ⊷ 9 at 110–200F.

MIONNAY 01390 Ain **RN 83 Map 2-A2**

⚓⊗ **LE RELAIS BRESSAN** (N° RR MAI 26 550) (Mme Monique **Millet
Desmaris**) Route Nationale 83 ☎ 78-91-82-22. Closed Sat, Sun and
2 weeks Aug, 1 week in Dec.

MIRAMAS 13140 Bouches-du-Rhône **RN 569 Map 24-A3**

⚓⊗ **LE RELAIS** (N° RR DEC 25 762) (Mme **Bouvier**) 72, avenue
Charles de Gaulle ☎ 90-58-05-89. **Minitel**. Closed Sun. Coaches
welcome. Rest. seats 90. Home cooking. Specialities: paella,
couscous, lasagne. Lunch 12–2.30pm. Dinner 7–10pm. Garden
terrace. Parking. Sights: les Baux de Provence.

MIRAMONT-DE-GUYENNE 47800 Lot-et-Garonne **CD 933 Map 21-B1**

⚓⊗ ☆☆ **NN LE RELAIS DE GUYENNE** (N° RR NOV 27 097) (Mme
⌂ Raymonde **Rodes**) Route de Paris Saint-Pardoux-Isaac ☎ 53-93-
20-76. Closed Sat. Spanish and Italian spoken. Dinner to 10pm.
Rest. seats 100 ⊷ 8. Parking. Coaches welcome. Filling station
nearby, open 6am–10pm.

MITRY-MORY

MITRY-MORY 77290 Seine-et-Marne **Map 1-A3**

♈⊗ **LE RELAIS DE MITRY** (N° RR FEV 27 197) (Mme Josiane **Thyphonnet**) 3, rue Paul-Vallant-Courturier ☎ 64-27-11-61 and 64-27-32-79. **Minitel**. Closed 15 Jul–15 Aug. Modern décor. Rest. seats 50. ⟜ Parking for cars.

MODANE 73500 Savoie **RN 6 Map 19-B3**

♈⊗ **LA CROIX DU SUD** (N° RR JUL 26 599) (M. Bernard **Mestrallet**)
⌂ La Praz ☎ 79-05-34-47. Closed Sun, Aug. Italian spoken ⟜ 6. Coaches welcome. Rest. seats 120. Evening meals served until midnight. Bar open until 2am.

♈⊗ **LE RESTOPORT DU FREJUS** (N° RR OCT 27 412) (Joana S.A. M Starras **Stauridis**) Autoport du Frejus Le Freney. Directions: RN 6, 5km before the tunnel du Fréjus ☎ 79-05-29-98. Fax 79-05-14-83. **Minitel**. Closed Sun. English, Greek and Italian spoken. Restaurant. Regional home cooking. Menu à la carte. Self-service. Credit cards accepted. Rest. seats 150. Rest room. ⟜ Parking. Coaches welcome. Currency facilities. Filling station 100m, open 24 hours.

MOIDIEU-DETOURBE 38440 Isère **RD 502 Map 2-B2**

♈⊗ **CHEZ DÉDÉ** (N° RR OCT 26 079) (M. André **Seigle**) St-Jean-de-Bournay. Direction: Route de Vienne/Grenoble ☎ 74-58-13-02. Closed 15–30 Aug. Evening meals served until 10pm. Home cooking. Coaches welcome. Rest. seats 40. Parking.

MOIRANS 38430 Isère **RN 85 Maps 18-B3, 19-A3 and 24-B1**

♈⊗ **LE VIADUC** (N° RR JUL 27 319) (M Ferland **Barral-Poulet**) 4,
⌂ route de Grenoble ☎ 76-35-31-01 ⟜ 4. Closed Sat, Sun. Evening meals served until midnight. Rest. seats 25. Filling station nearby, open 5.30am–10pm.

MOISSAC 82200 Tarn-et-Garonne **RD 127 Maps 21-B2 and 22-A1**

♈⊗ ☆ **NN LE RELAIS AUVERGNAT** (N° RR AOU 15 344) (M. Jacques
⌂ **Ginisty**) 31, boulevard Camille-Delthil place du Palais. Direction: centre of town (A9) ☎ 63-04-02-58 or 63-04-93-02 ⟜ 10 100–160F (with bath). Closed Sun evening. Full-board 160–180F per night. Rest. seats 75. Meals served until 11pm. Menus 50–80F. Home cooking. Specialities: cassoulet, confit, grillade. Children's menu. À la carte. Spanish spoken. ⟜ Parking cars. Credit cards accepted. Sights: Boudou, Montauban (30km), cathedral, museum.

MOLINET 03510 Allier **RN 79 Map 16-A3 and 18-A1**

♈⊗ **LES ARCADES CHEZ YOYO** (N° RR AVR 25 876) (Mme Anne-Marie **Fongarnand**) Moulins ☎ 85-53-15-18. **Minitel**. Closed Sat afternoon and Sun. Rest. seats 24. Parking for HGV.

MOLOMPIZE 15500 Cantal **RN 588 Map 17-A3**

♈⊗ **LE RELAIS DU CENTRE** (N° RR AVR 18 067) (Mme Marie-Louise
⌂ **Filliat**) ☎ 71-73-61-97 ⟜ 12. Closed Sat, Sun, part of Nov. Rest. seats 30.

MONASTIER (LE) 48100 Lozère known locally as LES AJUSTONS **RN 9 Map 17-B3 and 23-A1**

♈⊗ ☆ **NN LE RELAIS DES AJUSTONS** (N° RR MAR 20 128) (M. Guy
⌂ **Gibelin**) crossroads of Nationales 9 and 88 ☎ 66-32-70-35. ⟜ 27 80–150F. Breakfast from 16F. Closed Sat, Sun in winter, 18 Dec–18 Jan. Coaches welcome. Rest. seats 80. Fishing local. ⟜ Sights: Gorges du Tarn, Aubrac.

MONT DE MARSAN

MONDAVEZAN 31220 Haute-Garonne **RN 117 Map 21-B3**
☖ **LA FERMIERE** (N° RR MARS 26 488) (Mme Alexine **Ferrage**) RN 117 ☎ 61-97-01-52 ⊷ 16. Closed Sun.

MONDOUBLEAU 41170 Loir-et-Cher **Map 8-B3**
☖ **HOTEL DE LA GARE** (N° RR MAI 23 297) (M. Gérard **Lucas**) 6, rue de la Gare ☎ 54-80-90-59 ⊷ 6.Closed Sat, Aug. Evening meals to 8pm. Rest. seats 90.

MONESTIER DE CLERMONT 38650 Isère **RN 75 situated 30 km South of Grenoble Map 19-A3 et 24-B1**
☖ **REST DU NORD** (N° RR JUN 26 905) (M. Michel **Capogna**) 44, Grande Rue ☎ 76-34-03-75. Closed Sun, 23 Dec–1 Jan. Dinner to 10pm. Filling station nearby.

MONETAU 89470 Yonne **RD 84 Map 13-A2**
☖ **AU RENDEZ-VOUS DES PECHEURS** (N° RR AVR 22 751) (M. R. **Gaufillet**) 14, rue d'Auxerre ☎ 86-40-63-32 ⊷ 6. Closed Sun, Aug. Rest. seats 128. Evening meals. Spanish spoken.

MONLET near d'ALLEGRE 43270 Haute-Loire **RD 13 Map 17-A3**
☖ ☆ **NN LE ROULIS** (N° RR FEV 20 650) (M. Pierre **Marec**) ☎ 71-00-73-54. Closed Oct ⊷ 10 from 60–98F. Coaches welcome. Rest. seats 100. English spoken. Menu 48–55F. Children's menu. Dinner to 9pm. Home cooking. Specialities: champignons à la crème, potée auvergnate. Car park. Bar. ⚑ Recreations: pétanque. Sights: Richard's Windmill (Ambert), châteaux, lakes, forests.

MONNAI 61470 Orne **RN 138 Map 8-A2**
☖ **LE RELAIS DU CHEVAL BAI** (N° RR JAN 7 428) (M. Gilbert **Roussel**) Route Nationale 138 ☎ 33-39-42-00. **Minitel** ⊷ 6. Closed Sun, 15 Nov–15 Feb. Coaches welcome. Rest. seats 110. Evening meals until 11pm.

MONNAIE 37380 Indre-et-Loire **RN 10 Map 12-A3**
☖ **GRILL DE TOURAINE** (N° RR 1841) (M. Jean-Jacques **Bigot**) Aire de Tours, La Longue Vue Sens Paris/Bordeaux autoroute ☎ 47-56-44-94.
☖ **L'ARCHE DE TOURS** (N° RR 2028) (M. Christophe **Ozenne**) Aire de Tours, Val de Loire Sens Bordeaux/Paris autoroute ☎ 47-56-15-49.

MONT-A-LA-QUESNE par BRIX 50700 Manche **RN 13 Map 4-A1**
☖ **LES CLOS NORMAND** (N° RR SEPT 26 628) (Mme **Germain**) ☎ 33-41-94-35. Evening meals.

MONT CRESSON 45700 Loiret **Map 13-A2**
☖ **BAR DE L'ETOILE** (N° RR OCT 27 410) (Mme Gisèle **Dicicco**) 16, rue de Verdun ☎ 38-90-00-50. **Minitel**. Evening meals to 9pm. Home cooking. Menu à la carte. Credit cards accepted. Rest. seats 50. Parking. Coaches welcome. Filling station nearby.

MONT DE MARSAN 40000 Landes **Maps 20-B2 and 21-A1**
☖ **BARDES SPORTS** (N° RR FEV 24 508) (Mme Josiane **Ledoux**) Place des Arènes ☎ 58-75-05-08. Regional home cooking. Menu 47–60F. Lunch 12–2pm. Dinner 7–11pm. Closed Sun. Rest. seats 60 ⊷ 20. Spanish spoken.

MONT SOUS VAUDREY

MONT SOUS VAUDREY 39380 Jura **Map 14-A3**
Ⓧ **HOTEL DU CENTRE CHEZ COLETTE** (N° RR JUN 24 259) (M.
Maurice **Creusot**) 1, rue Jules Grevy ☎ 84-71-71-94. **Minitel**.
Restaurant: dinner to 10pm. Closed Mon, 15–30 May and 20
Oct–11 Nov. Rest. seats 50 ← 7.

MONT ST MICHEL (LE) 50170 Manche **Map 7-A3 and 8-A1**
Ⓧ **LES CAMPINGS DU MONT-SAINT-MICHEL La Rôtisserie** (N°
RR AVR 15 191) (M. Phillipe **François**) locally The Caserne BP8
☎ 33-60-09-33. **Minitel**. Dinner to 9pm. Closed 15 Nov–1 Feb.
Rest. seats 480 ← 83. English and German spoken.

MONTAIGUT-EN-COMBRAILLE 63700 Puy-de-Dôme **Map 16-B2**
Ⓧ **CHEZ CLAUDINE** (N° RR AUG 27 355) (Mme Claudine **Legrand**)
Rue de la Chapelle ☎ 73-85-15-32. Closed Wed afternoon,
June/July. Evening meals served until 10pm. Rest. seats 40.
Parking. Coaches welcome. Filling station nearby, open 7am–
9pm.

MONTANDON 25190 Doubs **Map 10-A3**
Ⓧ **LE GRAND CLOS** (N° RR DEC 26 418) (Mme Martine **Lepeme**)
Saint-Hippolyte ☎ 81-96-51-12 ← 6 90–120F with showers, WC.
German spoken. Home cooking. Menu 42F. Menu à la carte.
Dinner to 10pm. Closed on Sat. Credit cards accepted. Tradi-
tional décor. Rest. seats 50. Open 7am–11pm. Garden terrace. ⌒
Parking. Coaches welcome. Sights: château (30km), Saut du
Doubs, grottos (40km).

MONTAREN 30700 Gard **RN 981 Map 24-A2**
Ⓧ **LES ROUTIIERS CHEZ RÉGIME** (N° RR NOV 26 101) (Mme
Régine **Hangard**) 7, rte d'Alès ☎ 66-22-25-26 ← 9. Closed Sun.

MONTARGIS 45200 Loiret **Map 9-B2**
Ⓧ **LE PARIS – MONTARGIS** (N° RR MARS 27 556) (M. **Darbier**) 221
rue Emile Mangin ☎ 38-85-63-04 or 38-93-91-58. Restaurant
closed Sun ← 10. English spoken.

MONTAUBAN-DE-BRETAGNE 35360 Ille-et-Vilaine **RN 12 and 164 bis**
Map 7-B3
Ⓧ ☆☆ **NN HOTEL DE FRANCE** (N° RR AOU 7 884) (M. Gabriel **Le**
Métayer) 34, rue du Gl-de-Gaulle ☎ 99-06-40-19 ← 12 98–195F
with showers, WC, tel, television. Closed Mon, 20 Dec to 20 Jan.
Coaches welcome. Rest. seats 80. Evening meals until 10pm.
Credit cards accepted. Car park. ⌒ English, Spanish, some
German spoken. Menus 55–135F. Children's menu. À la carte.
Specialities: seafood, coq au muscadet, far breton.
Ⓧ ☆☆ **NN LE RELAIS DE LA HUCHERAIS** (N° RR SEPT 27 032) (M.
Alain **Meheust**) ☎ 99-06-40-29 ← 12 100–170F. Closed Sun.
English spoken. Evening meals served until 10pm. ⌒ TV. Bar and
lounge. Coaches welcome. Rest. seats 110. Garage.

MONTAUDIN 53220 Mayenne **RN 799 Map 8-B1**
Ⓧ **HÔTEL DE PARIS** (N° RR MAI 21 111) (M. Daniel **Doudard**) route
d'Ernée ☎ 43-05-30-79. **Minitel** ← 5. Closed Mon. Full-board
155F. Evening meals served until 9pm. English spoken. Coaches
welcome. Rest. seats 550.

MONTAUROUX 83440 Var **RN 562 Map 25-B2**
☆☆ **NN RELAIS DU LAC** (N° RR 26 110) (M. **Hernandez**) RN 562
☎ 94-76-43-65. **Minitel** ⮞ 37. Coaches welcome. Rest. seats 400.
Evening meals. English, Spanish spoken.

MONTBAZON 37250 Indre-et-Loire **Map 12-B2**
LA GRANGE BARBIER (N° RR DEC 27 473) (M. William
Laborde) La Grange Barbier. Directions: leave south to Poitiers
on RN 10 ☎ 47-26-01-60 ⮞ 5 100–150F. Closed Sun evening.
Evening meals. Home cooking. Children's menu. Garden terrace. ⮞ Parking. Coaches welcome. Rest. seats 70. Nearby
service station, open 24 hours. Sights: Les châteaux de la Loire.

MONTBENOIT 25650 Doubs **Map 14-B3**
RELAIS DES VOYAGEURS (N° RR JANV 26 152) (M. Pierre
Magnin-Feysot) Place de l'Abbaye ☎ 81-38-10-85 ⮞ 6 120–170F
with shower. Closed Tue evening. Regional home cooking.
Specialities: croûte fôrestière, jambon de montagne. Menu 50–
140F. Children's menu. À la carte. Lunch 11.30–1.30pm. Dinner
6.30–8.30pm. Coaches welcome. Rest. seats 150. Credit cards
accepted. ⮞ Parking. Sights: Montbenoit Abbey.

MONTBOUCHER 23400 Creuse **CD 941 Map 16-A2**
LA BERGERIE (N° RR DEC 26 760) (Mme Brigitte **Belz**) Bour-
ganeuf ☎ 55-64-20-18. Closed Mon in winter and 15 days in Feb.
Coaches welcome. Rest. seats 60.

MONTBRISON 42600 Loire **RN 496 Map 18-A2**
LE RELAIS DE LA GARE (N° RR JAN 20 369) (M. Jean-Pierre
Gacon) 2, place de la Gare ☎ 77-58-30-33 ⮞ 8. Closed Sun, Aug.
Evening meals to 10pm.

MONTDAUPHIN 05600 Hautes-Alpes **RN 94 Maps 19-B3 and 25-A1**
☆ **NN LE RELAIS DE LA GARE** (N° RR JUN 10 820) (Mme
Francine **Lacour**) ☎ 92-45-03-08 ⮞ 24 105–200F. Closed Sat, 1
May–30 June, 1 Sept to 25 Dec. Coaches welcome. Evening
meals served until 9pm. English spoken. Menus 54–140F.
Specialities: truite aux morilles, filet de boeuf, côte d'agneau. ⮞
Parking. Coaches welcome. Rest. seats 80.

MONTDIDIER 80500 Somme **RN 30 and 35 Maps 3-A3 and 5-B3**
LE RELAIS DU MOUTON D'OR (N° RR AVR 19 734) (M. Christian
Parmentier) 10, boulevard Debeney ☎ 22-78-03-43 ⮞ 5. Closed
Sun, 1–21 Aug, 24–31 Dec. Coaches welcome. Rest. seats 70.

MONTEBOURG 50310 Manche **RN 13 Map 4-B1**
AUBERGE DES ROUTIERS – CHEZ LE CHAROLAIS (N° RR SEP
25 649) (M. Serge **Charenton**) 19, place Albert Pélerin ☎
33-41-14-57. **Minitel** ⮞ 4.

MONTECH 82700 Tarn-et-Garonne **RN 128 Map 22-A1**
LE RELAIS DE L'AVENUE (N° RR AVR 21 515) (M. Georges
Taupiac) 7, boulevard Lagal ☎ 63-64-72-26. Closed Sun, public
holidays, 20 Dec–10 Jan. Rest. seats 60. Evening meals to 9pm.

MONTÉLIMAR

MONTÉLIMAR 26780 Drôme **Autoroute A7 Map 24-A2**

♉⊗ **SODEXAS RELAIS P.L.M.** (N° RR 1811) (M. **Arletti**) Aire de Service de Montélimar ☎ 75-46-60-00. Open 24 hours. Self-service café and restaurant. Showers. TV. Shop.

MONTEREAU 77130 Seine-et-Marne **RN 1 Map 9-B2**

♉⊗ **LES ROUTIERS** (N° RR SEP 25 644) (M. Claude **Spinato**) RN 105 ☎ 64-32-44-93. Closed Sun, July.

MONTFAVET 84140 Vaucluse **RN 100 and A7 Map 24-A2**

♉⊗ ☆ **NN LE RELAIS DE BONPAS** (N° RR JUN 21 138) (M. Alain
⌂ **Laugier**) locally Pont de Bonpas RN 7 ☎ 90-23-07-01. **Minitel** ⊸ 14 85–120F. Rest. seats 110. Evening meals. English spoken. ⊢ Sights: Fontaine de Vaucluse, Avignon, Baux de Provence.

MONTFIQUET 14490 Calvados **RD 572 Map 4-B1**

♉⊗ **RELAIS DE LA FORÊT** (N° RR MAI 27 606) (M. Christian
⌂ **Desobeaux**) locally L'Embranchement ☎ 31-21-39-78 ⊸ 10.

MONTGENÈVRE 05100 Hautes-Alpes **RN 94 Map 19-B3**

♉⊗ **LE TRANSALPIN** (N° RR JUN 22 385) (Mme Yvette **Silvestre**) ☎ 92-21-92-87. Closed Sat afternoon, Sun, 15 Aug–15 Sept. Rest. seats 60. Evening meals to 10pm.

MONTHUCHON 50200 Manche **Map 4-B1)**

♉⊗ **LES CHARMILLES** (N° RR MARS 27 577) (M. Ludovic **Lecadet**) Le Bourg Coutances ☎ 33-07-59-59. English spoken. Parking. Coaches welcome.

MONTILS (LES) 41120 Loir-et-Cher **RN 764 Map 12-A3**

♉⊗ **LES DEUX ROUES** (N° RR MAI 23 299) (M. Jean-Pierre **Levaux**) 28, rue du Bel-Air ☎ 54-44-02-40. **Minitel**. Closed Sun. Rest. seats 110.

MONTLHÉRY 91300 Essonne **RN 20 Map 1-B2**

♉⊗ ☆ **NN LE SOLOGNE** (N° RR MAY 25 933) (M. Jacques **Cheron**)
⌂ 65, Route d'Orléans ☎ 69-01-00-98 ⊸ 8. Closed Sun and 3rd week in Aug. Rest. seats 40. Evening meals served until 9pm.

MONTLUÇON 03100 Allier **RN 145 Map 16-A2**

♉⊗ **CADET ROUSSEL** (N° RR AVR 27 594) (M. Edouard **Gawron**) 53,
⌂ rue de Pasquis ☎ 70-29-32-27. Restaurant closed Sun ⊸ 8. Polish and a little Russian spoken.

MONTMARAULT 03390 Allier **RN 145 Map 16-A2**

♉⊗ **LE RELAIS DE L'UNION** (N° RR AVR 24 932) (Mme Monique **Desbordes**) 2, route de Montluçon ☎ 70-07-60-05. Closed 15 Sept–7 Oct. Coaches welcome. Rest. seats 120.

♉⊗ **LE CHALET** (N° RR FEV 26 815) (M. Alain **Vassort**) 18, boulevard Tourret ☎ 70-07-60-23. Closed Sat evening and Sun, 3 weeks in Aug. English spoken. Coaches welcome. Rest. seats 144. Evening meals.

♉⊗ **RELAIS DE L'ÉTAPE** (N° RR AUG 27 358) (M. Robert **Legal**) Route de Moulins ☎ 70-07-36-03. Closed Sat evening, Sun. Parking. Coaches welcome. Filling station nearby, open 24 hours.

MONTMARTIN-SUR-MER 50590 Manche **RD 20 Maps 4-B1 and 8-A1**
☆☆ **NN HOTELLERIE DU BON VIEUX TEMPS** (N° RR JUIN 26 257) (M. Érick **Bourbonnais**) ☎ 33-47-54-44. Minitel ⚊ 20 from 108–242F with shower and bath, WC, telephone in room. Open 7am–11pm. Restaurant: local cooking. Menu 53–175F. Children's menu. À la carte. Closed Sun evening (out of season). Credit cards accepted. Garden terrace. Coaches welcome. Rest. seats 200. Evening meals. English spoken. Car park. ⚐ Bar. Tobacconist. Sights: Baie de la Sienne (2km), quick lime furnace, manor houses.

MONTMELIAN 73800 Savoie **RN 6 Map 19-A2**
LE GRAND SCHLEM (N° RR JANV 27 158) (Mme Lucie **Karpy**) (SARL Le Grand Schlem) RN 6 ☎ 79-65-23-63. English, Spanish and Italian spoken. Parking. Coaches welcome. Filling station nearby, open 24 hours.

MONTMIRAT 30260 Gard **RN 110 Map 23-B2**
LE CASTELAS (N° RR OCT 27 423) (Mme Josiane **Gatel**) route Nationale 10 ☎ 66-77-81-33. Restaurant: home regional cooking. Specialities: lotte à l'americaine, gardiane, bourride, sole hollandaise. Menu 55F, 72–125F. Children's menu. Dinner to 9pm. Closed Sat and Sun (low season) and Aug. Credit cards accepted. Traditional décor. Rest. seats 77. Garden terrace. ⚐ Parking. Coaches welcome. Sights: Anduze (30km), Trabuc grottos (30km), Nîmes (Roman city 30km), Pont du Gard (30km).

MONTMOREAU 16190 Charente **RN 674 Map 15-B2/3**
LE RELAIS DES ROUTIERS (N° RR AVR 12 793) (Mme Ernestine **Ferrier**) Route d'Angoulême 3 ☎ 45-60-21-17 ⚊ 5.

MONTOIR DE BRETAGNE 44550 Loire-Atlantique **Map 11-A2**
LE RELAIS DES NOES (N° RR AUG 27 652) (Mme Brigitte **Liberge**) Route Nationale 171 Les Noès ☎ 40-45-55-67. Showers available for drivers. Restaurant closed on Sat and Sun. Filling station nearby.

MONTOIRE-SUR-LE-LOIR 41800 Loir-et-Cher **Map 21-A3**
À LA DESCENTE DU PERCHE (N° RR MAI 27 281) (M. François **Detalle**) 2, rue du Docteur Schweitzer ☎ 54-85-21-39. Closed Sun pm. Evening meals served until 8.30pm. Filling station 200m.

MONTPELLIER-FABRÈGUES 34690 Hérault **LA LANGUEDOCIENNE A9 Map 23-B2**
L'ARCHE DE FABRÈGUES (N° RR 1815) (M. Jean-Mary **Nicolle**) Aire de Service de Fabrègues 2 sens Passerelle ☎ 67-85-15-06.

MONTPEZAT-de-QUERCY 82270 Tarn-et-Garonne **RN 20 Map 22-A1**
☆ **NN LE RELAIS DE L'ETAPE QUERCY** (N° RR JUN 21 121) (Mme Sylviane **Molinie**) La Madeleine Route Nationale 20 ☎ 63-02-07-58 ⚊ 14. Closed Sat low season, Sept.

MONTPINCHON 50210 Manche **RD 73 Map 8-A1**
BAR DES AMIS (N° RR SEPT 27 665) (Mr Joel **Hebert**) Le Bourg ☎ 33-45-70-95. Lorry park. Filling station nearby, open 8am–8pm.

MONTPON MENESTEROL

MONTPON MENESTEROL 24700 Dordogne **RN 89 Map 15-B3**
ॱ⊗ **LAS DAVALDAS DE MÉNESPLET** (N° RR MAR 23 717) (M. René **Duvillard**) Route Nationale 89 ☎ 53-81-83-67 ◄ 12. Coaches welcome. Rest. seats 50. Evening meals.

MONTREAL 11290 Aude **RD 119 Map 22-B2**
ॱ⊗ **LE MALEPERE** (N° RR OCT 25 696) (M. Gabriel **François**) Les Giscarels. Direction: leave towards Limouy. ☎ 68-76-29-43 ◄ 3 80F with bathroom, WC, TV. Closed Sat, Sun. Home cooking. Menu à la carte. Evening meals until 10pm in winter. Spanish, English spoken. Rest. seats 40. Garden terrace. ◄ Coaches welcome. Parking.

MONTREDON-CORBIÈRES 11100 Aude **RN 113 Map 23-A2/3**
ॱ⊗ **LE STÉPHANOIS** (N° RR MAI 26 246) (M. Paul **Chanut**) RN 113 ☎ 68-42-08-41. Closed Sat and Sun. Coaches welcome. Rest. seats 100. Evening meals. English, some Spanish, Italian spoken.

MONTREUIL-LE-CHÉTIF 72130 Sarthe **Map 8-B2**
ॱ⊗ **AU RENDEZ-VOUS DES CHASSEURS** (N° RR OCT 27 434) (Mme Françoise **Bordeau**) Le Grand Gué ☎ 43-33-39-90. Restaurant: home cooking. Children's menu. Credit cards accepted. Traditional décor. Rest. seats 80. Garden terrace. ◄ Parking. Coaches welcome. Shower. Filling station nearby. Sights: Château Sainte Suzanne, grottes de Sauges, Fresnay, museum of head-dresses, Abbaye de Champagne.

MONTREUIL-SOUS-BOIS 93100 Seine-St-Denis **Map 1-A3**
ॱ⊗ **CHEZ MAMY** (N° RR MAY 22 354) (Mme Michelle **Garnier**) 51, rue Léon Loiseau ☎ 42-87-06-08. Restaurant open 6.30am–8.30pm. Closed Sat, Sun. Rest. seats 35. ◄
ॱ⊗ **LE RELAIS DES ROUTIERS** (N° RR NOV 11 914) (Mmes **Sol** and **Puech**) 70, rue de Lagny ☎ 48-51-54-41. Closed Sun, Aug.

MONTREUIL SUR LOZON 50570 Manche **Map 4-B1**
ॱ⊗ **AUBERGE DE LA TRUITE DE LOZON** (N° RR JUL 27 635) (M. André **Hebert**) Le Bourg Marigny ☎ 33-55-03-43. Open 7.30am–9.30pm. English spoken.

MORANCE 69480 Rhône **Map 2-A1**
ॱ⊗ **REST DE LA MAIRIE** (N° RR JUL 26 274) (Mme Ginette **Roy**) Le
⌂ Bourg ☎ 78-43-60-82 ◄ 5. Closed Sat, Sun evening, 15 days in May. Coaches welcome. Rest. seats 70.

MORANGIS 91420 Essonne **Map 1-B2**
ॱ⊗ **CHEZ GIGI ET MOMO** (N° RR JAN 27 146) (M. Madjid **Belaidi**) 3 avenue Pierre Corneille ☎ 69-09-14-38. Restaurant closed Sat and July.

MORDELLES 35310 Ille-et-Vilaine **Map 7-B3**
ॱ⊗ **L'ISATIS** (N° RR OCT 27 432) (M. Michel **Edet**) La Croix Ignon ☎ 99-60-41-33. Closed Sun and Aug. Filling station nearby.

MOREAC 56500 Morbihan **RN 24 Map 7-B2**
ॱ⊗ ☆☆ **LE RELAIS DU BARDERFF** (N° RR FEV 26 453) (M. Jean **Lamour**) Z.I. Le Barderff ☎ 97-60-18-60. Fax 97-60-25-25. **Minitel**.

Open 5am–midnight. Closed Sun. Evening meals served. Restaurant. Regional home cooking. Menu 42–56F. Children's menu. Self service. Lunch 12–2pm. Dinner 7–10pm. Closed on Sun. Credit cards accepted. Modern décor. Rest. seats 290 ⬌ 20 200–350F with showers, bathrooms, WC, TV, telephone. Open 5am–midnight. Sitting room. Parking. Coaches welcome. Archaeology, hunting, fishing, the sea (30km).

MOREILLES 85450 Vendée **Map 11-A1**
AU CHEVAL BLANC (N° RR SEPT 27 673) (M. Christian **Sarraud**) 9, Route Nationale Le Bourg ☎ 51-56-11-02 ⬌ 5. Closed Sundays after 3pm, 24 Dec–2 Jan. Coaches welcome. Rest. seats 70. Evening meals until midnight. Filling station nearby.

MORNANT 69440 Rhône **Map 2A-1**
LE RELAIS DE BELLEVUE (N° RR DEC 27 739) (M. Patrick **Coupard**) Route départementale 42 Bellevue. Directions between Brignais and Rive de Gier ☎ 78-81-22-26. Restaurant: regional cooking. Specialities: poulet aux écrevisses, coquelet au champagne, lotte à l'americaine. Menu 55–145F. Children's menu. À la carte. Lunch 11.30–3pm. Dinner 7–10pm. Credit cards accepted. Modern décor. Rest. seats 70. ➥ Parking. Coaches welcome. Filling station nearby. Sights: Mornant.

MORNAS 84420 Vaucluse **Autoroute A-7 Map 24-A2**
L'ARCHE DE MORNAS (N° RR 1833) (Mme Corinne **Perez**) Aire de Mornas towards village Lyon/Marseille Autoroute ☎ 90-37-03-09.
RELAIS DE LA CASCADE (N° RR DEC 27 746) (Mme Margareth **Micheletti**) RN 7 ☎ 90-37-02-67. Restaurant: menu 54F. Open 5am–11pm. Closed Sat, Sun and 15 days in Aug. Spanish and Italian spoken. Lorry parking. Filling station 3km.

MORNAY-SUR-ALLIER 18600 Cher **RN 76 Map 13-B2**
LE RELAIS DE LA ROUTE (N° RR DEC 15 044) (Mlle Jacqueline **Chevrot**) 57, Bis RN ☎ 48-74-53-54 ⬌ 5 60–90F with WC. German, English spoken. Restaurant: home cooking. Menu 50F. Open 24 hours. Closed Sat 3pm and Sun. Credit cards accepted. Rest. seats 64. Sights: Apremont (15km), Parc de Saint Augustin (7km).

MORTAGNE-AU-PERCHE 61400 Orne **RN 12 Map 8-A2/3**
★ **HOTEL DES VOYAGEURS** (N° RR FEV 25 798) (Mme Cassimira **Blochel**) 60, fbg St-Éloi ☎ 33-25-25-46 ⬌ 10. Closed Sun evening, Mon evening, 20 Dec–20 Jan. Rest. seats 110. Evening meals served until 10pm.

MORTAGNE-SUR-SÈVRE 85290 Vendée **RN 160 Maps 11-B3 and 12-B1**
LE RELAIS DE LA GARE (N° RR AOU 26 299) (M. Jean-Luc **Arrouet**) 52, route de Cholet ☎ 51-65-11-56. Closed Sat evening, Sun, Aug.

MORTRÉE 61570 Orne **RN 158 Map 8-A2**
LE POINT DU JOUR (N° RR JUIN 25 948) (M. Jacques **Montier**) 139, Grande-Rue ☎ 33-35-35-22. Closed Sat, Sun. Coaches welcome. Rest. seats 220.

MOUCHARD

MOUCHARD 39330 Jura **RN 72 Map 14-B3**
♀⊗ **SARL LA TONNELLE** (N° RR AOUT 26 303) (M. Bernard **Miller**)
⌂ **Pagnoz** ☎ 84-37-81-17. **Minitel** ◄ 11. Closed Sat, Aug. Coaches
welcome. Rest. seats 70. Evening meals served until 10pm.

MOUEN 14790 Calvados **RN 175 Map 4-B2**
♀⊗ **LA BRUYÈRE** (N° RR FEV 27 528) (Mme Jeannine **Lechevalier**)
⌂ 1546, route de Bretaque ☎ 31-80-96-77 ◄ 5.

MOULEYDIER 24520 Dordogne **Map 21-B2**
♀⊗ **RELAIS DU BARRAGE** (N° RR JUIN 27 309) (M. Patrick **Delmas**)
Tuilières ☎ 53-23-20-55. Closed Sun. English, German and
Spanish spoken. Evening meals served until 11pm. Filling station
nearby, open 7am–7pm.

MOULINS 03000 Allier **RN 7 Map 16-A3**
♀⊗ **LE RELAIS DES TROIS RUBANS** (N° RR AOU 7 841) (M. Pierre
Moline) 1, route de Paris ☎ 70-44-08-51. Closed Sat, Sun and
Aug. Evening meals served until 8pm.

MOULINS-DES-MALADES par ORCHAMPS 39700 Jura **RN 73 Map
14-A5/B3**
♀⊗ **AU RENDEZ-VOUS DE LA MARINE** (N° RR MAI 6 142) (Mlle
Bullet) 73, Route Nationale ☎ 84-71-32-10. Closed Aug.

MOULISMES 86500 Vienne **RN 147 Map 15-B1**
♀⊗ ☆ **NN LA TABLE OUVERTE** (N° RR AVR 22 752) (**SARL**
⌂ **Gransagne-Baudet**) 147, Route Nationale Montmorillon ☎ 49-91-
90-68. ◄ 7 from 80–150F with shower, bathroom. Open 6am–
10pm. Home cooking. Menu 45–95F. Menu à la carte. Access for
disabled. Closed Sat afternoon, Sun afternoon (except Aug). Car
park 5,500m². Coaches welcome. Rest. seats 75. Evening meals.
Bar. ⊨ Credit cards accepted. Sights: Vallée de la Gartempe,
Futuroscope.

MOUZEUIL ST MARTIN 85370 Vendée **RN 148 Map 11-A1**
♀⊗ **CENTRAL ROUTIER** (N° RR JUN 21 961) (M. Jean-Marie **Guil-**
⌂ **baud**) 33, rue Louis Appraille RN 148 ☎ 51-28-72-44 ◄ 8.
Coaches welcome. Rest. seats 200. Evening meals served until
10pm.

MOYON 50860 Manche **CD 999 Map 8-A1**
♀⊗ **LE SUPER ROUTIERS** (N° RR NOV 27 091) (M. Pierre **Borau**)
Carrefour Paris Route départmentale 999 Moyon ☎ 33-05-59-74.
Minitel. Closed Sun and Feb. Restaurant; home cooking. Specialities: pied de veau. Children's menu. À la carte. Credit cards
accepted. Parking. Filling station 3km open 6am–8pm. Portuguese, English and Spanish spoken. Coaches welcome. Rest.
seats 120. Evening meals served until 11pm.

MUREAUX (LES) 78130 Yvelines **RN 14 Maps 1-A1 and 3-B2**
♀⊗ **LE RELAIS ICI ON COUPE LA SOIF** (N° RR JUL 12 328) (Mme
⌂ **Compagnon**) 102, avenue du Maréchal Foch ☎ 34-74-05-04.
Minitel ◄ 7. Closed Sun, Aug.
♀⊗ **CAFÉ D'ARMOR** (N° RR OCT 26 700) (Mme Germaine **Dolais**)
29, rue J.-Jaurès ☎ 34-74-04-95. Closed Wed. English spoken.

NANTEUIL LE HAUDOUIN

MURON 17630 Charente-Maritime **Map 11-B1**

♀⊗ **LE KOALA** (N° RR NOV 27 711) (Mme **Vezin** and **Duret**) rue du Champ de Foire, place de l'Eglise ☎ 46-27-74-71. Restaurant: regional cooking. Menu 48.50–110F. Children's menu 29F. À la carte. Dinner to 1am. Closed Sun (out of season). Credit cards accepted. Traditional décor. Rest. seats 38. Garden terrace. ⌁ Parking. Coaches welcome. Filling station 500m open 8am–8pm. Sights: Roman church at Genouille (3km), Château de Surgères (11km), Dolmen d'Ardillères (5km).

MUSSIDAN 24400 Dordogne **Map 15-B3**

♀⊗ **RELAIS LE PERIGORD** (N° RR MARS 27 564) (Mme Annie
⌂ **Callens**) 37, avenue Gambetta ☎ 53-81-05-85 ⊷ 6. Filling station nearby, open 7.30am–7.30pm.

MUY (LE) 83490 Var **RN 7 Map 25-A2**

♀⊗ **LA CHAUMIÈRE** (N° RR AOUT 26 625) (M. Louis **Fogola**) 7, quartier de la Gare ☎ 94-45-10-81 ⊷ 7. Closed Sun. Coaches welcome. Rest. seats 80. Evening meals served until 11pm.

NAINTRÉ 86530 Vienne **RN 10 Map 15-B1**

♀⊗ **LA HALTE** (N° RR NOV 20 892) (M. and Mme **Henni-Houas**) Nationale 10 ☎ 49-90-09-69. **Minitel**. Situated on exit south of Châtellerault from Autoroute Aquitaine. Closed Sat, Sun. Coaches welcome. Rest. seats 150. Evening meals. English, Arabic, Spanish, German spoken.

NANCY 54000 Meurthe-et-Moselle **RN 4 Maps 10-A2 and 14-B1**

♀⊗ **LE RELAIS DU PORT** (N° RR FEV 18 314) (M. Claude **Dopp**)
⌂⊶ 5, rue Henri-Bazin ☎ 83-35-49-85 ⊷ 9. Closed Fri evening, Sat, Sun, Aug. English, German spoken. Evening meals.

♀⊗ **RELAIS VICTOR** (N° RR SEPT 29 641) (M. Jean-Marie **Hecht**) 7, rue Victor ☎ 83-36-53-27. **Minitel** ⊷ 9. Closed Sat, Sun. Evening meals served until 9pm. Coaches welcome. Rest. seats 46. ⌁

NANTES 44000 Loire-Atlantique **RN 43 Maps 11-A/B2 and 12-B1**

♀⊗ **L'ANCRE D'OR** (N° RR AOUT 26 295) (M. Serge **Desmortiers**)
⌂ 55, boulevard Gustave Roch ☎ 40-35-39-30. **Minitel** ⊷ 5. Closed Sat afternoon, Sun, 1–25 Aug. Evening meals served until 9.30pm. Coaches welcome. Rest. seats 110.

♀⊗ **CAFÉ DE L'AVENIR** (N° RR SEPT 26 043) (Mme Viviane **Baron**) 1, rue de la Pompe ☎ 40-43-46-03. Closed Sat lunch, Sun. Coaches welcome. Rest. seats 54. Evening meals until 10pm.

♀⊗ **LES TILLEULS** (N° RR JANV 26 784) (Mme Marie-Thérèse
⌂ **Poirier**) 9, rue de la Petite Baratte ☎ 40-49-68-29 ⊷ 13. Closed Sat, Sun, Aug.

♀⊗ **AU RENDEZ-VOUS DES SPORTIFS** (N° RR OCT 27 405) (M. Bernard **Aubert**) 40, quai Malakoff ☎ 40-47-75-39. Closed Sat, Sun and July. Evening meals served until 9pm. Home cooking. Specialities: paella, couscous. Rest. seats 70. Credit cards accepted. Filling station nearby.

NANTEUIL LE HAUDOUIN 60440 Oise **Map 3-B3**

♀⊗ **RESTAURANT DU CHEMIN DE FER** (N° RR JUL 27 639) (Mme
⌂ Jeanik **Camusat**) place de la Gare ☎ 44-88-03-18. Restaurant: open 4pm–midnight. Closed Sat and Sun (unless booked) ⊷ 6 80–120F. Parking. Coaches welcome.

NARBONNE

NARBONNE 11100 Aude **RN 9 Map 23-A3**

♀⊗ **LE NOVELTY** (N° RR JAN 10 223) (M. Claude and Louis
⌂ **Strazzera**) 33, avenue des Pyrénées ☎ 68-42-224-28. Fax 68-42-
13-37. **Minitel** ➝ 21 80–175F. Open 7am–midnight. Ideal home
cooking. Specialities: cassoulet, choucroute, paella. Menu
49–85F. À la carte. Lunch 12–2.30pm. Dinner 7.30–10.30pm.
Coaches welcome. Rest. seats 250. Evening meals. English,
Arabic, Spanish, Italian spoken. Credit cards accepted. ↙ Car
parking.

♀⊗ ☆ **NN LE RELAIS DES 2 MERS** (N° RR JAN 23 601) (M. Franco
⌂ **Mattei**) route de la Nautique. Directions: leave autoroute south
Narbonne ☎ 68-41-00-21. **Minitel** ➝ 39. Restaurant: home
cooking. Children's menu. Open 5am–midnight. Closed Sun.
Modern décor. Rest. seats 224. Rest room. Garden terrace. ↙
Parking. Coaches welcome. Italian spoken. Sights: cathedral,
museums, pool, beach.

♀⊗ **LA TOUPINE** (N° RR NOV 27 112) (M. Yannick **Canessa**) 3, route
⌂ de Coursan ☎ 68-65-11-01. **Minitel** ➝ 4. English and Spanish
spoken. Closed Sat evening, Sun evening. Coaches welcome.
Rest. seats 90. Evening meals served until midnight. Filling
station nearby open 6.45am–8pm.

NASSANDRES 27550 Eure **RN 13 Map 4-B3**

♀⊗ **LE PARIS CAEN/CHERBOURG INTERNATIONAL** (N° RR OCT
26 686) (M. Patrice **Boutel**) SARL Le Paris Caen/Cherbourg 11,
RN 13 ☎ 32-45-00-26. **Minitel**. Closed Sat afternoon, Sun. Evening
meals to 1am. Credit cards accepted. Rest. seats 90. ↙ Lorry
parking. Sights: Abbeye de Bec-Hellouin.

NAUCELLE 12800 Aveyron **RN 88 Map 22-B1**

♀⊗ **RELAIS DE LA MOTHE** (N° RR JAN 27 513) (M. Michel **Cousin**)
RN 88. La Mothe ☎ 65-69-03-00. Closed Monday. Evening meals
until 9pm. Parking.

NAVILLY 71270 Saône-et-Loire **RN 83 Bis Map 14-A3**

♀⊗ **AU BOIS DE BOULOGNE** (N° RR FEV 10 347) (M. **Grapinet**)
☎ 85-49-10-40. Closed Wed, 21 Dec–21 Jan. Coaches welcome.
Rest. seats 100.

NEAUX 42470 Loire **Map 16-B3**

♀⊗ **CHEZ GINOU** (N° RR FEV 27 537) (Mme Geneviève **Decreux**)
RN 7 La Croix. Directions: between Lyon and Roanne ☎
77-62-10-32. Restaurant: home cooking. Lunch 11.30am–2pm.
Dinner to 10pm. Closed Mon and Sun from midday and in Aug.
Traditional décor. Rest. seats 32. ↙ Filling station 30m open
7.30am–8.30pm. Sights: the river Loire and its châteaux.

NÉGRONDES 24460 Dordogne **Map 15-B3**

♀⊗ **LA FRINGALE** (N° RR JAN 27 764) (M. Henri **Ribeyrol**) Les
Riviers ☎ 53-62-15-62. **Minitel**. Specialities: périgourdines. Menu
50–140F. À la carte. Parking. Coaches welcome. Filling station
nearby open 7am–9pm.

NEMOURS 77140 Seine-et-Marne **Autoroute A6 Map 9-B2**

⊗ **RESTOP DE NEMOURS** (N° RR 1829) Aire de Service de
Darvault – both directions of the autoroute. Directions: bridge
which crosses autoroute. ☎ 64-28-11-97. Restaurant: regional

cooking. Menu 25% discount to lorry drivers. Children's menu. À la carte. Self service. Open 24 hours. Credit cards accepted. Rest. seats 250. Garden terrace. ⊨ Parking. Coaches welcome. TV. Shower facilities. In addition to the fast self-service restaurant, "La Ferme" offers a varied and cheaply priced menu.

NERE 17510 Charente-Maritime **RD 133 Map 15-A2**
⛾⊗ **LES ROUTIERS** (N° RR JUN 23 828) (Mme Monique **Metois**) route d'Aulnay-les-Égaux ☎ 46-33-00-30.

NEUFBOURG (LE) 50140 Manche **RN 177 Map 8-A1**
⛾⊗ **LES ROUTIERS** (N° RR AOUT 26 025) (Mme Françoise **Hamel**)
⌂ 13, rue de Vire ☎ 33-59-00-59 ⊨ 4.

NEUFCHATEL-EN-SAOSNOIS 72600 Sarthe **RN 155 Map 8-B2**
⛾⊗ **CHEZ CHRISTIANE Tobacconist** (N° RR AOU 18 500) (Mme
⌂ Christiane **Chapellier**) ☎ 43-97-74-10 ⊨ 12. Closed Aug. Evening meals until 10pm. Rest. seats 40.

NEUILLY 89113 Yonne **Map 13 A-2**
⛾⊗ **AUBERGE DE LA POSTE** (N° RR OCT 27 685) (Mme Nicole
⌂ **Weiberg**) 51, Grande Rue ☎ 86-73-71-27. **Minitel**. Restaurant: home cooking. Menu 49 50–75F. Dinner to 11pm. Closed Tue. Credit cards accepted ⊨ 5 65–100F. Rest room. Garden terrace. ⊨ Parking. Sights: museums, pool.

NEUSSARGUES MOISSAC 15170 Cantal **RN 122 Map 17-A2**
⛾⊗ **LE SPORTING BAR** (N° RR OCT 27 428) (Mme Joelle **Allanche**) rue des Écoles ☎ 71-20-56-89. Closed Sun, last 2 weeks Aug. Evening meals served until 10pm. Filling station nearby.

NEUVE-LYRE (LA) 27330 Eure **RN 830 Map 8-A3**
⛾⊗ **LE RELAIS DES AMIS** (N° RR AVR 21 047) (M. Jean-Claude **Guyot**) Hameau de Chagny ☎ 32-50-50-60. Closed Sun, 15–30 Aug.

NEUVILLE-AU-PLAIN 50480 Manche **RN 13 Map 4-B1**
⛾⊗ **LA RENCONTRE** (N° RR AOU 25 079) (M. Jean-Pierre **Alix**) Ste Mère Eglise ☎ 33-41-31-46. Closed Aug. English spoken. Coaches welcome. Rest. seats 52. Evening meals served until 9pm.

NEUVY 41250 Loir-et-Cher **RD 18 and 923 Map 12-A3**
⛾⊗ **LA CHEMINÉE** (N° RR JUL 26 613) (M. Philippe **Masclet**)
⌂ Bracieux ☎ 54-46-42-70 ⊨ 9. Closed Wed in winter, 15–30 Sept, 1–15 Mar. Rest. seats 110. Evening meals served until 10pm.

NEUVY-SAINT-SÉPULCRE 36230 Indre **RD 927 Map 16-A1**
⛾⊗ **LA CHARRETTE** (N° RR FEV 26 454) (M. Nicholas **Pavlicevic**) 21,
⌂ place du Champ-de-Foire. Directions: between La Châtre and Montluçon ☎ 54-30-84-77 ⊨ 7 120–170F with shower, WC. Italian, Yugoslavian, Polish, Russian, English spoken. Restaurant: home cooking. Specialities: coq au vin, boeuf bourguignon, blanquette de veau (on request). Children's menu. À la carte. Lunch 12.30–2pm. Dinner 7–11pm. Traditional décor. Rest. seats 100. Sights: basilique, château, plan d'eau.

NEUVY-SAUTOUR

NEUVY-SAUTOUR 89570 Yonne **RN 77 Map 9-B2**
♀⊗ **AU BON COIN CHEZ GÉRARD ET ANNIE** (N° RR JUL 26 292)
(M. Gérard **Charpignon**) 29, route de Troyes ☎ 86-56-35-52.
Minitel. Closed Sat afternoon, Sun. Rest. seats 40. Evening meals
until 9pm.

NEVERS 58000 Nièvre **RN 7 Map 13-B2**
♀⊗ **HOTEL NIVERNAIS** (N° RR SEP 23 481) (M. Marcel **George**) 106,
⌂ route de Lyon-Plagny ☎ 86-37-58-32. **Minitel** ➔ 6. Closed Sun
evening and first fortnight Sept. English, Spanish, Italian spoken.
Evening meals served until 10pm.
♀⊗ **HOTEL DU LION D'OR** (N° RR OCT 26 682) (M. Thierry **Petillot**)
⌂ 13, faubourg de Lyon ☎ 86-37-55-48 ➔ 4. Closed Wed (low
season) and Sept. Some English spoken. Rest. seats 60. Evening
meals served until 9.30pm.

NICOLE 47190 Lot-et-Garonne **RN 113 Map 21-A/B1**
♀⊗ **LE PLAISANCE** (N° RR JUN 24 615) (M. Bernard **Lambert**) Rte
⌂ Nle 113 Aiguillon ☎ 53-79-64-07 ➔ 7. Closed Sat, last Sun of
month and Aug. Rest. seats 100. Evening meals until 10pm.

NIEPPE 59850 Nord **RN 42 Map 5-A1**
♀⊗ **LE RELAIS DE L'ARMONIE** (N° RR SEPT 27 014) (Mme
Christiane **Boulet**) 127, rue d'Armentières ☎ 20-48-74-29. Closed
Mon, Aug. Filling station nearby.

NIEUL-LE-DOLENT 85430 Vendée **RD 36 Map 11-B3**
♀⊗ **CHEZ JACQUES** (N° RR MAR 23 210) (M. Jacques **Pinel**) 8, rue de
Lattre-de-Tassigny between la Roche-sur-Yon and les Sables-
d'Olonne ☎ 51-07-93-71. Closed Sun. Coaches welcome. Rest.
seats 40. HGV parking (2,000m^2).

NIMES 30900 Gard **Map 23-B2 and 24-A3**
♀⊗ **L'AVONAGE** (N° RR NOV 26 099) (Mme Gabriel **Finiels**) route
de Generac, Camping du Domaine de la Bastide ☎ 66-38-06-99.
Closed Sun (low season), Oct. Coaches welcome. Rest. seats 70.
Evening meals served until 9.30pm. English, Spanish spoken.
Restaurant: regional home cooking. Specialities: escargots à la
provençale, jambonneau aux lentilles, gardianne de taureau.
Menu à la carte. Credit cards accepted. Modern décor. Garden
terrace. ⌫ Parking. Sights: Nimes, La Camargue, the sea, pont du
Gard.

NIORT 79000 Deux-Sèvres **RN 150 Map 15-A1**
♀⊗ **LE BON ACCUEIL** (N° RR OCT 24 743) (Mme Thérèse **Deni-
baud**) 424, avenue St-Jean-d'Angély ☎ 49-79-27-60. Closed Sun,
Aug. Home cooking. Coaches welcome. Rest. seats 96. Evening
meals until 10pm. Parking. Credit cards accepted. Sights: the zoo
at Forêt Chicè (20km), Marais Beitevin.

NOAILLES 19600 Corrèze **RN 20 Map 17-A1**
♀⊗ **RELAIS D'ATAN** (N° RR JUL 26 606) (Mme Josiane **Berthelot**)
Fontrouvée ☎ 55-85-85-76. Italian, Spanish, Portuguese spoken.

NOCLE-MAULAIX (LA) 58250 Nièvre **RD 3 Map 16-A3**
♀⊗ **LE RELAIS DE LA POSTE** (N° RR JAN 17 715) (M. Marcel
Senotier) ☎ 86-30-80-32. Closed Mon, 1–21 Sept. Menu à la carte.
Lunch 12–1.30pm. Traditional décor. 3 rooms.

LA NOË POULAIN 27560 Eure **CD 810 Map 4-B3**

♈⊗ **CHEZ MANU ET JOJO** (N° RR NOV 27 088) (Mme Josiane **Langin**) Lieurey ☎ 32-57-90-35. Closed Sat and July/Aug. Dinner to 10pm. Filling station nearby.

NOEUX LES MINES 62290 Pas-de-Calais **Map 5-B2**

♈⊗ **LE DIAMANT NOIR** (N° RR FEV 27 793) (M. Lionel **Renoult**) 94 RN ☎ 21-26-74-74. Restaurant: menu to 50F. Children's menu. Open 11am–11pm. Rest. seats 30. Terrace garden. Parking. Sights: Notre dame de Lorette.

NOGENT-LE-PHAYE 28630 Eure-et-Loir **RN 10 Map 8-B3**

♈⊗ **RELAIS DU MOULIN ROUGE** (N° RR NOV 26 716) (M. Christian **Bru**) Le Moulin Rouge. Directions: leave for Chartres on the RN 10 towards Paris 3km ☎ 37-31-62-68. **Minitel**. Closed Sat, Sun, Aug. Evening meals served until 9pm. Restaurant: home cooking. Menu 58F. Credit cards accepted. Traditional décor. Rest. seats 30. ⚑ Parking.

NOGENT LE ROTROU 28400 Eure-et-Loir **Map 8-B3**

⚑ **TOTAL SERVICE STATION – ALLIANE AUTO** (N° RR 27 726) (Mme Danielle **Blottin**) Route du Mans ☎ 37-52-90-02. Restaurant: open 6pm–midnight. Credit cards accepted. Rest room. Parking cars and HGV. Showers (10F). Shop. Repairs and maintenance assured.

NOHANT-EN-GOUT 18390 Cher **Map 13-B2**

♈⊗ **RELAIS DU BERRY** (N° RR AVR 27 251) (SARL Ligot) RN 151 ☎ 48-30-42-90. German, English, Spanish and Italian spoken. Filling station nearby open 24 hours.

NOLAY 21340 Côte-d'Or **RD 73 Map 13-B3**

♈⊗ ☆☆ **NN LE RELAIS DU CHEVREUIL** (N° RR AOU 20 799) (Mme 🏠 Rachelle **Suissa**) place de l'Hôtel de Ville ☎ 80-21-71-89. **Minitel**. English, Spanish spoken. Restaurant: regional cooking. Specialities: écrevisses au gratin, poulet de bresse, filet de boeuf. Children's menu. À la carte. Dinner to 10pm. Closed Wed (low season) and Dec. Rest. seats 80. Hotel ⇔14 at 170–290F with shower, bathroom, WC, TV, Tel. Open 8am–11pm. Rest rooms. Garden terrace. ⚑ Parking. Sights: Burgundy vineyard and cellars.

NONANT-LE-PIN 61240 Orne **RN 26 Map 8-A2**

♈⊗⇔**LE RELAIS DES HARAS** (N° RR MAR 25 345) (M. Jacques **Lampin**) Grand-Rue. Directions: towards Argentan ☎ 33-39-93-35. Closed Sun. Children's menu. Home cooking. Specialities: tripes maison, andouillette garnie. Menu to 45F without reservation. Coaches welcome. Rest. seats 49. Evening meals until 10pm. Traditional décor. ⚑ Sights: Haras du pin.

NOTRE-DAME-DE-GRAVENCHON 76330 Seine-Maritime **RD 428 Map 4-B3**

♈⊗ **AU LE COUP DE FREIN** (N° RR AVR 897) (Mme Marie-Josée **David**) rue Claude-Bernard ☎ 35-94-61-35.

NOUZONVILLE 08700 Ardennes **RD 1 Map 6-A2**

♈⊗ **LE RELAIS DE LA PLACE** (N° RR SEP 21 243) (Mme Annie 🏠 **Boquillon**) 15, place Gambetta ☎ 24-53-80-43. Restaurant: home

Nouzonville continued
cooking. Dinner to 8.30pm. Closed Sun. Rest. seats 40 ⊸ 6 with
showers and WC. Open 7am–10pm. ⌐ Parking. Sights: Vallée de
la Meuse (10km), Belgium (10km).

NOVES 13550 Bouches-du-Rhône **RN 7 Map 24-A3**
♈⊗ **RELAIS DE LA BASSAQUE** (N° RR SEPT 26 325) (M. Joseph
Masi) RN 7 ☎ 90-94-26-84. Closed Sun. Italian spoken.

NOVION-PORCIEN 08270 Ardennes **RN 985 Map 6-A2**
♈⊗ **LE FRANCO-BELGE – LE RELAIS DES ROUTIERS** (N° RR AVR
17 499) (Mme Simone **Boniface**) place de la Gare ☎ 24-38-70-06.
Minitel ⊸ 2. Evening meals. Parking.

NOYAL-SUR-VILAINE 35530 Ille-et-Vilaine **Map 8-B1**
♈⊗ **LE RELAIS 35** (N° RR FEV 27 521) (Mme Pascale **Sejelin**) 20,
⌂ avenue du Général-de-Gaulle ☎ 99-00-51-20 ⊸ 13. Closed Sat
4pm to Sun. Coaches welcome. Rest. seats 80. Evening meals
until 11pm. English spoken. Filling station 200m.

NOYANT-LA-PLAINE 49700 Maine-et-Loire **Map 12-B2**
♈⊗ **L'ÉTAPE** (N° RR FEVR 25 821) (M. Michel **Eono**) RD 761
⌂ ☎ 41-59-30-40 ⊸ 7. Closed Sun. Coaches welcome. Rest. seats
80. Evening meals.

NOYAREY 38360 Isère **RN 532 Maps 19-A3 and 24-B1**
♈⊗ **AU BON ACCUEIL DES ROUTIERS** (N° RR FEVR 25 815) (M.
⌂ Jean-Claude **Compe**) rue de la Gare Le Maupas Sassenage ☎
76-53-95-61. **Minitel** ⊸ 11 at 80–130F. Restaurant: home cooking.
Closed Sat afternoon and Sun. Traditional décor. Rest. seats 100.
German, Italian, Spanish spoken. Open 5.30am–11.30pm. Garden
terrace. ⌐ Parking. Sights: le Vercors, Chartreuse.

NOYERS SUR CHER 41140 Loir-et-Cher **Maps 12-A/B3**
♈⊗ **LES NOUETTES** (N° RR JAN 27 510) Mme Beatrice **Lacou**) 110,
rue Nationale ☎ 54-32-76-66. Parking. Service station nearby.

NOYON 60400 Oise **Maps 3-A3**
♈⊗ **LE PARIS-BRUXELLES** (N° RR JUIL 27 644) (M. Dominque
Gugnot) 33, avenue de la Libération ☎ 44-44-01-24. **Minitel** ⊸ 4
at 110F. English spoken. Restaurant: home cooking. Menu to 48F.
À la carte. Dinner to 9.30pm. Closed Sun. Credit cards accepted.
Rest. seats 40. Garden terrace. Parking. Filling station nearby.

NUITS-SAINT-GEORGES 21700 Côte-d'Or **RN 74 Map 14-A3**
♈⊗ ✩✩ **NN HOTEL DES CULTIVATEURS** (N° RR JUN 1 894) (MM.
⌂ **Villemagne Père et Fils**) 12, rue du Général-de-Gaulle ☎
80-61-10-41 ⊸ 15 at 125–260F with showers, bathrooms, WC.
Closed Sun, 15 Dec to 15 Jan. Coaches welcome. Rest. seats 60.
Evening meals to 9pm. English spoken. ⌐ Parking. Sights:
Hospices et chateaux de Beaune, caves de Dijon.

OBJAT 19130 Corrèze **Map 17-A1**
♈⊗ **RELAIS DU PARC** (N° RR JAN 27 492) (Mme Monique **Richard**)
⌂ 1, avenue Poimcaré ☎ 55-84-11-11 ⊸ 14. Filling station nearby.

OCTEVILLE 50130 Manche **RD 3 and 900 Map 4-A1**
♀⊗ **LE VENT D'AMONT** (N° RR MAI 26 885) (M. Jacky **Travers**)
1, rue Jules Ferry ☎ 33-52-16-16. Closed Mon after lunch. Private
car and HGV park (2,200m²). English spoken. Filling station near.

OGEVILLER 54450 Meurthe-et-Moselle **RN 4 Map 10-A2**
⚑ **RELAIS D'OGEVILLER** (N° RR FEV 5500000 13) (M. Christian
Perrette) 8, route de Strasbourg ☎ 83-72-27-82. German spoken.
Restaurant closed Sun.
♀⊗ **RELAIS DE LA VERDURETTE** (N° RR SEP 21 653) (Mme
Besnard) ☎ 33-26-81-97 ⇥ 4. Closed Sat from Oct–Apr. Rest.
seats 60.

OISSEAU LE PETIT 72610 Sarthe **N 138 Map 8-B2**
♀⊗ **HOTEL DE L'ESPERANCE** (N° RR SEP 21 653) (Mme **Besnard**)
☎ 33-26-81-97 ⇥ 4. Closed Sat from Oct–Apr. Rest. seats 60.

OLEMPS 12510 Aveyron **Map 22–B1**
♀⊗ ☆ **NN RELAIS DU PAS** (N° RR JUIN 27 300) (M. Jean-Marc
⌂ **Mayrand**) RD 994 Le Pas Druelle ☎ 65-69-39-11 ⇥ 8 80–100F.
English and Spanish spoken. Evening meals to midnight. Park-
ing. Filling station 800m open 7am–10pm.

ORANGE 84100 Vaucluse **RN 7 Map 24-A2**
♀⊗ **LE MOULIN A VENT** (N° RR JUN 25 031) (M. Henri and Joachim
Garcia) Pont de l'Aigue ☎ 90-34-02-41. Spanish, Italian spoken.

ORBEC 14290 Calvados **RD 31 Map 8-A2**
♀⊗ **LE RELAIS DES ROUTIERS** (N° RR JUN 20 760) (Mme Marie-
Claude **Morel**) 37, rue de Bernay ☎ 37-32-70-70. Closed Sun,
Aug. Evening meals to 8.30pm.

ORGENOY par PONTHIERRY 77310 Seine-et-Marne **RN 7 Map 9-B1**
♀⊗ **LE RELAIS DU KM43** (N° RR OCT 14 982) (M. **Saint-Jean**) ☎
⌂ 60-65-71-01. **Minitel** ⇥ 8. Closed Sat evening, Sun, Aug, Christmas to New Year. Evening meals served until 11.30pm.

ORGON 13660 Bouches-du-Rhône **RN 7 Maps 24-A3 and B3**
♀⊗ **LE BELLEVUE** (N° RR MAI 27 617) (Mme Danielle **Mulatierri**) RN
7 ☎ 90-73-00-24. Evening meals. English and Italian spoken.
Parking.
♀⊗ **AU BEC FIN** (N° RR JUIL 26 948) (M. Michel **Toesca**) RN 7 ☎
90-73-00-49. Closed Sun. Private car park (6,000m²). English,
Italian, Spanish spoken. Filling station open 24 hours.
♀⊗ **RELAIS DES FUMADES** (N° RR AVR 27 256) (M. Jean **Etch-**
⌂ **everry**) ☎ 90-73-00-81. **Minitel** ⇥ 11 100–150F. German and
English spoken. Evening meals served until midnight. Rest. seats
130. Parking. Filling station 3km.

ORLEANS 45100 Loiret **RN 20 and D 951 Map 13-A1**
♀⊗ **LE RELAIS DES QUATRE MARCHES** (N° RR DEC 16 327) (M.
⌂ Pierre **Guyot**) 163, route de Saint-Mesmin ☎ 38-66-31-12 ⇥ 5.
Open 7am–10pm. Closed Sat evening, Sun, Aug. Evening meals
to 10pm. Home cooking. Menu 46–50F. Modern décor. Rest.
seats 65. Sights: Les Bords du Loiret.

ORNANS

ORNANS 25290 Doubs **RD 67 Map 14-B3**
☆ **NN HÔTEL LE PROGRÈS** (N° RR AOU 20 800) (M. **Perriot-Comte**) 11, rue Jacques-Gervais ☎ 81-62-16-79. Minitel ◄ 16 at 140–220F with shower, bathroom, telephone. Directions: route Besançon/Pontarlier through the Loue valley. Restaurant: regional home cooking. Specialities: truite, terrine maison, escargots maison. Menu 55–180F. Children's menu. À la carte. Self-service. Closed Sun evening (out of season). Credit cards accepted. 2 dining rooms 180 seats. Rest rooms. ◄ Parking. Coaches welcome. Pursuits: fishing, shooting, canoeing, swimming, tennis. Sights: Vallée de la Loue, lakes, maison nationale de la pêche à Ornans, Trépot museum of cheese-making and vineyards and wine.

OUISTREHAM 14150 Calvados **RD 514 Map 4-B2**
AU COIN DU PORT (N° RR MAI 27 278) (M. Claude **Morin**) 90, avenue Michel-Cableu ☎ 31-97-15-22. Closed Sun afternoon (all day low season), Oct and 1 Apr–30 May. Coaches welcome. Rest. seats 60. Evening meals served until midnight.

OURVILLE-EN-CAUX 76450 Seine-Maritime **Map 4-A3**
BAR DE LA PLACE (N° RR MAI 25 924) (M. Jean-Pierre **Pouchet**) place Jean-Picard ☎ 35-27-60-01 ◄ 10. Rest. seats 45.

OZOIR LA FERRIERE 77330 Seine-et-Marne **Map 1-B3**
LA TERRASSE (N° RR FEV 27 525) (M. Jean-François **Audebert**) 17, avenue du Général-de-Gaulle ☎ 60-28-20-36. Closed Sun, Aug. Filling station nearby open 24 hours.

PACADIÈRE (LA) 42310 Loire **Map 16-B3**
LE RELAIS DU LAC (N° RR MARS 27 210) (M. Marcel **Vernay**) RN 7 ☎ 77-64-36-08 ◄ 5. Dinner to 2am. Closed Sat and Jun. Rest. seats 80. HGV Parking.

PACÉ par ALENÇON 61250 Orne **RN 12 Map 8-B2**
LE RELAIS DES ROUTIERS Tobacconist (N° RR SEPT 12 434) (M. Marcel **Bruneau**) 12, route de Bretagne (7 km from Alençon) ☎ 33-27-70-69. Closed Sat afternoon, Sun afternoon, Jan. Coaches welcome. Rest. seats 70. Evening meals to 9.30pm. ◄ Parking.

PAIMPOL 22500 Côtes-du-Nord **Map 7-A2**
LE TRISKEL (N° RR NOV 27 729) (Mmes Martine Josiane **Dagorrio Pettier**) 15, avenue Chateaubriand ☎ 96-20-82-72. A little English spoken. Restaurant: home cooking. Menu 42F. Open 7am–9pm. Lunch 11.45am–2pm. Dinner 6–9.30pm. Closed Sat afternoon, Sun, bank holidays, Aug. Lorry parking. Filling station nearby.

PAJAY 38260 Isère **RD 73 Map 18-B3**
LE RELAIS DE MA PETITE AUBERGE (N° RR JUL 19 435) (Mme Huguette **Vivier**) La Côte-Saint-André ☎ 74-54-26-06. Minitel ◄ 6. Closed Sept 15 days. Rest. seats 80. English, some German spoken. Evening meals served until 9pm. Menus 50–120F. Specialities: grenouilles, lotte à l'Américaine, gratin Dauphinois.

PANTIN 93500 Seine-St-Denis Porte de Pantin **RN 3 Map 1-A/2-3**
RESTODEM SARL (N° RR JUN 25 026) (M. **Demougin**) 110, bis avenue du Général Leclerc. Directions: take CD 115 to SNCF

☎ 48-44-75-84. **Minitel**. Closed Sat, Sun. Coaches welcome. Rest. seats 280 + 40. Showers for drivers. Restaurant: menu à la carte. Self-service. Credit cards accepted. Rest room. Garden terrace. ⊮ Parking. Sights: Paris (1km), Museum of carts at Pantin.

♀⊗ **EUROPE TABAC SABRIE** (N° RR AVR 23 220) (M. Georges **Sabrie**) 203, avenue Jean-Lolive ☎ 48-45-03-17. Closed Sun. German, English, Spanish, Italian spoken. Evening meals. International coach station.

♀⊗ **LE RELAIS DU PONT** (N° RR DEC 27 472) (SARL) 25, avenue Edouard Vailant ☎ 48-45-80-73. Closed Sat, Sun and Aug. Evening meals. English, German, Spanish, Italian, Portuguese spoken.

PARIGNÉ 35133 Ille-et-Vilaine **CD 19 ET 108 Map 8-A/B1**

♀⊗ **FRANK'ELLE** (N° RR OCT 27 066) (M. Franck **Rousset**) 12, rue de la Mairie ☎ 99-97-22-90. Closed Mon pm. Filling station 2.5km.

PARIGNE-LE-POLIN 72330 Sarthe **RN 23 Map 12-A2**

♀⊗ **LA CHESNAIE** (N° RR AOUT 27 650) (Mme Chantal **Marg**) RN 33 La Chesnaie ☎ 43-87-90-70. Dinner to 9.30pm. Closed Sat. Parking. Filling station nearby open 7am–10pm.

PARIGNY 50600 Manche **Map 8A-1**

♀⊗ **HOTEL DU CHEMIN DE FER** (N° RR FEV 27 519) (M. Gilbert **Lecornu**) La Gare. Direction: the road Caen/Rennes between Mortain and St. Hilaire ☎ 33-49-10-55. Restaurant: home cooking. Menu to 47F. Menu à la carte. Lunch 11.30am–3pm. Dinner 7–10pm. Closed Sun (low season). Rest. seats 25 in 2 rooms ⊨ 4 80–160F with shower. Open 6.45am–11pm. ⊮ Parking. Filling station nearby. Sights: Le Mont St Michel (40km), Lac de Vezins (8km), Villedieu (city of copper).

PARIS 75000

♀⊗ **LE RELAIS CHEZ LEON** (N° RR JAN 37 789) (Mme **Grange**) 5, rue de l'Isly ☎ 43-87-42-77. Closed Sun, Aug. Dinner to 9pm.

PARIS 75013

♀⊗ **AU RENDEZ-VOUS DES ROUTIERS – CHEZ SMAIL** (N° RR JUL ⌂ 22 881) (M. Mohand **Naït**) 117, quai de la Gare ☎ 45-84-57-06 ⊨ 24. Evening meals to 11pm.

PARIS 75018

♀⊗ **LE RELAIS DES ROUTIERS** (N° RR OCT 15 413) (M. Bernard **Dubreuil**) 50 bis, rue Marx-Dormoy. Direction: the gate to the Chapelle Gare du Nord ☎ 46-07-93-80. Closed Sun and Aug. Evening meals served until 10pm. Coaches welcome. Rest. seats 50. Home cooking. Specialities: couscous, paella, choucroute. Menu 55–75F. Credit cards accepted. Traditional décor.

PARIS 75020

♀⊗ **ETOILE DE LISBONNE** (N° RR AOUT 26 622) (M. Manuel **Duarte**) 139, boulevard Davout ☎ 43-61-04-80. Closed Aug. Spanish, Portuguese spoken.

PARON 89100 Yonne **RN 60 Map 9-B2**

♀⊗ **LE RELAIS DE ST-BOND** (N° RR MARS 25 835) (M. Daniel **Millard**) 32, avenue Jean-Jaurès ☎ 86-95-41-41. Closed Sun.

PAU

PAU 64000 Pyrénées-Atlantiques **RN 117/134 Maps 20-B3 and 21-A3**
♈⊗ ☆ **NN HOTEL DU BOIS LOUIS** (N° RR SEPT 23 482) (M. **Bareille**)
⌂ 18, avenue Gaston-Lacoste ☎ 59-27-34-98 ⊷ 8. Closed Sun and
first 2 weeks Aug. Rest. seats 65. Evening meals served until
10pm.

PAUILLAC 33250 Gironde **RD 2 Maps 15-A3 and 20-A1**
♈⊗ **LE YACHTING** (N° RR JAN 26 136) (Mme Louisette **Puyfourcat**)
⌂ 12, Port de Plaisance ☎ 56-59-06-43 ⊷ 16. Closed Sat in winter.
Coaches welcome. Rest. seats 100. Evening meals.
♈⊗ **LA TORCHE** (N° RR NOV 27 099) (Mme Maryse **Eesinger**) 2,
⌂ quai A. Depichon ☎ 56-59-19-20 ⊷ 5 50–120F with showers.
Closed Sat, Jan. English spoken. Home cooking. Menu 55–150F.
Children's menu. À la carte. Lunch 12–3pm. Dinner 7–10.30pm.
Rest. seats 50. Evening meals served until 10.30pm. Parking for
cars.

PAULHAGUET 43230 Haute-Loire **RN 102 Map 17-A3**
♈⊗ **LE COQ HARDI** (N° RR MAR 22 715) (Mme Marie-Louise
⌂ **Meyronneine**) La Chomette ☎ 71-76-62-29. Closed Sat, Nov.
Rest. seats 60.

PAVILLONS-SOUS-BOIS (LES) 93320 Seine-St-Denis **RN 3 Map 1-A3**
♈⊗ **CAFÉ DU STADE** (N° RR NOV 27 453) (M. Marc **Muller**) 31, rue
Anatole-France ☎ 48-48-10-98. Closed Sun, Aug.

PEAGE (LE) (SERAZEREUX par CHATEAUNEUF-EN-THYMERAIS)
28210 Eure-et-Loir **RN 154 Map 8-A3**
♈⊗ **AU BON ACCUEIL** (N° RR JUL 27 328) (Mme Élaine **Herisson**) Le
Péage ☎ 37-65-22-49. **Minitel**. Closed Sat evening and Sun.
Evening meals served to 10pm. Parking. Filling station nearby.

PECHEREAU (LE) 36200 Indre **Map 16 A-1**
♈⊗ **RESTAURANT DE L'AERODROME** (N° RR SEPT 27 671) (Mme
Christiane **Luduc**) RD 929 La Bourdine ☎ 54-24-20-91. **Minitel**.
Phone point. Filling station nearby open 6am–10pm.

PEDERNEC 22540 Côtes-du-Nord **Map 7-A2**
⊗♈ **RELAIS DE MAUDEZ** (N° RR JUL 26 614) (M. Denis **Dutillet-
Maudez**) ☎ 96-45-31-28. Closed Sun.

PELLEVOISIN 36180 Indre **RD 11 Map 12-B3**
♈⊗ **LES ROUTIERS DE LA POSTE CHEZ BABETTE** (N° RR MARS 28
⌂ 837) (Mme Elisabeth **Petit**) 30, rue Jean-Giraudoux ☎ 54-39-03-78
⊷ 5. Closed Mon evening and 1 week in Feb and 1 in Sept. Rest.
seats 70. English spoken. Filling station nearby open 8am–
8.30pm.

PELUSSIN 42410 Loire **Map 2-B1**
♈⊗ **LE CLUB** (N° RR JUN 26 932) (M. Alan **Daveau**) rue Antoine
⌂ Eyraud ☎ 74-87-61-69 ⊷ 6. English and German spoken. Evening meals served until 11pm. Rest. seats 60. Parking. Filling
station nearby open 8pm.

PERCY 50410 Manche **RD 999 Map 8-A1**
♈⊗ **LE RELAIS DE LA GARE** (N° RR OCT 24 704) (M. Bernard
Guillotte) 4, rue de l'Ancienne Gare. Directions: turn left on

entering Percy to Saint Lo ☎ 33-61-20-96. **Minitel**. Restaurant: home cooking. Specialities: jambon fumé and omelette. Menu to 42F (midday) and 50F (evening). Lunch 12. Dinner 7–10pm. Closed Sun, bank holidays and 15–28 Feb. Modern décor. Rest. seats 70 ⊨ 4 at 80–100F with shower, WC. Open 7am–10pm. ⊨ Parking. Sights: Villedieu les Poêles (9km), Le Mont St Michel (55km).

PERIGNY 03120 Allier **Map 16 A/B-3**

♀⊗ ☆ **LE RELAIS DE PERIGNY** (N° RR DEC 27 483) (M. Patrice
⌂ **Cardinaud**) Le Bourg. Directions: 3km along the RN 7 to La-palisse ☎ 70-99-84-57. Restaurant: regional home cooking. Menu 51F. Open 24 hours. Closed Sat and Sun. Credit cards accepted. Traditional décor. rest. seats 60 ⊨ 6 from 100–150F. Rest room. Parking. Sights: Vichy (20km), Lapalisse (5km).

PERN 46170 Lot **Map 22 A-1**

♀⊗ **LE RELAIS DES CIGALES** (N° RR MARS 27 573) (M. José-Manuel **Fernandez**) RN 20 Saint Barthelemy, Castelnau Montratier ☎ 65-21-97-49. Restaurant specialities: confit d'ole, magrets, cassoulets au confit d'ole. Menu 55–70F. Closed Sun (low season) ⊨ 4. Parking.

PERONNE 80200 Somme **RN 17 Maps 5-B3 and 6-A1**

♀⊗ **CHEZ BÉATRICE** (N° RR SEPT 26 320) (M. Serge **Seilier**) 61,
⌂ route de paris ☎ 22-84-10-82. **Minitel** ⊨ 6. Closed Sun, 2nd fortnight Aug. Easter week. Meals served until 9.30pm.

PERONNE-ASSEVILLERS 80200 Somme **Autoroute A1 Maps 5-A3 and 6-A1**

♀⊗ **ACCOR L'ARCHE** (N° RR 1831) (M. Christian **Soma**) Aire de Service d'Asservilliers Ouest sens Paris/Lille Autoroute ☎ 22-85-20-35.

PERPIGNAN 66000 Pyrénées-Orientales **Map 23-A3**

♀⊗ **POLYGONE NORD** (N° RR JAN 27 756) (SARL **Gemini**) 10, rue Beau de Rochas ZI Nord ☎ 68-61-35-15. Closed Sun. Specialities: paella, grillades à la Plancha, Parillades. Menu 50–70F. Lunch 11am–2.30pm. Dinner 6.30–10pm. Lorry park. Filling station 500m.

PERROS GUIREC 22700 Côtes-du-Nord **Map 7 A-2**

♀⊗ **LE CORMORAN** (N° RR JUN 27 628) (M. Bernard **Spas**) 41,
⌂ boulevard Clémenceau ☎ 96-26-20-65. Restaurant: dinner to 11pm. Closed 10 days in Feb ⊨ 7 at 100–180F.

PERRUSSON 37600 Indre-et-Loire **RN 143 Map 12-B3**

♀⊗ **LE RELAIS DES ROUTIERS** (N° RR JUN 16 590) (M. Kleber
⌂ **Lanchais**) 3, rue de l'Indre ☎ 47-59-39-76 ⊨ 8. Closed Sun evening, 15 days in Aug. Rest. seats 120.

PERTUIS 84120 Vaucluse **Map 24-B3**

♀⊗ **LE VICTOR HUGO** (N° RR OCT 27 705) (M. Jacky **Chalot**) 143, boulevard Victor Hugo. Directions: route de Cavaillon ☎ 90-79-12-29. Closed Sun. Italian and English spoken. Restaurant: home cooking. Menu 54F. Dinner to 11pm. Traditional décor. Rest. seats 40. Garden terrace. ⊨ Parking. Filling station 1km, open 6.30am–9pm. Sights: Château d'Ansouis-Lourmavin (15km), étang de la Bonde (10km), Château de la Tour d'Aigues (8km).

PERUSE (LA)

PERUSE (LA) 16270 Charente **RN 141 Map 15 B-2**
Ⓨ⊗ **LES ROUTIERS** (N° RR JAN 27 493) (M. André **Troussieux**)
Roumazieres Loubert. Directions: Limoges-Angoulèmes ☎ 456-
71-11-73. Restaurant: home cooking. Lunch 11am–2pm. Closed
Sun, Aug. Credit cards accepted. Traditional décor. Rest. seats
30. ⊶ Parking. Service station open 8.30am–7pm 30m away.

PETIT-FOSSARD (LE) 77130 Seine-et-Marne **RN 5 Map 9-B2**
Ⓨ⊗ **LE RELAIS DU PETIT-FOSSARD** (N° RR OCT 20 572) (M. Jean
🏠 **Guillard**) ☎ 64-32-03-28 and 64-32-17-47. Restaurant: home
cooking. Menu à la carte. Dinner to 11pm. Closed Sat afternoon,
Sun, Aug. Credit cards accepted. Rest. seats 118 ⊶ 8 with
showers. Parking.

PETIT-REDERCHING 57410 Moselle **RN 410 Map 10-B1**
Ⓨ⊗ **REST DE LA GARE** (N° RR OCT 8 908) (M. Bernard **Vogel**) 6, rue
de Strasbourg. Directions: near to the station ☎ 87-09-81-09.
Minitel. Closed Sat, 15 July–16 Aug. Evening meals to 8.30pm.
Restaurant: home cooking. Credit cards accepted. Rest. seats 95.
Garden terrace. ⊶ Parking. Sights: Citadelle de Bitche, musée et
fabrique de cristal de Meisenthal.

PETIVILLE 14390 Calvados **RD 513 Map 4-B2**
Ⓨ⊗ **LE COLOMBIER** (N° RR NOV 26 103) (M. Gèrard **Baudel**)
Cabourg ☎ 31-78-00-67. **Minitel.** Closed Sun, Dec. Restaurant:
home cooking. Menu 50F. Children's menu. Dinner to 8.30pm.
Credit cards accepted. Rest. seats 35.

PEYREHORADE 40300 Landes **Map 20 A-2**
Ⓨ⊗ **BAR DES SPORTS** (N° RR NOV 27 731) (Mme Marysie **Dulucq**) 6,
rue du Château ☎ 58-73-09-51. Restaurant: menu 50F. Closed
Thurs and beg. of Jun. Filling station nearby open 6am–9pm.

PEYRIAC-DE-MER 11440 Aude **RN 9 Map 23-A3**
Ⓨ⊗ **RELAIS PORTE DES CORBIÈRES** (N° RR NOV 27 109) (Mme
Béatrice **Vincent**) Route N9. Directions: opposite the Sigean
African Reserve ☎ 68-48-30-88. Closed Sun. Restaurant: home
cooking. Specialities: confit de canard, fruits de mer. Menu 50F.
Menu à la carte. Lunch 11am–3pm. Dinner 6–11.30pm. Rest. seats
85.

PEZOU 41100 Loir-et-Cher **RN 10 Map 12-A3**
Ⓨ⊗ **RELAIS D'ARGENTEUIL** (N° RR JAN 26 142) (M. Pierre **Hauville**)
🏠 locally called Fontaine RN 10 ☎ 54-23-42-47. **Minitel.** Restaurant:
home cooking. Lunch 11.30am–2pm. Dinner to 10.30pm. Closed
Sat from 11am, Sun, Aug and end of Dec. Credit cards accepted.
Traditional décor. Rest. seats 70 ⊶ 6 at 77–150F with shower.
Open 5am–11.30pm. ⊶ Parking.
Ⓨ⊗ **L'ÉTAPE** (N° RR MARS 27 214) (M. Claude **Chève**) RN 10 ☎
54-23-42-85. Closed Sat pm, Sun and 1st 2 weeks Aug. Filling
station nearby open 6am–midnight.

PIA 6380 Pyrénées-Orientales **Map 23-A3**
Ⓨ⊗ **AU P'TIT NICE** (N° RR OCT 26 358) (M. Jean Louis **Leone**)
RN 9 5km ☎ 68-61-05-70. Closed Sun. Spanish, Italian, Arabic
spoken. Evening meals served until 11pm. Coaches welcome.
Rest. seats 50.

PIOLENC

PIACE 72170 Sarthe **RN 138 Map 8-B2**
♈⊗ **LES DEUX RENARDS** (N° RR SEPT 27 004) (M. Jérôme **Brilliet**) RN 138 Le Bourg ☎ 43-97-02-16. Closed Sat, Sun. Regional home cooking. Children's menu. Coaches welcome. Rest. seats 66. Evening meals served until 11.30pm. Filling station 4km. Credit cards accepted. Parking. Sights: Les Alpes Mancelles (20km).
♈⊗ **AU RENDEZVOUS DES ROUTIERS** (N° RR JAN 27 498) Mme Brahim **Ghozrane-Ghozrane**) 71, avenue Lenine ☎ 48-26-53-59. Evening meals. Closed Sun.

PIERREFITTE-NESTALAS 65260 Hautes-Pyrénées **RN 21 Map 21-A3**
♈⊗ **LE RELAIS DE BEL-AIR** (N° RR JUN 21 131) (M. Raymond ⌂ **Bellocq**) 5, rue Lavoisier ☎ 62-92-75-22 ⇥ 11. Spanish spoken. Coaches welcome. Rest. seats 25.

PIERREFITTE-RONAI 61160 Orne **RN 158 Map 8-A2**
♈⊗ **LE PIERREFITTE** (N° RR JANV 27 143) (M. Yves **Delaunay**) Direction: towards Argentan/Falaise 9km from Argentan ☎ 33-35-95-06. Closed Mon and Feb. Restaurant: home cooking. Lunch 11.30am–2.30pm. Dinner 7–11.30pm. Credit cards accepted. Parking. Traditional décor. Garden terrace. ⇥ Filling station nearby open 24 hours. Sights: Falaise (10km).

PIERREFITTE SUR SEINE 93380 Seine-St-Denis **Map 1-A3**
♈⊗⇥**LE NORMANDIE** (N° RR JUN 24 982) (Mme **Vidal**) 105, avenue Galliéni ☎ 48-26-55-62. **Minitel**. Closed Sun, 2nd fortnight Sept. Evening meals served until 10pm. Some English, Spanish spoken. Restaurant: regional home cooking. Specialities: confit de canard, paella, escalope Normande. Menu from 53–74F. Children's menu. À la carte. Credit cards accepted. Rest. seats 35. Hotel with showers. Garden terrace. ⇥ Parking. Sights: Château d'Ecouen (5km), Abbaye de Royaumont, Château de Chantilly (15km).

PIEUX (LES) 50340 Manche **RD 904 and 265 Map 4-A/B1**
♈⊗ **T'CHEU P'TIT LOUIS** (N° RR MAR 23 687) (M. Louis **Mabire**) 17, rue Centrale ☎ 33-52-43-18.

PINEUILH 33220 Gironde **Map 21 A-1**
♈⊗ **L'ABBALESTRIER** (N° RR DEC 27 743) (Mme Andrée **Teysier**) route de Bergerac. Direction: the Bordeaux/Libourne road towards Bergerac ☎ 57-46-27-90. Showers for drivers. Restaurant: regional home cooking. Specialities: gratin dauphinois, lotte à l'américaine. Menu from 50–160F. Children's menu. À la carte. Lunch 11.30am–3pm. Dinner 7–10pm. Closed the 2nd week of Jan. Credit cards accepted. Traditional décor. Rest. seats 120 ⇥ 5 to 130F (breakfast included) with shower, WC. Garden terrace. ⇥ Parking for cars. Filling station nearby open 7–9pm. Sights: Château de Duras (28km), Bordeaux (60km), Sainte Foy la Grande (1km), Saint Emilion (30km), goose and duck farm.

PINOLS 43200 Haute-Loire **RN 590 Map 17-A3**
♈⊗ **HÔTEL DES VOYAGEURS** (N° RR JUL 19 853) (Mme **Cornet**) ☎ ⌂ 71-74-11-42 ⇥ 9 per night. Rest. seats 50. Meals until 10pm.

PIOLENC 84420 Vaucluse **Autoroute A7 Map 24-A2**
♈⊗ **LE COMMERCE** (N° RR NOV 25 182) (M. Roger **Sambucini**) ⇥ place Cours Corsin ☎ 90-29-60-14. Closed Wed, Nov. Coaches

PIPRIAC

Piolenc continued
welcome. Rest. seats 60. English spoken. Evening meals served until 9pm. Restaurant: home cooking. Specialities: fillet de boeuf aux morilles, poulet, écrevisses. Menu 51F. Menu à la carte. Garden terrace. ⌗ Parking. Sights: Arc de Triomphe à Orange (5km), Palais des Popes, Pont Saint Benèzet.

PIPRIAC 35550 Ille-et-Vilaine **RD 777 Map 7-B3**
☖⊗ ☆ **NN LE RELAIS DE LA TOUR D'AUVERGNE** (N° RR NOV 22 093)
🏠 (M. Michel **Gérard**) 7, rue de l'Avenir ☎ 99-34-41-34 and 99-34-34-85 ◄ 10 90–140F (additional beds for children) with shower, WC, TV. Open 7am–midnight. Restaurant: regional cooking. Speciality: poissons au beurre blanc. Menu 48–140F. Dinner to 9pm. Closed Mon evening and 15 days in Feb. Credit cards accepted. Rest. seats 105. Sights: castle, glass blowing and craft shops.

PITHIVIERS 45300 Loiret **Map 9 B-1**
☖⊗ **RELAIS D'INTVILLE – CHEZ LULU** (N° RR SEPT 27 387) (Mme Lucienne **Loeillet**) 15, Grande Rue ☎ 38-39-71-70. Restaurant: home cooking. Menu to 53F. Children's menu. Lunch 11.30am–3pm. Dinner 7–8pm. Closed Sat, Sun, Aug. Filling station nearby.

PLAINE-SAINT-DENIS 93210 Seine-St-Denis **RN 1 Porte de la Chapelle Map 1-A2**
☖⊗ **LE CRISTAL** (N° RR AVR 27 584) (Mme Janine **Paliwoda**) 101, avenue du Président-Wilson ☎ 42-43-75-58. Closed Sat, Sun.

PLAINTEL 22940 Côtes-du-Nord **Map 7-A2**
☖⊗ **A LA DESCENTE DES CHAOS** (N° RR AOU 25 616) (M.
🏠 Jean-Claude **Bonenfant**) gare de Plaintel ☎ 96-32-16-05 ◄ 8. Closed Tue afternoon, Sun afternoon, Aug. English spoken.
☖⊗ **LE SÉBASTOPOL** (N° RR MARS 26 474) (Mme Colette **Helary**) route de Sébastopol ☎ 96-32-15-74. Closed Sun, Aug. Coaches welcome. Rest. seats c.100. English, German spoken.

PLAISANCE-DU-GERS 32160 Gers **RN 646 Map 12-A2**
☖⊗ **LA PERGOLA** (N° RR OCT 14 040) (Mme Christiane **Lagisquet**)
🏠 11, allée des Ormeaux ☎ 62-69-30-22. **Minitel** ◄ 10 75–150F with shower. Open 7am–11pm. Closed Sat in low season, 24 Dec–3 Jan. Regional home cooking. Specialities: foie gras, confit, magret. Menu 50–150F. Menu à la carte. Coaches welcome. Rest. seats 80. Evening meals until 9pm. Credit cards accepted. Sights: Pyrénées and sea.

PLEINE SELVE 33820 Gironde **Map 15 B-3**
☖⊗ ☆ **RELAIS DU CHATEAU** (N° RR SEPT 27 658) (Mme Martine
🏠 **Boucher**) RN 137 Bel-Air ☎ 57-32-90-58. Restaurant: dinner until midnight. Closed Wed (low season). English spoken ◄ 12 110–180F. Parking. Filling station 3km open 6.30am–8pm.

PLENÉE JUGON 22640 Côtes-du-Nord **RN 12 Map 7-A3**
☖⊗ **LES GARENNES** (N° RR SEPT 27 007) (M. Jean **Elings**) locally known as **Les Garennes** ☎ 96-34-52-11. English, Spanish and Dutch spoken. Direction: take the exit to Rennes on going towards St Brieuc. Restaurant: regional home cooking. Specialities: fruite farcie aux cèpes, paella, couscous, cassoulet. Dinner to midnight. Closed Sun. Credit cards accepted. Rest. seats 70. ⌗ Parking. Sights: Abbaye de Bacquin, Lac de Jugon.

PLEUMEUR-GAUTIER 22740 Côtes-du-Nord **CD 33 Map 7-A2**
Ⓨ⊗ **CHEZ CINDY** (N° RR OCT 27 402) (M. Herré **Le Foll**) route de
Tréquier, La Croiz Neuve ☎ 96-92-42-19. Closed Sat and 3 weeks
in Aug. Evening meals served until 9pm. Restaurant: home
cooking. Rest. seats 38. Garden terrace. Credit cards accepted.
Parking. Filling station nearby open 9am–10pm.

PLEYBEN 29190 Finistère **RN 787 and Dle 787 Map 7-A2**
Ⓨ⊗ **HÔTEL DES VOYAGEURS** (N° RR SEPT 26 648) (M. Jean-Yves
Marzin) 17, Grande Place, Charles de Gaulle ☎ 98-26-61-06 ➥ 7
85–120F. Restaurant: home cooking. Specialities: fruits de mer,
couscous. Children's menu. À la carte. Lunch 12–2pm. Dinner
7.30–9pm. Closed Sun, 3 last weeks Aug. Credit cards accepted.
Rest. seats 64. ➥ Parking. Sights: Château de Trévarez, Lou-
crouau, Quimper (30km).

PLOERMEL 56800 Morbihan **RN 24 Map 7-B3**
Ⓨ⊗ **LES ROUTIERS** (N° RR DEC 20 052) (Mme Solange **Rio**) route de
⌂ Rennes ☎ 97-74-00-48. **Minitel** ➥ 11 70–95F. Closed Sat, Sept.
Home cooking. Menu 45–110F. Children's menu. Coaches wel-
come. Rest. seats 150. Evening meals served until 10pm. Credit
cards accepted. Parking.

PLOMBIERES-LES-BAINS 88370 Vosges **RN 57 Maps 14-B2 and 10-A3**
Ⓨ⊗ ☆ **NN LE RELAIS STRASBOURGEOIS** (N° RR AVR 6 049) (M.
⌂ Alain **Robert**) 3, place Beaumarchais ☎ 29-66-00-70. **Minitel**.
Restaurant: regional home cooking. Specialities: terrine maison,
fruites à la crème, vacherin glacé. Menu à la carte. Dinner to
9pm. Closed on Sun (1 Oct–1 Apr) and Nov ➥ 13 80–160F with
shower, bathroom, WC, TV. Open 7am–10pm. Garden terrace.
➥ Parking. Filling station opposite hotel. Ping pong. Sights:
thermal resort.

PLOMELIN 29000 Finistère **RN 785 Map 7-B1**
Ⓨ⊗ **LE RELAIS DE L'AVANTAGE** (N° RR JUN 10 737) (M. Alain **Le
Vergos**) ☎ 98-94-22-06.

PLOUAGAT 22170 Côtes-du-Nord **RN 12 Quintin exit CD7 7-A2**
Ⓨ⊗ **CHEZ PIERRETTE** (N° RR AOUT 26 296) (**SARL Drouin**) ZA de
Fournello Sortie Quintin ☎ 96-74-28-23. Closed Sat midday, Sun,
bank holidays. Coaches welcome. Rest. seats 124. Evening meals
until 1am. Parking. Filling station open 24 hours.

PLOUEDERN 29220 Finistère **RN 12 Map 7-A1**
Ⓨ⊗ **LE RELAIS KERIEL** (N° RR JUN 24 264) (Mme Marie **Gac**)
Keriel-Landerneau ☎ 98-20-82-53. **Minitel**. Closed Fri evening,
last 2 weeks Sept. Coaches welcome. Rest. seats 125. Evening
meals served until 9pm. English spoken.

PLOUER-SUR-RANCE 22490 Côtes-du-Nord **RD 366 Map 7-A3**
Ⓨ⊗ **LE BON ACCUEIL CHEZ THEO** (N° RR MARS 26 483) (M. Théo
⊸ **Yris**) La Gourbanière ☎ 96-86-91-67. Closed Mon, Aug. Dinner to
9pm. Rest. seats 130.

POLOUGOUMELEN 56400 Morbihan **RN 165 Map 11-A1**
Ⓨ⊗ **LE KENYAH**(N° RR MAI 26 893) (M. Joël **Boriller**), Zone
Commerciale du Kenyah ☎ 97-56-25-37. Closed Sun. Public car

Polougoumelen continued
park. English spoken. Filling station near. Coaches welcome.
Rest. seats 120. Evening meals to 11pm.

PLOUGUENAST 22150 Côtes-du-Nord **RN 168 Map 7-A2**
♈⊗ **LE RELAIS DU SQUARE** (N° RR JUL 20 257) (Mme Sylviane
Lafon-Sagory) 5 rue d'Enfer ☎ 96-28-760-47. Dinner to 9pm.
Closed Sat and Aug.

PLOUHINEC 29780 Finistère **Map 7 B-1**
♈⊗ **RESTO GRILL "AN DOAL MEN"** (N° RR DEC 27 470) (M. Daniel
Ogor) 3, rue du General-Leclerc ☎ 98-70-76-20. Closed Sun.
Evening meals until 9pm. English spoken. Parking. Filling station
nearby open 8am–8pm.

PLOUIGNEAU 29610 Finistère **Map 7-A2**
♈⊗ **LE RELAIS DES SPORTS** (N° RR JAN 26 151) (M. Paul **Talguen**)
18, rue du 9 Août. Direction: towards centre of town ☎ 98-67-71-
37. Closed Sun (except for banquets), 15 days in Aug. Coaches
welcome. Rest. seats 65. Restaurant: regional. Specialities: fruits
de mer, choucroute maison, couscous. Menu 45F. Children's
menu. Lunch 12–2.30pm. Dinner 7–10pm. Credit cards accepted.
Modern décor. Parking.

PLOUNEVEZ-MOEDEC 22810 Côtes-du-Nord **RN 12 main road exit
D 11 Map 7-A2**
♈⊗ **AUX ROUTIERS – LE RELAIS DU BEG-AR-C'HRA** (N° RR JAN 3
⌂ 717) (M. Jean-Marie **Rubeus**) N 12 Berg-ar-c'hra exit (D11)
☎ 96-38-61-08. **Minitel** ⊷ 11 (6 deluxe) Closed Sat, Sun, 10 days
between 20 Aug–20 Sept. Restaurant: home cooking. Specialities:
fruits de mer. Lunch 12–2pm. Dinner 7.30–10pm. Coaches welcome. Rest. seats 160. English spoken. Credit cards accepted.
Traditional décor. Rest. seats 140. Parking. Sights: the sea
(20km), lakes (10km).

PLOUNEVEZ-QUINTIN 22110 Côtes-du-Nord **RN 790 Map 7-A/B2**
♈⊗ **LE RELAIS DES ROUTIERS** (N° RR MAR 14 273) (Mme **Martin**)
place de l'Eglise ☎ 96-24-54-05. **Minitel**. Closed Sat, 15 Aug
–1 Sept.

PLOURAY 56770 Morbihan **Map 7-B2**
♈⊗ **LE RELAIS DES SPORTS** (N° RR JUL 24 642) (M. Léandre **Le
Lain**) 2, rue de l'Ellé ☎ 97-23-90-18.

POITIERS 86000 Vienne **RN 10 Map 15-B1**
♈⊗ **LE RELAIS DES DOUVES** (N° RR OCT 20 854) (Mme **Gremillon**)
2, avenue de la Libération ☎ 49-37-80-04 ⊷ 5 80–140F with
shower, bathroom. Open 7am–1am. Regional home cooking.
Children's menu. À la carte. Coaches welcome. Rest. seats 90.
Evening meals served until 11.30pm. English, German spoken.

POIX TERRON 08430 Ardennes **Map 6-A2**
♈⊗ **LE GODILLOT** (N° RR OCT 26 080) (M. José **Michel**) 26, place de la
Gare opposite the chemist ☎ 24-35-61-46. **Minitel**. Restaurant:
home cooking. Specialities: couscous, lasagnes maison. Menu
49.50F. Lunch 11.45am–2pm. Dinner 7.30–9pm. Closed Sat, Sun.
Credit cards accepted. Rest. seats 30 ⊷ 6 80F with shower. ⌁ Lorry
parking. Sights: Vallée de la Meuse (30km), Lac de Bairen (15km).

POMMEVIC 82400 Tarn-et-Garonne **RN 113 Map 21-B2**
♀⊗ ☆☆ **A LA BONNE AUBERGE** (N° RR OCT 12 514) (M. Pierre
⌂⇌ **Hume**) Route Nationale ☎ 63-39-56-69 ⊶ 15 150–250F with
shower, bath, WC, TV, telephone. Open 7am–11pm. Closed Sat
evening and 2 weeks in Nov. Coaches welcome. Rest. seats 180.
Evening meals served until 9pm. Regional home cooking.
Specialities: magret de canard, pintade au porto, foie gras.
Menus from 55–130F. Children's menu. À la carte. Credit cards
accepted. ⊭ Parking.

POMPAIRE 79200 Deux-Sèvres **Map 15 A-1**
♀⊗ **LA CLE DES CHAMPS** (N° RR JANV 27 749) (Mme Yolande
Dubin) Route de Saint Maixent ☎ 49-95-20-75. **Minitel**. Restau-
rant: home cooking. Specialities: cuisses de grenouilles, anguille
provençale, plateau de fruits de mer. Menu 50–99F. Children's
menu. À la carte. Open 7am–7pm. Lunch 11am–3pm. Closed Sun.
Credit cards accepted. Modern décor. Rest. seats 40. ⊭
Parking. Filling station nearby. Sights: Parthenay (medieval city).

PONS 17800 Charente-Maritime **Map 15-A2**
♀⊗ **RESTO-GRILL CHARENTOTEL** Autoroute A10 Aire de Saint-
Léger ☎ 46-91-95-30. Coaches welcome. Rest. seats 200. Even-
ing meals served until 10.15pm.

PONT-AUDEMER 27500 Eure **RN 180 Map 4-B3**
♀⊗ **A LA MIRABELLE** (N° RR JUN 25 439) (M. Renaud **Pierrel**) 4, rue
Notre Dame-du-Pré ☎ 32-41-04-36. Restaurant closed Sun. Rest.
seats 40 ⊶ 3.
♀⊗ **RELAIS DU BOULANGARD** (N° RR AVR 23 023) (M. Francis
Égret) Corveville-sur-Riscle ☎ 32-57-01-27.

PONT-AVEN 29930 Finistère **RN 783 Map 7-B1**
♀⊗ **CHEZ MELANIE ET MONIQUE** (N° RR OCT 17 916) (M.
⌂⇌ Bertrand **Le Goc**) Croissant-Kergoz ☎ 98-06-03-09. Closed Mon
in Summer, Sept.

PONT-CHRETIEN-CHABENET 36800 Indre **RN 727 Map 16-A1**
♀⊗ **LE RELAIS DE BOUZANNE** (N° RR OCT 24 000) (M. Gilbert **Boileau**)
15, rue Principale opposite château ☎ 54-25-81-54. Closed Wed
afternoon, 10–25 Aug. Evening meals to 8pm. Home cooking. Menu
42F. Sights: Château de Chabenet, Pont de Bais 1km.
♀⊗ **AUBERGE DU PONT** (N° RR JUIN 27 302) (Mme Yvelisé **Lar-
deau**) 46, rue Nationale ☎ 54-25-81-03. **Minitel** ⊶ 6. Closed Thurs
and 15–30 Sept. Evening meals. Filling station 4km.

PONT-D'AIN 01160 Ain **Map 18-B13**
♀⊗ **CRISNO** (N° RR NOV 26 731) (M. Christian **Sanchez**) 56, rue
St-Expéry ☎ 74-39-01-22. Coaches welcome. Rest. seats 50.
Parking.

PONT-DE-CHERUY 38230 Isère **RD 517 and 18 Map 2-A2**
♀⊗ **RELAIS CHEZ ZEPI** (N° RR AVR 26 490) (SARL **Delaur**) 30, rue
⌂ Giffard ☎ 78-32-20-02. **Minitel** ⊶ 30. Closed Sun. Meals served
until 10pm. English spoken.

PONT-DE-MENAT 63500 Puy-de-Dôme **RN 144 Map 16-B2**
♀⊗ **LE RELAIS CHEZ ROGER** (N° RR JUN 13 786) (Mme Marie **Pinel**)
⌂⇌ ☎ 73-85-50-17 ⊶ 8. Closed Thurs. Coaches welcome. Rest. seats

PONT DE PANY

Pont-De-Menat continued

80. Menus 55–70F and more. Specialities: jambon d'Auvergne, potée auvergnate, trout.

PONT DE PANY 21410 Côte-d'Or **Map 14 A-3**

Y⊗ **BAR DE LA POSTE** (N° RR MAI 27 595) (M. Jacques **Veaulin**) ☎
⌂ 80-23-62-70. Restaurant: open 6–midnight. Closed 24 Dec–1 Jan
⊷ 5 80–110F. Public parking. 20 lorries.

PONT-DES-BEIGNERS 45530 Loiret **RN 60 Map 13-A1**

Y⊗ **LE RELAIS DU PONT DES BEIGNERS** (N° RR JUL 17 581) (M.
Jean-Pierre **Gueru**) ☎ 38-59-47-72. **Minitel**. Closed Sat evening,
Sun, mid Aug to mid Sept. Evening meals served to 10pm.
Coaches welcome. Rest. seats 80.

PONT-DES-SABLES 47200 Lot-et-Garonne **Map 21-A1**

Y⊗ **LE MARINIER** (N° RR JUN 24 991) (M. **Flores**) Coussan-
Marmande toll exit ☎ 53-93-60-37. **Minitel**. Closed Sat, Sun, 11–19
Aug. Evening meals served to 10pm. English, Italian, German,
Spanish spoken. Parking.

PONT-HÉBERT 50880 Manche **RN 174 Map 4-A1**

Y⊗ **LE MADRILÉNE** (N° RR FEV 27 185) (Mme Marie-Thérèse
⌂ **Hamlet**) Quartier du Pont-la-Meauffe ☎ 33-56-44-18 ⊷ 6. Dinner
to 9pm. Rest. seats 35. Filling station nearby.

PONT-L'ABBE PICAUVILLE 50360 Manche **Map 4-B1**

Y⊗ **HOTEL DES VOYAGEURS** (N° RR MAR 24 886) (Mme Fabienne
⌂ **Françoise**) 43, rue de Périer ☎ 33-41-00-59 ⊷ 9. Closed Sun
1 Sept–Easter. English spoken.

PONT-REMY 80580 Somme **Map 5-A3**

Y⊗ **LE CONTINENTAL** (N° RR JUL 25 480) (Mme Ginette **Therasse**)
SARL 9, rue Robert-Bordeux ☎ 22-27-12-89. Closed Aug. Coaches welcome. Rest. seats 100.

PONT-ROYAL 08300 Ardennes **Map 6-B2**

Y⊗ **LE RELAIS PONT-ROYAL** (N° RR AVR 24 561) (M. Yves
Detruiseux) Chatelet-sur-Retourne ☎ 24-38-93-27. Closed Tue
evening. Evening meals to midnight. Rest. seats 60.

PONT SUR YONNE 89140 Yonne **Map 9B-2**

Y⊗ **CARRE D'AS** (N° RR JUN 27 620) (M. Daniel **Pirony-Rousseau**) 29,
⌂ avenue du Général Leclerc ☎ 86-67-03-03. English, Italian
spoken ⊷ 7.

PONT TRAMBOUZE 69240 Rhône **Map 18 A-1**

Y⊗ **"LA TRAMBOUZE"** (N° RR MAI 27 597) (M. Pascal **Gidel**) Place
Henri Michalot ☎ 74-64-11-30. Restaurant: open 6.30am–10pm.
Closed Sun pm. Parking (place municipale).

PONTARLIER 25300 Doubs **Map 14-B3**

Y⊗ **CAFÉ DE LA LIBERTÉ** (N° RR SEPT 27 029) (Mmes Michèle
Besand and Martine **Petit**) 36, rue de Salins ☎ 81-39-01-68.
Closed Sun and 15 Aug–5 Sept. Coaches welcome. Rest. seats 60.
Filling station nearby.

PONTAULT-COMBAULT 77340 Seine-et-Marne **RN 304 Map 1-B3**
♈⊗ **SARL LE RELAIS DU PAVÉ** (N° RR DEC 27 115) (M. José **Da**
⌂ **Silva**) 9, route de Paris ☎ 60-28-00-21. Closed Sun and Aug.
Home cooking. Menu à la carte. Lunch 12–2pm. Dinner 7–10pm.
Filling station nearby open 6am–9pm.

PONTCHARRA 38530 Isère **RN 90 Map 19-A2**
♈⊗ **LE RELAIS DU PONT DE LA GACHE** (N° RR AVR 25 357) (M.
Jean-Pierre **Rubatat**) RN 90 La GACHE ☎ 76-97-30-08. Closed
Sat, 15–30 Aug, 15 days at Christmas. Coaches welcome. English
spoken. HGV parking. Showers for drivers.

PONTCHATEAU 44160 Loire-Atlantique **RN 165 Map 11-A2**
♈⊗ **LE RELAIS DE BEAULIEU** (N° RR AOU 7 869) (SARL Louisette
⌂⊸ **Praud**) ☎ 40-01-60-58. ⊨ 15. Coaches welcome. Rest. seats 70 +
café, annexe. Evening meals until midnight. Menus from 42.30–
140F. Specialities: eels in cider, grilled salmon with butter,
prawns à la Beaulieu. English spoken.
♈⊗ ☆ **NN L'AUBERGE DU CALVAIRE** (N° RR NOV 20 885) (Mme
⌂⊸ **Couvran**) 6, route de la Brière 4km from centre of Pontchâteau
on Herbignac road. Le Calvaire ☎ 40-01-61-65 ⊨ 12. Coaches
welcome. Rest. seats 60. Evening meals served until 10pm.

PONTET (LE) 84130 Vaucluse **RN 7 Map 24-A3**
♈⊗ **LA CROIX VERTE** (N° RR DEC 24 439) (M. Guy **Prat**) route de
Lyon ☎ 90-86-39-56. **Minitel**. Closed Sun, Sat evening. Coaches
welcome. Rest. seats 100.

PONTGIBAUD 63230 Puy-de-Dôme **RN 141 Map 16-B2**
♈⊗ **LE RELAIS DES VOYAGEURS** (N° RR NOV 15 448) (M. **Sardier**)
⌂ avenue de Verdun ☎ 73-88-70-35 ⊨ 16. Closed Nov. Coaches
welcome. Rest. seats 60.

PONTHIERRY 77310 Seine-et-Marne **RN 7 Map 8-B1**
♈⊗ **LE RELAIS DES TROIS MARCHES** (N° RR DEC 24 054) (Mme
Odette **Pothier**) 7, rue de la Saussale ☎ 60-65-77-67. Closed Sun,
Aug. Evening meals served to 9pm.

PONTIGNY 89230 Yonne **RN 77 Map 13-A2**
♈⊗ **RELAIS DE PONTIGNY** (N° RR AOUT 26 619) (Mme Carole
⌂ **Leducq**) 9, rue Paul-Desjardins ☎ 86-47-42-83 ⊨ 8. Closed Sun.
English, German, Italian spoken.

PONTOISE 95300 Val-d'Oise **RN 14 Maps 1-A2 and 9-A1**
♈⊗⊸**RESTAURANT DE LA POSTE** (N° RR SEPT 27 016) (M. Alain
Louat) 68, rue Pierre-Butin ☎ 30-32-47-72. Closed Sat evening
and Sun. English spoken. Evening meals served to 9pm.

PONTS-ET-MARAIS 76260 Seine-Maritime **RD 1015 Bis Map 4-A2**
♈⊗ **LA FERME NIÇOISE** (N° RR JAN 26 777) (M. Patrick **Nalais**)
route de Gamache ☎ 35-86-50-37. Closed Sun.

PORCHERIE (LA) 87380 Haute-Vienne **RN 20 Map 17-A1**
♈⌂ **RELAIS DE LA BORNE 40** (N° RR JUIL 27 347) (M. Michel
Reyrolle) Beasoleil ☎ 55-71-90-30 ⊨ 7. Closed Sat evening and
Sun. Evening meals served to 10pm. Parking. Filling station
nearby open 6am–11.30pm.

PORT-A-BINSON

PORT-A-BINSON 51700 Marne **Map 9-A2**
🍷⊗ **LE RELAIS DE LA GARE** (N° RR OCT 26 363) (Mme Nadine
🏠 **Negri**) 22, rue du Gl-Leclerc ☎ 26-58-30-41 ⇥ 4. Closed Sun.
Coaches welcome. Rest. seats 60.

PORT DE BOUC 13110 Bouches-du-Rhône **Map 24 A-3**
🍷⊗ **RELAIS DE LA GARE** (N° RR MAI 27 609) (Mlle Brigitte **Streiff**)
Quartier de la Gare ☎ 42-06-43-43. Open 6.30am–11pm. Dinner
to 11pm. Closed Sun pm (low season). German spoken.

PORT DE PILES 86220 Vienne **Map 12 A-3**
🍷⊗ **RESTAURANT DE LA CREUSE** (N° RR JANV 27 770) (M. Lionel
Leberquier) 6 RN 10. Directions: the Poitiers/Tours road. ☎
49-85-66-48. Restaurant: regional home cooking. Speciality:
truites au cidre. Menu 46–118F. Children's menu. À la carte.
Open 7am–10pm. Closed on Tue. Parking. Filling station 200m
open 7am–7pm. Credit cards accepted. Traditional décor. Rest.
seats 158. ⇥ Sights: Musée des Acadiens, Les troglodytes de
Saint Rémy.

POUILLY EN AUXOIS 21490 Côte-d'Or **Map 14 A3**
⊗ **RELAIS DE L'AUXOIS** (N° RR 2029) Aire de Service du Chien
Blanc Sens Paris/Lyon Autoroute ☎ 80-90-74-25. Restaurant:
regional cooking. Menu 25% discount to Routiers. Children's
menu. À la carte. Self-service. Open 7am–11pm. Credit cards
accepted. Rest. seats 190. Garden terrace. ⇥ Parking. Nursery.
The restaurant offers a varied selection of regional wines and
dishes. English spoken.
⊗ **RELAIS DE L'AUXOIS** (N° RR 2040) Aire de services des
Lochères Sens Lyon/Paris Autoroute ☎ 80-90-83-28. Restaurant
regional cooking. 25% discount for Routiers. Children's menu.
Self-service. Open 24 hours. Credit cards accepted. English
spoken. Rest. seats 130. Garden terrace. ⇥ Parking.

POURIERRES 83910 Var **RN 7 Map 24-B3**
🍷⊗ **LE LORRAINE PROVENCE** (N° RR JUIL 27 339) (Mme Mireille
Mohr) ☎ 94-78-41-28. English and Italian spoken. Evening meals
served up to 10pm. Closed Sun. Rest. seats 80. Parking. Filling
station nearby.

POUSSAN 34140 Hérault **RN 113 Map 23-B2**
🍷⊗ **LE LANDRY** (N° RR NOV 27 722) (M. Yannick **Carreau**) RN 113.
Direction: leave autoroute turn right to Béziers Nle 113 2km to
Landry ☎ 67-78-24-74. English, Spanish, Italian, German spoken.
Restaurant: home cooking. Specialities: hûitres, moules, sèches
rouille. Menu 55F. Menu à la carte. Dinner to 10pm. Closed Sat
pm and Sun pm. Rest. seats 75. Hotel with showers. Garden
terrace. ⇥ Parking. Filling station nearby. Sights: Le Litoral.
🍷⊗ **LE 7 SUR SETE** (N° RR FEV 27 774) (SARL Le 7 sur Sète) RN 113
☎ 67-78-33-29. English spoken. Menu 51F. Open 6am–1am.
Filling station nearby.

POUSSAY 88500 Vosges **RN 413 Map 10-A2 and 14-B1**
🍷⊗ **AUBERGE DES PECHEURS** (N° RR NOV 2 282) (M. **Hingray**) ☎
🏠 29-37-07-73 ⇥ 7. Closed Tue, mid Dec–mid Jan. Evening meals
until 9pm.

POUZIN (LE) 07250 Ardèche **RN 86 Map 24-A1**
♈⊗ ☆ **NN ROUTIERS** (N° RR AVR 21 048) (Mme Juliette **Vialatte**) 64,
⌂ rue Olivier-de-Serres ☎ 75-63-83-45 ━ 5 from 55–85F. Closed
Sun, 15 days Aug, 15 days Sept. Evening meals.

POZIERES 80300 Somme **RN 29 Map 5-B3**
♈⊗ **LE RELAIS DES ROUTIERS** (N° RR SEP 24 345) (Mme Josiane
Brihier) Route Nationale ☎ 22-75-23-05.

PREIXAN 11250 Aude **Map 22 B-2**
♈⊗ **L'OISEAU BLEU** (N° RR FEV 27 552) (Mme Nadia **Abredine**) ☎
⌂ 68-26-89-50. Dutch spoken. Dinner to midnight. Closed Sun ━ 7.
Filling station nearby open 6am–8pm.

PREMERY 58700 Nièvre **Map 13 B-2**
♈⊗ **LE ROUTIER** (N° RR JANV 27 767) (M. Jean-Jacques **Lemarié**) 8,
rue de Lurcy ☎ 86-37-97-59. German and English spoken. Menu
46F. Filling station 500m open 7am–8pm.

PRESSAC 86460 Vienne **RN 148 Map 15-B2**
♈⊗ **LE RELAIS** (N° RR MAI 25 409) (Mme Francine **Bouyer**) Place de
l'Eglise Mauprevoir ☎ 49-48-56-99. **Minitel**. Closed Sat, 15 Aug–
1 Sept. Coaches welcome. Rest. seats 60. Evening meals.

PREZ-SOUS-LAFAUCHE 52700 Haute-Marne **Map 14-A1**
♈⊗ **LES 3 VALLEES** (N° RR AVR 24 550) (Mme Eliane **Trommensch-
lager**) ☎ 25-31-57-84. Closed Sun pm (except for banquets) and
Aug. Coaches welcome. Rest. seats 180. Evening meals. Open 24
hours. Parking.

PRIMAUBE (LA) 12450 Aveyron **RN 88 Map 22-B1**
♈⊗ **LES ROUTIERS** (N° RR MAI 26 534) (Frères **Castanie**) 3, avenue
de Rodez ☎ 65-71-40-31. Closed Sun.

PRIVAS 07000 Ardèche **RN 104 Map 24-A1**
♈⊗ **LA RENAISSANCE** (N° RR MAR 21 437) (M. **Monteil**) 4, place du
Champ-de Mars ☎ 75-64-21-60. Closed Sun, Aug.

PROSNES 51400 Marne **RD 31 Map 6-B2**
♈⊗ **LE RELAIS CONSTANTINE** (N° RR NOV 14 593) (M. René
Roselet) known as 'Constantine' Route Nationale ☎ 26-61-70-70.
Minitel. Closed Sat, Sun, 15–31 Aug. Coaches welcome. Rest.
seats 80. Evening meals until 9pm. Home cooking. Menu 41F.
Menu à la carte. Credit cards accepted. Parking. Sights: caves
and vineyard museums, war cemetery, Reims Cathedral, Le
Moulin de Valmy.

PROVINS 77160 Seine-et-Marne **RN 19 Map 9-A/B2**
♈⊗ **LE RELAIS DE LA CURE D'AIR** (N° RR NOV 3 083) (M. **Amroun**)
⌂━ 54, avenue du Général-de-Gaulle ☎ 64-00-03-21 ━ 8. Closed Fri
and last 2 weeks July.

PROYART 80121 Somme **RN 29 Map 5-B3**
♈⊗ **LA RAPERIE** (N° RR MAI 19 350) (Mme Odete **Mourier**) Route
⌂━ Nationale, known as 'La Raperie' ☎ 22-85-37-30 ━ 8. Closed Sat
and Sun evening, 23 Dec–10 Jan. German, Italian, Spanish
spoken.

PRUNAY-LE-GILLON

PRUNAY-LE-GILLON see FRAINVILLE 28360 Eure-et-Loir **RN 154 and RD 28 Maps 8-B3 and 9-B3**

♈⊗ **LE RELAIS DE LA GERBE D'OR** (N° RR MAI 14 347) (M. Charles **Miklos**) 10, rue du Pavillion ☎ 37-25-72-38. Closed Sun in winter. Coaches welcome. Rest. seats 50. English spoken.

PUJAUT 30131 Gard **RN 580 Map 24-A2**

♈⊗ **CHEZ ODETTE** (N° RR DEC 25 765) (Mme Odette **Quinquemelle**) Les Gravières ☎ 90-25-19-70. Closed Sat and Sun. Evening meals until 11pm. Restaurant: home cooking. Menu 55F (drinks and coffee included). Menu à la carte. Credit cards accepted. Modern décor. Rest. seats 50. Rest room. Garden terrace. ⊷ Parking. Sights: Pont du Gard, Palais des Papes, Pont d'Avignon, Chartreuse.

PUNTOUS 65230 Hautes-Pyrénées **Map 21 A-3**

♈⊗ **AUBERGE DES PYRENEES** (N° RR FEV 27 775) (M. Olivier **Vanoni**) Cap de côte. Directions: 1.5km after leaving Puntous, left to Tarbes ☎ 62-39-83-31. Restaurant: regional home cooking. Specialities: confit de canard, magrets, couscous, paella. Menu 50–90F. Menu à la carte. Dinner to midnight. Closed Mon, Jan. Lorry parking. Filling station nearby.

PUTOT-EN-AUGE 14430 Calvados **RN 175 Map 4-B2**

♈⊗ **LE DAUPHIN** (N° RR NOV 25 733) (M. Jacques **Ribourg**) ☎
⌂ 31-79-20-29. **Minitel** ⊸ 6. Closed Sun (low season), 15 Dec–15 Jan. Evening meals until 11pm. German spoken.

PUY (LE) 43000 Haute-Loire **Maps 17-A3 and 18-A3**

♈⊗ **LA TAVERNE** (N° RR JUN 10 835) (M. René **Rolland**) 50, boulevard Carnot ☎ 71-09-35-16 ⊸ 10. Coaches welcome. Rest. seats 50.

♈⊗ ☆ **NN LA VERVEINE** (N° RR FEV 24 844) (M. Gaston **Malthieu**) 6,
⌂ place Cadelade ☎ 71-02-00-77 and 02-14-66. **Minitel** ⊸ 30. Closed 15 Dec–15 Jan. Coaches welcome. Rest. seats 100. Evening meals.

PUY-MAURY 63380 Puy-de-Dôme **RN 141 and RD 108 Map 16-B2**

♈⊗ **LE RELAIS CHEZ LUCETTE** (N° RR JAN 19 631) (Mme Lucette **Condon**) ☎ 73-79-00-40. Closed 2nd fortnight Aug. Coaches welcome. Rest. seats 40. Home cooking. Lunch 12–2.30pm. Dinner 7.30–10pm. Garden terrace. ⊷ Parking. Sights: the Faoles viaduct, Puy de Dôme (50km).

PUYDROUARD par FORGES 17290 Charente-Maritime **Map 11-B1**

♈⊗ **CHEZ RENE** (N° RR SEPT 26 630) (M. **Bourieau**) Aigrefeille ☎ 46-35-07-83. **Minitel**. Closed Sun. Coaches welcome. Rest. seats 80. Weekends only. Evening meals until 9.30pm. English spoken.

PUYRICARD 'LA PETITE-CALALE' 13540 Bouches-du-Rhône **RN 7 Map 24-B3**

♈⊗ **LE TOURANGEAU** (N° RR MAI 21 533) (Mme Danielle **Roccia**)
⌂ Route Nationale 7 ☎ 42-21-60-65 ⊸ 14. Closed Sun, Aug. Italian spoken. Dinner to midnight. Rest. seats 80.

QUAEDYPRE 59380 Nord **CD 9 16 Map 5-A/B2**

♈⊗ **AUBERGE DU BON COIN - CHEZ L'GITAN** (N° RR JAN 21 368) (M. Pierre **Lammin**) (SARL La Flamanderie) Chemin Départmental 916 ☎ 28-68-76-94. Closed Mon, Aug. Coaches welcome. Rest. seats 550. English spoken. Regional home cooking. Menu 55F. Children's menu. À la carte. Parking.

QUEVEN 56330 Morbihan **RD 6 Map 7-B2**
♈⊗ **LE RELAIS DE LA MAIRIE** (N° RR JUL 17 317) (Mme Yvonne **Le Gallic**) rue Principale ☎ 97-05-07-50 ◄ 8.

QUIMPER 29000 Finistère **RN 165 Map 7-B1**
♈⊗ **LE TRUCK** (N° RR JANV 27 165) (M. Jacques **Le Grand**) 96, avenue de la Libération ☎ 98-95-35-62. **Minitel**. English spoken. Restaurant: home cooking. Menu 45F. Lunch 12–2.30pm. Dinner 7–10pm. Closed Sat evening, Sun. Credit cards accepted. Traditional décor. Rest. seats 124. ⚑ Parking. Filling station nearby. Sights: the seaside.

QUIMPERLÉ 29130 Finistère **Map 7-B1**
♈⊗ **LA FOURCHE** (N° RR OCT 27 421) (Mme Solarge **Le ball**) route de Loriert ☎ 98-39-11-45. Restaurant: home cooking. Specialities: choucroute, couscous, andouillette. Lunch 12–2pm. Dinner 7.30–9.30pm. Closed Sun. Rest. seats 50. ⚑ Parking. TV. Filling station nearby open 6am–10.30pm. Sights: Forêt de Carnoêt, the beaches.

QUINCY-SOUS-SENART 91480 Essonne **Map 1 B-3**
♈⊗ **A LA BONNE TABLE** (N° RR JANV 27 170) (M. Pierre **Walter**) 3, avenue Henri-Chasles ☎ 69-00-93-81. Restaurant: regional home cooking. Speciality: Normandes. Menu à la carte. Lunch 11.45am–2.45pm. Dinner 7.45–9.30pm. Closed Mon and Feb. Modern décor. Rest. seats 30 ◄ 5. Open 5.30am–10pm. Garden terrace. ⚑ Parking. Sights: Forêt de Senart, Fontainebleu.

QUINTIN 22800 Côtes-du-Nord **St-Brieux/Quimper Map 7-A2**
♈⊗ **RELAIS JACOB** (N° RR SEPT 26 032) (M. Pierre **Jacob**) Zl St Brandan ☎ 96-74-88-19. Closed Sat afternoon, Sun. Coaches welcome. Rest. seats 30. Evening meals until 10pm.

RACHECOURT-SUR-MARNE 52170 Haute-Marne **RN 67 Map 14-A1**
♈⊗ **L'AURORE** (N° RR DEC 26 413) (M. **Narat**) avenue de Belgique ☎ 25-04-41-58 ◄ 4 90–200F with shower, WC. Closed Mon, Aug. Home cooking. Menu 50–90F. Children's menu. Coaches welcome. Rest. seats 36. Garden terrace. Car park. Situated in the middle of the country.

RANES 61150 Orne **RN 916 Map 8-A2**
♈⊗ **HOTEL DU PARC** (N° RR JUL 17 316) (M. Rogé **Cantin**) 9, rue du Parc ☎ 33-39-73-85 ◄ 6. Evening meals until 9pm.

RASSATS (LES) 16590 Charente **RN 141 Map 15-B2**
♈⊗ **L'AUBERGE DES ROUTIERS** (N° RR NOV 19 204) (SARL **Doré and Son**) ☎ 45-65-90-24. **Minitel**. Closed Sun, Aug. Evening meals until 9pm. Home cooking. Menu 48F. Menu à la carte. Coaches welcome. Parking – 5,000m². Rest. seats 64. Credit cards accepted. Rest room. ⚑

RAVOIRE (LA) 73490 Savoie **RN 6 and CD 21 Map 19-A2**
♈⊗ **LA PETITE TARENTAISE** (N° RR DEC 27 476) (M. Hervé **Bray**) ☎ 79-72-94-27. **Minitel**. Restaurant: home cooking. Specialities: cuisses de grenouilles. Menu 60F. Menu à la carte. Closed

RAZES

Ravoire continued
Sunday. Evening meals until 11pm. Credit cards accepted. Traditional décor. Rest. seats 74. Garden terrace. ⋈ Parking. Service station nearby.

RAZES 87640 Haute-Vienne **Map 16-B1**
♟⊗ **LE PECHER** (N° RR DEC 263 98) (M. Marc **Lamotte**) RN 20 ☎ 55-71-02-52. Closed Sun.

REBENACQ 64260 Pyrénées-Atlantiques **Map 20-B3**
♟⊗ **CHEZ PALU** (N° RR DEC 24 776) (M. Alain **Palu**) RD 134 ☎ 59-05-54-11. Restaurant: regional home cooking. Menu 50–70F. Children's menu. À la carte. Traditional décor. Hotel with showers, TV. Parking. Coaches welcome. Rest. seats 80. Evening meals until 10pm. Sights: Vallée d'ossau, Spanish border.

REDON 35600 Ille-et-Vilaine **Map 11-A2**
♟⊗ ☆ **NN LE RELAIS** (N° RR FEV 26 172) (M. Noël **François** SARL)
⌂⊷ route de Rennes ☎ 99-71-46-54. **Minitel** ⊷ 18 120–140F. Coaches welcome. Rest. seats 120. Evening meals. English spoken. Bar. ⋈ 'Casserole' menus 38–145F.

REFFANNES 79420 Deux-Sèvres **RD 938 Map 15-A1**
♟⊗ **LE CHEVAL BLANC** (N° RR SEPT 26 033) (M. **Chevallier**) Avenue de la Grande Auberge le Bourg ☎ 49-70-25-18. Evening meals until 9pm. Closed Sat. Home cooking. ⋈ Parking.

REGUISHEIM 68890 Haut-Rhin **RN 422 Map 10-B3**
♟⊗ **SARL A L'ANGE** (N° RR JUN 19 085) (M. Raymond **Bertrand**) 90,
⌂ Grande-Rue ☎ 89-81-12-66. **Minitel** ⊷ 5. Closed Sat, Sun, Aug. German spoken. Evening meals to midnight.

REIMS 51400 Marne **Autoroute A4 Maps 6-B12**
♟⊗ **RESTOP DE REIMS** (N° RR 1819) (M. Patrice **Jezequel**) Aire de Service de Reims Champagne Les Petites Loges par Mourmelon-le-Grand ☎ 26-03-93-57. Self-service restaurant. Restaurant: regional cooking. Menu 25% discount for Routiers. Children's menu. À la carte. Open 24 hours. Credit cards accepted. Rest. seats 225. Garden terrace. Parking. Local shop. Tourist office. Hotel booking. Nursery. In delightful surroundings the restaurant offers a varied menu of local wines and dishes.

REMOULINS 30210 Gard **RN 86 Map 24-A3**
♟⊗ ☆☆ **NN AUBERGE DES PLATANES** (N° RR NOV 24 421) (M.
⌂⊷ Gérard **Reynaud**) Castillon-du-Gard-les-Croisées ☎ 66-37-10-69. **Minitel** ⊷ 35 160–200F with showers, bathroom, WC, TV. Open 7am–11.30pm. Rest room. Garden terrace. Coaches welcome. Rest. seats 250. Evening meals until 10pm. English, Spanish spoken. Menus 55–110F. Specialities: rouille d'encornets carmagueuse, potée du pêcheur aux fruits de mer (made to order), taureau sauvage. Children's menu. À la carte. Credit cards accepted. ⋈ Parking.

RENAC 35660 Ille-et-Vilaine **RD 177 Map 7-B3**
♟⊗ **BEAUREGARD** (N° RR FEV 27 192) (Mme Marie-Annick **Bonno**) ☎ 99-72-07-83. Closed Mon and 10 days in Mar. Rest. seats 50. Filling station nearby.

RENESCURE 59173 Nord **RN 42 Map 5-A1**

♈⊗ **LA CLÉ DES CHAMPS** (N° RR JAN 15 505) (Mme Marlène **Lamiaux**) locally known as La Clé des Champs. RN 42 ☎ 28-49-81-12. Coaches welcome. Rest. seats 60. Home cooking. Menu 40F. Lunch 11.30am–2pm. Closed Sat pm, Sun. Credit cards accepted. Traditional décor. ⊨ Parking. Sights: Cassel (10km).

REVIN 08500 Ardennes **RN 388 Map 6-A2**

♈⊗ **CHEZ ALEX** (N° RR JAN 17 985) (M. **Mahut**) 6, rue Voltaire ☎ 24-40-12-91 ⊷ 4. Dinner to 9pm. Rest. seats 30.

REYRIEUX 01600 Ain **Map 2-A2**

♈⊗ **BAR RESTAURANT DE LA GARE** (N° RR MAI 27 271) (Mme Yvonne **Oritz**) ☎ 74-00-12-00.

RHODES 36170 Indre **RN 20 Map 16-A1**

♈⊗ **LE RELAIS ROUTIERS DE RHODES** (N° RR AVR 25 375) (M. Jean-Pierre **Perez**) Mouhet-Rhodes ☎ 54-47-65-26. **Minitel**. Closed Sat afternoon, Sun, Aug. Evening meals until 10.30pm.

RIAILLE 44440 Loire-Atlantique **Map 11-A3**

♈⊗ **AU RENDEZ-VOUS DES PECHEURS** (N° RR AVR 26 528) (M. Joël **Aspot**) 7, rue de Bretagne ☎ 40-97-80-95. Closed Wed afternoon (low season), 1, 15 August. Coaches welcome. Rest. seats 60. Evening meals until 10pm.

RIBAUTE-LES-TAVERNES 30720 Gard **RN 110 Map 23-B1**

♈⊗ **LE VIEUX MOULIN** (N° RR JUN 26 920) (Mmes **Coste** and **Riminucci**) ☎ 66-83-07-94. Closed Tue. English, Spanish, Italian spoken. Filling station near. Coaches welcome. Evening meals. Rest. seats 50 on a terrace. Dinner to 11pm.

RIBAY (LE) 53640 Mayenne **RN 12 Map 8-B1**

♈⊗ **LE LION D'OR** (N° RR 23 351) (Mme Simone **Reboux**) Le Bourg
⌂ ☎ 43-03-90-27 ⊷ 7. Closed 20 Dec–2 Jan. Coaches welcome. Rest. seats 80. Evening meals until 9pm. English spoken.

RIBERAC 24600 Dordogne **RN 708/710 Map 15-B3**

♈⊗ **LAKANAL** (N° RR MARS 27 202) (Mme Jean-Marie **Lagarde**) 1, avenue Lakanal ☎ 53-90-04-77. Closed Thurs and 10 days in June. Evening meals until 2am. Rest. seats 48. English spoken. Parking.

♈⊗ **CAFÉ DU COMMERCE** (N° RR MAR 23 172) (M. Paul **Ratineau**)
⌂ La Borie Villetoureix ☎ 53-90-05-24 ⊷ 9. Closed Sun except high season. Evening meals.

RICAMARIE (LA) 42150 Loire **RN 88 Map 2-B1**

♈⊗ **AU RELAIS SYMPA RICAMONDOIS** (N° RR SEPT 27 008) (M. Franck **Bonnaire**) 5 bis, rue de la Libération ☎ 77-57-89-31. Closed Mon pm. Open 7.30am–midnight. English and German spoken. Filling station open 7.30am–9pm.

RICHEVILLE 27420 Eure **RN 14 Map 3-B1**

♈⊗⊷**LE RESTOROUTE LE BALTO** (N° RR FEV 27 173) (M. Pierre **Sadok**) RN 14 ☎ 32-27-10-55. Closed Sun, Aug. English spoken. Restaurant: home cooking. Specialities: escalopes Normandes,

RIEUPEYROUX

Richeville continued
filet au poivre. Menu 44F. Children's menu. À la carte. Dinner to 10pm. Credit cards accepted. Traditional décor. Rest. seats 170. ⊨ Parking. Sights: Château Gaillard (9km), Les Andelys (25km), museum of Claude Monet and Giverny (21km).

RIEUPEYROUX 12240 Aveyron **RD 905 Map 22-B1**
⛾⊗ ☆ **NN CHEZ PASCAL** (N° RR OCT 23 965) (M. Claude **Bou**) rue
⌂ de l'Hom ☎ 65-65-51-13. **Minitel**. Restaurant: regional home cooking. Specialities: tripous, confits. Children's menu. À la carte. Dinner to 9pm. Closed Sun pm (low season) and 1–15 Oct. Credit cards accepted. Rest. seats 90 ⊨ 14 70–170F with shower, bathroom, WC. Open 7am–10pm. Sights: Château de Belcastel (15km), grottes de Foissac (30km), viaduc de Viaur (30km), Rodez Cathedral (38km).

RIEUTORT-DE RANDON 48700 Lozère **CD 1 Map 17-B3**
⛾⊗ **RELAIS DE LA POSTE** (N° RR JUL 26 611) (Mme Annie **Magne**) place de la Poste ☎ 66-47-34-67. Closed weekends.

RIGNAC 46500 Lot **Map 17-B1**
⛾⊗ **AUBERGE DE DARNIS** (N° RR OCT 27 435) (M. Lawrence **Stucke**) Darnis ☎ 65-33-66-84. English and Dutch spoken. Dinner to 9.30pm. Closed Wed (low season) ⊨ 4.

RILLIEUX-LA-PAPE 69140 Rhône **Map 2-A2**
⛾⊗ **RELAIS DU BUGEY** (N° RR FEV 26 455) (M. Alain **Rebout**) 1270, avenue Victor Hugo. Directions: opposite the station ☎ 78-88-09-60. **Minitel**. Closed Sat, Sun, Aug. Lunch 11.45am–2.30pm. Evening meals 8–10pm. Rest. seats 50. ⊨ HGV parking.

RIOM 63200 Puy-de-Dôme **RN 9 Map 16-B3**
⛾⊗ **LE CANTALOU** (N° RR MAI 24 939) (M. Jean-Louis **Tholonias**) 12, avenue de Clermont ☎ 73-38-03-68. Closed Sun, 15 days Aug. English spoken.
⛾⊗ **AU STAND** (N° RR OCT 25 680) (Mme **Dassaud-Riquier**) 24, avenue de Clermont ☎ 73-38-04-06. Closed Sun, Aug. Home cooking. Credit cards accepted. Rest. seats 110. ⊨ Sights: Volcais d'Auvergne.

RIOTORD 43200 Haute-Loire **RD 503 Map 18-A3**
⛾⊗ **BAR RESTAURANT DES CHASSEURS** (N° RR MARS 26 824) (Mme Dominique **Arnaud**) route de Dunières ☎ 71-75-31-40. Closed Sun, July. Dinner to 9pm. Filling station 3km. Coaches welcome. Rest. seats 40.

RIS/PUY GUILLAUME 63290 Puy-de-Dôme **Map 16-B3**
⛾⊗🏠**HOTEL DE LA GARE** (N° RR JANV 27 154) (M. Robert **Nicholas**) Gare De Ris ☎ 73-94-68-68. **Minitel**. Restaurant: home cooking. Menu 46F. Children's menu. Closed Sun (low season), mid Sept– mid Oct. Credit cards accepted. Traditional décor. Rest. seats 40 ⊨ 10 75–200F. Open 5am–10pm. Garden terrace. ⊨ Parking. Filling station open 6am–9pm. Sights: L'Auvergne et ses monts.

RISCLE 32400 Gers **RD 135 Map 21-A2**
⛾⊗ ☆ **NN RELAIS DE L'AUBERGE** (N° RR DEC 21 307) (Mme **Portes**)
⌂ place de la Mairie ☎ 62-69-70-49 ⊨ 10 (with WC) from 65–80F.

Closed Sun, Oct. Coaches welcome. Rest. seats 100. Bar. Parking. ⚑ Sights: cave de Saint-Mont, Tour de Termes d'Armagnac, foie gras cannery.

RIVE-DE-GIER 42800 Loire **Map 2-A1**
Ɩ⊗ **RESTAURANT DE LA GARE** (N° RR JUL 27 335) (Mme Paulette **Perrier**) 6, Vallée de Couzon ☎ 77-75-45-52. Evening meals until midnight. Nearby service station open 7am–9pm.

RIVIERE (LA) 33126 Gironde **Map 15-A3**
Ɩ⊗ **LA RIVIERE** (N° RR NOV 27 732) (Mme Jeanine **Rastoul**) ☎ 57-24-94-26. **Minitel**. Spanish spoken. Restaurant: home cooking. Menu 50–95F. Children's menu. À la carte. Dinner until 11pm. Traditional décor. Rest. seats 50. Garden terrace. ⚑ Parking for cars. Filling station nearby open 7am–11pm. Showers available for customers. Sights: Fronsac Bordeaux vineyard.

RIVIERE-DE-CORPS (LA) 10300 Aube **RN 60 Map 9-B3**
Ɩ⊗ **LA QUEUE DE LA POELE** (N° RR MAI 25 404) (M. Gaby **Barbier**) RN 60 Sens road, Troyes exit ☎ 25-74-47-94. Closed Sun evening.

RIVIÈRE SAINT SAUVEUR (LA) 14560 Calvados **Map 4-B2**
Ɩ⊗ **LES OISEAUX DE MER** (N° RR JAN 27 505) (M. Pascal **Quesney**) 28, route des 4-Francs ☎ 31-89-11-62. Closed Sat afternoon, Sun, Aug. Lunch 11am–3pm. Evening meals 7–9pm. Menu 47–50F. Children's menu. Home cooking. Sights: Honfleurs, Deauville (15km), Lisieux (33km).

ROANNE 42120 Loire **RN 7 Map 18-A2**
Ɩ **LE JOCKEY BAR** (N° RR NOV 27 455) (M. Joseph **Vera**) 1, place du Champ-de-Foire ☎ 77-71-43-09. Closed Wed pm. Filling station nearby.

ROCHE-CHALAIS (LA) 24490 Dordogne **RD 730 Map 15-A3**
Ɩ⊗⌐**CAFÉ DU MIDI** (N° RR AVR 21 884) (Mme Violette **Rawyler**) 32, avenue du Stade ☎ 53-91-43-65. English, German spoken. Closed Mon, Tue afternoons. Home cooking. Rest. seats 40. ⚑ Parking.

ROCHE-LA-MOLIERE 42230 Loire **Map 18-A2**
Ɩ⊗ **LE FLORENCE** (N° RR SEPT 26 659) (M. Michel **Bruyas**) 3, rue des Carrières ☎ 77-90-58-41. Closed Aug. Home cooking. Rest. seats 42.

ROCHE-SUR-YON 8500 Vendée **RN 137 Maps 11-B2/3 and 12-B1**
Ɩ⊗ ☆☆ **NN LE SULLY** (N° RR OCT 22 072) (Mme Natalie **Maliclin**) ⌂ boulevard Sully ☎ 51-37-18-21 and 51-37-54-02. **Minitel** ⇥ 34 135–280F with shower, bath, WC, TV, tel. Open 6am–midnight. Home cooking. Specialities: jambon de Vendée et haricots blancs. Children's menu. À la carte. Coaches welcome. Rest. seats 250. Evening meals until midnight. English, Spanish spoken. Car park. Bar. ⚑ Credit cards accepted. Recreations: skating, swimming. Sights: Haras, museum, dam at Papon.

ROCHE-VINEUSE 71960 Saône-et-Loire **RN 79 Map 18-B1**
Ɩ⊗ **RELAIS ROUTIERS** (N° RR 24 115) (Mme France **Brouillon**) Place du Chaucher ☎ 85-37-71-51. **Minitel**. Closed Sat afternoon, Sun, Aug. Coaches welcome. Rest. seats 50. Evening meals until 11pm. Home cooking. Credit cards accepted. ⚑ Parking. Sights: Roche de Solutré prehistoric sites, Cluny Abbey.

ROCHECORBON

ROCHECORBON 37210 Indre-et-Loire **RN 152 Map 12-B3**

♀⊗ **RELAIS DE PATYS** (N° RR FEV 27 198) (M. Jean-Marc **Nourry**) 1, rue de Patys ☎ 47-52-61-75. English and Spanish spoken. Restaurant: home cooking. Menu 43–52F. Children's menu. À la carte. Lunch 12–2pm. Dinner 7–9pm. Closed Sun, Aug. Modern décor. Rest. seats 31 ⊷ 4 90–120F. Rest room. ⍦ Parking. Sights: châteaux of the Loire.

ROCHELLE (LA) 17000 Charente-Maritime **Map 11-B1**

♀⊗ **LES EMBRUNS** (N° RR OCT 27 701) (M. René **Poultier**) 413, ⌂ avenue Jean Guiton ☎ 46-42-61-68. **Minitel**. Restaurant: home cooking. Specialities: couscous, paella, choucroute. Menu 48F. Children's menu. Lunch 11.30am–4pm. Dinner 6–10pm. Traditional décor. Rest. seats 110. Rest room. ⍦ Parking. Filling station 500m open 6am–10pm. Sights: Base sous-marine (300m), the beach (800m), the fishing port and le pont de l'Ile-de-Ré (8km).

♀⊗ **LE GOELAND** (N° RR OCT 27 700) (M. Jacques **Durandeau**) Place du Marche ☎ 46-42-05-29. English spoken. Home cooking. Menu 45F. Open 6.30am–midnight. HGV park. Filling station 500m open 6am–10pm.

ROCHELLE-PALLICE (LA) 17000 Charente-Maritime **Map 11-B1**

♀⊗ **L'OCÉANIC** (N° RR JUL 27 648) (M. Phillipe **Alzin**) 22, rue du ⌂ Docteur ☎ 46-42-62-37 ⊷ 5. Closed Fri from 6pm, Mon from 6.30. Evening meals until 9.30pm. Coaches welcome. Filling station 150m open 6am–8pm.

♀⊗ **CHEZ ANNIE** (N° RR AVR 27 262) (Mme Annie **Bernelas**) Ancien Embarcadère de l'Ile de Ré ☎ 46-42-53-61. Closed Sun. Evening meals served until 11pm. Nearby service station open 6am–9pm.

ROCHEMAURE 07400 Ardèche **RN 86 Map 24-A2**

♀⊗ **LE RELAIS DE LA CONDAMINE** (N° RR NOV 14 069) (Mme Josiane **Sircoit**) ☎ 75-52-96-26. Closed Sun, 20 Dec–31 Jan. Coaches welcome. Rest. seats 40. Evening meals.

ROCHETAILLÉE 38520 Isère **RN 91 and RD 526 Map 19-A3**

♀⊗ ☆ **NN HOTEL BELLEDONNE** (N° RR JAN 22 965) (Mme Mireille ⌂⊷ **Esposito**) ☎ 76-80-07-04 ⊷ 21 100–250F with shower, bath. Some English spoken. Restaurant: home cooking. Specialities on request. Menu 65–110F. Dinner until 9pm. Closed Sat, Sun (low season). Credit cards accepted. Rest. seats 100. Rest room. Garden terrace. Parking. TV. Sights: Grand Maison dam, ski station (3 and 50km).

ROCROI 08230 Ardennes **RN 51 and 377 Map 6-A2**

♀⌂ **HÔTEL DE LA GARE** (N° RR JAN 23 633) (SARL **Minucci**) 1, avenue du Général-Moreau ☎ 24-54-10-32 ⊷ 10 100–200F with shower and bath. Home cooking. Lunch 12–2pm. Evening meals 7–9pm. Menu 50–100F. À la carte.

RODEZ 12000 Aveyron **RN 88 and 595 Map 22-B1 see also BERTHOLENE**

♀⊗ ☆ **NN LA ROCADE** (N° RR AOU 18 491) (M. **Gayraud**) La ⌂⊷ Roquette RN 88 ☎ 65-67-10-44 and 64-67-17-12. **Minitel** ⊷ 14 95–125F with shower, telephone. Open 7am–10pm. Closed Fri evening, Sat, 1–14 July, 24 Dec–12 Jan. Coaches welcome. Rest. seats 120. Evening meals until 9pm. Car park. Bar. ⚓ Garden. Menu 43–100F. Specialities: confit de canard, civet d'oie, tripoux, grillades au feu de bois. Sights: lakes, the Tarn Gorge.

⚓⊗ **LE VICTOR HUGO** (N° RR FEV 27 524) (M. Christian **Guigard**)
🏠 19, avenue Victor Hugo ☎ 65-68-14-59 ⊷ 10. Parking. Filling station nearby open 7am–10pm.

ROFFIAC 15100 Cantal **RD 926 Map 17-A2/3**
⚓⊗ **AUBERGE DE LA VALLÉE** (N° RR MAR 23 193) (M. Pierre **Farges**) St Flour ☎ 71-60-04-50. Closed Sat, Sun, 15–30 Aug. Regional home cooking.

ROGNAC 13340 Bouches-du-Rhône **RN 113 Map 24-B3**
⚓⊗ ☆☆ **NN CADET ROUSSEL** (N° RR AVR 25 353) (M. Jack **Schiele**)
🏠 Autoroute exit-Berre ☎ 42-87-00-33 ⊷ 13 150–210F with shower, bath, WC, TV, telephone. Open 7am–10pm. Closed Sun. Regional home cooking. Menu 51–85F. Evening meals until 10pm. Some German spoken. Car park. Bar. ⚓ Rest. seats 90. Garden terrace.

ROMAGNY 50140 Manche **Map 8-A1**
⚓⊗ ☆☆ **AUBERGE DES CLOSEAUX** (N° RR OCT 24 717) (M.
🏠 Bernard **Clouard**) Les Closeaux ☎ 33-59-01-86 ⊷ 10 160–200F with shower, bath, WC, TV, telephone. Restaurant: regional cooking. Specialities: pintade au cidre, crutacés, poisson. Menu 50–115F. Children's menu. À la carte. Dinner until 8.30pm. Closed Sun (low season). Credit cards accepted. Modern décor. Rest. seats 100. Rest room. Garden terrace. Parking. Sights: Mont St Michel (20km), La côte de Granuille.

ROMANVILLE 93230 Seine-St-Denis **Map 1-A2**
⊗ **LE REFUGE – CHEZ ANNA** (N° RR JANV 27 771) (Mme Maria **Vuko**) 79, boulevard Henri Barbusse ☎ 48-91-04-85. Spanish, Portuguese spoken. Restaurant. Menu 57F. Lunch 11.30am– 3.30pm. Closed Sun. HGV parking.

ROMAZY 35490 Manche **Map 8-A1**
⚓⊗ **LE RELAIS** (N° RR 27 365) (M. Jean-Claude **Moncel**) ☎ 99-39-50- 83. Dinner until 10pm. Closed Sun. Rest. seats 30.

ROMORANTIN-LANTHENAY 41200 Loir-et-Cher **RN 722/765 Map 13-B1**
⚓⊗ **RELAIS DE L'AVENIR** (N° RR SEPT 27 667) (Mme Jocelyne **Breton**) 44, avenue de Villefranche ☎ 54-76-14-28. **Minitel**. Closed Sat, Sun. Coaches welcome. Rest. seats 60. A little English and Spanish spoken. Filling station nearby open 7am–9pm.
⚓⊗ ☆ **NN LES AUBIERS** (N° RR MAR 23 703) (M. Guy **Boivin**)
🏠 1, avenue de Blois ☎ 54-76-05-59. **Minitel** ⊷ 24 80–200F with shower, bath, WC, TV, telephone. Open 7am–11pm. Restaurant: home cooking. Menu 50–120F. Children's menu. À la carte. Dinner until 9pm. Closed Sun pm. Credit cards accepted. Rest. seats 120. Rest room. Parking. Sights: château at Chambord and Blois.

RONCHAMP

RONCHAMP 70250 Haute-Saône **RN 19 Map 10-A3**
☆ **NN LE RELAIS DE LA POMME D'OR** (N° RR FEV 18 622)
(MM. **Cenci Frères**) Rue Le Corbusier ☎ 84-20-62-12. Fax
84-63-51-95 **Minitel** ⇀ 30 95–160F with shower, bath, WC, TV,
telephone. Open 6am–midnight. Restaurant: regional home
cooking. Menu 45–180F. Children's menu. À la carte. Dinner
7–10.30pm. Credit cards accepted. Rest. seats 220. ⚓ Parking.
Sights: Le Corbusier, museum, plans d'eau.

ROQUE-D'ANTHÉRON (LA) 13640 Bouches-du-Rhône **CD 561 and 543
Map 24-B3**
AU RELAIS FLEURI (N° RR OCT 27 058) (M. Guy **Auguste**)
Hameau de St Christophe ☎ 42-50-20-24 ⇀ 9 120–150F. English,
Italian, German and Spanish spoken. Home cooking. Menu
50–80F. Children's menu. À la carte. Lunch 12–2pm. Dinner
7.30–10pm. Credit cards accepted. Traditional décor. Coaches
welcome. Rest. seats 80. Garden terrace. ⚓ Parking. Filling
station 4km open 7am–9pm. Sights: Le Luberón, Château de
Lourmarin.

ROSOY 89100 Yonne **RN 6 Map 9-B2**
LA MAISON BLANCHE (N° RR JUL 10 864) (M. **Reinhold**) rte
d'Auxerre ☎ 86-97-13-01 ⇀ 15 66–68F (single), 96–98F (double).
Coaches welcome. Rest. seats 150. Evening meals. Menus 50–
110F. Home cooking. Specialities: moules à la chablisienne,
couscous. Open 24 hours. ⚓ Parking. Sights: Sens Cathedral,
museum, the Yonne river.

ROSPORDEN 29140 Finistère **RN 165 Map 7-B1**
LES ROUTIERS (N° RR 26 703) (Mme Maryvonne **Michal**) 9, Pont
Biais ☎ 98-59-20-40. **Minitel** ⇀ 17 110–140F. Closed Sat, Sun, Aug
(res. only). Home cooking. Menu 46F. Lunch 11.30am–1.30pm.
Evening meals 7.30–8.30pm. ⚓ Parking. Sights: Concorneau
(13km).

ROSTASSAC 46150 Lot **Map 17-B1**
AUBERGE DU VERT (N° RR AVR 27 590) (M. Bernard **Joucias**)
RD 660 ☎ 65-36-22-85 ⇀ 7 100–150F. English spoken. Restaurant.
Specialities: confit de canard, magret (2 people minimum order),
foie gras. Menu 70–140F. Dinner until 9.30pm. Closed Mon night,
Tue (1 Sept–30 June), 4th week in Sept and 2 Feb–15 Mar.
Parking.

ROSTRENEN 22110 Côtes-du-Nord **Map 7-B2**
LE RELAIS DES ROUTIERS (N° RR MAI 14 345) (M. Corentin
Cerno) 32, rue Olivier Perrin ☎ 96-29-01-30. **Minitel**.

ROTS 14980 Calvados **RN 13 Map 4-B2**
LE RELAIS DU COUP DE POMPE (N° RR JAN 27 163) (M.
Valentine **Castander**) 22, route de Caen ☎ 31-26-63-56 ⇀ 5.
Closed Sun. English, Spanish spoken. Dinner to 9pm. Filling
station nearby.

ROUANS 44640 Loire-Atlantique **Map 11-A2**
LA CHAUSSÉE LE RETZ (N° RR JUN 26 911) (Mme Claudette
Biton) La Chaussée le Retz ☎ 40-64-22-23 ⇀ 6. Rest. seats 60.
Evening meals until 9pm. Filling station 2km.

ROUBAIX 59100 Nord **Map 5-B1**

ⵣⵣ **LE CALAIS** (N° RR OCT 27 073) (Mme Josette **Vaze**) 2, quai de Calais ☎ 20-26-14-01. Closed Sat pm, Sun and Aug. German, Dutch and English spoken.

ROUDOUALLEC 56110 Morbihan **Map 7-B1**

ⵣⵣ **RESTAURANT TYKORN** (N° RR DEC 27 468) (Mme Mineille **Glet**) ☎ 97-34-50-38. English spoken. Restaurant: home cooking. Specialities: couscous, bourguignon, ragout du pêcheur. Menu 44F. Lunch 11am–3pm. Dinner 7–8pm. Closed Sun. Credit cards accepted. Traditional décor. Rest. seats 48. ⵗ Parking. Sights: Château du Faou, Quimper.

ROUEN 76100 Seine-Maritime **RN 13 Bis and RN 14 Map 3-A1**

ⵣⵣ **LES PLATANES** (N° RR MARS 26 468) (M. Roger **Sannier**) 57, avenue du Mont-Riboudet ☎ 35-71-01-52. **Minitel** ⵗ 20. Closed Sat pm, Sun, 24 Dec–2 Jan, bank holidays. Evening meals.

ⵣⵣ **RELAIS 207 CHEZ JOËLE ET PATRICK** (N° RR JAN 26 775) (M. **Mebarki**) 46, quai Cavelier-de-la-Salle ☎ 35-73-18-55. Closed Sat, Sun.

ⵣⵣ **LONDON BAR** (N° RR JAN 25 278) (M. Dominique **Merchi**) 55, quai Cavelier-de-la-Salle ☎ 35-73-03-01. Closed Sat, Sun. Evening meals until 11pm. English, Arabic spoken.

ROUFFIGNAC-DE-SIGOULES 24240 Dordogne **15-B3**

ⵣⵣ **RELAIS LA TAVERNE ALSACIENNE** (N° RR AVR 27 245) (Mme Francine **Thomann**) La Tabaline ☎ 53-58-84-13. Evening meals. German spoken. 24 hour filling station 8km.

ROUFFILLAC-DE-CARLUX 24370 Dordogne **RD 703 Map 17-A1**

ⵣⵣ ☆☆ **NN AUX POISSONS FRAIS** (N° RR MAR 12 788) (**Cayre and Son**) ☎ 53-29-70-24 ⵗ 18 130–225F with bath. Closed 1–31 Oct. Coaches welcome. Rest. seats 140. Evening meals until 9pm. Bar. Parking. ⵗ Recreation: swimming, tennis, canoeing, fishing. English spoken. Sights: les grottes de Lascaux, Rocamadour, Padirac, les Eyzies et Cougnac.

ROUGEMONTIER 27350 Eure **RN 180 Map 4-B3**

ⵣⵣ **LE LUDO** (N° RR FEV 24 871) (M. Jean-Claude **Duboc**) RN 175 ☎ 32-56-85-22. Closed Sat afternoon, Sun, Aug. Evening meals until 9pm. ⵗ Parking.

ⵣⵣ **AU RENOUVEAU** (N° RR OCT 27 437) (Mlle Nathalie **Dumège**) RN 175 ☎ 32-42-07-89. Closed Mon. Evening meals. English spoken. Filling station nearby.

ROUILLAC 16170 Charente **RN 139 Map 15-A2**

ⵣⵣ **LA BOULE D'OR SARL** (N° RR AOUT 26 304) (M. Franck **Chiron**) 56, rue Général-de-Gaulle ☎ 45-96-50-45 ⵗ 9. Closed Sat pm, Sun. Coaches welcome. Rest. seats 80. Evening meals until 9pm. English spoken.

ROUMAZIÈRES-LOUBERT 16270 Charente **RN 141 Map 15-B2**

ⵣⵣ **LES 3 CHENES CHEZ YVETTE** (N° RR NOV 27 713) (M. Raymond **Bisserier**) Chantrezac ☎ 45-77-71-83. Basin, bidet, WC on corridor. Restaurant: home cooking. Menu 55F. Children's menu. Dinner until 11pm. Traditional décor. Rest. seats 55 ⵗ 7 90–110F with shower. Open 6am–midnight. Garden terrace. ⵗ Parking. Sights: Château de Nieul (8km), La Rochefoucaud (26km).

ROUSSET

ROUSSET 13790 Bouches-du-Rhône **Map 24-B3**

♈⊗ **LA CENGLE** (N° RR JUN 24 609) (M. **Hoffmann**) 110, RN 7 ☎
⌂ 42-29-00-40 ◄ 5 90–150F. Closed Sat pm, Sun. Coaches welcome.
Rest. seats 110. Evening meals. Italian spoken. Dinner until 10pm.

♨ **RELAIS DE ROUSSET Total Service Station** A8 ☎ 42-29-01-95.

ROUXIÈRE (LA) 44370 Loire-Atlantique **D28, D29 Map 11-A3**

♈⊗ **CAFÉ DES SPORTS – CHEZ RAOUL ET SYLVIE** (N° RR MAI 26
898) (M. Raoul **Mahé**) 123, rue de la Croix Bouvier ☎ 40-96-98-12.
Minitel. English spoken. Filling station near. Coaches welcome.
Rest. seats 60.

ROYAN 17200 Charente-Maritime **Maps 11-B1 and 20-A1**

♈⊗ **L'ESPÉRANCE** (N° RR SEPT 27 669) (M. G. **Alexandra**) 72,
boulevard d'Aquitaine ☎ 46-05-01-02. Coaches welcome. Rest.
seats 45. Evening meals. Filling station nearby open 8am–8pm.

♈⊗ **LE SYMPATIC** (N° RR SEPT 26 672) (M. Yves **Boinard**) 30, av de la
⌂ Libération ☎ 46-05-67-21 ◄ 12 120–190F with shower, WC. Open
6am–10pm. Home cooking. Children's menu to 9pm. Closed Sun,
24–31 Dec. Coaches welcome. Rest. seats 30. ⊨ Parking.

ROYE 70200 Haute-Saône **RN 19 Map 10-A3**

♈⊗ **LE RELAIS DES ROUTIERS** (N° RR AOU 15 771) (Mme Huguette
Kuhn) 50, rue de la Verrerie ☎ 84-30-06-48. Closed Sun. Car Park.
Coaches welcome. Rest. seats 25.

ROZIERES EN BEAUCE 45130 Loiret **Map 13-A1**

♈⊗ **LA BAGATELLE** (N° RR FEV 27 542) (Mme Sylvie **Bihel**) 1, rue
Bagatelle ☎ 38-74-22-03 ◄ 3 100–150F. Restaurant: home cooking.
Menu 48–50F. Children's menu. Lunch 11am–3pm. Dinner 6.30–
11pm. Closed Sat. Credit cards accepted. Rest. seats 44. ⊨
Parking. Filling station open 5am–10pm. Sights: Orléans.

RUFFEC 16700 Charente **RN 10 Map 15-B2**

♈⊗ **CAFE DE LA GARE** (N° RR OCT 27 706) (Mme Marie-Hélène
Chinier) 15, boulevard de Verdun ☎ 45-31-18-09. **Minitel**. Restau-
rant: home cooking. Menu 48F. Children's menu. Closed Sun.
Credit cards accepted. Traditional décor. Rest. seats 30. ⊨
Parking. Showers. TV. Filling station 500m open 8am–8pm.

♈⊗ **LE LANDAIS** (N° RR JANV 26 799) (M. Jean-Michel **Lapegue**) 34,
avenue Célestin Sieur ☎ 45-31-04-16. Restaurant: regional home
cooking. Menu 50F. À la carte. Lunch 12.15–1pm. Dinner 7–9pm.
Closed Sun, Dec. Credit cards accepted. Traditional décor. Rest.
seats 25. ⊨ Parking. Sights: Angouléme (45km), the futuroscope at
Poitiers (70km).

RUFFEC-LE-CHATEAU 36300 Indre **Map 16-A1**

♈⊗ **CHEZ P'TIT JEAN** (N° RR NOV 26 728) (Mme Micheline **Meran-**
⌂ **don**) Le Bourg ☎ 54-37-70-05. **Minitel** ◄ 6. Closed Sept. Coaches
welcome. 2 rest. 30 seats. Evening meals served until 9pm.

RUNGIS CEDEX 94150 Val-de-Marne **RN 7 Map 1-B2/3**

♈⊗ **LE GRAND COMPTOIR DE RUNGIS** (N° RR OCT 25 698) (SARL
Sogere) place St-Hubert Halles de Rungis ☎ 46-86-29-30. Restaurant: home cooking. Menu à la carte. Closed Sat, Sun. Coaches
welcome. Rest. seats 25. ⊨ Parking.

RYE 39230 Jura **Map 14-A3**
♈⊗ **CHEZ LUCETTE** (N° RR AVR 27 263) (Mme Lucette **Cambazard**)
☎ 84-48-61-60. Closed Thurs afternoon, 1–15 Aug. Rest. seats 50.

SABLES-D'OLONNE (LES) 85100 Vendée **RN 160/149 Map 11-A1**
♈⊗ **AU COQ HARDI** (N° RR MAI 20 453) (Mlle Françoise **Pajot**)
⌂ 7, avenue Alcide-Gabaret ☎ 51-32-04-62 ⊷ 8. Closed Sun low
season, end of Sept/beginning of Oct. Coaches welcome. Rest.
seats 90.

♈⊗ **LES VOYAGEURS** (N° RR AOU 26 307) (M. Clément **Pacory**) 17,
⌂ rue de la Bauduère ☎ 51-95-11-49 ⊷ 11. Closed Fri pm, Sat, end of
Dec/beginning of Jan. Evening meals until 9pm.

SABLONNIERES 38460 Isère **RD 522 and 517 Crossroads Map 2-B2**
♈⊗ **LE RELAIS DE LA PLACE** (N° RR OCT 24 366) (M. Maurice
Mailler) Crémieu ☎ 74-92-80-19. Evening meals.

SACEY 50170 Manche **RD 80/D 169 Map 8-A1**
♈⊗ **LES VOYAGEURS** (N° RR NOV 25 168) (Mme Marcelle **Belan**) Le
⌂ Bourg ☎ 33-60-15-11. **Minitel** ⊷ 8 120–135F. Regional home
cooking. Lunch 12–3pm. Rest. seats 180. Evening meals 7–9pm.
Specialities: fruits de mer, homard à l'américaine (on request).
Children's menu. Traditional décor. ⊨ Parking. Coaches wel-
come. Sights: Mont St Michel, le jardin des plantes à Avranches
(12km).

SACLAS 91690 Essonne **RN 20 Map 9-B1**
♈⊗ **RELAIS DE MONDÉSIR** (N° RR SEPT 27 386) (M. Jean **Picq**)
Guillerval ☎ 64-95-60-76. Closed Sat, Sun, Aug. Evening meals
until 10.30pm. Spanish, Portuguese spoken.

SAILLANS 26340 Drôme **RN 93 Map 24-B1**
♈⊗ **LE NATIONAL** (N° RR SEP 18 179) (Mme Jeannine **Chauvet**) place
⌂ du Prieuré – Grand-Rue ☎ 75-21-51-33 ⊷ 6 100–150F. Closed Wed
and 5 weeks Sept/Oct. Full-board 160–170F per night. Regional
home cooking. Specialities: gigot d'agneau, daube provençale.
Children's menu. Garden terrace. ⊨ Parking. Coaches welcome.
Rest. seats 35. Evening meals until 8pm. Sights: Vallée de la Drome
church.

**SAINT, SAINTE: for compound names beginning with Saint or Sainte, see
the end of this section.**

SAINTENY 50500 Manche **CD 971 Map 4-B1**
♈⊗ **LE RELAIS DES FORGES** (N° RR NOV 27 092) (Mme Francine
Cousin) Les Forges Carentan ☎ 33-42-39-36. Closed Tue and Aug.
Evening meals to 8pm. Coaches welcome. Rest. seats 70. ⊨
Parking. Filling station nearby.

SALAISE-SUR-SANNE 38150 Isère **Map 18-B3**
♈⊗ **LE RELAIS DE LA SANNE** (N° RR MAR 24 522) (M. Marc **Giraud**)
RN 7 ☎ 74-86-37-91. **Minitel**. English, German spoken. Dinner to
11pm. Closed Sun.

SALINS-LES-BAINS

SALINS-LES-BAINS 39110 Jura **Map 14-B3**

♟⊗ **RESTAURANT DES SPORTS** (N° RR JUL 27 344) (Mme Denise **Reverchon**) 107, rue de la République ☎ 84-73-11-18. Closed Wed afternoon, Sept. Evening meals until 11pm. Parking. Filling station 1km open 7am–10pm.

SALLE (LA) 71260 Saône-et-Loire **RN 6 Map 18-B1**

♟⊗ **RELAIS DU MACONNAIS** (N° RR JUL 26 590) (Mme Valérie **Zorzi**) Lugny ☎ 85-37-51-34. Closed Sat afternoon, Sun. Italian spoken. Evening meals until 11pm.

SALOUEL 80480 Somme **RN 29 Map 5-A3**

♟⊗ **LE TROU NORMAND** (N° RR MAI 27 270) (M. Jean-Michel **Picard**) 75, route de Rouen ☎ 22-95-53-90. Closed Sun. English and German spoken. Filling station nearby open 24 hours.

SAMADET 40320 Landes **Map 20-B2**

♟⊗ **AU PELLE** (N° RR OCT 26 346) (Mme **Darolles-Cassou**) route d'Hagetmau ☎ 58-79-19-81. Coaches welcome. Evening meals to 8pm. English, Spanish spoken. Closed Sun, 1st 2 weeks Aug.

SAMMERON 77260 Seine-et-Marne **RN 3 Map 9-A2**

♟⊗ **LES CICOGNES** (N° RR OCT 27 566) (Mme Gloria **Bento**) 2, rue de
🏠 Metz ☎ 60-22-79-40 ⊷ 5 90–120F with showers. Portuguese spoken. Restaurant: home cooking. Specialities: Portuguese. Menu to 60F. Children's menu. À la carte. Open 7am–9.30pm. Lunch 11.30am–3pm. Dinner 7–9.30pm. Closed Sun, Aug. Credit cards accepted. Rest. seats 80. Parking.

SANCERGUES 18140 Cher **RN 151 Map 13-B2**

♟⊗ **LE RELAIS AU BON LABOUREUR** (N° RR JAN 22 148) (Mme
🏠 Martine **Dubois**) 54, Grande-Rue ☎ 48-72-78-13 ⊷ 5 80–90F. Open 7am–9pm. Restaurant: home cooking. Specialities: poisson, choucroute. Menu to 56–50F. Children's menu. Lunch 11.45–1.45pm. Dinner 7–8.30pm. Closed 15 July–15 Aug. Traditional décor. Coaches welcome. Rest. seats 90. German, Italian spoken. ⊷ Parking for cars. Sights: Sacerre (25km), Bourges cathedral (40km), Noirlac Abbey (60km).

SARCEY 69490 Rhône **2km from RN 7 Map 2-A1**

♟⊗ **LE RELAIS DES MARRONIERS** (N° RR AVR 26 223) (M. Patrick **Parisi**) place de l'Église ☎ 74-26-86-65. Closed Wed afternoon. English spoken.

SARGE-SUR-BRAYE 41170 Loir-et-Cher **Map 12-A3**

♟⊗ **LE RELAIS DE MONPLAISIR Tobacconist** (N° RR DEC 27 737) (M. Roger **Moujeard**) RN 157 ☎ 54-72-72-21. Restaurant: home cooking. Menu to 49F. Lunch 11.30am–3.30pm. Dinner 6.30–10pm. Closed Sat, Sun, Aug. Credit cards accepted. Rest. seats 45. ⊷ Parking. Filling station nearby. Sights: Vallée du Loir.

SARLAT 24200 Dordogne **CD 46/57 Map 17-B1**

♟⊗ **RELAIS DU PONTET** (N° RR FEV 27 543) (M. Jean-Pierre **Bouy**) avenue de la Dordogne. Direction on the road to Bergerac ☎ 53-31-05-36 or 53-31-05-85. Restaurant: regional family cooking. Speciality: gibiers (wild boar). Children's menu. Self-service. Lunch 11.30am–4pm. Dinner 7–11pm. Closed 15 Dec–1 Jan. Credit cards accepted. Modern décor. Rest. seats 50. Rest room. Garden terrace. ⚐ Parking. Filling station 300m open 7am–10pm. Sights: Sarlat, Rocamadour, gouffre de Padirac, Castelnaud.

SARREGUEMINES 57200 Moselle **RN 74 Map 10-A/B1**

♈⊗ **AU RELAIS DES ROUTIERS – CHEZ EDMOND** (N° RR SEPT 18 829) (M. Camille **Fasel**) 19, rue du Bac ☎ 87-98-15-39 ━ 11 65–85F. Showers and WC on landing. Closed Sun during July. Open 5am–midnight. Coaches welcome. Rest. seats 60. Evening meals until midnight. German spoken. Home cooking. Specialities: choucroute garnie. Parking.

SARTILLY 50530 Manche **Map 8-A1**

♈⊗ **LE VIEUX LOGIS** (N° RR OCT 27 394) (M. Gerard **Cadiot**) Grand Rue ☎ 33-48-80-31. Closed Sun afternoon. English spoken. Home cooking. Menu to 48F. Rest. seats 30. ⚐ Filling station nearby open 8am–8pm. Sights: the bay of Mont St Michel.

SATOLAS ET BONCE 38290 Isère **Map 2-A/A2**

♈⊗ **LE RELAIS DU CHAFFARD** (N° RR NOV 27 717) (Mme Annette and Didier **Zanoni**) CD 75 ☎ 74-94-16-16. English, German, Italian spoken. Restaurant. Menu 55F. Closed Sat, Sun and 25 Dec–1 Jan. Parking. Filling station open 6am–9pm.

SAUJON 17600 Charente-Maritime **Map 11-B1**

♈⊗ ☆ **NN HÔTEL DE LA GARE** (N° RR OCT 24 404) (M. Michel **Mellot**) 2, rue Clémenceau ☎ 46-02-80-33 ━ 12 from 120–180F with showers. Home cooking. Children's menu. Access for disabled. Closed Sun, Christmas to New Year. Coaches welcome. Rest. seats 110 in 2 rooms. Evening meals until 9pm. Bar. ⚐ Sports (table tennis, petanque, swings). Garden terrace. Parking.

SAULCE 26270 Drôme **RN 7 and RD 26 motorway exit Loriol, Montélimar Nord Map 24-A1**

♈⊗ **LE DISQUE BLEU** (N° RR OCT 25 134) (M. Jacques **Brillo**) quartier des Blaches à Cliouscat. Directions: leave Autoroute at Loriol and Montélimar North ☎ 75-63-00-08 ━ 8 60–80F. Closed Sun afternoon. Open 4am–midnight. Coaches welcome. Rest. seats 140. Evening meals to midnight. Washbasin and WC on landing. Restaurant: home cooking. Menu to 53F. Children's menu. À la carte. Credit cards accepted. ⚐ Parking.

SAULIEU 21210 Côte-d'Or **RN 6 Map 13-B3**

♈⊗ **LE RELAIS AUX POIDS LOURDS** (N° RR FEV 12 693) (M. Michèle **Godet**) 30, rue Courte-epée ☎ 81-64-19-83 ━ 8 60–75F. Open 7am–10pm. Home cooking. Menu to 48F. Lunch 12–2.30pm. Closed Sat, Sun, Aug. Credit cards accepted. Traditional décor. Rest. seats 40. Parking. Sights: Lac de Settons (25km).

SAULNIÈRES 35320 Ille-et-Vilaine **RD 777 Map 7-B3**

♈⊗ **LA TAVERNE BRETONNE** (N° RR MAI 26 540) (Mme Nicole **Scoazec**) Bourg de Saulnières, Bel de Bretagne ☎ 99-44-70-61. **Minitel**. Coaches welcome. Rest. seats 180. Casserole menus 45–120F. Dinner to 10pm. Closed Sat. Specialities: confit de poule, filet de loup pipérade, coquilles St Jacques.

SAUMUR

SAUMUR 49400 Maine-et-Loire **RN 152 Map 12-B2**

☆☆ **NN HÔTEL DE LA GARE** (N° RR FEV 17 188) (M. Jacques **Gaudicheau**) 16, avenue David-d'Angers (opposite the station) ☎ 41-67-34-24 ⊶ 18, 13 with shower or bath. WC. TV. Telephone. Open 7am–midnight. Access for disabled. View of Loire and castle. Coaches welcome. Rest. seats 200. Evening meals until 10pm. English, German spoken. Proprietorship passed from father to son since 1919. Car park patrons only. Secure. Bar. ⊷ Menus 28–80F. Specialities: cuisses de poulet bonne femme, rôti à la saumuroise, omelette arc-en-ciel. Sights: stone circles, châteaux, museums, churches, wine cellars.

SAUQUEVILLE 76550 Seine-Maritime **RN 27 Map 4-A3**

LA FALAISE (N° RR NOV 25 214) (Mme **Capeyrou**) Bas de Tourvilles/Arques ☎ 35-85-44-77 ⊶ 11. Closed Sun evening. English, Italian, Spanish spoken.

SAUVETAT SUR LEDE (LA) 47150 Lot-et-Garonne **Map 21-B1**

LA RENAISSANCE (N° RR FEV 27 776) (M. Alain **Soressi**) Le Bourg ☎ 53-41-94-50. Italian spoken. Menu 75–120F. Menu Routiers, 55F ⊶ 7 at 100–130F. Parking.

SAUVETERRE DE GUYENNE 33540 Gironde **Map 21-A1**

☆ **HOTEL DE GUYENNE** (N° RR AVR 27 578) (M. Jean-Paul **Daldoss**) route de Libourne Pringis ☎ 56-71-54-92. English spoken. Restaurant. Specialities: escargots à la Bordelaise, magret, foie gras. Menu at 65–70F. Dinner to 10pm ⊶ 9 at 90–160F. Parking.

SAUVIAT-SUR-VIGE 87400 Haute-Vienne **RN 141 Map 16-B1**

☆ **NN HÔTEL DE LA POSTE** (N° RR AOU 10 941) (M. Pierre **Chassagne**) ☎ 55-75-30-12 ⊶ 12 (10 with WC) from 75–145F. Closed Wed, Sept. Coaches welcome. Rest. seats 160. Evening meals to 10pm. Parking. Bar. ⊷ Recreations: fishing, hunting, countryside to explore. Sights: vineyards (St Emilion, Pomerol).

SAUZE-VAUSSAIS 79190 Deux-Sèvres **RN 148 Map 15-A1/2 LES ALLEUDS (Chaignepain)**

LE RELAIS DES ROUTIERS (N° RR JAN 20 089) (M. Joël **Quintard**) ☎ 49-29-34-61. Closed Sat. Coaches welcome. Rest. seats 90. Lunch 11.30am–2.30pm. Evening meals 7–10pm. Home cooking. Menu to 45F. Traditional décor. ⊷ Parking.

SAVENAY 44260 Loire-Atlantique **RN 165 Map 11-A2**

RELAIS 165 (N° RR FEV 27 193) (M. Claude **Bourgine**) Le Pas de l'Auline Prinquiau on the Nantes/Vannes road. ☎ 40-56-64-99. Home cooking. Menu 47F. Open 5am–2am. Rest. seats 64. ⊷ Parking. Filling station nearby. Sights: the sea.

SAVERDUN 09700 Ariège **RN 20 Map 22-A2**

A LA BONNE AUBERGE (N° RR AVR 21 880) (Mme **Boutet**) RN 20 – rue du Lion-d'Or ☎ 61-69-30-33 ⊶ 6. Closed Mon, Sept. Spanish spoken.

SENE

SAZILLY 37220 Indre-et-Loire **RD 760 Map 12-B2**

♈⊗ **LE RELAIS DE LA PROMENADE** (N° RR MARS 25 862) (Mme Jocelyne **Bigot**) Le Bourg ☎ 47-58-55-50. Closed Sun. Coaches welcome. Rest. seats 80.

SCIEZ 74140 Haute-Savoie **RN Map 19-A1**

♈⊗ ☆ **NN LE LEMAN** (N° RR AVR 25 358) (M. Roger **Berthet**)
⌂ Bonnatrait ☎ 50-72-60-04 ⊷ 12 60–110F. Closed Sat in winter, Oct. Coaches welcome. Rest. seats 70. Evening meals. Parking. Bar. English, German spoken. Sights: Evian, Geneva, mountain walks.

SCOURY 36300 Indre **RN 151 Map 16-A1**

♈⊗ **LE RELAIS DES ROUTIERS** (N° RR JANV 26 791) (Mme Roselyne
⌂ **Pilet**) RN 151 ☎ 54-37-98-09 ⊷ 4 110F. Closed Sun, Dec. Coaches welcome. Rest. seats 40. Evening meals until 10pm. Modern décor. Sights: La Brenne (20km).

SÉBAZAC 12850 Aveyron **CD 904 Map 22-A1**

♈⊗ **LE LONGCHAMP** (N° RR SEPT 27 033) (Mme Monique **Guilpin**) 56, avenue Tabardelle ☎ 65-74-93-62. Coaches welcome. Rest. seats 50. Evening meals until 10pm. Filling station open 8am–8pm.

SECONDIGNY 79130 Deux-Sèvres **RN 148 Map 15-A1**

♈⊗ **LE RELAIS DES ROUTIERS** (N° RR JAN 19 615) (M. Noël
⌂ **Duranceau**) 43, rue de la Vendée ☎ 49-95-61-35. Directions: leaving the town towards La Roche sur Yon. Restaurant: regional home cooking. Specialities: escargots farcie, salade gourmande. Menu 48–120F. Children's menu. À la carte. Lunch 11.30am–2.30pm. Dinner 7–9pm. Closed Sun, 1 week Sept. Credit cards accepted. Rest. seats 165 ⊷ 5 95–160F with shower, bath, WC. Hotel open 7am–10pm. Parking. Swimming. Tennis. Miniature golf. Sights: Roman church, Château de Saint Loup (40km), Mervent (forest 25km), the futuroscope at Poitiers (70km).

SEGLIEN 56160 Morbihan **RN 782 Map 7-B2**

♈ **LE CAFE DE LA PAIX** (N° RR MAR 20 134) (M. Armand **Bigouin**) ☎ 97-28-02-48 Lann-Blomen.

SEGRE 49500 Maine-et-Loire **RN 775 Maps 11-A3 and 12-A1**

♈⊗ **LE RELAIS DU COMMERCE** (N° RR DEC 18 576) (M. Emile
⌂ **Georget**) 1, place de la Gare ☎ 41-92-22-27 ⊷ 10.

SENAN 89710 Yonne **RD 955 Map 13-A2**

♈⊗ **HOTEL DE LA CROIX BLANCHE** (N° RR NOV 26 104) (M. Jean-Claude **Lecourt**) 16, rue d'Aillant ☎ 86-63-41-31. Closed Sun after lunch.

SENAS 13560 Bouches-du-Rhône **RN 7 Map 24-B3**

♈⊗ **L'ETAPE** (N° RR MARS 21 043) (SNC Veyrier Frères) RN 7 ☎ 90-59-22-81. Closed Sat, Sun, 25 Dec–5 Jan.

♈⊗ **LE RESTO GRILL** (N° RR SEPT 26 326) (M. **Degoul**) RN 7 ☎ 90-57-27-82. Closed Sat afternoon, Sun.

SENE 56860 Morbihan **RN 165 Map 11-A1/2**

♈⊗ ☆ **NN LE POULFANC** (N° RR FEV 16 886) (S.A. **Penru**) route de
⌂ Vannes ☎ 97-47-47-97 ⊷ 45. Closed Sat (low season), 23 Dec–2 Jan. Evening meals until 9pm. Parking.

SENLIS

SENLIS 60300 Oise **Map 3-B3**

♀⊗ **RELAIS DU POTEAU** (N° RR AVR 27 579) (Mme Jeanine **Ronald**) 11, avenue du Poteau ☎ 44-53-12-10. Restaurant: closed Sat, Sun, Aug.

SENNECEY-LE-GRAND 71240 Saône-et-Loire **RN 6 Map 8-B3**

♀⊗ **L'ARCHE DE CHALON LA FERTE** (N° RR 1828) (M. Fabrice **Leonard**) Aire de la ferté Sens Paris/Lyons autoroute ☎ 58-44-21-79.

♀⊗ **L'ARCHE DE CHALON SAINT AMBREUIL** (N° RR 1808) (M. Bruno **Brenez**) Aire de Saint Ambreuil Sens Paris/Lyons autoroute ☎ 85-44-20-64.

SEREILHAC 87620 Haute-Vienne **Map 16-B1**

♀⊗ **AUBERGE DES ROUTIERS** (N° RR FEV 24 846) (Mme Denis
⌂ **Vignaud**) RN 21 ☎ 55-39-10-46 ⇌ 6. Coaches welcome. Rest. seats 100. English spoken. Dinner to 11pm.

SERIFONTAINE 60590 Oise **Map 3-A/B2**

♀⊗ **LE RELAIS FLEURI** (N° RR MARS 27 553) (Mme Annick **Fon-**
⌂ **taine**) 22, rue Hacque ☎ 44-84-89-17. Restaurant: closed Fri pm, Sat after 3pm, last 2 weeks Aug ⇌ 9. Filling station nearby.

SÉRIGNY 17230 Charente-Maritime **Map 11-A1**

♀⊗ **CHEZ JOHAN** (N° RR MAI 27 288) (M. Johan **Mercier**) RN 137 towards Nantes ☎ 46-01-40-03. **Minitel**. Closed Sun. Evening meals to midnight. Rest. seats 70. Filling station 2.5km open 6am–midnight.

SERRES-CASTET 64121 Pyrénées-Atlantiques **Maps 20-B3 and 21-A3 on the road to Bordeaux**

♀⊗ **LES ROUTIERS** (N° RR MAR 23 199) (M. Léon **Salis**) ☎ 59-33-91-
⌂ 06 ⇌ 4. Closed Sat, Sun, Aug. Evening meals to 10pm. Spanish spoken. Regional home cooking. Speciality: béarnaises. Children's menu. Rest room. Parking.

SERVAS 01000 Ain **RN 83 Map 18-B2**

♀⊗ **LE RELAIS DU POSTILLON** (N° RR AVR 25 364) (M. Kaddour
⌂ **Lastab**) RN 83 ☎ 74-52-79-10 ⇌ 5. Closed Sat, Aug. Rest. seats 80.

SETE 34200 Hérault **RN 108 Map 23-B2**

♀⊗ **LE PAVILLON** (N° RR MARS 26 471) (Mme Marie-France **Petitfils**) 23, route de Montpellier ☎ 67-48-62-53. Closed Sat afternoon, Sun. English and German spoken. Evening meals to 10pm.

♀⊗ **RESTOROUTE LA PENICHE** (N° RR AVR 23 758) (Mme Paquerette **Dupuy**) 1, quai des Moulins ☎ 67-48-64-13. Evening meals to 11pm. Rest. seats 100.

♀⊗ **RESTAURANT ROUTIERS** (N° RR DEC 27 116) (Mme Savita **Barthe**) 1, quai de la République Place Delille. Directions: on entering town opposite the port ☎ 67-74-32-92. English, Spanish, Italian spoken. Restaurant: regional home cooking. Paella, couscous. Menu to 55F. Children's menu. À la carte. Open 8am–1am. Lunch 12–3pm. Dinner 7–10pm. Traditional décor. Rest. seats 40. Garden terrace. Filling station nearby open 7am–10pm.

SEURRE 21250 Côte-d'Or **Map 14-A3**

♈⊗ **RELAIS DU CHAMP DE FOIRE** (N° RR JUL 26 580) (M. Jacky **Madesclaire**) 13, place du Champ de Foire ☎ 80-21-03-43. Closed Sun. Rest. seats 50. Evening meals until 9pm.

SEXCLES 19430 Corrèze **RN 120 Map 17-A2**

♈⊗ **AUBERGE DES ROUTIERS** (N° RR JUL 26 597) (M. Claude
⌂ **Gubert**) Le Mas ☎ 55-28-70-70.

SEYCHES 47350 Lot-et-Garonne **RN 133 Map 21-B1**

♈⊗ **AU BON ACCUEIL** (N° RR NOV 14 086) (Mme Madec **Laliette**) ☎ 53-83-60-10. Closed Sat. Evening meals until 11.30pm.

SEYNOD 74600 Haute-Savoie **RN 201 Map 21-B1**

♈⊗ ☆ **NN LE RELAIS SAINTE-CATHERINE** (N° RR MARS 9 372) (M.
⌂ Lucien **Zerbola**) 181, route d'Aix ☎ 50-69-00-86. **Minitel** ⌐ 10 at 110–150F with shower. Closed Sat/Sun, 3 weeks in summer. Regional home cooking. Specialities: steak aux morilles, fondue savoyarde. Coaches welcome. Rest. seats 120. Evening meals. English spoken. Parking. Bar. ⌐ Garden terrace. Sights: Annecy.

♈⊗ **L'AUBERGE** (N° RR JAN 27 514) (SARL Carroz) (N° RR JANV 27 514) (Mmes **Curlioz** and **Rozier**) 1152, route d'Aix les Bains ☎ 50-46-71-02 ⌐ 10. Closed Sun. Evening meals until 10pm. English, Italian spoken. Service station nearby. Parking.

SIDIALLES 18270 Cher **Map 16-A2**

♈⊗ **CHEZ MIMI** (N° RR MAI 27 268) (M. Lucien **Le Bellego**) Le Bouquet ☎ 48-56-63-02. Filling station 4km open 7am–8pm.

SIGOTTIER 05700 Hautes-Alpes **RN 5 Map 24-B2**

♈⊗ **PONT LA BARQUE** (N° RR MARS 25 841) (M. and Mme Claude **Faizende**) Serres ☎ 92-67-04-15. Coaches welcome. Rest. seats 100. Italian spoken. Restaurant: home cooking. Menu à la carte. Lunch 11am–3pm. Dinner 7–11pm. Closed 25 Dec–7 Jan. Credit cards accepted. Traditional décor. Garden terrace. ⌐ Parking.

SILLE-LE-GUILLAUME 72140 Sarthe **CD 37 Map 8-B2**

♈⊗ **HÔTEL DE L'OUEST** (N° RR OCT 26 676) (M. Jean-Jacques **Aubert**) RD 304, 8, place de la Gare ☎ 43-20-10-58 ⌐ 4. Closed Sun evening, Aug. Rest. seats 35. Evening meals until 9pm.

♈⊗ **LA COQUE** (N° RR SEPT 27 005) (M. Claude **Rouzier**) 11 bis, route de Mans, St Rémy de Sillé ☎ 43-20-11-84. Closed Sun, 15–30 Aug. Evening meals to 10pm. Home cooking. Filling station nearby open 7am–10pm. Parking. ⌐ Sights: Lac sous le forêt.

SIMARD 71330 Saône-et-Loire **Map 18-B1**

♈⊗ **RESTAURANT DE L'AMITIE** (N° RR FEV 27 540) (M. Gérard **Sixdenier**) le Bourg ☎ 85-72-25-57. Parking. Filling station 50m open 8am–7pm.

SIZUN 29450 Finistère **RD 167 Map 7-A1**

♈⊗ ☆ **NN HÔTEL DES VOYAGEURS** (N° RR MAR 14 263) (M. Joseph
⌂⌐ **Corre**) 2, rue de l'Argoat ☎ 98-68-80-35 ⌐ 28 from 70–135F. Closed Sat evening (off season), 14 Sept–7 Oct. Rest. seats 290. Evening meals. English spoken. Menus 40–65F. Specialities: terrine de lapin, mousseline de truite, fruits de mer.

SOMMERY

SOMMERY 76440 Seine-Maritime **Map 3-A1**
♈⊗ **LE MONTESTRUC** (N° RR MARS 27 208) (M. Jean-Luc **Édet**) La
  Cavée ☎ 35-90-56-16. Closed Wed pm. Filling station 2km.

SOMMIERES-DU-CLAIN 86160 Vienne **RD 1 Map 15-B1**
♈⊗ **LES TROIS PILIERS** (N° RR JUIL 26 937) (M. Martial **Richard**)
⌂ place de l'Église ☎ 49-87-70-09 ⊸ 5. Closed Mon, Feb. Evening
  meals until 11pm. Rest. seats 80. Coaches welcome.

SORINIERES (LES) 44840 Loire-Atlantique **RN 137 and 178 Maps
11-A/B2 and 12-B1**
♈⊗ **LE RELAIS – CHEZ PIERRETTE ET JEAN-LOUIS** (N° RR SEP 24
⌂ 673) (M. Jean-Louis **Benoît**) 16, rue du Général-de-Gaulle ☎
  40-31-22-91 ⊸ 7. Closed Sat evening, Sun, 15 Dec–5 Jan. Coaches
  welcome. Rest. seats 50 in 3 rooms.

SOUAL 81580 Tarn **RN 126 Map 22-B2**
♈⊗ **LE MAÏZOU** (N° RR JUN 26 912) (M. Jean-Marie **Lemaire**) 12–14,
⌂ Grand-Rue ☎ 63-75-52-24 ⊸ 6. Closed Tue evening. Rest. seats
  150. Dinner to 10pm. Filling station 100m. Coaches welcome.

SOUBERAC 16130 Charente **RN 141 Map 15-A2**
♈⊗ **AUX CHASSEURS** (N° RR MAI 26 254) (M. Raymond **Joffrion**)
  Gensacla-Pallue ☎ 45-32-13-80. Closed Sat, Aug.

SOUCHEZ 62153 Pas-de-Calais **RN 37 Map 5-A1**
♈⊗ **AU RENDEZ-VOUS DES ROUTIERS** (N° RR DEC 20 352) (Mme
  Antoinette **Loup**) 5, rue Carnot ☎ 21-45-15-01.

SOUDAN 44110 Loire-Atlantique **RN 775 Maps 11-A3 and 12-A1**
♈⊗ **CAFE DE LA POSTE** (N° RR SEP 24 321) (M. Claude **Fruchard**) 7,
  place Tolhouët – place de la Poste ☎ 40-28-62-36. Coaches
  welcome. Rest. seats 70 in 2 rooms. ⊨ Parking. Sights: Châteaubriant.

SOUDE 51320 Marne **Map 9-A3**
♈⊗ **CHEZ PHILLIPE** (N° RR SEPT 27 385) (SNC Menis Père et **Fils**)
  ☎ 26-69-71-10. Parking.

SOUILLAC 46200 Lot **RN 20 Map 17-B1**
♈⊗ ☆ **NN LE RELAIS DE L'ESCALE** (N° RR MARS 27 201) (M. Alain
  Fage) 39, avenue Louis-Jean Malvy ☎ 65-37-82-65. Closed Sun.
  Filling station nearby open 7am–10pm.

SOULAINES-DHUYS 10200 Aube **RD 960 Map 9-B3**
♈⊗ **LE RELAIS DES ROUTIERS** (N° RR 20 866) (M. Guy **Demongeot**)
  RN 960 ☎ 25-92-76-10. Restaurant: regional home cooking. Menu
  40–70F. Dinner 11pm. Credit cards accepted. Rest. seats 30 (2
  rooms). Parking. Tobacconist. Petrol. Sights: Lac du Dër (15km),
  nautical port of Dienville (20km).

SOULGE-SUR-OUETTE 53210 Mayenne **RN 157 Map 8-B1**
♈⊗ **LA BELLE ÉTOILE** (N° RR OCT 26 710) (M. Gérard **Couillebault**)
⌂ Le Point du Jour ☎ 43-02-30-18 ⊸ 10. Rest. seats 40. Evening
  meals until 11.30pm. Coaches welcome.

STRASBOURG MEINAU

SOULIGNY par BOUILLY 10320 Aube **RN 77 Map 9-B3**

�⊗ ☆ **NN AU RELAIS DE MONTAIGU** (N° RR AVR 18 374) (M. René
⌂ **Braux)** 300, rue au Febvres. Directions: Troyes 12km ☎ 25-40-20-
20. **Minitel**. Restaurant: regional home cooking. Menu à la carte.
Dinner to 9pm. Credit cards accepted. rest. seats 120 (2 rooms)
⌐ 13 70–140F with showers, WC, TV, tel. Open 6am–11pm. ⌐
Parking. Sights: Troyes, museums, lakes, foret d'Orient.

SOUMOULOU 64420 Pyrénées-Atlantiques **RN 117 Maps 20-B3 and
21-A3**

�⊗ **LE RELAIS BEARNAIS** (N° RR FEV 18 644) (Mme Anne-Marie
⌂ **Delroise)** 5, rue de Platanes ☎ 59-04-60-45. **Minitel** ⌐ 6. Closed
Sat and 3 weeks Aug, 1 week Christmas. Evening meals to 9pm.

SOURDEVAL 50150 Manche **Map 8-A1**

�⊗ **AU BON ACCUEIL** (N° RR JANV 27 760) (M. Daniel **Delaunay**)
1, place du Champ-de-Foire. Directions: between Caen and Vire
☎ 33-59-62-91. **Minitel**. English spoken. Restaurant: home
cooking. Menu 47–100F. À la carte. Open 6am–11pm. Dinner to
10pm. Closed Sun (without reservation) Credit cards accepted.
Traditional décor. Rest. seats 115 (3 rooms) ⌐ 4 70–100F (with
wash basin). Garden terrace. ⌐ Parking. Shower and bath (10F).
Filling station nearby.

SOURDEVAL-LES-BOIS 50450 Manche **RN 799 Map 8-A1**

�⊗ **LE RELAIS DES ROUTIERS** (N° RR FEV 20 659) (Mme Colette
Dufour) La Croix ☎ 33-61-77-99. **Minitel**. Home cooking. Menu
40F. Lunch 12–2pm. Sights: Hambye Abbey (2km).

STEENVOORDE 59114 Nord **RN 25 Map 5-A1**

☓⊗ **CAFETERIA DE STEENVOORDE** (N° RR 1824) (M. Michel
Jaminion) Aire de service de Saint-Laurent and Province/Paris
directions ☎ 28-49-71-88.

STENAY 55700 Meure **D 947 Map 6-B3**

☓⊗ **LA MANGEOIRE** (N° RR MARS 26 841) (M. Daniel **Demaçon**)
1, rue Carnot ☎ 29-80-60-06 ⌐ 7 (4 single) Closed Sun afternoon,
15–31 Aug. German, English (some) spoken. Evening meals until
9pm. Parking. Filling station 300m.

STRASBOURG 67000 Bas-Rhin **RN 4 Map 10-B2**

☓⊗ **AU PETIT RHIN** (N° RR AVR 27 588) (Mr René **Mayrignac)** 4, rue
du Port-du-Rhin ☎ 88-61-35-00. Closed Sat, Sun, Aug. Evening
meals to 10pm.

☓⊗ **AU RHIN FRANÇAIS** (N° RR DEC 25 227) (M. Marcel **Wend-**
⌂ **ling)** 83, route du Rhin. Directions: towards frontier bridge
opposite the customs ☎ 88-61-29-00. Closed Sat, Sun. Restaurant:
regional home cooking. Menu 50F. À la carte. Self-service.
Dinner to 11pm. Credit cards accepted. Modern décor. Rest.
seats 150 (3 rooms) ⌐ 10 140F with showers, WC. German,
English, Italian, Spanish, Dutch spoken. Coaches welcome.
Parking.

STRASBOURG MEINAU 67100 Bas-Rhin **Map 10-B2**

☓⊗ **BRASSERIE DES BATELIERS** (N° RR JUIN 27 306) (M. and Mme
Jean-Claude **Pccinelli)** rue de la Plaine des Bouchers ☎ 88-39-
19-50. Closed Sat from 3pm, Sun and 24 Dec–21 Jan, Easter and 3

Strasbourg Meinau continued

weeks in September. German spoken. Evening meals served until 10pm. Filling station 1.5km open 6.30am–9pm.

SUEVRES 41500 Loir-et-Cher **RN 152 Map 12-A3**
♀⊗ **LA PROVIDENCE – CHEZ JACQUES** (N° RR SEPT 27 674) (M.
⌂⇔ Michel **Grosse**) 1, place de la Mairie ☎ 54-87-80-88. **Minitel** ⇥ 7.
Closed Sat evening, Sun evening. Evening meals to 10pm.
Spanish, English spoken. Parking. Filling station nearby.

SUIPPES 51600 Marne **RN 77 and 31 Maps 6-B2 and 9-A3**
♀⊗ **AU BON COIN** (N° RR JUL 24 623) (SDF **Tiloca**) 25, rue de la
Libération ☎ 26-70-05-84. Coaches welcome. Rest. seats 100.
Italian spoken.

SULLY-SUR-LOIRE 45600 Loiret **RN 152 Map 13-A1**
♀⊗ **LE ST GERMAIN** (N° RR FEV .21 807) (M. and Mme **Schwartz**)
⌂ 2, place Saint-Germain ☎ 38-36-27-02. Directions: leave Sully
towards Orléans. Restaurant: regional home cooking. Specialities: andouillette de Jargeou, coq au vin maison. Children's menu.
À la carte. Lunch 11.45am–1.45pm. Dinner 7–9pm. Closed Fri
evening, Sun evening and last 2 weeks Dec. Traditional décor.
Rest. seats 148 in 3 rooms ⇥ 6 100–140F with showers. ⊬ Parking.
Sights: Château de Sully sur Loire.

♀⊗ **CHEZ LIONEL – CAFÉ DE LA GARE** (N° RR OCT 26 077) (M.
⌂ Lionel **Funten**) 47, rue de la Gare ☎ 38-36-26-11 ⇥ 7. Closed Sat
afternoon, Sun, 8–23 Aug. Coaches welcome. Rest. seats 85.
Evening meals until 10pm.

SURESNES 92150 Hauts-de-Seine **Porte de St-Cloud Map 1-A/B2**
♀⊗ **LE RELAIS DES ÉCLUSES** (N° RR JUN 19 083) (M. Henri **Bodin**)
30, quai Gallieni ☎ 45-06-11-48. Closed Sun, public holidays,
Aug.

SURVILLIERS 95470 Val-d'Oise **Map 3-B3**
♀⊗ **LE COQ CHANTANT** (N° RR FEV 27 526) (Mme Edith **Ressien**)
RN 17 ☎ 34-68-24-65. Closed Sun. Filling station nearby.

⊗ **RELAIS ILE DE FRANCE** (N° RR 1839) Aire de service de
Vemars in both directions of the autoroute ☎ 34-68-39-20.
English, German spoken. Restaurant: regional cooking. 25%
discount to Routiers. Children's menu. Self-service. Open 24 hrs.
Credit cards accepted. Garden terrace. ⊬ Parking. Drivers'
shop. Bureau de change. Hotel reservation service. Showers.

SURY-LE-COMTAL 42450 Loire **RD 8 Map 18-A2**
♀⊗ **LE PARILLY P.M.U.** (N° RR OCT 27 690) (M. Eric **Simonet**) 13,
rue du 11-Novembre on the RD 8 towards Montbrison ☎
77-30-80-14. Closed Sun. Home cooking. Rest. seats 40. Evening
meals until 10pm. English, Spanish spoken. Garden terrace. ⊬
Parking.

SUZAY 27420 Eure **RN 14 Map 3-B1**
♀⊗ **LE RELAIS MODERNE** (N° RR AOU 26 977) (M. Jean-Claude
Laurent) ☎ 32-55-65-01. Filling station nearby.

SAINT-AUBIN-DU-CORMIER

SAINT-AGATHON 22200 Côtes-du-Nord **RN 12 Map 7-A2**
☆ **NN HÔTEL BELLE VUE** (N° RR OCT 20 294) (M. **Février**)
Bel-Orme ☎ 96-43-80-53 ◄ 20 from 120–195F, tel. Closed Sun.
Car park. Bar. ⚓ Fishing excursions. Rest. seats 300. Dinner to
11pm.

SAINT-AGNANT-LES MARAIS 17620 Charente-Maritime **Map 11-B1**
RENDEZ-VOUS DES AMIS (N° RR JUN 26 266) (M. Alain **Neveur**)
Le Pont ☎ 46-83-30-36. Closed Sat (low season). Coaches
welcome. Rest. seats 100. German spoken.

SAINT-AIGNAN-LE-JAILLARD 45600 Loiret **RD 951 Map 13-A1**
LE SAINT-AIGNAN (N° RR FEV 26 464) (Mme Claudine **Gasnier**)
78, rue Nationale ☎ 38-36-38-21. Closed Wed, end of Feb and
Aug. Coaches welcome. Evening meals until 9pm. Rest. seats 40.

SAINT-AMAND-LE-PETIT 81720 Haute-Vienne **Map 16-B1**
LE PROMENADE (N° RR AVR 25 356) (M. Fernand **Rouby**)
Eymoutier ☎ 55-69-15-38 ◄ 3.

SAINT-ANDRÉ-DE-LÉPINE 50680 Manche **RD 85 2km from D 972
St-Là/Caen Map 4-B1**
SAINT-ANDRÉ BAR (N° RR DEC 25 751) (M. Raymond **Harl**)
Bourg, St Cerisy-lap Forêt ☎ 33-57-24-00. Closed Wed afternoon,
Aug. Coaches welcome. Rest. seats 50. Evening meals until
10pm. Home cooking. Menu 47.50F. Children's menu. Modern
décor. Parking.

SAINT-ANTOINE DE BREUILH 24230 Dordogne **Maps 17-A/B3 and
21-A1**
RELAIS DE FRANCE (N° RR NOV 27 077) (M. Christian **Noble**)
Sarl ☎ 53-24-78-97. Closed Sun. Evening meals until 9pm. Filling
station nearby.

SAINT-ANTOINE-DE-FICALBA 47340 Lot-et-Garonne **RN 21 Map
21-B1**
LE RELAIS DES ROUTIERS (N° RR DEC 17 153) (Mme Rosette
Crozes) ☎ 53-70-36-08 ◄ 5. Closed Sun, public holidays.

SAINT ARNOLT DES BOIS 28190 Eure-et-Loir **Map 8-A/B3**
AU REGAL (N° RR DEC 27 480) (Mme Françoise **Cornueau**) 26,
Grande Rue ☎ 37-22-51-77. Closed Sun pm. Filling station
nearby.

SAINT-AUBIN-DE-BLAYE 33820 Gironde **RN 137 Map 15-A3**
SARL LES GLYCINES (N° RR JUN 27 634) (M. Mohammad
Sefibargeh) ☎ 57-32-62-11 ◄ 4. English, Spanish spoken.
Specialities: plâteau de fruits de mer. Menu 80F. Coaches
welcome. Rest. seats 50. Evening meals. Filling station nearby.
HGV park.

SAINT-AUBIN-DES-BOIS 28300 Eure-et-Loir **RN 23 Map 8-B3**
LA MORICERIE (N° RR FEV 26 184) (M. Dominique **Libératore**)
RN 23 ☎ 37-32-99-25. Coaches welcome. Rest. seats 163. Evening
meals. Open 24 hrs.

SAINT-AUBIN-DU-CORMIER 35140 Ille-et-Vilaine **Map 8-B1**
LES VOYAGEURS (N° RR OCT 27 397) (M. Max **Tizon**) 13, route
de Rennes ☎ 99-39-17-80. Closed Aug. Evening meals to 9pm.

Saint-Aubin-du-Cormier continued
Home cooking. Menu 45F. 24 hr service station. Credit cards accepted. Traditional décor. Rest. seats 50. Garden terrace. ⌐⌐ Parking.

SAINT-AUBIN-EN-BRAY 60650 Oise **RN 31 Map 3-A2**
Ⓨ⊗ **RELAIS DES FONTAINETTES** (N° RR SEPT 27 384) (M. Jose
⌂ **Albert**) Les Fontainettes ☎ 44-80-50-26 ▬ 5. Closed Sun and 1st 2 weeks of May. Evening meals until 9pm. English spoken.

SAINT-AUBIN-SUR-LOIRE 71140 Saône-et-Loire **RN 979 Map 16-A3**
Ⓨ⊗ **BAR DE L'AMITE** (N° RR OCT 27 063) (M. Didler **Gaumard-Maison**) SNC Le Bourg 85-53-91-09. Closed Mon pm. English, German and Spanish spoken. Evening meals until 9pm. Coaches welcome. Rest. seats 30. Filling station 5km open 7am–8pm.

SAINT-AUBIN-SUR-SCIE 76550 Seine-Maritime **Map 4-A3**
Ⓨ⊗ **CHEZ FRANÇOISE** (N° RR FEV 24 513) (Mme Françoise **Soichet**) rue du Gouffre ☎ 35-85-91-09. Closed Sun, 1 Aug–1 Sept.

SAINT-AVOLD 57740 Moselle **Autoroute A 32 Map 10-A1**
⊗ **RELAIS DE LORRAINE** (N° RR 1823) Aire de Service de Saint-Avolo in both directions of the autoroute ☎ 87-92-23-89. English, German spoken. Restaurant: regional cooking. 25% discount to Routiers. Children's menu. À la carte. Self-service. Open 24 hrs. Credit cards accepted. Rest. seats 200. Rest room. Garden terrace. ⌐⌐ Parking. Tourist office. Exchange. Hotel booking. Nursery. With contemporary décor the restaurant offers a wide variety of regional wines and dishes.

SAINT-BENOIT-DU-SAULT 01300 Ain **2-B3**
Ⓨ⊗ **AUBERGE DU FAROU** (N° RR FEV 27530) (M. Alain **Durierz**) ☎
⌂ 74-39-70-88. **Minitel**. English spoken ▬ 9. Filling station 25km.

SAINT-BERTHEVIN-LES-LAVAL 53940 Mayenne **RN 157 Map 8-B1**
Ⓨ⊗ ☆☆ **NN LE RESTAURANT DE L'AULNE – L'INTERNATIONAL**
⌂ (N° RR JUN 20 761) (M. Henri **Garnier**) L'Aulne ☎ 43-69-31-74 ▬ 22. 100–130F, telephone, access for disabled. Closed Sun. Regional home cooking. Menu à la carte. Self-service. Coaches welcome. Rest. seats 200 + 105. Evening meals. Bar. ⌐⌐ Rest room. Parking. Credit cards accepted.

SAINT-BOMER-LES-FORGES 61700 Orne **RD 962 Map 8-A1**
Ⓨ⊗ **LE SAINT BOMER** (N° RR MARS 26 845) (M. Pierre **Janniard**) Le Bourg ☎ 33-37-61-66. Closed Mon evening. Filling station near.

SAINT BONNET-DU-FOUR 03390 Allier **RN 145 Map 16-A2**
Ⓨ⊗ **TRANS EUROPEEN** (N° RR DEC 27 484) (Mme Ivane **Pignot**) ☎ 70-07-72-62. Closed Sun. Evening meals. English, Italian spoken. Filling station 2km.

SAINT-BONNET près **RIOM** 63200 Puy-de-Dôme **RN 143 Map 16-B3**
Ⓨ⊗ **AU BON COIN** (N° RR OCT 16 729) (M. **Levadoux**) 2, rue de la
⌂ République ☎ 73-63-31-14 ▬ 10. Closed 15 Sept–10 Oct. Coaches welcome. Rest. seats 90. Evening meals.

SAINT-BRÉVIN-LES-PINS 44250 Loire-Atlantique **RD 77 Map 11-A2**
☆ **NN LE RELAIS DU MARCHÉ** (N° RR AVR 16 002) (M. and
Mme **Taraud**) place Henri-Basle ☎ 40-27-22-21 ➝ 16. Closed
Mon (low season), 20 Dec–5 Jan. Evening meals. German spoken.
Parking.

SAINT-BRICE-EN-COGLES 35460 Ille-et-Vilaine **RN 155 Map 8-B1**
☆☆ **LE CHATEAU BRIAND** (N° RR MARS 27 559) (M. Bertrand
Clouard) 18, rue Châteaubriant ☎ 99-98-61-45. **Minitel** ➝ 5.
English, Spanish spoken. Dinner to 11pm. Closed Mon. Filling
station nearby.

SAINT-BRIEUC 22000 Côtes-du-Nord **RN 12 Map 7-A2**
☆ **NN AU BEAUFEUILLAGE** (N° RR JUL 6 292) (M. Claude
Andrieux) 2, rue de Paris ☎ 96-33-09-16. **Minitel** ➝ 29. Closed
Sun afternoon, 8 Aug–1 Sept. Coaches welcome. Rest. seats 60.
Evening meals.

SAINT-CAPRAISE-DE-LALINDE 24150 Dordogne **CD 660 Map 21-B1**
LES GABARIERS (N° RR DEC 27 128) (Mme Jacqueline **Stève**) ☎
53-23-26-74. Closed Sun. Filling station nearby.

SAINT-CERE 46400 Lot **RD 677 Map 17-B1**
HOTEL DU QUERCY (N° RR JUN 27 627) (Mme Colette **Gibre**)
21, avenue Anatole-de-Monzie ☎ 65-38-04-83 ➝ 10 100–170F.
Closed Fri evening (low season). Specialities: salade de gésiers,
confit de canard forestier. Menu 25–55F. Coaches welcome.
Rest. seats 100. English, Spanish spoken.

SAINT-CHÉLY-D'APCHER 48200 Lozère **RN 9 Map 17-B3**
LE BARCELONNE (N° RR MAR 27 228) (Mme Monique **Vitre**) 33,
avenue de la Gare ☎ 66-31-01-22 ➝ 5. Nearby service station
open 7.30am–8pm. Parking.

SAINT-CLAIR-DU-RHONE 38370 Isère **CD 4 Map 2-B3**
LE RELAIS FLEURI (N° RR DEC 22 602) (M. **Tognoloni**) 3, rue du
Commandant L'Herminier ☎ 74-56-43-12 ➝ 7. Open 24 hrs.
Closed 1 week in Aug. Italian spoken. Rest. seats 110. Coaches
welcome. Dinner to midnight. Parking.

SAINT-CYR-EN-PAIL 53140 Mayenne **RN 12 Map 8-B1**
LES ROUTIERS (N° RR FEV 27 182) (Mme Antoinette **Dupont**) Le
Bourg Pré-en-Pail ☎ 43-03-03-21. Closed Sun pm. English
spoken. Dinner to 9pm. Parking.

SAINT-CYR-SUR-MENTHON 01380 Ain **RN 79 Map 18-B1**
SARL LE SAINT CYR (N° RR JANV 27 769) (M. **Allek**) RN 79 Le
Logis ☎ 85-36-30-69. English spoken. Restaurant. Specialities:
couscous. Menu 50–55F. Open 6am–midnight. Lunch 11.30am–
2.30pm. Dinner 7–11pm. HGV parking. Filling station nearby.

SAINT-CYR-SUR-MER 83270 Var **Map 24-B3**
MICKEY RESTO (N° RR MARS 25 852) (M. Christian **Reverberi**)
20, rue d'Arquier ☎ 94-26-49-98. Closed Sun low season, 3 weeks
at Christmas and New Year. Rest. seats 42. Coaches welcome.

SAINT-DENIS 93200 Seine-St-Denis **Portes de la Chapelle et de
Clignancourt Map 1-A2**

SAINT-DENIS-DE-MAILLOC

Saint-Denis continued

℗⊗ **LE RELAIS DU FRET CHEZ DANIEL** (N° RR JUN 26 272) (M. **Dahan**) 53, avenue du Président Wilson ☎ 48-09-41-22. **Minitel**. Closed Sun. Coaches welcome. Rest. seats 60. Evening meals to midnight. Spanish, English spoken.

℗⊗ **AU RENDEZ-VOUS DES CHAUFFEURS** (N° RR FEV 7 482) (Mme **Sahut**) 1, rue Jules Gérovési ☎ 48-20-13-81. Closed Sat, Sun, Aug, bank holidays. ⊷ Evening meals. Home cooking.

℗⊗ **LA CHEMINÉE** (N° RR SEPT 26 665) (Mme Edwige **Brizot**) 56, rue Ambroise Croizat ☎ 48-09-92-92. Closed Sat, Sun, Aug. Evening meals until midnight.

℗⊗ **LE MORETTI** (N° RR JAN 758) (M. Ben **Messaoud**) 72, av. Paul-Vaillant-Couturier ☎ 48-27-35-02. Menu to 46F. Open 6am–midnight.

SAINT-DENIS-DE-MAILLOC 14100 Calvados RD 579 Map 4-B2

℗⊗ **LA FORGE** (N° RR AVR 26 871) (M. Yvan **Leroy**) Lisieux ☎ 31-63-73-19. Closed Sat, Sun. Rest. seats 44. Evening meals. Coaches welcome. Filling station nearby.

SAINT-DENIS-DE-MÈRE 14110 Calvados RD 562 Map 8-A2

℗⊗ **LE RELAIS DES LANDES** (N° RR JAN 25 271) (M. Jean-Hugues 🏠 **Neveu**) Condé-sur-Noireau ☎ 31-69-01-06 ⊷ 7. Coaches welcome. Rest. seats 80. Traditional décor. Sights: Clécy (10km).

SAINT-DENIS-DES-MONTS 27520 Eure RN 138 Map 4-B3

℗⊗ **LE LAMA Tabac** (N° RR OCT 27 068) (M. Christian **Chuette**) ☎ 32-42-60-10. Closed Sun. Evening meals until 9pm.

SAINT-DENIS-LES-SENS 89100 Yonne RN 5 Map 9-B2

℗⊗ **LES CERISIERS** (N° RR SEP 24 670) (M. Michel **Ferrière**) 1, rue de Paris ☎ 86-65-28-52. **Minitel**. Closed Sat, Sun, Aug. Coaches welcome. Rest. seats 53. Evening meals until 9pm. English spoken. Home cooking. ⊷ Parking.

SAINT-DENIS-SUR-SARTHON 61420 Orne RN 12 Map 8-A/B2

℗⊗ **LE RELAIS DE LA GARE – LES AMIS DES ROUTIERS** (N° RR 🏠 SEPT 27 380) (M. Guy **Ellien**) Mélivier ☎ 33-27-30-03 ⊷ 8. Closed Sun. HGV parking. Filling station nearby.

SAINT-DIDIER-DE-BEAUJEU 69430 Rhône C 37 Map 18-A2

℗⊗ **LE CLÉ BEAUJOLAIS** (N° RR SEPT 27 012) (M. Alex **Gras**) Les Dépôts ☎ 74-04-87-53. Closed Mon. Filling station nearby.

SAINT DIÉ 88100 Vosges RN 59 Map 10-A/B2

℗⊗ **LA CROISETTE** (N° RR AVR 25 884) (M. Bernard **Roumier**) 41, 🏠 av. de Verdun ☎ 29-56-14-37 ⊷ 14. Closed Sat, Sun, end of year. Rest. seats 100. Evening meals to 10pm.

SAINT-DIZIER 52100 Haute-Marne RN 401 and 4 Map 14-A1/9-A3

℗⊗ **LE MOLIERE** (N° RR JUL 25 978) (M. René **Castello**) 10, rue Le Moliere ☎ 26-56-63-05. **Minitel**. Closed Sat, Sun, Aug. Coaches welcome. Rest. seats 43. Evening meals until 12.30am. English, German spoken.

SAINT ELIX LE CHATEAU 31430 Haute-Garonne Map 22-A2

℗⊗ **LE RELAIS DU CHATEAU** (N° RR OCT 27 696) (M. Gérard **Serrano**) RN 117 Le Fousseret ☎ 61-87-60-23. English, Spanish spoken. Restaurant: home cooking. Speciality: sauces. Menu 45–65F. Dinner to 10pm. Closed Sat, Sun. Credit cards accepted. Traditional décor. Rest. seats 60. Garden terrace. ⌘ Parking. Filling station open 6.30am–10pm.

SAINT-ERBLON 35230 Ille-et-Vilaine **RD 82 Map 7-B3**
Ⓨⓧ **CHEZ MICHEL ET SYLVIE** (N° RR FEV 26 819) (M. Michel **Martin**) 3, allée des Leuzières, place de l'Eglise ☎ 99-52-28-40. English spoken. Closed Feb. Coaches welcome. Rest. seats 300. Parking.

SAINT-ETIENNE 42000 Loire **RN 82 Maps 2-B1 and 18-A2/3**
Ⓨⓧ **LE MISTRAL** (N° RR AVR 26 873) (Mme Martine **Gant**) 4, rue Jean-Neyret ☎ 77-32-95-39. Closed Sat, Sun, Aug. English, Spanish, Arabic spoken. Evening meals. Filling station near.

SAINT-ETIENNE-EN-BRESSE 71370 Saône-et-Loire **Map 18-B1**
Ⓨⓧ **LE RELAIS DE L'OASIS** (N° RR MARS 25 859) (M. Alain **Sarim**) ☎ 85-96-40-26. Evening meals. Closed Mon.

SAINT-EUGÈNE 17520 Charente-Maritime **Map 15-A2**
Ⓨⓧ **LES DEUX CHARENTES** (N° RR JUN 26 556) (Mme Marcelle **Blanchard**) Fontenelle Archiac ☎ 46-49-13-28. Closed Wed (off season), 15 days Feb. Coaches welcome. Rest. seats 210. Some German spoken. Dinner to 9pm.

SAINT-ÉVARZEC 29170 Fouesnant-Finestère **RD 783 Map 7-B1**
Ⓨⓧ ☆ **NN AU BON REPOS** (N° RR JUN 25 005) (M. Roger **Guillou**)
⌂ Poullogoden ☎ 98-56-20-09 ⊨ 20 120–180F with shower, bath, WC. Closed Sat (low season), 15 Dec–10 Jan. Home cooking. Specialities: coquilles St Jacques. Children's menu. Coaches welcome. Rest. seats 165. Evening meals. English spoken. ⌘ Parking. Sights: Bénodet (beach), Fouesnant.

SAINT-ÉVROULT-DE-MONTFORT 61230 Orne **RN 138 Map 8-A2**
Ⓨⓧ **HOTEL DU RELAIS** (N° RR SEP 26 050) (M. Daniel **Conan**) Le
⌂ Bourg ☎ 33-35-60-58 ⊨ 5 70–120F with shower. Closed Sun. Rest. seats 120. Evening meals until 10pm. Home cooking. Coaches welcome.

SAINT-FÉLIX-DE-LAURAGAIS 31540 Haute-Garonne **RN 622 Map 22-A/B2**
Ⓨⓧ **LE GRILLON** (N° RR DEC 23 582) (Mme Aliette **Bonnes**) Route de Castelnaudary ☎ 61-27-65-27. Restaurant: home cooking. Specialities: cassoulet au confit de canard. Dinner to midnight. Closed Sun, 15–31 Aug. Credit cards accepted. Modern décor. Rest. seats 120. ⊨ 5 56–58F with showers. Open 7am–midnight. ⌘ Parking. Sights: Black Mountain, dam, Lake St Péréol, village de cuivres.

SAINT-FIRMIN 05800 Hautes-Alpes **RN 85 Map 19-A3**
Ⓨⓧ ☆ **NN RELAIS DE LA TRINITÉ** (N° RR NOV 19 998) (M. Pascal
⌂ **Poncet**) Route Nationale ☎ 92-55-21-64 ⊨ 12 100–200F with showers, bath, WC. Lunch 12–2.30pm. Evening meals from 7–9pm. Closed Jan. Parking. Bar. ⌘ Games (children's swings, ping-pong). Credit cards accepted. Modern décor. Rest. seats 60.

SAINT-FLORENT-SUR-CHER

SAINT-FLORENT-SUR-CHER 18400 Cher **RN 151 Map 13-B1**

♈⊗ **L'IMPRÉVU** (N° RR AVR 27 252) (M. Bernard **Ruellan**) 60, rue Jean-Jaurès ☎ 48-55-12-00. **Minitel**. Restaurant closed Sunday afternoon and in August. Evening meals. Rest. seats 80. Filling station nearby. Open 6.30am–9pm.

SAINT-FLOUR 15100 Cantal **RN 9 Map 17-A/B3**

♈⊗ **LE RELAIS DU VIEUX PONT** (N° RR AOU 22 015) (Mme Liliane
⌂ **Teissèdre**) 49, place de la Liberté ☎ 71-60-23-00. **Minitel** ⊶ 8. Closed Sun, Mon, Jan, Feb. Coaches welcome. Rest. seats 45. Evening meals to 10pm. English, Spanish spoken.

♈⊗ ☆☆ **HÔTEL LE PROGRÈS** (N° RR AVR 23 757) (M. Alain
⌂ **Mourgues**) 61, rue des Lacs ☎ 71-60-03-06. **Minitel** ⊶ 16. Coaches welcome. Rest. seats 120. Evening meals.

SAINT-GAULTIER 36800 Indre **RN 151 Map 16-A1**

♈⊗ **LE COMMERCE** (N° RR JAN 25 266) (Mme Marie **Pilorget**) ☎ 54-47-14-81. Closed Thur.

SAINT-GAUX 33340 Gironde **RN 215 Map 20-A1**

♈⊗ **LE RELAIS Chez Monique** (N° RR AOU 26 974) (Mme Monique **Buscail**) Saint Germain-d'Esteuil, Lesparre Médoc ☎ 56-73-06-28. Closed Sun, 1st fortnight Oct. Evening meals to 10pm. Filling station 4km.

SAINT-GENCE 87510 Haute-Vienne **RD 20 Map 16-B1**

♈⊗ **LE CAMPANELLE** (N° RR FEV 26 445) (M. Albert **Denardou**) rte de St-Gence ☎ 55-48-02-83. Closed Sat (except for banquets or wedding receptions), Aug. Coaches welcome. Rest. seats 100. Evening meals to 9pm.

SAINT-GENIX-SUR-GUIERS 73240 Savoie **Map 2-B3**

♈⊗ **AUBERGE CAMPANARDE** (N° RR JUIL 27 351) (M. Louis **Ailloud**) Joudin ☎ 76-31-80-19. Closed Sat, Sep, Oct. Evening meals to 9pm. Filling station nearby. Parking 500m².

SAINT-GEOIRE-EN-VALDAINE 38620 Isère **Map 2-B3**

♈⊗⌕**LE MÉNUPHARD** (N° RR JUIL 27 352) (M. Raymond **Brigard**) La Combe ☎ 76-07-58-70. **Minitel**. Parking 3,000m².

SAINT-GEORGES-DE-MONTCLARD 24140 Dordogne **RD 21 Maps 15-B3**

♈⊗ **LE BON COIN** (N° RR JUIN 27 593) (Mme Catherine **Malnatt**) ☎ 53-82-98-47. Filling station 100m open from 8am–8pm.

SAINT-GEORGES-DES-GARDES 49120 Maine-et-Loire **RN 161 Maps 11-B3 and 12-B1**

♈⊗ **LE RELAIS DES ROUTIERS** (N° RR DEC 19 223) (M. Louis **Jolivet**)
⌂ Chemille ☎ 41-62-79-38 or 41-62-94-60 ⊶ 6 100F with shower, bathroom, WC. Open 6am–midnight. Home cooking. Menu 48F. Dinner to 10pm. Rest. seats 150. Parking.

SAINT-GEORGES-D'OLÉRON 17190 Charente-Maritime **Map 11-B1**

⊗ **AUBERGE D'ALIENOR** (N° RR DEC 26 751) (M. Patrick **Audouim**) 5, Place de Verdun ☎ 46-76-76-33. Restaurant: regional home cooking. Specialities: fruits de mer, poissons. Menu 50–115F Children's menu. À la carte. Lunch 12–2.30pm. Dinner 7–11pm. Closed Wed (low season) and last 2 weeks Nov. Credit

cards accepted. Traditional décor. Rest. seats 70. Parking.
Sights: Les Port de plaisance.

SAINT-GERMAIN-DU-BEL-AIR 46310 Lot **RD 23 Map 17-B1**
ℙ⊗ **CAFÉ DE FRANCE** (N° RR JANV 27 168) (Mme Mélina **Fran-coual**) Le Bourg ☎ 65-31-06-99. Closed Sun. Filling station nearby
open 8am–7.30pm.

SAINT-GERMAIN-DU-PLAIN 71370 Saône-et-Loire **RD 978 Map 18-B1**
ℙ⊗ **RELAIS DES SPORTS** (N° RR AVR 26 508) (M. Gilles **Tenedor**)
route de Louhans ☎ 85-47-37-27.

SAINT-GERMAIN-LA-GATINE 28300 Eure-et-Loir **RN 154 Map 8-A3**
ℙ⊗ **LE RELAIS DE SAINT-GERMAIN** (N° RR AVR 26 869) (Mme
Madeleine **Tarrou**) 1, avenue de Chartres ☎ 37-22-80-31. Closed
Sun. Coaches welcome. Rest seats 60.

SAINT-GERMAIN-LES-ARPAJON 91290 Essonne **RN 20 Map 1-B2**
ℙ⊗ **L'AS DE TRÈFLE** (N° RR NOV 26 084) (Mme Gisèle **Belin**) RN 7
20 La Petite-Folie. Directions: on the road to Orléans ☎
64-90-02-24. Closed Sun. Coaches welcome. Rest. seats 70.
English spoken. Lunch 11am–2.30pm. Evening meals 6–8.30pm.
Home cooking. Menu 50F. Self-service. Credit cards accepted.
Traditional décor. Sights: zoo de St Vrain.

SAINT-GERMAIN-SUR-MOINE 49230 Maine-et-Loire **Map 11-A3**
ℙ⊗ **LE TAILLIS DU VERGER** (N° RR FEV 27 538) (M. Paul **Eraud**)
Carrefour du Petit Lapin. Route de la Ran audière ☎ 41-64-64-61.
Minitel. Restaurant: regional home cooking. Menu 47F. Child-ren's menu. Lunch 11.30am–2.30pm. Dinner 7–10pm. Closed Sun.
Credit cards accepted. Rest. seats 80. Garden terrace. ⊨
Parking.

SAINT-GERMAIN-SUR-MORIN 77740 Seine-et-Marne **RN 34 Map 9-A2**
ℙ⊗ **LE RELAIS DE LA MAIRIE** (N° RR AVR 5 988) (Maldin **de Letter**)
29, rue de Paris ☎ 60-04-00-63. **Minitel**. Closed Sun. Coaches
welcome. Rest. seats 52.

SAINT-GERVAIN EN BELIN 72520 Sarthe **Map 12-A2**
LES RELAIS DES ARDRIENS (N° RR SEPT 27 663) (M. William
Royer) route du Lude "Les Ardriens" ☎ 43-42-02-19. Restaurant:
dinner to 9pm. Closed Mon. Filling station open 8am–8pm.

SAINT-GERVAIS-DE-VIC 72120 Sarthe **RD 303 Map 12-A3**
ℙ⊗ **CHEZ ODETTE-LE SAINT ELOI** (N° RR AVR 26 872) (Mme
Odette **Hervé**) ☎ 43-35-09-00. **Minitel**. Closed Sun, public holi-days. Italian spoken. Evening meals. Coaches welcome. Rest.
seats 120. Filling station 3km.

SAINT-GILDAS-DES-BOIS 44530 Loire-Atlantique **RN 773 Map 11-A2**
ℙ⊗ **LE RELAIS DES ROUTIERS** (N° RR NOV 19 193) (M. Michel
⌂ **Gaidano**) 27, rue du Pont, between Redon and Pontchâteau ☎
40-01-42-15. Restaurant: home cooking. Specialities: plateau de
fruits de mer, homard grillé. Menu 45–350F. Children's menu. À
la carte. Lunch 12–2.30pm. Dinner 8–9.30pm. Credit cards
accepted. Rest. seats 350 ⊨ 10 95–120F with TV. Open 8am–
11pm. ⊨ Parking. Sights: Calvaire de Pontchâteau (10km).

SAINT-GILLES

SAINT-GILLES 50180 Manche **RD 972 77 Map 4-B1**
♀⊗ **CARREFOUR SAINT-GILLES** (N° RR MAI 26 884) (M. Jean-Jacques **Billy**) Le Bourg-Agneaux ☎ 33-06-24-50. Closed Sun. English, German spoken. Filling station 3km. Parking by the church.
♀⊗ **LES RELAIS** (N° RR MAI 26 895) (Mme Jeanine **Abiven**) 23, rue de Rennes ☎ 99-64-63-04. English, German spoken. Dinner to 1am. Closed Sat, Sun and 1–15 Aug. Rest. seats 136. Parking. Filling station nearby.

SAINT GRATIEN 95210 Val-d'Oise **Map 1-A2**
♀⊗⌐**LE SAINT GRATIEN** (N° RR JANV 27 762) (Mme Joêlle **Faligand**) 79, boulevard Pasteur ☎ 39-89-13-26. Restaurant: menu 60–90F. Lunch 11.30am–3pm. Parking. Tobacconist. Papers. Lotto.
♀⊗ **LES ROUTIERS** (N° RR MARS 24 515) (M. Amar **Negaa**) 57, boulevard Foch ☎ 39-89-29-74.

SAINT-GRÉGORIE 35760 Ille-et-Vilaine **Map 7-B3**
♀⊗ **RESTAURANT DE L'ÉTANG** (N° RR JUIN 27 303) (M. Michel **Hubert**) rue de l'Étang au Diable ☎ 99-38-49-43. **Minitel**. Closed Sat and Sun, 3–20 Aug. Evening meals served until 9pm. Filling station 100m.

SAINT-GUYOMARD 56460 Morbihan **Map 7-B2**
♀⊗ ☆ **NN LES RELAIS DES DOLMENS DE LANVAUX** (N° RR DEC
⌂ 27 469) (M. Pierre **Legrand**) "Le Passoir" ☎ 97-93-81-05 ⊷ 7 from 110–140F. Closed Sunday. Evening meals until 10pm. Parking. Filling station nearby.

SAINT-HELEN 22100 Côtes-du-Nord **Map 7-A3**
♀⊗ **RELAIS DE LA CROIX DU FRENE** (N° RR AVR 27 260) (M. Guy **Gabillard**) La Croix du Frene ☎ 96-83-25-02. Closed Sat pm, Sun and bank holidays. Filling station 3km.

SAINT-HILAIRE-DE-LA-CÔTE 38260 Isère **RD 73 Map 18-B3**
♀⊗ **AUBERGE DE LA FONTAINE** (N° RR MARS 27 218) (Mme Raymonde **Glandut**) La Côte St-André ☎ 74-54-60-17. Closed Mon. English and Italian spoken. Dinner to midnight. Rest. seats 45. Filling station 3km open 7am–11pm. HGV parking.

SAINT-HILAIRE-DE-LOULAY 85600 Vendée **RN 137 Map 12-B1**
♀⊗ ☆☆ **LE RELAX** (N° JUIL 23 361) (M. Luc **Van Wanghe**) Les
⌂♟ Landes de Roussais ☎ 51-94-02-44. A little German and English spoken. Restaurant: regional cooking. Specialities: grillades au feu de bois, poissons au beurre blanc. Menu 58–145F. Children's menu. À la carte. Dinner to 2am. Open 24 hrs. Closed Sat midday and 24 Dec–6 Jan. Credit cards accepted. Rest. seats 220 ⊷ 11 170–200F with shower, WC, TV, telephone. Hotel open 6am–2am. ⊮ Parking. Garage. Money exchange. Routiers shop. Sights: château, Muscadet wine, gardens.

SAINT-HILAIRE-DU-ROSIER VILLAGE 38840 Isère **RN 92 Map 18-B3**
♀⊗ **LE RELAIS DOMENECH** (N° RR OCT 17 652) (Mme Domenech
⌂ **Lopez**) RN 92 ☎ 76-36-53-84. **Minitel** ⊷ 5 90F (single), 135F (double) with bath. Closed Sat, Sept, Oct. Restaurant: regional cooking. Menu 45–98F. Children's menu. Credit cards accepted. Modern décor. ⊮ Parking.

SAINT-JEAN-DE-MAURIENNE

SAINT-HILLAIRE-LA-GRAVELLE 41160 Loir-et-Cher **RN 19 Maps 12-A3 and 8-B3**

♈⊗ **AUBERGE DU LOIR** (N° RR OCT 22 066) (M. **Pierdos**) 10, rue Léon Cibié ☎ 54-82-65-00. **Minitel**. Closed Wed evening, Aug. Evening meals. English spoken. Restaurant: home cooking. Children's menu. À la carte. Credit cards accepted ⇌ 2 at 150F with shower, TV. Rest. seats 35. Coaches welcome.

SAINT-INGLEVERT 62250 Pas-de-Calais **RN 1 Map 5-A2**

♈⊗ **LA MURAILLE** (N° RR JAN 26 422) (Mme Jocelyne **Salmon**) RN 1 ☎ 21-33-75-44. Closed Sat, Sun and 3 weeks in July. English spoken. Coaches welcome. Rest. seats 80. Evening meals. Home cooking. Menu 58F. Menu à la carte. Traditional décor. Showers. Parking. Garden terrace. ⌐ Credit cards accepted.

SAINT-JACQUES-DE-LA-LANDE 35136 Ille-et-Vilaine **Map 7-B3**

♈⊗ **LA GAITÉ** (N° RR OCT 27 396) (M. Yannide **Echelard**) 26, boulevard Roger Rodin, route de Redon ☎ 99-31-27-56. Closed Sat, Sun, 15 days in Aug and 1 week between Christmas and New Year. English spoken. Evening meals to 9.45pm. Filling station nearby open 7am–9.30pm. Credit cards accepted. ⌐ Parking.

SAINT JACQUES-SUR-DARNETAL 76160 Seine-Maritime **Map 3-A1**

♈⊗ **LE RELAIS DES FORGETTES** (N° RR JUIL 27 329) (M. Gérard **Peudeiun**) route de Gournay ☎ 35-02-10-76. Closed Sun and Sept. Dinner to 9pm. Filling station across road. Parking on side of road.

SAINT JEAN BREVELAY 56661 Morbihan **Map 7-B2**

♈⊗ **LE SAINT-YANN** (N° RR NOV 27 728) (M. Rémy **Verdeau**) 21, rue de Rennes ☎ 97-60-30-10. A little English, Spanish spoken. Closed Mon pm. HGV parking. Fina filling station open 7.30am–9pm. Showers for drivers.

SAINT-JEAN-DE-BEUGNE 85210 Vendée **RN 137 Map 11-B2**

♈⊗ **L'OASIS** (N° RR JUN 953) (M. Guy **Teillet**) Ste-Hermine ☎ 51-27-38-80. Closed Sat pm, Sun, end of Dec. Evening meals to 10pm. Rest. seats 60.

SAINT-JEAN-DE-CHEVELU 73170 Savoie **RN 504 A Map 19-A2**

♈⊗ ⌂ **LE RELAIS DES QUATRE CHEMINS** (N° RR NOV 26 388) (M. Jean **Rubad**) Directions: between Lyon and Chambérg ☎ 79-36-80-06. **Minitel**. English spoken. Restaurant: home cooking. Menu 59–78F. Lunch 12–2pm. Dinner 7–8pm. Open 4am–midnight. Closed Sat pm, Sun, end of Dec–beginning Jan. Credit cards accepted. Traditional décor. Rest. seats 120 ⇌ 9 110–175F with showers, WC. Rest room. ⌐ Parking. Sights: Abbaye de Haute Combe (12km).

SAINT JEAN DE DAYE 50620 Manche **Map 4-B1**

♈⊗ **AU P'TIT TROT** (N° RR JUN 27 630) (Mme Agnés **Lesaulnier**) rue de la libération ☎ 33-55-48-00. English spoken.

SAINT-JEAN-DE-MAURIENNE 73300 Savoie **RN 6 Map 19-B3**

♈⊗⌐**RESTAURANT RELAIS R** (N° RR JUN 21 971) (Mme Angèle **Dompnier**) Place du Champs du Foire, 66, rue Louis-Sibuè ☎ 79-64-12-03. Closed Sun. Italian spoken. Home cooking. Coaches welcome. Rest. seats 80. Garden terrace. ⌐ Parking. Sights: La Maurienne and all the sights around.

SAINT-JEAN-DE-MOIRANS

SAINT-JEAN-DE-MOIRANS 38430 Isère **RN 92 Map 19-A3**
♀⊗ **LE RIO BRAVO** (N° RR JUIL 27 321) (M. M. **Speranza**) rue
Gaston-Bouardel ☎ 76-05-28-65. Evening meals to 9pm. English
and Italian spoken. Closed Sun. Filling station nearby open
7am–8.30pm.

SAINT-JEAN-SUR-COUESNON 35140 Ille-et-Vilaine **RN 12 and D 23
Map 8-B1**
♀⊗ **LA JUHUELLERIE** (N° RR NOV 27 449) (M. **Garel**) La Juhuellerie
☎ 99-39-11-85. **Minitel**. Closed Sat. Evening meals to 10pm.
Filling station nearby.

SAINT-JEAN-SUR-VILAINE 35220 Ille-et-Vilaine **RN 157 Map 8-B1**
♀⊗ **RELAIS DU CHEVAL BLANC** (N° RR DEC 26 118) (M. Alain
⌂ **Bellevin**) 4, rue de Rennes ☎ 99-00-32-67 ⊷ 10. **Minitel**.

SAINT-JOSEPH-DE-RIVIÈRE 38134 Isère **CD 520 A Map 19-A2**
♀⊗ **LE RELAIS CHAMPÊTRE** (N° RR OCT 27 051) (Mme Adeline
⌂ **Mandrillon**) Le Pont Demay ☎ 76-55-49-08 ⊷ 7. Closed Fri pm,
Sat (low season) and 15 Oct–15 Nov. Italian spoken. Coaches
welcome. Rest. seats 60. Filling station 2km.

SAINT-JULIEN-DE-CIVRY 71610 Saône-et-Loire **RD 985 Map 18-A1**
♀⊗ **RESTAURANT DES VOYAGEURS** (N° RR MAR 26 855) (M.
Hubert **Dumoulin**) the station ☎ 85-70-62-10. Closed Tue afternoon, last 2 weeks of Aug. English, German spoken. Filling
station 3km.

SAINT-JULIEN-DE-PIGANIOL 12300 Aveyron **RD 963 Map 17-B2**
♀⊗ **A L'AUBERGE DE ST-JULIEN** (N° RR SEPT 26 657) (Mme Yvette
Carrière) Rte Dle 963 ☎ 65-64-05-92. Closed Mon. Coaches
welcome. Rest. seats 95. Evening meals to 8pm.

SAINT-JULIEN-LA-VÊTRE 42440 Loire **RN 89 Maps 18-A2 and 16-B3**
♀⊗ **L'ESCALE 89** (N° RR OCT 27 065) (M. René **Pasinetti**) ☎
77-97-85-30. German, Italian and English spoken. Filling station
nearby.

SAINT-JULIEN-LE-FAUCON 14140 Calvados **RN 511 Map 4-B2**
♀⊗ **LES ROUTIERS** (N° RR JUN 26 261) (Mme Gisèle **Goupil**) Livarot
☎ 31-63-80-96. Closed Sat pm, Sun. English spoken. Evening
meals until 8pm.

SAINT-JULIEN-LES-ROSIERS 30340 Gard **RD 904 Map 23-B1 Route de
Saint Ambraux**
♀⊗ **LE MISTRAL** (N° RR OCT 27 424) (M. José **Garcia**) ☎ 66-86-15-
⌂ 29. Restaurant: regional home cooking. Specialities: tripous,
paella, rouille du pêcheur. Children's menu. À la carte. Dinner to
10pm. Closed Wed (low season). Rest. seats 60 ⊷ 15 from
100–150F with showers. Open 7am–11pm. Garden terrace. ⊯
Parking. Filling station nearby. Sights: grottes Cocalières (20km),
grottes Trabuc (20km), pont du Gard (40km).

SAINT-JUNIEN 87200 Haute-Vienne **RN 141 Map 16-B1**
♀⊗ **L'ETOILE** (N° RR AVR 25 872) (M. Alain **Noble**) 8, avenue
⌂ Barbusse ☎ 55-02-15-19 ⊷ 7. Closed Fri evening in winter,
20 Dec–6 Jan. Summer open every day. Coaches welcome. Rest.
seats 130. Evening meals. English spoken.

SAINT-JUST-LE-MARTEL 87590 Haute-Vienne **RN 141 Map 16-B1**

♊⊗ **LE PETIT SALÉ** (N° RR FEV 25 310) (M. Jean-Pierre **Teyti**) Les Chabanes ☎ 55-09-21-14. Coaches welcome. Rest. seats 80. Evening meals until midnight.

SAINT-LANGIS-LES-MORTAGNES 61400 Orne **RD 938 after 138 bis, 1km from Nle Map 8-A2**

♊⊗ **HÔTEL DE LA GARE** (N° RR SEPT 27 390) (M. Jean **Lonak**) rue
⌂ de la Gare ☎ 33-25-16-10 ➡ 7 75–120F. Open 6am–11pm. Closed Sun. Evening meals to 11pm. Home cooking. Children's menu. À la carte. ⊮ Parking.

SAINT-LAURENT-DU-VAR 06700 Alpes-Maritimes **Map 25-B2**

♊⊗ **AU COUP DE FUSIL** SARL Floreje (N° RR JANV 27 159) (M. Eugène **Bagi**) boulevard Pierre-Marie Curie ZI Secteur B ☎ 93-31-60-55. Home cooking. Menu 50F. À la carte. Closed Sun, bank holidays, Aug. Rest room. Garden terrace. ⊮ Parking. Italian spoken. Filling station 150m open 7am–8pm.

SAINT LÉGER 17800 Charente-Maritime **RN 137 Map 15-A2**

♊⊗ **LES TROIS MOULINS** (N° RR FEV 27 188) (M. Robert **Decker**) RN 137 Pons ☎ 46-96-91-38 ➡ 6. Closed Sun. Rest. seats 66. German spoken. Dinner to 11pm. Filling station 3km open 7am–10pm.

♊⊗ **L'ARCHE DE SAINT LÉGER** (N° RR 2 026) (M. Phillipe **Pelé**) Aire de Saint Léger in both directions of the autoroute ☎ 46-91-95-30. Restaurant. Children's menu. À la carte. Self-service. Dinner 7–11pm. Credit cards accepted. Rest. seats 100. Terrace garden. ⊮ Parking. Sights: Cognac (40km), Royan (30km), La Rochelle (80km).

SAINT-LÉGER-CARCAGNY 14740 Calvados **RN 13 Map 4-B2**

♊⊗ **AUX JOYEUX ROUTIERS** (N° RR SEP 24 683) (M. Charles **Candavoine**) Hameau de St-Léger ☎ 31-80-22-01. Closed Sun in winter.

SAINT-LÉGER-SUR-DHEUNE 71510 Saône-et-Loire **RD 978 Maps 18-A1 and 13-B3**

♊⊗ **AU BON ACCUEIL** (N° RR JAN 22 147) (Mme Nelly **Roland**)
⌂ avenue de la Gare ☎ 86-45-30-65 ➡ 5. Evening meals.

SAINT-LON-LES-MINES 40300 Landes **CD6 Map 20-A2**

♊⊗ ✩ **NN HOTEL DU FRONTON** (No RR MAI 26 880) (M. Daniel
⌂ **Laffitte**) Au Bourg ☎ 58-57-80-45. **Minitel** ➡ 10 (8 with WC, 2 with shower) 130–160F. Closed Feb. Spanish spoken. Filling station 2km distant. Telephone. Bar. ⊮ Games (table football). Coaches welcome. Rest. seats 200. Evening meals to 1am. Parking 1,500m². Sights: Château de Peyrehorade (7km), Bayonne (35km).

SAINT-LOUP-DE-VARENNES 71240 Saône-et-Loire **RN 6 Map 18-B1**

♊⊗ **LA PETITE AUBERGE** (N° RR AOU 26 980) (M. Jacques **Demeu-zoy**) ☎ 85-44-21-87. Closed Sun. Dinner to 1am. Rest. seats 40. Parking. Filling station near.

SAINT-LOUP-SUR-SEMOUSE 70800 Haute-Saône **RN 64 Maps 10-A3 and 14-B2**

♊⊗ **LE RELAIS DE LA TERRASSE** (N° RR MAI 6 059) (Mme Jean

Saint-Loup-sur-Semouse continued
Ballot) rue de la Gare ☎ 84-49-02-20. **Minitel** ⊷ 4. Closed Sun,
1–15 Aug.

SAINT-MALO 35400 Ille-et-Vilaine **RN 157 Map 7-A3**
☽⊗ **HOTEL DE L'ARRIVÉE** (N° RR FEV 27 191) (Mme Edith **Eveill-**
⌂ **ard**) 83, rue Ville-Pépin, Saint-Servan-sur-Mer ☎ 99-81-99-57 ⊷
16. Closed Sun in low season, Oct. English spoken. Rest. seats 70.
Dinner to 9pm. Filling station nearby.

SAINT-MARC-SUR-SEINE 21450 Côte-d'Or **RN 71 Map 13-A3**
☽⊗ **LE SOLEIL D'OR** (N° RR DEC 22 133) (Mme Geneviève **Girard**)
⌂ ☎ 80-93-21-42 ⊷ 7. Closed Sat, 22 Dec–2 Jan. English spoken.
Coaches welcome. Rest. seats 50.

SAINT-MARCEL 27950 Eure **Map 3-B1**
☽⊗ **LE TERMINUS** (N° RR JANV 27 506) (M. Claude **Hard**) 30, RN 15
⌂ Le Goulet ☎ 32-52-50-07 ⊷ 18 100–125F. Home cooking. Menu
50F. Lunch 11.30am–3pm. Dinner 7.30–8.30pm. Rest. seats 100.
Closed Sun, Aug. Evening meals. Sights: Claude Monet Garden
at Giverny.

SAINT-MARCEL LÈS-VALENCE 26320 Drôme **RN 532 à 100m Map
18-B3.**
☽⊗ **LA PRAIRIE** (N° RR SEPT 27 021) (M. Michel **Montusciat**) 8, rue
de la Liberté. Directions: between Valanco and Romans ☎
75-58-70-38. Italian and English spoken. Coaches welcome. Rest.
seats 120. Evening meals to 10pm. Home cooking. Children's
menu. À la carte. Credit cards accepted. ⊬ Filling station nearby
open 7am–9pm and 4km open 24 hrs.

SAINT-MARS-LA-BRIERE 72680 Sarthe **RN 157 Map 8-B2**
☽⊗ **AUBERGE DU NARAIS** (N° RR OCT 27 067) (M. Rémy **Tressy**)
RN 157 ☎ 43-89-87-30. **Minitel**. Closed Sat, Sun. Aug. Evening
meals to midnight. Rest. seats 150. Garden terrace. ⊬ Parking.

SAINT-MARTIAL-D'ARTENSET 24700 Dordogne **RN 89 Map 15-B3**
☽⊗ **RELAIS DU CHAPEAU** (N° RR AOUT 27 655) (M. Roland
Torreborre) Le Chapeau ☎ 53-81-33-83. Filling station nearby.

SAINT-MARTIN-DE-CLELLES 38930 Isère **Map 19-B3**
☽⊗ **MON REGAL** (N° RR FEV 27 533) (Mme Moniqüe **Flandin**) RN 75
☎ 76-34-42-84. Restaurant: home cooking. Children's menu.
Dinner to 9pm. Filling station nearby.

SAINT-MARTIN-DE-CRAU 13310 Bouches-du-Rhône **RN 113 Map
24-B3**
☽⊗ **LA CABANE BAMBOU** (N° RR AVR 13 594) (M. Jacques and
⌂ Georgette **Giraud**) RN 113 between Salon and Aries ☎ 90-58-17-
25 and 90-58-02-52. **Minitel** ⊷ 10. Closed Sun (except summer
time). Open 24 hrs. Coaches welcome. Rest. seats 100. Evening
meals all night. English, Italian, Spanish spoken.
☽⊗ **LE RELAIS DES SPORTS** (N° RR NOV 27 728) (M. Daniel
Nivaggiol) La Dynamite ☎ 90-47-05-24. Spanish, Italian spoken.
Menu 50F. Menu à la carte. Open 6am–11pm. Closed Aug. HGV
parking. Filling station 5km.

SAINT-MARTIN-DE-RE 17410 Charente-Maritime **Map 11-B1**

♈⊗ **EL PANCHO** (N° RR OCT 27 699) (Mme Brigitte **Raguenaud**) route de la Flotte Venelle de la Cristallerio ☎ 49-09-02-05. Restaurant: home cooking. Speciality: pizza. Menu 50–76F. Children's menu. À la carte. Open 8am–11pm. Lunch 12–2pm. Dinner 6.30–10pm. Closed Mon pm. Traditional décor. Rest. seats 50. Garden terrace. ⚐ Parking. Filling station 100m open 8am–10pm. Sights: les ramparts de Saint-Martin (1km), phare des baleines, l'abaye, La flotte (5km), la cristallerie à visitor sur les yeux.

SAINT-MARTIN OSMONVILLE 76680 Seine-Maritime **RN 28 Map 4-A3**

♈⊗ **LA GRANGE** (N° RR JAN 25 784) (Mme Denise **Dubois**) De La Boissière ☎ 35-34-14-34. **Minitel**. Dinner to midnight. Closed Sun (low season).

SAINT MATHIEU 87440 Haute-Vienne **Map 15-B2**

♈⊗ **LA GRANGE DU LAC** (N° RR OCT 27 708) (M. Franck
⌂ **Varachaut**) 'Les Champs' ☎ 55-00-35-84. English spoken. Restaurant: regional cuisine. Specialities: magret, confits, cèpes. Menu 46–125F. Children's menu. À la carte. Dinner to 1am. Closed Mon evening. Credit cards accepted. Traditional décor. Rest. seats 150 ⊨ 120F (90F for Routiers) with shower, WC. Hotel open 7am until midnight. Garden terrace. ⚐ Parking. Games. Filling station nearby open 8am–9pm. Lakes close by. Sights: Monbrun, Oradour sur Glane Vallée Bandiat-Tardoire.

SAINT-MAUR-DES-ROSSÉS 94100 Val-de-Marne **Map 1-B3**

♈⊗ **LA PASSERELLE** (N° RR OCT 26 699) (M. Jean **Dias**) 45, Boulevard Général Ferrier ☎ 42-83-21-71. Portuguese, Spanish spoken. Closed Christmas and New Year. Evening meals served to 10pm.

SAINT-MAURICE-SUR-DARGOIRE 69440 Rhône **RD 42 Map 2-B1**

♈⊗ **CHEZ ROSE** (N° RR JUL 26 604) (Mme Rosiane **Blé**) Le Grand Buisson ☎ 78-81-20-10. Coaches welcome. Rest. seats 40. Evening meals to 10pm.

SAINT-MAURICE-SUR-FESSARD 45700 Loiret **Map 9-B1**

♈⊗ **RESTAURANT DE LA GARE** (N° RR JANV 26 800) (Mme Colette **Jehl**) RN 60 Villemandeur ☎ 38-97-81-00. Closed Sat pm and Sun pm. Evening meals. English, Spanish spoken.
LE RELAIS DE SAINT-MAURICE (N° RR MARS 26 840) (M. Pascal **Crouvisier**) RN 60 Villemandeur ☎ 38-97-80-59. Closed Wed. Coaches welcome. Dinner to 9pm. Rest. seats 90. Total filling station nearby.

SAINT-MEEN-LE-GRAND 35290 Ille-et-Vilaine **RN 164 Bis and 166 Map 7-B3**

♈⊗ **LE RELAIS DU MIDI** (N° RR NOV 26 732) (M. Christian **Posnic**) SARL 25, place Patton ☎ 99-09-60-02. Home cooking. Menu 40F. Children's menu. Closed Sat after lunch, 15–31 Aug. Coaches welcome. Rest. seats 30. Evening meals. Lunch 12–2.30pm Dinner 7–10pm. Credit cards accepted.

SAINT MICHEL DE CASTELNAU 33840 Gironde **Map 21-A1**

♈⊗ **LE PETANQUE** (N° RR JANV 27 753) (Mme Rose-Marie
⌂ **Claverie**) between Bazan and Casteljaloux ☎ 57-65-82-47. Evening stop 50F. Restaurant. Specialities: confits, magret, fruits de

SAINT-MIHIEL

Saint Michel de Castelnau continued
mer. Menu at 45–90F. Dinner to midnight. Credit cards accepted. Traditional décor. Rest. seats 136 ⚏ 5 at 105–145F with shower, bath, TV, telephone. Open 7am until midnight. Rest room. Garden terrace. ⚲ Parking. Filling station nearby. Sights: Vallée Touristique, Ecomusée des landes.

SAINT-MIHIEL 55300 Meuse **RD 964 Map 14-A1**
🍷⊗   **LES ROUTIERS** (N° RR AOU 22 460) (M. Claude **Rousselot**) 19,
🏠   rue de Verdun ☎ 29-89-00-44 ⚏ 8. Closed Sat, Sun. Aug. Evening meals served until 9pm. English spoken.

SAINT-NAUPHARY 82370 Tarn-et-Garonne **RD 999 Map 22-A1**
🍷⊗   **LES AYÈRES** (N° RR FEV 22 645) (M. **Monruffet**) ☎ 63-67-85-09
🏠   ⚏ 11. Coaches welcome. Rest. seats 160. Evening meals. Closed Fri pm, Sat, 3 weeks Aug.

SAINT-NAZAIRE 30970 Gard **RN 86 Map 24-A2**
🍷⊗   ☆ **NN LES TE RAILLES** (N° RR NOV 19 219) (Mme **Menu**) RN 86
🏠   ☎ 66-89-66-14 ⚏ 12. Closed Sat pm, Sept.

SAINT-NAZAIRE 44600 Loire-Atlantique **RN 771 Map 11-A2**
🍷   **LE LAFAYETTE** (N° RR SEP 24 671) (M. Gilbert **Renou**) 7, avenue de Penhoët ☎ 40-22-53-82. **Minitel**. Closed Sat, Sun, July. Coaches welcome. Terrace seats 40. Credit cards accepted. ⚲ Parking. Sights: naval base, ship yards.

SAINT-NICOLAS-DE-BOURGUEIL 37140 Indre-et-Loire **CD 035 Map 12-B2**
🍷⊗   **LE RELAIS** (N° RR OCT 25 717) (M. Joël **Joulin**) Le Bourg – place de Église ☎ 47-97-75-39 ⚏ 3. Closed Sun, 15–31 Aug. Evening meals to 9pm – Routiers only.

SAINT-NICOLAS-DE-REDON 44460 Loire-Atlantique **Map 11-A2**
🍷⊗   **LE RELAIS DES ROUTIERS** (N° RR JAN 23 081) (Mme Marie-Annick **Hemery**) 84, avenue Jean-Burel ☎ 99-71-01-96. **Minitel**. Closed Sun, Aug. Coaches welcome. Rest. seats 72. Evening meals until 11pm.

SAINT-NOLF 56250 Morbihan **RN 166 Map 11-A2**
🍷⊗   **LE RELAIS DE BELLEVUE** (N° RR FEV 27 578) (Mme Edith
🏠   **Hureau**) Bellevue ☎ 97-45-44-04. Closed Sun. Evening meals to 10pm.

SAINT-OMER 62500 Pas-de-Calais **RN 43 Map 5-A2**
🍷⊗   **LE RELAIS DE LA RENAISSANCE** (N° RR AVR 10 573) (SARL
🏠   **Vanyper Fils**) 10, place du 11-Novembre ☎ 21-38-26-55 ⚏ 7. Closed Sun. Coaches welcome. Rest. seats 100. Evening meals until 9pm. English spoken.

SAINT-OUEN 93400 Seine-St-Denis **Pont de St-Ouen Map 1-A2**
🍷⊗   **AU ROUTIER SYMPAS** (N° RR SEP 22 466) (M. Bernard **Delouv-**
🏠   **rier**) 93, boulevard Victor-Hugo ☎ 40-11-00-31 ⚏ 9 at 50F per person. WC and showers on landing. Closed Sun, Aug. Evening meals to 8.30pm. ⚲ Coaches welcome. Rest. seats 70.
🍷⊗   **LE RELAIS DU PAVILLON BLEU** (N° RR JUN 23 830) (M. Ramdane **Kerdous**) 7, quai de Seine ☎ 40-11-03-67. Closed Sat pm, Sun. Coaches welcome. Rest. seats 60. Evening meals.

SAINT-PAUL-TROIS CHATEAUX

SAINT-PARDOUX-L'ORTIGIER 19270 Corrèze **Map 17-A1**
℗⊗ **LA ROUTE MAUVE** (N° RR JANV 27 765) (M. Jean Marc Bienvenu) Les Quatre Routes ☎ 55-73-72-33. **Minitel**. English spoken. Restaurant. Specialities: périgourdines. Menu 50–130F. À la carte. Closed on Sun pm. Parking. Filling station nearby.

SAINT-PAUL 60650 Oise **RN 31 Map 3-A2**
℗⊗ **AU RELAIS SAINT-PAUL** (N° RR SEPT 27 035) (Mme Marie-France **Mouligneaux**) ☎ 44-82-20-19. Closed Sun and 24 Dec–1 Jan. English spoken. Coaches welcome. Home cooking. Rest. seats 42. Evening meals to 10pm. Filling station nearby open 7am–9pm. ⚑ Sights: Cathédrale de Beavais.

SAINT-PAUL-CAP-DE-JOUX 81220 Tarn **RD 112 Map 22-B2**
℗⊗ **LES GLYCINES** (N° RR SEPT 23 452) (M. Claude **Peyrard**) rue Philippe Pinel ☎ 63-70-61-37. **Minitel**. Closed Mon (midday meal assured). Coaches welcome. Rest. seats 180. Evening meals to 8pm. Home cooking. ⚑ Parking.

SAINT-PAUL-DE-LOUBRESSAC 46170 Lot **RN 20 Map 22-A1**
℗⊗ ☆ **NN LE RELAIS DE LA MADELEINE** SARL (N° RR JUL 9 786)
⌂⇌ (M. Bernard **Devianne**) 100m from the RN 20 in the direction of La Madeleine ☎ 65-21-98-08 ⊨ 16 from 95–170F with shower, bath, WC. Open 7am–10pm. Access for disabled. Closed Sat, Sun (low season), 1 Nov for 8 days, 15 days at Christmas. Coaches welcome. Rest. seats 65 plus terrace. Evening meals. English spoken (Spanish in summer). Car park. Bar. ⚑ Recreations: pétanque, children's games. Menus 55–98F. Specialities: foie gras, quercynoise, confit, magret. Credit cards accepted. Garden terrace.

SAINT-PAUL-DU-BOIS LA REVEILLERE 49310 Maine-et-Loire **RN 748 Map 12-B1**
℗⊗ **LES ROUTIERS** (N° RR FEV 20 394) (M. Gérard **Bonnin**) ☎ 41-75-81-44. Restaurant: home cooking. Specialities: anguille à la creme, cuisses de grenouilles (on request). Menu 44–125F. Children's menu. À la carte. Lunch 12–2.30pm. Dinner 7–9pm. Closed Tue. Rest. seats 125. ⚑ Parking.

SAINT-PAUL-LE-JEUNE 07460 Ardèche **RD 104 Map 23-B1**
℗⊗ **LE RELAIS ROUTIERS DE CHEYRÈS** (N° RR JUN 23 309) (Mme Marie-Thérèse **Vernède**) Cheyres-Banne ☎ 75-39-30-09. **Minitel**. Closed Sun. Coaches welcome. Rest. seats 70. Evening meals. Car park 5,000m².

SAINT-PAUL-LES-DAX 40990 Landes **RN 124 Map 20-A/B2**
℗⊗ **RELAIS PLAISANCE** (N° RR MAI 23 784) (M. Alain **Escos**) route de Bayonne ☎ 58-74-04-70. English, Spanish spoken.

SAINT-PAUL-TROIS CHATEAUX 26130 Drôme **RN 59 near Autoroute A7 Map 24-A2**
℗⊗ **LE RELAIS DE PROVENCE** (N° RR MAI 21 109) (Mme Hélène
⌂ **Entringer**) 11, avenue du Général-de-Gaulle ☎ 75-04-72-48 ⊨ 7 65–130F with shower. Closed Feb. Evening meals. Home cooking. Specialities: omelette truffée, agneau du Tricostin. Menu 78–125F (Routier menu 55F). Lunch 12–1.45pm. Dinner to 9pm. Rest. seats 142.

SAINT PAY D'ARMENS

SAINT PAY D'ARMENS 33330 Gironde **15 A-3**
♔⊗ **RELAIS DE GASCOGNE** (N° RR SEPT 27 660) (M. Eric **Samson**)
RD 936 ☎ 57-47-15-02. English spoken. Dinner to 10pm. Closed
Sat pm and Sun.

SAINT-PELLERIN 50500 Manche **RN 13 Map 4-B1**
♔⊗ **AUBERGE DE LA FOURCHETTE** (N° RR DEC 25 752) (Mme
Henriette **Letourneur**) Carantan ☎ 33-42-16-56. English spoken.
Regional home cooking. Specialities: pied de veau, rillettes,
tripes. Menu à la carte. Dinner to 10pm. Closed Sun, Feb. Credit
cards accepted. Traditional décor. Rest. seats 50. Garden ter-
race. ⚓ Parking. Filling station 2km. Sights: landing beach,
Church Sainte Mère et les marais en bâteaux.

SAINT-PHAL 10130 Aube **Map 9-B3**
♔⊗ **RESTAURANT DU COMMERCE** (N° RR FEV 26 821) (M. Daniel
Godefroy) Evry-le-Châtel ☎ 25-42-16-39. Closed Mon, Aug.
Coaches welcome. Rest. seats 100. Regional cooking. Menu
50–130F. Children's menu. Lunch 11am–1.30pm. Dinner 7–
8.45pm. Credit cards accepted. Garden terrace. ⚓ Parking.

SAINT-PHILBERT-DE-GRAND'LIEU 44310 Loire-Atlantique **RD 18 Bis**
Map 11-B2
♔⊗ **LA BOULOGNE** (N° RR MAR 24 162) (M. Bernard **André**) 11,
🏠 place de l'Abbatiale ☎ 40-78-70-55. Closed Sat, Sun. Coaches
welcome. Rest. seats 80. Evening meals to 9pm.

SAINT-PIERRE DE CHANDIEU 69780 Rhône **RD 149 Map 2-B2**
♔⊗ **LE BLE D'OR** (N° RR NOV 27 451) (Mme Marthe **Jacquenool**)
avenue Amédée-Ronin ☎ 78-40-32-41. Closed Sun pm. English
spoken. Evening meals to 11pm. Filling station 600m open
7am–8pm. Parking 300m².

SAINT-PIERRE-DE-QUIBERON 56510 Morbihan **RD 768 Map 11-A1**
♔⊗ **LA CHALOUPE** (N° RR MAI 21 916) (Mme **Le Bellour**) place du
Marché Kerhostin ☎ 97-30-91-54. Closed Sun (low season), 15
Oct–15 Nov. Coaches welcome. Rest. seats 80.

SAINT-PIERRE-DES-CORPS 37700 Indre-et-Loire **RN 751 Map 12-A3**
♔⊗ **LE GRILLON** (N° RR DEC 21 721) (M. and Mme **Latour**) 9, quai
de la Loire ☎ 47-44-74-90. Closed Sat, Sun, July or Aug. Evening
meals served to 11.30pm. Coaches welcome. Rest. seats 60.

SAINT-PIERRE-LANGERS 50530 Manche **RN 173 Map 8-A1**
♔⊗ **A LA GRILLADE** (N° RR JUN 27 632) (M. Eric **Rome**) Hameau de
🏠 la Havaudière (5km from Sartilly) ☎ 33-48-83-71 ⊷ 8 from
70–170F. Restaurant open 7.30am–11pm. Closed Sun (low season). Dinner to 9pm. Hotel open 7am–11pm.

SAINT-PIERRE-LES-ELBEUF 76320 Seine-Maritime **Map 3-B1**
♔⊗ **LA SAUVAGINE** (N° RR OCT 27 418) (M. Patrick **Clivaz**) 611,
chemin du Halage ☎ 35-78-37-70. Closed Sun, 15 days in Jan or
Feb, 3 weeks in Aug. English spoken. Evening meals to 11pm.
Filling station 500m.

SAINT-PIERRE-SUR-DIVES 14170 Calvados **D 511 Map 8-A2**
♔⊗ **LE PRESSOIR** (N° RR OCT 27 416) (Mme Florence **Villain**) 17,
route de Caen ☎ 31-20-56-03. Closed Sun. Evening meals to

11pm. Filling station 300m. Home cooking. Menu 45F. Modern décor. Rest. seats 26. ⚑ Parking.

SAINT-PIERREMONT 88700 Vosges **RD 414 Map 14-B1**

♟⊗ ☆☆ **LE RELAIS VOSGIEN** (N° RR NOV 145 81) (Mme **Prevost**)
⌂ Rambervilliers ☎ 29-65-02-46. **Minitel**. Restaurant: home cooking. Menu 58–180F. Children's menu. À la carte. Lunch 12–2pm. Dinner 7–9pm. Closed Mon evening. Credit cards accepted. Rest. seats 130 ⇤ 14 at 190–280F with shower, bath, WC, TV, telephone. Open 7am until midnight. Garden terrace. Parking. ⚑ Lecture room and TV. Amusement park. Sights: Lunéeville, cristallerie Baccaret, sources and étangs.

SAINT-POL-DE-LÉON 29250 Finistère **Map 7-A1**

♟⊗ ☆ **LES ROUTIERS** (N° RR JUN 26 267) (M. Jean-Louis and Marie-
⌂ Pierre **Floch**) 28, rue Pen-Àr-Pont ☎ 98-69-00-52. Closed Sun, Aug (not hotel). Coaches welcome. Rest. seats 140. English, German spoken. Evening meals. Home cooking. Children's menu. Credit cards accepted ⇤ 18 at 120–160F with shower, WC, TV. Open 7am until midnight. ⚑ Parking. Sights: Cathédrale de Roscoff (4km).

SAINT-PRIEST-DE-GIMEL 19800 Corrèze **RN 89 Map 17-A1**

♟⊗ **LE RELAIS CHEZ MOUSTACHE** (N° RR JUL 20 791 bis) (M. Jean-Claude **Laval**) Gare de Corrèze ☎ 55-21-39-64. **Minitel** ⇤ 3. Closed Sun, Aug. Dinner to 10pm.

SAINT-PRIVAT-DES-VIEUX 30340 Gard **RD 216 Map 23-B1**

♟⊗ **L'ESCALE Tobacconist** (N° RR JAN 18 303) (Mme Ginette **Calcat**)
⌂ 59, route de Bagnois ☎ 66-30-09-40. **Minitel** ⇤ 8. English spoken. Evening meals to 11pm. Coaches welcome. Rest. seats 170. Parking 6,000m^2.

SAINT-PROUANT 85110 Vendée **RD 760 Map 11-B3**

♟⊗ **LE ZODIAC** (N° RR MAR 24 159) (M. Daniel **Arru**) 2, rue G.
⌂ Clemenceau Le Bourg ☎ 51-66-40-55 ⇤ 5. Closed Mon, Feb. Coaches welcome. Rest. seats 80. Evening meals to 9pm. English, Spanish spoken.

SAINT-QUAY-PORTRIEUX 22410 Côtes-du-Nord **RN 786 Map 7-A2**

♟⊗ **LES ROUTIERS** (N° RR DEC 27 738) (M. Claude **Bailleu**) 42, rue
⌂ des 3 Frères Salaûn ☎ 96-70-40-19. Restaurant. Speciality: couscous. Menu 44–150F. Closed Sun (low season) ⇤ 11 from 80–120F. Parking. Filling station.

SAINT-QUENTIN 02100 Aisne **RN 44 Maps 5-B3 and 6-A1**

♟⊗ **BRASSERIE DE LA VALLÉE** (N° RR MAI 27 291) (M. Jean **Boyard**) 28 bis, Chaussée Romaine ☎ 23-62-43-67. Restaurant: regional home cooking. Menu 35–59F. À la carte. Lunch 12–2pm. Closed Sat midday, Sun, Aug. Credit cards accepted. Modern décor. Rest. seats 35. ⚑ Parking. English, German and a little Dutch spoken. Filling station nearby open 24 hrs. Sights: basilique de Saint Quentin, musée Quentin de la Tour, parc d'Isle forêt de Saint Gobain, souterrain de Riqueval.

SAINT-QUENTIN-LES-ANGES 53400 Mayenne **RD 26 Map 12-A1**

♟⊗ **LE RELAIS** (N° RR NOV 24 419) (Mme Marie-Annick **Trottier**) Le
⌂ Bourg ☎ 43-06-10-62. **Minitel**. Restaurant: home cooking. Specialities: coquilles Saint Jacques à la Nantaise, filet de canard

SAINT-QUENTIN-SUR-ISÈRE

Saint-Quentin-Les-Anges continued

à la Craonnaise, filet de sandre grille au beurre blanc. Menu 44–150F. Children's menu. Self-service. Lunch 12–2.30pm. Dinner 7.30–9.30pm. Closed end of Aug. Credit cards accepted. Traditional décor. Rest. seats 210 ⊷ 9 from 75–110F with shower. Open 7am–11.30pm. ⊨ Car parking. Sights: Château de Craon, Château de Mortiercrolles, Nine Bleue, musée Robert Tatin.

SAINT-QUENTIN-SUR-ISÈRE 38210 Isère **RN 532 Map 19-A3**
♀⊗ **LE GIBRALTAR** (N° RR NOV 27 716) (M. Pierre **Barreau**) RN 532
☎ 76-93-65-28. Closed Sat, Sun, 15 days in Aug. Evening meals to 11pm. Menu 52F. Parking. Filling station nearby.

SAINT-RAPHAEL 83700 Var **RN 98 Map 25-B2**
♀⊗ ☆ **NN LE RELAIS BEL AZUR** (N° RR FEV 19 663) (Mme
⌂⊷ Marguerite **Magnani**) 247, boulevard de Provence ☎ 94-95-14-08
⊷ 20. Closed Sat, Sun pm, 15 Sept, 1 June, 22 Dec–5 Jan. Coaches welcome. Rest. seats 115. Evening meals until 9am. Italian spoken. Parking. Bar. ⊨ Specialities: bouillabaisse Aïoli paella. Menus 49.50–110F. Sights: Gorges du Verdun et de Lup, Roman ruins.

SAINT-RIQUIER 80135 Somme **Map 5-A3**
♀⊗ **LE CENTULOIS** (N° RR JUIL 26 970) (Mme Lili **Colinet**) 70, rue du Général-de-Gaulle ☎ 22-28-88-15. Closed Wed afternoon. Filling station near.

SAINT-ROMAIN-DE-COLBOSC 76430 Seine-Maritime **Map 4-A3**
♀⊗ **LE RELAIS DU FRESCOT** (N° RR JAN 25 257) (M. Jacques **Chapelet**) 18, Nationale on the road to Havre ☎ 35-20-15-09 ⊷ 7. Open 5.30am–10pm. Closed Sun. Coaches welcome. Home cooking. Menu 45F. À la carte. Lunch 11.30am–2.30pm. Dinner to 9pm. Rest. seats 90. Garden terrace. ⊨ Parking.

SAINT-ROMAIN-LA-MOTTE near ROANNE 42640 Loire **RN 7 Map 16-B3**
♀⊗ **AU BON ACCUEIL** (N° RR JUN 25 463) (Mme Lucienne **Galichon**) Les Baraques ☎ 77-70-12-03. **Minitel** ⊷ 3. Coaches welcome. Rest. seats 50. Evening meals to 11pm. Closed Sat pm.

SAINT-ROMAIN-LE-PUY 42610 Loire **Map 18-A2**
♀⊗ **LE PETIT VINCENNES** (N° RR JANV 26 774) (M. Alain **Bouchet**) 16, rue Léon Portier ☎ 77-76-63-54. English spoken.

SAINT-ROME-DE-CERNON 12490 Aveyron **Map 23-A1**
♀⊗ **RELAIS CHEZ PIERROT** (N° RR JUL 27 642) (M. Jean-Pierre
⌂ **Bousquet**) avenue de Millau ☎ 65-62-33-56 ⊷ 7 75–110F. Coaches welcome. Rest. seats 70. Evening meals. English, Spanish spoken. Specialities: truite au roquefort, écrevisses à l'Américaine.

SAINT-SAMSON-DE-LA-ROQUE 27680 Eure **RN 815 A Map 4-B3**
♀⊗ **LE RELAIS NORD BRETAGNE** (N° RR OCT 27 417) (M. Marcel **Poiraud**) route du Pont-de-Tancarville ☎ 32-57-67-30. Closed Sat, Sun. Evening meals until 11pm. English, Spanish spoken.

SAINT-VICTURNIEN

SAINT-SAUVEUR 70300 Haute-Saône **RN 57 Maps 10-A3 and 14-B2**
♈⊗ **LE RELAIS CHEZ MAXIM** (N° RR AVR 21 055) (Mme Colette
⌂ **Lack**) 10, avenue Georges-Clémenceau ☎ 84-40-02-91. **Minitel**
⊷ 8. Closed Sun evening, Feb. Coaches welcome. Rest. seats
228. Evening meals. German, English spoken.

SAINT-SAUVEUR D'EMALLEVILLE 76110 Seine-Maritime **CD 925**
Map 4-A2/3
♈⊗ **RELAIS DE SAINT SAUVEUR** (N° RR SEPT 27 017) (M. Phillippe
Guèrin) Route Nationale Goderville ☎ 35-27-21-56. Closed 15
days July. Home cooking. Credit cards accepted. Evening meals
to 10pm. Rest. seats 100. Garden terrace. ⊶ Parking. Filling
station 5km. Sights: Etretat, Fécamp.

SAINT SAVINIEN 17350 Charente-Maritime **Map 15 A-2**
♈⊗ **LE SAINT SAVINEN** (N° RR JUIL 27 646) (Mme Jacqueline
⌂ **Chauvin**) 27, rue de Champeroux ☎ 46-90-20-33 ⊷ 10. Filling
station open 7am–8pm.

SAINT-SORNIN 16220 Charente **TD 6 Map 15-B2**
♈⊗ **LES ROUTIERS Tobacconist** (N° RR AVR 25 914) (M. Jean-Michel
Dubois) Le Bourg Montbron ☎ 45-23-12-83. Closed Mon after-
noon, 2 weeks in Aug.

SAINT-SULPICE-DE-GRAINBOUVILLE 27210 Eure **RD 312 Map 4-B3**
♈⊗ **LE RELAIS DE ST SULPICE** (N° RR MAI 27 277) (M. Pierre
Dulong) La Place ☎ 32-41-50-99. **Minitel**. Closed Sun pm. English
spoken. Evening meals to midnight. Rest. seats 60. HGV park.

SAINT-SULPICE-LES-FEUILLES 87160 Haute-Vienne **Map 16-A1**
♈⊗ **HOTEL DU COMMERCE** (N° RR JAN 23 626) (M. Robert
⌂ **Dionnet**) 1, rue du Commerce ☎ 55-76-70-72 ⊷ 6. Evening
meals.

SAINT-SYMPHORIEN-DES-MONTS 50640 Manche **RN 176 Map 8-A1**
♈⊗ ☆ **NN LE RELAIS DU BOIS LEGER** (N° RR JUL 10 872) (M. and
⌂⊷ Mme Raymond **Pinet**) Lapenty ☎ 33-49-01-32. **Minitel**. Restaurant: regional home cooking. Specialities: pintade aux pommes,
terrine du chef. Children's menu. À la carte. Dinner to 9pm.
Closed 3 weeks Sept, 1 week Feb. Credit cards accepted. Rest.
seats 50 ⊷ 9 from 100–160F with shower, bathroom. Open
6am–11pm. Rest room. Garden terrace. ⊶ Parking. Fish in rivers
and ponds. Sights: animal park, rose garden. Mont St Michel.

SAINT-THEGONNEC 29223 Finistère **RN 12 Map 7-A1**
♈⊗ **REST DU COMMERCE** (N° RR NOV 25 198) (M. Alain **Mevel**)
1, rue de Paris ☎ 98-79-61-07. Closed Sat and Sun. Coaches
welcome. Rest. seats 92.

SAINT-VICTURNIEN 87420 Haute-Vienne **RN 141 Map 16-B1**
♈⊗ **LE RELAIS DE LA MALAISE** (N° RR JUL 26 293) (M. Jean-Marie
Faure) La Malaise ☎ 55-03-87-03 ⊷ 4. Coaches welcome. Rest.
seats 80. Evening meals to 10pm. English spoken. Closed Sat pm,
Sun pm and beginning Sept.

241

SAINT-VIGOR-LE-GRAND

SAINT-VIGOR-LE-GRAND see BAYEUX 14400 Calvados **RN 13 Map 4-B2**

♈⊗ **CHEZ PEPONNE** (N° RR MAI 27 601) (M. Jean-François **Victoire**) 3, rue du Pont Trubert, La Maison Brulée ☎ 31-92-28-39.

SAINT-VINCENT-DE-CONNEZAC 24190 Dordogne **CD 709 Map 15-B3**

♈⊗ **AU BON ACCUEIL** (N° RR JANV 27 592) (M. René **Ravier**) route de Mussidan ☎ 53-91-82-17.

SAINT-VINCENT-DE-PAUL 33440 Gironde **RN 10 Map 20 B-2**

♈⊗ ☆ **NN CHEZ ANATOLE** (N° RR MAR 23 718) (M. Michel
⌂ **Denechaud**) Ambarès ☎ 56-38-95-11 ⊷ 8 from 75–120F with shower. Rest. seats 100. Home cooking. Specialities: lamproie bordelaise, cèpes, fruit de mer, poissons. Menu 49–165F. Closed Sat. Car park. ⊶ Sports and recreations (pool table, pétanque, swings, shaded garden). Sights: Citadelle de Blaye Grot 'Pair non Pair', Bec d'Ambes.

SAINT-VINCENT-DE-PAUL 40990 Landes **RN 124 Map 20-B2**

♈⊗ **AUX PLATANES** (N° RR OCT 20 315) (M. **Vicente**) ☎ 58-73-90-13. Closed Sun. Spanish spoken.

SAINT-YAN 71600 Saône-et-Loire **RN 982 (via Flèche Bison Fûté) Maps 18-A2 and 16-A3**

♈⊗ **HOTEL DE LA GARE** (N° RR FEV 26 463) (M. Pascal **Germain**)
⌂ 12, rue de la Gare ☎ 85-84-97-20 ⊷ 6. Closed Tue, Sept. Coaches welcome. Rest. seats 45. Evening meals until 11pm.

SAINT-YORRE 03270 Allier **RN 106 Map 16-B3**

♈⊗ **NOUVEL HOTEL** (N° RR JUN 26 559) (Mme Pascale **Rougelin**)
⌂ 17, route de Vichy ☎ 70-59-41-97. **Minitel** ⊷ 12. Closed Sat midday, Feb. Coaches welcome. English, some German spoken. Evening meals to 9pm. Rest. seats 150.

SAINTE-CATHERINE 62223 Pas-de-Calais **RN 25 Map 5-B3**

♈⊗ **L'AUBERGE DU MOULIN** (N° RR MAR 27 227) (M. Eric **Gagno**)
⌂ 135, route de Lenz ☎ 21-23-41-56 ⊷ 7. Closed Sun. Filling station nearby.

SAINTE-CECILE 62223 Manche **RN 24 Bis Map 8-A1**

♈⊗ **LE CÉCILIA** (N° RR MAI 26 883) (M. Daniel **Le Huby**) Le Bourg
⌂ ☎ 33-61-07-81. **Minitel** ⊷ 5. Closed Sat and Sun. English, German spoken. Filling station 2km.

SAINTE-CROIX-HAGUE 50440 Manche **RD 901 Map 4-A1**

♈⊗ **LE PETIT BACCHUS** (N° RR MARS 27 233) (M. Michel **Oury**) ☎
⌂ 33-52-77-53 ⊷ 11. Closed Sat, Sun. Filling station nearby.

SAINTE-FOY-DE-MONTGOMERY 14140 Calvados **Map 8-A2**

♈⊗ **LE RELAIS DE MONTGOMERY** (N° RR AOU 14 917) (Mme **Planckeel**) ☎ 31-63-53-02. Closed Sun ⊷ 4.

SAINTE-FOY-L'ARGENTIERE 69610 Rhône **Map 2-A12**

♈⊗ **AUBERGE DE LA PLACE** (N° RR AVR 24 915) (Mme Yvonne **Goubier**) 49, Grande Rue ☎ 74-70-00-51. Closed Sat, Aug.

SAINTE-TERRE

SAINTE-LIVRADE 47110 Lot-et-Garonne **RN 111 Map 21-B1**
♈⊗ ☆ **NN AU BON ACCUEIL** (N° RR JUL 19 426) (M. **Cougouille**)
⌂ route de Villeneuve ☎ 58-01-02-34. **Minitel** ⊷ 10. Closed Sun
evening, 24 Dec–2 Jan. Coaches welcome. Rest. seats 140.

SAINTE-LUCE sur LOIRE 44980 Loire-Atlantique **Maps 11-A/B2 and
12-B1**
♈⊗ **LA BOUGRIERE** (N° RR JANV 23 491) (M. Pierre **Pertue**) 4, rue
du Pavillon ☎ 40-25-60-84. **Minitel**. English, Spanish spoken.
Restaurant: regional home cooking. Specialities: beurre blanc,
grenouilles, anguilles. Menu à la carte. Dinner to 11pm. Closed
Fri evening, Sat, Sun (except banquets), Aug, Christmas and
New Year. Rest. seats 280. Parking. Sights: le nouveau pont de
Chevré, port de plaisance et de pêche de Pornic.

SAINTE-MARGUERITE 88100 Vosges **RN 59 Map 10-B2**
♈⊗ ☆ **NN LE RELAIS DES AMIS** (N° RR JUN 16 108)⁻(M. François
⌂ **Bernat**) rue d'Alsace ☎ 29-56-17-23 ⊷ 16 from 80–140F with
shower. Open 7am–10pm. Home cooking. Garden terrace. ⌁
Parking. Coaches welcome. Rest. seats 72. Evening meals to
10pm. Opportunities to walk in woods, on hills.

SAINTE MARIE DE GOSSE 40390 Landes **Map 20-A2**
♈⊗ ☆ **LES ROUTIERS** (N° RR AVR 12 815) (M. Marc **Deloube**) RN
⌂⇌ 117 ☎ 59-56-32-02. **Minitel** ⊷ 15. Restaurant. Specialities: confits,
foie gras, poissons régionaux (in season). Menu from 45F. Dinner
to 10pm. Closed Sat, Oct. Rest. seats 200. Spanish spoken.

SAINTE MARTHE 47430 Lot-et-Garonne **Map 21-A1**
♈⊗ **LE RELAIS DU PONT DE L'AVANCE** (N° RR FEV 24 860) (M.
Hervé **Pouchet**) ☎ 53-20-63-39. Menu to 50F. Open 6am–
midnight. Closed Sun. Parking. Filling station 2.5km.

SAINT-MAURE-DE-TOURAINE 37800 Indre-et-Loire **RN 10 Map 12-B3**
♈⊗ **LA PIERRE PERCEE** (N° RR MAI 25 937) (MM. **Malin Bouquet**)
RN 10 ☎ 47-65-08-64. **Minitel**. Closed Sat, Sun, Aug. Evening
meals until 11.30pm. English, some Portuguese, Italian spoken.
Parking.

SAINTE-SCOLASSES SUR SARTHE 61170 Orne **CD 8 and CD 6 Map
8-A2**
♈⊗ **HOTEL DU CHEVAL BLANC** (N° RR SEPT 26 995) (M. Daniel
⌂ **Millière**) place de l'Eglise ☎ 33-27-66-30. Showers and WC on
landing. Restaurant: home cooking. Specialities: lanque sauce
piquante, rognons au madère. Dinner to 11pm. Closed Sun pm, 8
days in Feb, 1st week Sept. Credit cards accepted. Rest. seats
110 ⊷ 3 70–85F. Garden terrace. ⌁ Parking. Filling station
nearby. Sights: haras du pin, lac du Merle.

SAINTE-SIGOLENE 43600 Haute-Loire **RD 43 Map 18-A3**
♈⊗ ☆ **LE RELAIS DE LA POSTE** (N° RR NOV 18 246) (M. **Mounier**) 2,
⌂ place Leclerc ☎ 71-61-61-33 ⊷ 20. Closed Aug and Sun.
Coaches welcome. Rest. seats 60. Evening meals to 9pm.

SAINTE-TERRE 33350 Gironde **Map 15-A3**
♈⊗ **CHEZ RÉGIS** (N° RR JANV 25 783) (M. Jacques **Astarie**) Avenue
⌂⇌ du Général-de-Gaulle ☎ 57-47-16-21. Closed Mon and Jan, Oct.
Restaurant: regional cooking. Specialities: lamproie, anguille,

TALMONT-ST-HILAIRE

Sainte-Terre continued

cèpes. Menu à la carte. Children's menu. Dinner 7–9pm. Credit cards accepted. Traditional décor. Rest. seats 255 ⊨ 6 from 100–120F with shower. Open 7.30am–10pm. Garden terrace. ⊨ Parking. Sights: Saint Emilion 15km.

TALMONT-ST-HILAIRE 85440 Vendée **Map 11-A1**

♈⊗ **HOTEL DU CENTRE** (N° RR OCT 26 698) (M. Michel **Leblond**) 1, rue du Centre ☎ 51-90-60-35. **Minitel**. Restaurant: regional home cooking. Speciality: fruits de mer. Children's menu. À la carte. Dinner to 9pm. Closed Sat, Oct. Credit cards accepted. Rest. seats 100 in 2 rooms ⊨ 12 from 100–180F with showers, WC, TV, telephone. Open 8am–10pm. Garden terrace. ⊨ Parking. Sights: Château de Talmont. Car museum.

TARARE 69170 Rhône **RN 7 Map 2-A1**

♈⊗ **BAR PROVENÇAL** (N° RR MAI 23 294) (M. Georges **Bidot**) 8, avenue Edouard-Herriot ☎ 74-63-33-64. Closed Sat afternoon, Sun, public holidays, 1 week in Aug. Evening meals until 8pm.

♈⊗ **HOTEL SAINT-PIERRE** (N° RR NOV 27 458) (M. Jean **Goutlemoire**) Les Sauvages ☎ 74-89-30-09. Restaurant: home cooking. Specialities: grenouilles. Lunch 12–1.30pm. Dinner 7–8.30pm. Closed Wed. Credit cards accepted. Traditional décor. Rest. seats 80 in 3 rooms ⊨ 7 from 80–220F, with showers, WC, TV. Parking.

TARBES 65000 Hautes-Pyrénées **RN 21 Map 21-A3**

♈⊗ ☆ **NN LE VICTOR HUGO** (N° RR FEV 26 438) (Mme Patricia **Jouanlong**) 52, rue Victor-Hugo ☎ 62-93-36-71 ⊨ 8 (with WC) from 60–70F. Closed Sun. Restaurant: regional home cooking. Specialities: confit de canard maison, magret de canard, gambas flambées. Menu 60–70F. Children's menu. À la carte. Lunch 11am–2.30pm. Dinner 6–9.30pm. Modern décor. Rest. seats 96 in 2 rooms. Open 6.45am–10.30pm. English, Spanish spoken. Parking. ⊨ TV. Sights: Donjon des Aigles, Pyrénées National Park (ski-runs), grottos de Bétharron.

♈⊗ **LE CLAUZIER** (N° RR OCT 25 665) (M. Didier **Chaussalet**) 2, place Germain Claverie ☎ 62-93-18-57. Closed Sun.

TATINGHEM 62500 Pas-de-Calais **Map 5 A-2**

♈⊗ **LE TRUCK WASH** (N° RR FEV 27 791) (M. **Leroy**) ZA de Tatinghem ☎ 21-98-45-45. **Minitel**. English spoken. Restaurant: menu to 50F. Children's menu. Open 7am–midnight. Closed Sun. Rest. seats 36. Garden terrace. Parking. Washing facilities for HGVs.

TAUXIGNY 37320 Indre-et-Loire **12 B-3**

♈⊗ **AUBERGE DE LA CHAUMIERE** (N° RR DEC 27 490) (M. Dominique **Garon**) 1, avenue de la Gare ☎ 47-43-40-26 ⊨ 2. Closed Fri afternoon and Sat morning. Evening meals until 9pm. Service station 1km.

TAVERS 45190 Loiret **RN 152 Map 12-A3**

♈⊗ **LA PIERRE TOURNANTE** (N° RR OCT 27 057) (Daniel **Lecoq**) 36, RN 152 ☎ 38-44-92-25. Restaurant closed Sunday. Service station open 7.30am–7.30pm, closed Mon.

TEIL (LE) 07400 Ardèche **RN 86 Map 24-A2**

♈⊗ **AU BON COIN** (N° RR DEC 20 616) (Mme Marie **Gineste**) 11, rue Henri-Barbusse ☎ 75-49-02-61. Closed Aug.

LE TEMPLE-SUR-LOT 47110 Lot-et-Garonne **RN 911 Map 21-B1**
Ⓨⓧ **LE VAL DU LOT "GOUNOT"** (N° RR MAR 21 817) (MM. Lionel
Ⓗ and Christian **Hutrel**) ☎ 53-84-90-26 ⊷ 5. Closed Sat except in
summer and 25 Aug–15 Sept. Coaches welcome. Rest. seats 60.
English spoken.

TENCE 43190 Haute-Loire **Map 18-A3**
Ⓨⓧ **RESTAURANT DES CARS** (N° RR MARS 27 567) (M. David
Bonnet) 13, Grande-Rue ☎ 71-59-84-01.

TENDU 36200 Indre **RN 20 Map 16-A1**
Ⓨⓧ **LE RELAIS DES ROUTIERS** (N° RR DEC 11 179) (M. André **Luneau**)
Ⓗ Nle 20 ☎ 54-24-14-10 ⊷ 9 of 100–150F. Closed Wed (low season), 1
week at end of Sept/Oct, 1 week Feb. Coaches welcome. Rest.
seats 70. Evening meals to 8pm. Credit cards accepted.

TERCIS-LES-BAINS
Ⓨⓧ **L'ÉTOILE** (N° RR MAI 27 284) (M. Thierry **Mortelette**) route de
Ⓗ Payrehorade ☎ 58-57-68-49 ⊷ 5. English and Spanish spoken.
Filling station 50m open 7am–8pm.

TERNAY 69360 Rhône **Map 2 B-1**
Ⓨⓧ **LE GAULOIS** (N° RR MARS 27 237) (M. Jean-Pierre **Coursat**) 2,
rue Saint Nicolas ☎ 78-73-07-34. English spoken. Restaurant:
home cooking. Specialities: oeufs pochés aux escargots, fricassé
de Faison à la moutarde de Meaux, coquelet aux morilles. Menu
55–175F. À la carte. Lunch 11.30am–3pm. Dinner 6.30–10pm.
Closed Sun, Mon. Credit cards accepted. Rest. seats 60 in 2
rooms. Garden terrace. ⊷ Parking. Filling station nearby. Sights:
Vienne (Roman town) 15km.

TERRASSON-LA-VILLEDIEU 24120 Dordogne **RN 89 Map 17-A1**
Ⓨⓧ **LE RELAIS DES ROUTIERS** (N° RR MAR 9 404) (M. Charles
Ⓗ **Leyrie**) 62, avenue Émile-Zola ☎ 53-50-00-75 ⊷ 12.

TERRENOIRE 42100 Loire **Map 2-B1 and 18-A2**
Ⓨⓧ **RELAIS DE L'AUTOROUTE** (N° RR DEC 26 771) (Mme Régine
Roux) 57, Les Marandes ☎ 77-95-70-92. Closed Sat, Sun. Evening
meals to midnight.

TESSY-SUR-VIRE 50420 Manche **Map 4-B1**
Ⓨⓧ **LES ROUTIERS** (N° RR MAR 26 854) (M. Maurice **Robert**) place
du Marché ☎ 33-56-35-25. Closed Thur afternoon. Filling station
150m. Coaches welcome. Rest. seats 55.

THAON-LES-VOSGES 88150 Vosges **RN 57 Map 14-B1**
Ⓨⓧ **RELAIS ROUTIER 6010** (N° RR JAN 26 148) (M. Robert **Gehin**)
Ⓗ 200, rue de Lorraine ☎ 29-39-21-67. **Minitel**. Restaurant: regional
home cooking. Speciality: tête de veau. Menu to 50F. Open
5am–9pm. Closed Sat, Sun. Credit cards accepted. Modern
décor. Rest. seats 35 in 2 rooms ⊷ 4 at 110F with shower, WC,
TV. Open 6am–9pm. ⊷ Parking. Museum of Fantasy at Epinàl
(9km).

THEIL (LE) 61260 Orne **Map 8-B3**
Ⓨⓧ **LE RELAIS DE L'ARCHE** (N° RR AOU 24 665) (M. Gérard
Leroux) La Rouge ☎ 37-49-62-92. Coaches welcome. Rest seats
55. Evening meals to 1am.

THENON

THENON 24210 Dordogne **RN 89 Maps 15-B3 and 17-A1**

♀⊗ **LES TOURNISSOUS – CHEZ SERGE** (N° RR MAR 23 159) (M.
⌂ Serge **Leymarie**) ☎ 53-05-20-31 ➡ 10. Coaches welcome. Rest.
seats 80 + 100 on terrace. English, Spanish spoken. Evening
meals to 11pm.

THIMERT 28170 Eure-et-Loir **RN 839 Map 8-A3**

♀⊗ **LA CRÉMAILLÈRE** (N° RR MAR 21 829) (Mme Madeleine
Breton) 1, rue de Chartres ☎ 37-51-60-90. **Minitel**. Closed Sun
afternoon and 3 weeks of Aug. Coaches welcome. Rest. seats 60.
Evening meals to 9pm.

THIVARS 28630 Eure-et-Loir **RN 10 Map 8-B3**

♀⊗ **CHEZ BARBICHE** (N° RR NOV 26 717 (M. Serge **Noel**) 15, rue
⌂ Nationale ☎ 37-26-40-05 ➡ 9. Closed Sun. Coaches welcome.
Rest. seats 25. Evening meals to 10pm.

THOMER LA SOGNE 27240 Eure **Map 8 A-3**

♀⊗ **LE RELAIS 154** (N° RR NOV 27 727) (Mme Nicolle **Vandecande-
laere**) route d'Orléans ☎ 32-67-41-00. English spoken. Restaurant: home cooking. Menu 50F (with coffee). Dinner to 10pm.
Closed Sun, 8 days at Christmas, 1 week in Aug. Modern décor.
Rest. seats 100 in 2 rooms. ➤ Parking.

THONES 74230 Haute-Savoie **RN 509 Map 19-A2**

♀⊗ ☆ **NN L'HERMITAGE** (N° RR AVR 26 523) (M. Pierre **Bonnet**)
⌂ avenue du Vieux-Pont ☎ 50-02-00-31. **Minitel** ➡ 40. Closed Fri
afternoon, 25 Oct–15 Nov. Coaches welcome. Rest. seats 160.

THORÉE-LES-PINS 72800 Sarthe **CD 306 Map 12-A2**

♀⊗ **CAFÉ RESTAURANT DES PÊCHEURS** (N° RR DEC 27 135) (M.
Marcel **Guillaume**) Le Bourg ☎ 43-45-03-79. Closed Wed after-
noon and Aug. English and German spoken. Dinner to 10pm.
Rest. seats 90.

THOU 45420 Loiret **RN 65 Map 13-A2**

♀⊗ **AU LIT ON DORT** (N° RR MAI 18 413) (M. Bernard **Bertrand**) ☎
38-31-62-07. Closed Mon afternoon and Aug.

THOUARS 79100 Deux-Sèvres **RN 1 Map 12-B2**

♀⊗ **LE MILLE PATTES** (N° RR MAI 24 957) (Mme Martine **Valleau**)
17, rue de Launay ☎ 48-56-36-53. **Minitel**. English and German
spoken.

THUET-PONTCHY 74130 Haute-Savoie **RN 506 Map 19-B2**

♀⊗ **LE RELAIS DES CYCLAMENS** (N° RR AUG 13 654) (Mme
Delavenay) ☎ 50-97-02-39.

THUILES (LES) 04400 Alpes-de-Haute-Provence **Map 25-A1**

♀⊗ **LES SEOLANES** (N° RR JUL 24 620) (M. Hubert **Maure**) Barce-
⌂ lonnette ☎ 92-81-07-37 ➡ 6. Closed one day a week, Jan.
English, Italian spoken. Dinner to 9pm.

TIGNIEU 38230 Isère **RD 18 Map 2-A2**

♀⊗ **AUBERGE DES CHARMILLES** (N° RR DEC 24 444) (Mme Josiane
Renon) 71, route de Bourgoin ☎ 78-32-23-57. Closed Sun afternoon. Home cooking. Menu 50F. Lunch 12–2pm. Rest. seats 30.

TOULOUSE-SAINT-MARTIN-DU-TOUCH

TOLLEVAST 50470 Manche **RN 13 Map 4-A1**
⊗ **LES CHEVRES** (N° RR OCT 26 705) (M. André **Maleuvre**) Brix ☎ 33-43-77-92. Closed Sat, Sun, Aug. English spoken. Evening meals to 10pm. Menu to 48F. Home cooking.

TONNAY-CHARENTE 17430 Charente-Maritime **RN 137 Map 11-B1**
🍸⊗ **L'OASIS CHEZ VACHON** (N° RR JAN 23 093) (M. **Vachon**) 27, rue de Lattre-de-Tassigny ☎ 46-88-70-84. Closed Mon, 1–15 Aug. Coaches welcome. Rest. seats 60. Lunch 12–2pm. Home cooking. Children's menu. À la carte. Closed Sun and between Christmas and New Year. ⊢ Parking.
🍸⊗ **LES FONTAINES** (N° RR DEC 27 122) (M. Jean Paul **Revelaud**) 110, avenue d'Aunis ☎ 46-83-79-11. **Minitel**. Restaurant: home cooking. Menu 50F. Children's menu. Lunch 11.30am–2.30pm. Dinner 7–9pm. Closed Sun. Traditional décor. Rest. seats 40 in 2 rooms. Garden terrace. ⊢ Parking. Restaurant closed Sunday. Service station open 6am–10pm. Sights: Cordeleries Royale, Rochefort. Maison de Pierre Loti.

TOTES 76890 Seine-Maritime **RN 27 Map 3-A1 Map 4-A3**
🍸⊗ **LES AMIS RÉUNIS** (N° RR FEV 19 282) (M. Michel **Guilbert**) Route de Dieppe ☎ 35-79-91-27.
🍸⊗ **LE NORMANDY** (N° RR MARS 26 187) (Sté de Fait M. **Perrero-Morel**) route d'Yvetôt ☎ 35-32-91-35. Closed Sat evening, Sun.

TOUL 54200 Meurthe-et-Moselle
⊗ **LE MIRABELLIER** (N° RR 2 048) Aire de Service de Toul – Dommartin Dans les deux sens autoroute ☎ 83-64-64-01. Restaurant: self-service. Open 6am–11pm. Rest. seats 180, covered terrace 60 seats, open terrace 120 seats. **Minitel**. Shower. Shop. TV. Message facility.

TOULON 83000 Var **RN 8 Map 25-A3**
🍸⊗ **LE RELAIS DE L'ESCAILLON** (N° RR MAI 24 967) (M. Bernard **Lemaire**) 1, rue Chateaubriand ☎ 94-24-21-02. Closed 15 Aug–3 Sept.
🍸⊗ **LA FRINGALE – CHEZ JO** (N° RR JUL 25 059) (SARL **Prim** and **Gonzales**) 522, avenue de la République ☎ 94-36-00-47. Closed Sun in winter, 1 week Oct, 1 week Feb. Coaches welcome. Rest. seats 25. English, Italian spoken. Dinner to 10pm. Garden terrace.

TOULON-SUR-ALLIER 03400 Allier **RN 7 Map 16-A3**
🍸⊗ **LE RELAIS FLEURI** (N° RR NOV 22 088) (M. **Belain**) RN 7 ☎ 70-44-47-16. Closed Sun, Aug.
🍸⊗ **LE FLAMBEAU** (N° RR OCT 27 710) (SARL **des Iles**) RN 7 ☎ 70-20-90-28. Restaurant: menu 50–60F. Parking.

TOULOUSE 31200 Haute-Garonne **RN 20 Map 22-A2**
🍸⊗ **LE NOUVEAU CORTIJO** (N° RR OCT 25 659) (M. René **Andrieu**) 181, avenue des États-Unis ☎ 61-47-68-64. **Minitel**. Closed Sat, Sun, 1–15 Aug. Evening meals to 11pm. Spanish spoken.

TOULOUSE-SAINT-MARTIN-DU-TOUCH 31300 Haute-Garonne **RN 124 Map 22-A2**
🍸⊗ **LE RELAIS DU PROGRÈS** (N° RR DEC 20 037) (M. Félix **Ober**)
⌂ 185, route de Bayonne ☎ 61-49-22-75 ⊷ 6. Closed Sun, Aug. Coaches welcome. Rest. seats 100. Evening meals until 11pm.

TOUQUES-DEAUVILLE

TOUQUES-DEAUVILLE 14800 Calvados **Dles 74 and 52 Map 4-B2**
♈⊗ **AUBERGE LA CROIX SONNET** (N° RR OCT 26 344) (Mme **Pedrazzi**) La Croix-Sonnet 4km from Trouville-Marguerite ☎ 31-88-19-62. English, Spanish, Italian spoken. Restaurant specialities: mussels, fish. Menu 68–103F. Children's menu. À la carte. Lunch 12–2pm. Dinner 7–9pm. Traditional décor. Rest. seats 35 + 100 on terrace ⇐ 4 from 200–250F with shower. Open 8am–12pm. Garden terrace. ⊬ Parking. Playroom. Sights: Deauville (4km), Honfleur (9km).

TOUQUIN 77131 Seine-et-Marne **RD 231 Map 9-A2**
♈⊗ **LE TOUQUINOIS** (N° RR JAN 26 160) (M. Marcel **Breuil**) 8, rue du Commerce ☎ 64-04-18-37. Closed Sun.

TOURCOING 59200 Nord **RN Sortie Tourcoing ouest 17 Map 5-B1**
♈⊗ **AU SIGNAL D'ARRET** (N° RR DEC 24 452) (M. Michel **Guilbert**)
⌂ 28, rue des Francs ☎ 20-26-56-74. **Minitel** ⇐ 5 75–130F. Closed Sat, Sun, Aug. Restaurant: home cooking. Menu to 55F. Children's menu. Lunch 11.30am–3pm. Dinner 7.30–9.30pm. Credit cards accepted. Traditional décor. ⊬ Parking. Coaches welcome. Rest. seats 60.
♈⊗ **LE SAPHIR** (N° RR NOV 26 723) (M. Jacques **Mareel**) 11 bis, chaussée Berthelot ☎ 20-01-88-03. Closed Sun.

TOUR-DU-MEIX (LA) 39270 Jura **RN 470 Map 19-B1**
♈⊗ **AUBERGE DU PONT DE LA PYLE** (N° RR MAR 23 698) (M. Jacques **Berger**) RN 70 ☎ 84-25-41-92. Closed Wed, Oct. Coaches welcome. Rest. seats 150 in 2 rooms. Meals served until 9.30pm. English, German spoken.

TOUR-DU-PIN (LA) 38110 Isère **RN 516 RN 6 Map 2-B3**
♈⊗ **CHEZ BABETH** (N° RR NOV 25 744). (Mme Elisabeth **Rostaing**) St-Didier-de-la-Tour between Tour du Pin and Les Abrets ☎ 74-97-15-87. **Minitel**. Coaches welcome. Rest. seats 60. Evening meals 5–7pm. Lunch 12–2pm. Home cooking. Speciality: grenouilles. Menu à la carte.

TOURS 37000 Indre-et-Loire **RN 10 CD 152 Map 12-A2/3**
♈⊗ **L'AVIATION** (N° RR JUN 26 554) (Mme Michelle **Mary**) 295,
⌂ avenue Maginot ☎ 47-51-19-50. **Minitel** ⇐ 8 Closed Sat, Sun. Coaches welcome. Rest. seats 50 in 2 rooms. Evening meals to 10pm. Parking 5500m^2.

TOURY 28390 Eure-et-Loir **RN 20 Map 9-B1**
♈⊗ **LE RELAIS DE LA CHAPELLE** (N° RR FEV 25 797) (Mme Claudine **Comarlot**) 60, avenue de la Chapelle ☎ 37-90-64-96. Closed Sat, Christmas week. Coaches welcome. Rest. seats 150. Evening meals until 11pm.

TRAIT (LE) 76580 Seine-Maritime **RD 982 Map 3-A1**
♈⊗ **LE JEAN BART** (N° RR AOU 23 902) (M. **Mahier**) 488, rue Jean Bart ☎ 35-37-22-47. **Minitel** ⇐ 3. Closed Sun, 10–30 Aug. Coaches welcome. Rest. seats 100. Evening meals to 10pm.

TRAMAIN 22640 Côtes-du-Nord **RN 12 Map 7-A3**
♈⊗ **AU RELAIS DE TRAMAIN** (N° RR MAI 26 894 (M. Jack **Hutteau**) rue du Bourg ☎ 96-31-82-28. Closed Sat, Sun. Filling station 4km. Coaches welcome. Rest. seats 105.

TREBES 11800 Aude **RN 113 Map 22-B2**

☖☒ **LE RELAIS DES CAPUCINS** (N° RR JUL 25 041) (M. Gilbert
⌂ **Laffont**) 34, route de Narbonne ☎ 68-78-70-07 ↤ 14. Closed Sat,
Sun, 1 week in Jul, 3 weeks at Christmas. Coaches welcome.
Rest. seats 55. Evening meals to 9pm.

TREBEURDEN 22560 Côtes-du-Nord **Map 7-A2**

☖☒ **RESTAURANT DES SPORTS** (N° RR NOV 27 447) (M. Andre
Courageaux) 24, rue des Plages ☎ 96-23-50-12. Closed Tues
afternoon (low season), 15–30 Aug. English spoken. Filling station
300m. Open 7.30am–8pm. Parking 6000m². Home cooking. Children's menu. Lunch 11.45am–1.45pm. Credit cards accepted.
Traditional décor. Rest. seats 80 in 2 rooms. ↰ Parking. Sights: La
côte de granit rose, Euradom, le planétarium, l'aquarium, le
centre ornithologique.

TREFFENDEL 35580 Ille-et-Vilaine

☖☒ **RELAIS RN24** (N° RR DEC 24 477) (Mme **Guillemot**) SARL RN24
La Gare Direction: road to Lorient 30km from Rennes ☎ 99-62-
00-62. Closed Sun. Evening meals. Restaurant: home cooking.
Menu of 43–90F. Children's menu. À la carte. Lunch 11.30am–
3pm. Dinner 6.30–10.30pm. Closed Sun during July/Aug. Credit
cards accepted. Rest. seats 70 in 2 rooms. Garden terrace. ↰
Parking. Sights: Vallée de Broccliaude, forêt.

TREGUIDEL 22290 Côtes-du-Nord **RD 51/CD 6 Map 7-A2**

☖☒ **LE BOUTOU** (N° RR JUN 25 003) (M. Bernard **Glaudel**) Bourg de
Tréguidel ☎ 96-70-02-42. Coaches welcome. Rest. seats 110.
Minitel. English spoken. Closed Mon afternoon.

TREILLIÈRES 44119 Loire-Atlantique **RN 137 Map 11-A2**

☖☒ **LE PIGEON BLANC** (N° RR AVR 26 527) (Mme Règine **Plat**) Le
Pigeon Blanc ☎ 40-94-67-72. **Minitel.** Closed Sun (low season).

TRELIVAN 22100 Côtes-du-Nord **Map 7 A3**

☖☒ **AU LUCKY BAR** (N° RR SEPT 27 682) (M. Jean Luc **Leroy**) RN 176
Gros Bois ☎ 96-85-37-27. **Minitel.** English, German spoken.
Restaurant: regional home cooking. Specialities: couscous. Menu
48F. Dinner to 1am. Closed Sun. Credit cards accepted. Rest.
seats 60. Garden terrace. ↰ Parking.

TREMOREL 22230 Côtes-du-Nord **N 164 bis Map 7-B3**

☖☒ **LES ROUTIERS** (N° RR FEV 26 820) (M. Yvon **Sohier**) Bourg
between Rennes and Loudéac ☎ 96-25-21-70. Closed Mon
afternoon. Evening meals to 10pm. Restaurant: home cooking.
Menu to 42F. Children's menu. Modern décor. Rest. seats 55.
Parking.

TREON 28500 Eure-et-Loir **RN 828 Map 8-A3**

☖☒ **LE RELAIS DE TREON** (N° RR JUL 26 583) (Mme **Cuvellier**) 20,
⌂ rue de Chateauneuf ☎ 37-82-62-35 ↤ 7. Closed Sat, Sun. Evening
meals until 10pm. Coaches welcome. Rest. seats 72.

TRESNAY 58240 Nièvre **RN 7 Map 16-A3**

☖☒ **LA SCIERIE** (N° RR FEV 27 180) (M. Martial **Pettinger**) Route
Nationale 7 St-Pierre-le-Moutier ☎ 86-38-62-14. Closed Sat, Sun,
Aug. English spoken. Restaurant: home cooking. Menu to 52F.

TRETS

Tresnay continued
Menu à la carte. Self-service. Lunch 12–2.30pm. Dinner 7–11.30pm. Credit cards accepted. Modern décor. Rest. seats 100. Parking. 24 hours filling station 3km.

TRETS 13530 Bouches-du-Rhône **RN 7 Map 24-B3**
♀⊗ **BAR DE L'AÉRODROME** (N° RR MAR 26 853) (M. Christian **Daumas**) RN 7 ☎ 42-61-49-45. **Minitel**. English spoken. Filling station nearby.

TRIGAVOU 22490 Côtes-du-Nord **Map 7 A-3**
♀⊗ **LE MILL'PATT** (N° RR OCT 27 395) (M. Loïc **Renault**) Le Bourg ☎ 96-27-84-14. Closed Monday afternoon. Evening meals. Filling station 500m.

TRIMOUILLE (LA) 86290 Vienne **RN 675 Map 16-A1**
♀⊗ **L'AUBERGE FLEURIE** (N° RR FEV 15 533) (M. Monique **Dufour**)
⌂⇌ rue Octave-Bernard ☎ 49-91-60-64 ⊷ 5 of 50–150F. Closed Sun, public holidays after lunch. Menus 43–60F. Home cooking. Specialities: moules au vert, medaillon de ris de veau à la trimouillaise, langouste thermidor. Traditional décor. Rest. seats 38. Lunch 12–2pm. Dinner 6–9pm. Garden terrace. Parking.

TRONQUAY (LE) 14490 Calvados **RD 572 Map 4-B1**
♀⊗ **AU ROUTIER SYMPA** (N° RR MAI 26 531) (M. Jacques **Lerosier**) ☎ 31-92-38-68.

TRONSANGES par BARBELOUP 58400 Nièvre **RN 7 Map 13-B2**
♀⊗ **L'AUBERGE DU SOLEIL LEVANT** (N° RR AVR 18 065) (M. Jean **Reichhard**) ☎ 86-37-84-02. Closed Sun, Sept. Coaches welcome. Rest. seats 30.
♀⊗ **LE RELAIS DE LA CROIX DU PAPE** (N° RR DEC 24 770) (Mme Marinette **Beunardeau**) Nationale ☎ 86-70-01-04. **Minitel**. Closed Sat, Sun, 3 weeks Aug, one week Christmas. English spoken. Coaches welcome. Rest. seats 120. Parking 3000m².
♀⊗ **SARL DE LA CROIX DU PAPE** (N° RR JAN 27 497) (Mme Agnes **Dumaine**) Barbeloup ☎ 86-37-84-03. Filling station nearby open 5am–midnight. Parking.

TRONVILLE-EN-BARROIS 55310 Meuse **Map 14-A1**
♀⊗ **L'ESPÉRANCE** (N° RR OCT 27 036) (M. Robert **Schneider**) Route Nationale 64 ☎ 29-78-19-59 ⊷ 2. Closed Sun. Menu 50–60F. Dinner to 11pm. Filling station 3km. Parking.

TROSLY BREUIL 60350 Oise **Map 3-A3**
♀⊗ **LA TERRASSE** (N° RR FEV 27 517) (M. Joël **Archain**) 47, route de Reims. Directions: between Compiègne and Soissons ☎ 44-85-70-39. **Minitel**. English spoken. Restaurant: home cooking. Speciality: Savoyardes. Menu 52F. Lunch 11.30am–3.30pm. Dinner 6.45–9.30pm. Closed Sun. Credit cards accepted. Traditional décor. Rest. seats 25. Garden terrace. ⇀ Parking. Filling station nearby. Sights: Château et forêt de Compiègne (10km), château de Pierrefonds (8km).

TULLINS 38210 Isère **Map 18 B-3**
♀⊗ **RESTAURANT DU CENTRE** (N° RR NOV 27715) (Mme Monique **Ducios**) 10, boulevard Michel Perret ☎ 76-07-93-08. English

spoken. Restaurant: regional home cooking. Specialities on request. Menu 50F. Children's menu. Dinner to midnight. Closed Wed afternoon. ⊨ Parking. Filling station nearby open 7am–8pm.

UCKANGE 57270 Moselle **RD 952 Maps 6-B3 and 10-A1**
♈⊗ **LE PRESSOIR** (N° RR JAN 21 339) (M. Silvio **Piccin**) 22, rue Jeanne-d'Arc ☎ 82-58-20-38. Closed Sat, Sun, Aug and 15 days at Christmas. Pizza menu Fri evening. Open 2.30–8pm.

ULMES (LES) 49700 Maine-et-Loire **RD 960 Map 12-B2**
♈⊗ **LA GRAPPE D'OR** (N° RR AVR 26 498) (Mme Monique **Forestier**) Restau Gril Le Moulin Cassé ☎ 41-67-00-06. Closed Sun evening at 7pm. English, German spoken.

UNIENVILLE 10140 Aube **RD 46 Map 9-B3**
♈⊗ **CHEZ CHRISTIANE ET MARCEL** (N° RR JANV_ 21 760) (M. Marcel **Saget**) ☎ 25-92-70-80. Restaurant: home cooking. Menu 50F. Lunch 11.30am–1.30pm. Dinner 7–8pm. ⊨ Parking.

UROU ET CRENNES 61200 Orne **RN 26 Map 8-A2**
♈⊗ **LE CLOS FLEURI** (N° RR NOV 26 720) (M. Gilbert **Estelle**) route de Paris ☎ 33-67-08-25. English, German spoken. Closed Sun (except banquets). Coaches welcome. Rest. seats 120. Evening meals until 11pm. Coaches welcome.

VAILLY-SUR-SAULDRE 18260 Cher **RD 926 Map 13-A1**
♈⊗ **REST DU MARCHÉ** (N° RR JANV 27 516) (Mme Catherine **Géraud**) place du Marché ☎ 48-73-72-25. Spanish spoken.

VALDURENQUE 81090 Tarn **Map 22-B2**
♈⊗ **ICIX 2** (N° RR OCT 27 688) (M. Pascal **Picardat**) 1, chemin de la Richarde ☎ 63-50-57-10. Restaurant. Dinner to 9pm. Closed Sun evening. Parking. Filling station open 6am–10pm.

VALENCIENNES 59300 Nord **RN 29 Maps 6-A3 and 5-B1**
♈⊗ **AUBERGE DU RELAIS DE LA POTERNE** (N° RR DEC 17 689) (M.
🏠 **Demolle**) 9, boulevard Eisen (Place Poterne) bd extérieur Itinéraire P.L. Exit from autoroute. A2 – Valenciennes Sud ☎ 27-46-44-98. Minitel ⊶ 13 with shower, TV. Coaches welcome. Rest. seats 50. Evening meals until 9.30pm.

VALENTON-VAL-POMPADOUR 94460 Val-de-Marne **RN 5 Map 1-B3**
♈⊗ **AU BON ACCUEIL** (N° RR OCT 25 165) (M. **Girard**) 46, rue Henri-Barbusse ☎ 43-89-06-70. Closed Sun, Aug. Spanish spoken. Evening meals until 10pm.

VALERGUES 34130 Hérault **RN 113 Map 23-B2**
♈⊗ **RELAIS DE VALERGUES** (N° RR JUL 25 495) (M. Claude
🏠 **Bernabé**) RN 113 ☎ 67-86-75-27. Closed Sun, Dec. Spanish spoken. Dinner to 11pm. Rest seats 90. Parking.

VALEUIL 24210 Dordogne **15-B3**
♈⊗ **LA GRÉGOIRE – RELAIS DE SARRAZEGNAC** (N° RR JAN 27 502) (M. Claude **Distingin**) ☎ 53-05-75-95. Open 24 hrs. English, Spanish spoken. Closed Fri evening, Sat and Sun morning. Rest. seats 120. Parking.

VALLET

VALLET 44330 Loire-Atlantique **RD 756 and 763 Maps 11-A1/B3 and 12-B1**
🍷⊗ **LE RELAIS DE LA GARE** (N° RR AVR 20 151) (Mme **Jouy**) 43, rue
⌂ Saint ☎ 40-33-92-55. **Minitel** ⎯ 25. Closed Sun. Coaches welcome. Rest. seats 160. English spoken.

VALLON-PONT-D'ARC 07150 Ardèche **RN 579 Map 24-A2**
🍷⊗ **BAR DE LA POSTE** (N° RR OCT 22 952) (M. Bernard **Garrido**)
rue Jean-Jaurès ☎ 75-88-02-11. Closed Sun (low season), Dec.
Spanish spoken. Coaches welcome. Rest. seats 40.

VALOGNES 50700 Manche **RN 13 Map 4-B1**
🍷⊗ **AU PETIT MONTROUGE** (N° RR DEC 12 588) (M. and Mme
François **Leblond**) 104, rue des Religieuses.

VALS-LE-BAINS 07600 Ardèche **Map 24-A1**
🍷⊗ **LE TONNEAU** (N° RR MAI 23 255) (M. Patrick **Guériot**) 89, rue
Jean-Jaurès ☎ 76-37-45-36. Closed Mon evening, 15 days Sept.
Evening meals. Rest. seats 50.

VANNES 56000 Morbihan **RN 165 Map 11-A1/2**
🍷⊗ ☆ **NN LE RELAIS DE LUSCANEN** (N° RR NOV 27 104) (M.
⌂ Jean-Marc **Giteau**) Route d'auvay ☎ 97-63-45-92. Restaurant:
regional home cooking. Menu 45F. Children's menu. À la carte.
Dinner to 11pm. Closed Sat evening, Sun and 13–26 Aug. Credit
cards accepted. Rest. seats 200 in 3 rooms ⎯ 12 120F (half-board) 160F (full-board) with shower, bath, WC. Open 6am–
midnight. ⊨ Parking. Filling station nearby. Sights: La côte
Bretonne, golf du Morbihan.

VANVES 92170 Hauts-de-Seine **Porte de Vanves Map 1-B2**
🍷⊗ **LE RELAIS DES ROUTIERS** (N° RR DEC 26 395) (M. Émile
Bourget) 38, avenue Pasteur ☎ 46-42-36-08. Closed Sun, 20 Jul–20
Aug. Coaches welcome. Rest. seats 100. Evening meals until
9pm.

VARANGES 21110 Côte-d'Or **RN 5 Map 14-A3**
🍷⊗ **L'AUBERGE** (N° RR MARS 27 223) (M. Jean-Pierre **Hul**) rue
Nouvelle ☎ 80-31-30 17. **Mintel**. Open 6.30am–10.30pm. Dinner to
10pm. Rest. seats 60. Filling station nearby.

VARENNES-LE-GRAND 71240 Saône-et-Loire **RN 6 Map 18-B1**
🍷⊗ **RELAIS DE LA GARE** – SARL (N° RR OCT 27 697) (M. Rachid
⌂ **Loulha**) RN 6 ☎ 85-44-22-76. Menu 54–56F. Dinner to 9pm. Filling
station nearby.
🍷⊗ **LE MISTRAL** (N° RR OCT 27 042) (M. Mohand **Aitaoudia**) RN 6 ☎
⌂ 85-44-12-70. ⎯ 10. English spoken. Filling station nearby.
🍷⊗ **LE COMMERCE** (N° RR SEPT 27 375) SARL (Yves-Marie
⌂ **Goalabre**) ☎ 85-44-22-34. English spoken. Restaurant: home
cooking. Menu à la carte. Closed Sat, Sun. Credit cards accepted
⎯ 14 from 90–150F with showers. Open 5am–midnight. ⊨
Parking. Filling station 150m open 6.30am–9pm.
🐝 **RELAIS DE VARENNES** (N° RR JUL 27 325) (M. Bernard
Guinchard) RN 6 Chalon/Tournus road ☎ 85-44-20-43.

VARENNES LES MACON 71000 Saône-et-Loire **Map 18-A/B1**
🍷⊗ **LA HALTE DES ROUTIERS** (N° RR FEV 27 541) (M. René
⌂ **Massonneau** – SARL Sonuet) RN 6 ☎ 85-34-70-44. Restaurant:

closed Sat from 8pm, Sun from 3.30pm ◄ 24. Filling station opposite open 6am–11pm.

VARENNES-SUR-ALLIER 03150 Allier **RN 7 Map 16-A3**

LE RELAIS DES TOURISTES – REST. DE FRANCE (N° RR MAI 14 802) (M. André **Juniet**) 1, rue des Halles ☎ 70-45-00-51. Restaurant: home cooking. Dinner to 9pm. Closed Sat (from Oct–May). Meal vouchers accepted. ◄ 9 75–90F (single), 100–150F (double). Open 6am–midnight. ☛ Parking.

LA RENAISSANCE (N° RR MAR 24 887) (Mme **Gardel**) Bellevue Route Nationale 7 ☎ 70-45-62-86. Portuguese spoken.

VATAN 36150 Indre **RN 20 Map 13-B1**

LE RELAIS DU CHÊNE VERT (N° RR JAN 3 823) (Mme **Lahaye**) 12, avenue de Paris, sur la Nle 20 ☎ 54-49-76-56 ◄ 5 with shower, bathroom. Open 7.45am–9.30pm. Closed Sat evening, Sun, 1 Sept–29 Sept. Restaurant: home cooking. Lunch 12–2pm. Evening meals 7.30–9.30pm. Credit cards accepted. ☛ Parking.

VATRY 51320 Marne **RN 77 Map 9-A3**

L'ETAPE (N° RR JANV 27 149) (Mme Éliane **Fouquet**) RN 77 ☎ 26-67-41-06 ◄ 7. Closed Sat pm and Sun in winter.

VAUVERT 30600 Gard **RD 56 Map 23-A2**

LE CRISTAL (N° RR JUL 24 647) (Mme Roselyne **Guyon**) 13, rue de la République ☎ 66-88-21-77 ◄ 11. Closed Sat afternoon, Sun, 23 Dec–2 Jan. Coaches welcome. Rest. seats 70. Evening meals until 9.30pm.

VAUX-EN-BUGEY 01150 Ain **RN 75 Map 2-A2**

LE RAMEQUIN (N° RR NOV 27 094) (Mme Michelle **Gallon**) RN 75 ☎ 74-35-95-09. Closed Sat pm and Sun. Filling station 2km. Open 8am–8pm.

VENDENHEIM 67550 Bas-Rhin **RN 63 Map 10-B2**

LE RELAIS DE LA MAISON ROUGE (N° RR AOU 16 194) (Mme Germaine **Michielin**) 2, route de Brumath ☎ 88-69-51-79. Closed Tues pm and Wed. Evening meals until 10pm. German spoken. Rest seats 30. Parking.

VENDEUVRE 14170 Calvados **RD 511 Map 8-A2**

LE RELAIS DU VENDEUVRE (N° RR JUN 23 836) (M. André **Denis**) place de la Gare, Saint-Pierre-sur-Dives ☎ 31-40-92-77 ◄ 11. Closed Sat, 23 Dec–8 Jan and 15 days of August. Coaches welcome. Rest. seats 120. Evening meals until 9.30pm.

VENDOEUVRES 36500 Indre **Map 16 A-1**

☆☆ **LE SAINT LOUIS** (N° RR FEV 27 545) (Mr Lionel **Brunet**) place Saint Louis ☎ 54-38-30-68. **Minitel**. Restaurant: regional home cooking. Specialities: cuisses de grenouilles, filet de carpe au pouligny, escargots. Menu à la carte. Lunch 12–2pm. Dinner 7–9pm. Closed Sun evening, Mon evening (rest. only). Credit cards accepted. Traditional décor. Rest. seats 80 ◄ 7 155–200F, with shower, WC. Rest room. ☛ Parking. Filling station 1km open 6am–8pm. Sights: parc naturel de la Brenne, étang de Belle-bouché, the châteaux of the Loire.

VENDOME

VENDOME 41100 Loir-et-Cher **RN 10 and 817 Map 12-A3**
♀⊗ **CHEZ MEMÈRE** (N° RR AOU 19 132) (Mlle Andrée **Touchard**)
⌂ 127, faubourg Chartrain ☎ 54-77-00-32 ⬗ 14. Closed Mon, 15
Feb–10 Mar. Coaches welcome. Rest. seats 130 in 3 rooms.
Meals served until 10pm.

VENISSIEUX 69200 Rhône **Map 2-A2**
♀⊗ **LES ROUTIERS** (N° RR FEV 26 458) (M. Hervé **Ligier**) 66,
boulevard Irène-Joliot-Curie ☎ 78-76-49-94. Closed Sat, Sun.
Spanish spoken. Rest. seats 42. Lunch 11.30–3pm. Evening meals
7–9pm. Home cooking menu to 60F. Garden terrace. Parking.

VENOY 89290 Yonne **Autoroute A6 Map 13-A2**
♀⊗ **L'ARCHE DE VENOY** (N° RR 1835) (M. Bruno **Allegatière**) Air de
Grosse Pierre sens Paris/Lyon autoroute ☎ 86-40-31-71.
♀⊗ **L'ARCHE DE VENOY 2** (N° RR 1836) (M. Blaise **Soriel**) Aire de
Soleil Levant Sens Lyon/Paris autoroute ☎ 86-40-35-53 or 86-40-
22-44.

VENSAC 33590 Gironde **Map 20-A1**
♀⊗ **CHEZ NICOLE** (N° RR JUN 25·466) (Mme Nicole **Figerou**)
⌂ St-Vivien ☎ 56-09-44-05 ⬗ 6. Coaches welcome. Rest. seats 72.
Evening meals until 10pm.

VERDUN 55100 Meuse **RN 3 Map 6-B3**
♀⊗ **A LA BONNE AUBERGE** (N° RR SEPT 3102) (Mme **Gaiotti-
Morano**) 11, rue Garibaldi ☎ 29-86-05-16 ⬗ 10. Evening meals
until midnight. Rest. seats 140.
L'ARCHE DE VERDUN (N° RR 1822) (M. Serge **Monceau**) Aire
de Verdun Saint-Nicolas Sens Paris/Metz. autoroute ☎ 29-86-41-
18.

VERGEZE 30310 Gard **RN 113 Map 24-A3, 23-B2**
♀⊗ **RELAIS DE LA SOURCE** (N° RR JUL 26 279) (M. Richard
⌂ **Serquera**) RN 113 ☎ 66-35-05-51 ⬗ 9. English, Spanish spoken.

VERGT 24380 Dordogne **RD 21 Map 15-B3**
♀⊗ **LE PHENIX** (N° RR JUN 26 929) (Mme Raymonde **Legeard**) place
Jean-Jaurès ☎ 53-54-91-89. Closed Mon pm, 15–28 Feb, 15–30
Nov. German, Italian understood. Filling station nearby.

VERMENTON 89270 Yonne **RN 6 Map 13-A2**
♀⊗ **AU NOUVEAU RELAIS** (N° RR MAI 6 826) (M. Pierre **Jean**) 74,
⌂ RN 6 ☎ 86-53-51-51 ⬗ 12. Closed Sun, Dec.

VERN-SUR-SEICHE 35770 Ille-et-Vilaine **Map 7-B3**
♀⊗ **WELCOME-BAR** (N° RR MAI 27 280) (M. Phillippe **Brossault**) Le Clos
Berquet ☎ 99-62-83-18. Closed Sun in winter. Filling station nearby.

VERNET LA VARENNE 63580 Puy-de-Dôme **Map 17-A3**
♀⊗ **HOTEL DU CHATEAU** (N° RR JANV 27 751) (Bernard and Denis
⌂ – SNC **Charnay-Magaud**) ☎ 73-71-31-79. English spoken. Restaurant. Menu 45–85F. Lunch 12–2pm. Dinner 7.30–9pm ⬗ 7 65–
110F. Parking for lorries. Filling station 200m open 8am–9pm.

VERNEUIL-SUR-AVRE 27130 Eure **Map 8-A3**
♀⊗ **RELAIS DE L'ESPÉRANCE** (N° RR MARS 26 192) (M. **Agullo**), 65,
Porte de Breteuil.

VIC LA GARDIOLE

VERNON 27200 Eure **RN 181 and 13 Map 3-B1**

⍨⊗ **HOTEL DE FRANCE** (N° RR MARS 26 193) (M. Thierry **Bonté**) 70,
⌂ route de Rouen ☎ 32-51-53-55. **Minitel** ⌐ 8. Closed Sun. Coaches
welcome. Rest. seats 150. Evening meals.

⍨⊗ **CAFÉ NORMAND CHEZ GÉGÉ** (N° RR OCT 27 420) (M. Gérard
Boulet) 29–31, avenue de l'Ile-de-France Le Petit Val ☎ 32-51-08-
41. Closed Sun pm. German and English spoken. Evening meals
to 10pm. Credit cards accepted. Traditional décor. Rest. seats
70. ⌐ Parking. Filling station.

VERRUE 86420 Vienne **RN 147 Map 12-B2**

⊗⍨ **CHEZ RÉMY ET PAULETTE** (N° RR SEPT 27 011) (Mme Paulette
⌂ **Nativelle**) RN 147 Monts-sur-Guesnes ☎ 49-22-84-01 ⌐ 8. Closed
Sun pm and Mon, 5 Jan–5 Feb. Coaches welcome. Rest. seats
120. Evening meals to 10pm. Parking.

VESLY 27870 Eure **RD 181 Map 3-B2**

⍨⊗ **LE RELAIS DE L'AGRICULTURE** (N° RR MAI 24 225) (M. Claude
Benteyn) ☎ 32-55-62-37. Closed Sat. Coaches welcome. Rest.
seats 44.

VEUREY-VOROIZE 38113 Isère **RN 532 Map 19-A3**

⍨⊗ **AUBERGE DU VAL ROSE** (N° RR JUIN 26 904) (M. Jean-Louis
⌂ **Quercia**) chemin de la Rive ☎ 76-53-95-04 ⌐ 8. Closed Sun.
Filling station nearby.

VEYRINS THUELLIN 38630 Isère **RN 75 Map 2-B3**

⍨⊗ ☆ **L'ASTRAL** (N° RR AVR 25 874) (M. Raymond **Belingherl**) ☎
⌂ 74-33-94-27. **Minitel**. Italian, English spoken.

VEZENOBRES 30360 Gard **RD 106 Map 23-B1**

⊗ **LES GRES** (N° RR OCT 27 445) (M. Jean-Pierre **Geney**) Route
Nationale 106 de Nimes ☎ 66-83-52-89. **Minitel**. Restaurant: home
cooking. Specialities: gibier, couscous, charcuterie maison.
Menu 45F. Children's menu. À la carte. Lunch 11am–4pm. Dinner
7pm–midnight. Closed Fri evening. Credit cards accepted.
Traditional décor. Rest. seats 50. Rest room. Garden terrace. ⌐
Parking. Showers. Sights: Vézénbrex (medievel city), commune
de deux.

VIAS 34450 Hérault **RN 112 Map 23-A2**

⍨⊗ **LE PETIT VATEL** (N° RR MARS 26 476) (M. Albert **Matagotte**)
avenue de la Gare ☎ 67-21-63-06. Closed Mon, Nov. English,
Spanish spoken.

VIC-EN-BIGORRE 65500 Hautes-Pyrénées **Map 21-A3**

⍨⊗ **LE RANCH** (N° RR JAN 25 788) (M. Bernard **Griffon**) route de
d'Auch ☎ 62-96-72-32. **Minitel**. Closed Sat, Sep. Evening meals
8–11pm. Regional home cooking. Menu 50F. Menu à la carte.
Credit cards accepted. Traditional décor. Rest. seats 55. Rest
room. Garden terrace. ⌐ Parking. Sights: Lourdes.

VIC LA GARDIOLE 34110 Hérault **23-B2**

⍨⊗ **LA RESERVE** (N° RR MAI 27 607) (Mme Conception **Martinez**)
RN 112 ☎ 67-48-14-33. Spanish spoken. Restaurant menu 50–95F.
Open 6am–10.30pm. Lunch 11.30am–2.30pm. Closed Sun (low
season). Parking.

VIC-LES-FESQ

VIC-LES-FESQ 30260 Gard **Map 23-B2**
♀⊗ **RELAIS DE LA NOUVELLE** (N° RR JANV 27 752) (M. Hubert **Tani**) La Nouvelle ☎ 66-77-82-81. Restaurant: menu 50–85F. Menu à la carte. Closed Sun. Parking.

VICHY 03200 Allier **RN 9A Map 16-B3**
♀⊗ **LE RELAIS DE LA PASSERELLE** (N° RR MAI 14 797) (M. **Pesce**) 1, rue de Bordeaux ☎ 70-98-57-70 ⊷ 4. Closed Sun, 2 weeks in Aug. Evening meals.

VIEILLE-BRIOUDE 43100 Haute-Loire **RN 102 Map 17-A3**
♀⊗ ☆☆ **NN LES GLYCINES** (N° RR NOV 25 748) (Mme Viviane 🏠 **Chardonnal**) Direction 3km before Brioude. Avenue de Versailles ☎ 71-50-91-80. English spoken. Restaurant: home cooking. Speciality: salmon. Menu 59–180F. Dinner to 9pm. Closed Fri pm, Sat pm, Jan. Credit cards accepted Rest. seats 150 in 3 rooms ⊷ 13 170–290F with shower, bath, WC, telephone. Rest room. Garden terrace. ⊬ Parking. Sights: Vallée de l'allier, basilique, maison du saumon.

VIELLEVIGNE 44116 Loire-Atlantique **Map 11-B3**
♀⊗ **LE COMMERCE** (N° RR OCT 27 399) (SARL Le Commerce) 7, 🏠 place de Verdun ☎ 40-26-51-81. ⊷ 7. Evening meals until 11pm. English and German spoken. Filling station.

VIERZON 18100 Cher **RN 20 and 76 Map 13-B1**
♀⊗ **MODERN SPORT** (N° RR MARS 27 206) (Mme Jeanine **Madeleine**) 141, avenue E.-Vaillant ☎ 48-75-13-63. Closed Sat, Aug. Coaches welcome. Rest. seats 60. Evening meals to 10pm. Filling station nearby open 6am–9pm.
♀⊗ **AUX MILLE PATTES** (N° RR JUL 26 600) (M. Ludwig **Jakubik**) 85, route de Tours ☎ 48-75-46-38. **Minitel**. Close Sun. Coaches welcome. Rest. seats 35. Evening meals until midnight.

VILDE-GUINGALAN 22980 Côtes-du-Nord **RN 176 Map 7-A3**
♀⊗ **LA BORGNETTE** (N° RR FEV 27 520) (M. Alain **Lambard** – SARL Mélodie) la Borgnette. ☎ 96-27-61-10. Restaurant: home cooking. Menu to 45F. Children's menu. Lunch 11am–3pm. Dinner 7–10pm. Closed Sun. Credit cards accepted. Rest. seats 270 in 3 rooms. ⊬ Parking. Filling station nearby.

VILLEBAUDON 50410 Manche **RD 999 and 13 Map 8-A1/4-B1**
♀⊗ **LE SPORTIF** (N° RR JUN 26 918) (Mme Agnès **Osouf**) Le Bourg ☎ 33-61-20-52. **Minitel** ⊷ 3. Filling station nearby.

VILLEDIEU-LES-POELES 50800 Manche **RN 175 and Dle 799 Map 8-A1**
♀⊗ **HOTEL DES VOYAGEURS** (N° RR SEPT 26 626) (SNC. 🏠 **Louaintier-Lecannellier**) 36, avenue du Mal-Leclerc ☎ 33-61-00-76 ⊷ 5. Coaches welcome. Rest. seats 105. Evening meals until 10pm.

VILLEDIEU-SUR-INDRE 36320 Indre **RN 143 Map 12-B3**
♀⊗ **CAFE DES SPORTS** (N° RR MARS 26 828) (Mme Joëlle **Gatefin**) 69, rue de Général de Gaulle ☎ 54-26-56-18. Closed Mon. Filling station nearby. Coaches welcome. Rest. seats 60.

VILLEDOMER 37110 Indre-et-Loire **RN 10 Map 12-A3**
ᵧ⊗◠**LE RELAIS DES GRANDS VINS DE TOURAINE** (N° RR JUN 12 910) (M. Claude **Romain**) La Grand Vallée ☎ 47-55-01-05 ◠ 4 from 70–120F. Open 7am–10pm. Closed Wed, 17–27 Jul. Coaches welcome. Rest. seats 70. Evening meals until 10pm. Specialities: rabbit leg sausage with Vouvray and kidney sauce, frogs legs. Menu à la carte. Credit cards accepted. ➹ Parking.

VILLEFRANCHE-DE-ROUERGUE 12200 Aveyron **RD 926 Map 22-B1**
ᵧ⊗ **RELAIS DES CABRIÈRES** (N° RR JUL 26 592) (M. Alain **Toulouse**) route de Montauban ☎ 65-81-16-99. Closed Sun. Coaches welcome. Rest. seats 135 in 2 rooms. Parking.

VILLEFRANCHE-SUR-SAONE 69400 Rhône **Déviation Nle 6 Map 2-A1 Motorway exit Macon Paris**
ᵧ⊗ **RELAIS CALADOIS** (N° RR AVR 26 513) (M. Denis **Gimaret**) 300 rue Jacque Marie ☎ 74-60-69-88. **Minitel**. Closed Sat, Sun, 15–31 Aug. Coaches welcome. English, Spanish spoken. Rest. seats 150. Parking.

VILLE FRANCOEUR 41330 Loir-et-Cher **RD 957 Map 12-A3**
ᵧ⊗ **LE CONCORDE** (N° RR AOU 26 976) (Mme Andrée **Gehanno**) Le Breuil ☎ 54-20-12-04. Closed Sat, Aug. Italian spoken. Filling station nearby. Rest. seats 100. Dinner to 10pm.

VILLENEUVE 04180 Alpes-de-Haute-Provence **RN 96 Map 24-B2/25-A2**
ᵧ⊗ **LE RELAIS CHEZ ROGER** (N° RR OCT 15 814) (SARL Pierre ⌂ **Curri**) route de Marseille-Gap ☎ 92-78-42-47 ◠ 7. Closed Sat night, Sun, 3 weeks Aug, 21 Dec–5 Jan. Coaches welcome. Rest. seats 60. Evening meals until 11pm.

VILLENEUVE-D'AVEYRON 12260 Aveyron **RD 922 Map 22-B1**
ᵧ⊗ **L'ORÉE DU BOIS** (N° RR NOV 26 727) (M. Michel **Boulesque**) Septfonds Dle 922 ☎ 65-81-65-77. Closed Sat. Spanish spoken. Evening meals until 10pm. Coaches welcome. Rest. seats 120.
ᵧ⊗ **AUBERGE DE LA TOUR** (N° RR FEV 27 772) (Mme Rose-Mary **Laval Scudier**) boulevard de la Dime ☎ 65-81-75-62. Menu 55–90F. (Routiers menu 44F). Closed Sat. Parking.

VILLENEUVE DE RIVIERE 31800 Haute-Garonne **Map 21-B3**
ᵧ⊗ **L'ESCALE** (N° RR JUIL 27 647) (M. Gérard **Valentin**) RN 117 ☎ 61-89-39-05. Spanish spoken. Closed Sun evening. Parking. Filling station nearby.

VILLENEUVE-L'ARCHEVEQUE 89190 Yonne **RN 60 Map 9-B2**
ᵧ⊗ **L'ESCALE 60** (N° RR MARS 26 188) (M. Dominique **Boire**) 10, ⌂ route de Sens ☎ 86-86-74-42 ◠ 5. Closed Sat, Sun. Coaches welcome. Rest. seats 70. Evening meals 1pm–2am. English spoken.

VILLENEUVE-SUR-LOT 47300 Lot-et-Garonne **RN 21 Map 21-B1**
ᵧ⊗ **RELAIS DE GASCOGNE** (N° RR AVR 26 519) (M. Alain **Guiraud**) ⌂ 31, boulevard du Maréchal Leclerc ☎ 53-70-06-48. **Minitel** ◠ 8. Closed Sun (low season). Coaches welcome. Rest. seats 120. Evening meals. Spanish spoken.

VILLEROMAIN

VILLEROMAIN 41100 Loir-et-Cher **RD 957 Map 12-A3**
♀⊗ AU BON COIN (N° RR JUL 27 333) (Mme Isabelle **Renouf**) Grand
Rue ☎ 54-23-81-17. Closed Sun, Feb. Evening meals to 11pm.
Rest. seats 52. English, Spanish spoken. Credit cards accepted.
Filling station nearby.

VILLERS-BOCAGE 14310 Calvados **Map 4-B2**
♀⊗ HOTEL DE LA GARE (N° RR JUL 26 287) (Mme Paulette
⌂ **Golasse-Marie**) 6, rue du Mal-Foch ☎ 31-77-00-23 ⊷ 10. Closed
Sun. Rest. seats 170 in 3 rooms. Evening meals to 11pm.

VILLERS COTTERETS 02600 Aisne **Map 3-B3**
♀⊗ AU BOUT DU MONDE (N° RR OCT 27 684) **Minitel**. Home
⌂ cooking. Specialities: confit Pierre gourmande. Children's menu.
À la carte. Dinner to 10pm. Closed Sat after 3pm, Sun, bank
holidays, 1–4 Nov and 12 Dec–6 Jan. Credit cards accepted ⊷ 5
from 95–130F with shower, bath, WC. Hotel open 6am–11pm.

VILLERS-SUR-MER 14640 Calvados **RN 813 Map 4-B2**
♀⊗ ☆ NN LE NORMAND – Les Routiers (N° RR MAI 20 735) (Mme
⌂ Suzanne **Dujardin**) 44, rue du Maréchal-Foch ☎ 31-87-04-23 ⊷ 8
from 158–220F. Closed Sun (low season), Dec. Coaches wel-
come. Rest. seats 50. Evening meals until 9pm. Parking. Bar.
Beach. Horse-riding. Tennis nearby. Sights: Lisieux and Bayeux.

VILLEURBANNE 69100 Rhône **Map 2-A2**
♀⊗ CHEZ NICOLE (N° RR AVR 27 244) (Mme Nicole **Grass**) 165, rue
Jean Voillot ☎ 72-37-52-00. Closed Sat pm and Sun after 3pm,
Aug. Filling station nearby open 6am–10pm.

VILLEVALLIER 89330 Yonne **RN 6 Map 9-B2**
♀⊗ RELAIS 89 (N° RR JUIL 26 956) (Mme Yvette **Petit**) 9, rue de la
⌂ République ☎ 86-91-11-17. **Minitel** ⊷ 6. Closed Sat afternoons,
Sun. Coaches welcome. Rest. seats 52. Evening meals until 11pm.

VILLIERS-AU-BOUIN 37330 Indre-et-Loire **RN 159 and CD 959 Map
12-A2**
♀⊗ ☆☆ NN LE GRAND CERF (N° RR SEP 23 450) (M. Jean **Meunier**)
⌂ La Porerie ☎ 47-24-11-06. **Minitel**. Restaurant: regional home
cooking. Specialities: rillette de la Sarthe, ris de veau, aiguillette
de canard. Menu 48–180F. Children's menu. À la carte. Closed
Sat (in winter), Sun pm, 26 Oct–10 Jan, 1–15 March. Credit cards
accepted. Rest. seats 270 in 3 rooms. ⊷ 24 from 100–210F with
shower, bath, WC, TV, telephone. Open 7am–10pm. Garden
terrace. ⚓ Parking. Sights: châteaux du Lude, lac de Rille, zoo, la
Flèche.
♀⊗ L'ETAPE (N° RR JAN 26 778) (Mme Chantal **Hais**) 15, rue de la
Libération CD 135 ☎ 47-24-03-76. Closed Sun (unless booked),
Aug, 23 Dec–3 Jan. Evening meals. Coaches welcome. Rest.
seats 140.

VIMOUTIERS 61120 Orne **RN 179 Map 8-A2**
♀⊗ LE RELAIS DE LISIEUX (N° RR FEV 23 635) (Mme Yvette
⌂ **Larivière**) 37, avenue Lyautey ☎ 33-39-02-62 ⊷ 5. Closed Sun, 2
weeks Aug. Coaches welcome.

VINEZAC 07110 Ardèche **RN 104 Maps 23-B1 and 24-A2**
℡⊗ **L'AUBERGE DES COTES** (N° RR MAI 15 217) (M. Serge **Zagar**) Les Côtes ☎ 75-36-80-10. Closed Sat, 1 to 30 Sept. ⊷ 3.

VIRAZEIL 47200 Lot-et-Garonne **RD 933 Map 21-A1**
℡⊗ **LE RALLYE** (N° RR JANV 27 499) (M. Jean-Pierre **Léglise**) route de Périgueux ☎ 53-20-18-17. **Minitel**. German spoken. Restaurant: regional home cooking. Specialities: foie gras, magret de canard. Menu from 52F. Children's menu. Dinner to 11pm. Credit cards accepted. Modern décor. Rest. seats 80 in 3 rooms. Rest room. Garden terrace. ⊶ Parking. Sights: Château de Juras, vallée de la Garonne.

VIRE 14500 Calvados **RN 177 and 24 Bis Map 8-A1**
℡⊗ **L'AVENIR** (N° RR MAI 26 533) (M. Hervé **Gautherot**) 30, rue Émile-Chenel ☎ 31-67-76-94. Closed Sun (except in season), Dec. Coaches welcome. Rest. seats 55. English, Spanish, Portuguese spoken.

℡⊗ ☆☆ **NN HOTEL DE FRANCE** (N° RR OCT 24 705) (M. Roger
⌂⊷ **Carnet**) 4, rue d'Aignaux ☎ 31-68-00-35. **Minitel** ⊷ 50 at 145–260F with bath or shower, WC, telephone. Closed 20 Dec–10 Jan. Regional cooking. Lunch 12–2pm. Dinner 7–9pm. Children's menu. À la carte. Coaches welcome. Rest. seats 200. English spoken. Specialities: tarte aux pommes flambées aux calvados, ris de veau Vallée d'Auge. Rest room. ⊶ Credit cards accepted.

VIRONVAY 27400 Eure **Autoroute A 13 Map 3-B1**
℡⊗ **L'ARCHE** (N° RR 18/2) (M. Pascal **Legal**) Aire de Vironvay ☎ 32-40-21-51.

VIRY-CHATILLON 91170 Essonne **RN 7 and RD 91 Map 1-B2**
℡⊗ **AU BON ACCUEIL** (N° RR SEP 12 440) (M. Fernand **Gadreau**) 100, route de Fleury ☎ 69-05-28-46. Closed Sun, public holidays.

VITARELLE (LA) 12210 Aveyron **RN 121 Map 17-B2**
℡⊗ **LE RELAIS DE LA VITARELLE** (N° RR AVR 20 696) (Mme
⌂ Francine **Falguier**) Montpeyroux ☎ 65-44-36-01 ⊷ 6. Closed Sat low season. Coaches welcome. Rest. seats 80. Evening meals.

VITROLLES 13127 Bouches-du-Rhône **RN 113 Map 24-B3**
℡⊗ **LA FALAISE** (N° RR JUN 27 622) (M. Roger **Gairaud**) RN 113 les
⌂ Cadestraux ☎ 42-87-00-44. English, Spanish spoken. Restaurant. Open 5am–11pm. Closed Sun ⊷ 15 at 70–100F.

VITRY-EN-CHAROLAIS 71600 Saône-et-Loire **RN 79 Map 16-A3**
℡⊗ **TOM BAR** (N° RR AVR 26 232) (M. André **Borrego**) RN 79 ☎ 85-81-02-85. Closed Sat midday, Aug. Evening meals until midnight. Spanish spoken.

VITTEAUX 21350 Côte-d'Or **RN 5 and 70 Map 13-A/B3**
⊗⌂ **RELAIS DE LA ROUTE BLANCHE** (N° RR FEV 9 286) (M. **Le Gall**) route de Dijon ☎ 80-49-60-13 ⊷ 5. Closed Sept. Home cooking. Lunch 12–2.30pm. Evening meals 7–9pm. Menu 50F. Traditional décor. Rest. seats 50. Parking.

VITTONVILLE 54700 Meurthe-et-Mozelle **Map 6 B-3**
℡⊗ **L'AIGLE D'OR** (N° RR SEPT 27 666) (Eliane and Eric **Lanzi**) RN 57 Pont à Mousson ☎ 83-81-04-08. **Minitel**. Italian spoken. Restaurant.

Vittonville continued
Menu 57F. Open 5am–12pm. Rest room. 🚻 Parking. TV. Games:
billiards, table football, CB.

VIVIERS-SUR-RHÔNE 07220 Ardèche **RN 86 Map 24-A2**
♈⊗ ☆ **NN CHEZ ESPERANDIEU – LE RELAIS DU VIVARAIS** (N° RR
🏠⊷ FEV 7 485) (M. André **Esperandieu**) RN 86 Lieu-dit-Les-Sautelles
☎ 75-52-60-41 ⊷ 10 100–200F with bath, WC. Open 5am–9pm.
Restaurant: regional home cooking. Specialities: cuisses de
grenouille provençale, canard à l'orange. Menu 80–150F. Chil-
dren's menu. Lunch 12–2pm. Dinner 7–9pm. Closed Wed, Jan.
Traditional décor. Rest. seats 35. Rest room. Garden terrace.
Coaches welcome. English spoken. Parking. Bar. 🚻 Fishing and
tennis nearby. Note: this hotel is 2 km north of the town, towards
Lyons.

VIVONNE 86370 Vienne **RN 10 Map 15-B1**
♈⊗ **LE RELAIS ROUTIERS DE VIVONNE** (N° RR JAN 26 143) (M.
Fernand **Judes** SARL) RN 10 ☎ 49-43-41-03. **Minitel**. Open 24
hours. Coaches welcome. Rest. seats 220.

VIVY 49680 Maine-et-Loire **RN 147 Map 12-A2**
♈⊗ ☆ **NN LE RELAIS SAINT-PAUL** (N° RR OCT 16 736) (Mme
🏠⊷ Marie-Louise **Bidet**) 30, rue Nationale ☎ 41-52-50-13. **Minitel**.
Regional home cooking. Children's menu. À la carte. Credit
cards accepted ⊷ 27 at 100–250F with shower, bath, WC, TV,
telephone. Open 7am–midnight. Rest room. 🚻 Parking. Coaches
welcome. Rest. seats 150 and 250. Evening meals until 10pm.
Some English spoken. Specialities: brochette de loire au beurre
blanc. Sights: Saumur.

VOINSLES-ROZAY-EN-BRIE 77540 Seine-et-Marne **Map 9-A2**
♈⊗ **RELAIS DE VOINSLES** (N° RR NOV 27 452) (Martine and
Patrice-Klein **Renaudin**) RN 4 ☎ 64-07-75-20. Closed Sat, Sun.
Coaches welcome. Rest. seats 40 in 2 rooms.

VOISINS MOUROUX 77120 Seine-et-Marne **RN 34 Map 9-A2**
♈⊗ **LE RELAIS DU SOMMET** (N° RR AOU 16 173) (M. Jacques
🏠 **Santerre**) 968, rue du Général de Gaulle ☎ 64-03-05-47 ⊷ 7.
Closed Sun, Aug.

VOIVRES 72210 Sarthe **RD 23 Map 10-A3**
♈⊗ **LE TAMARIS** (N° RR MAI 26 252) (M. Patrick **Le Guy**) route de la
🏠 Suze ☎ 43-88-52-60 ⊷ 5. Closed Sun evening. Coaches welcome.
Rest. seats 200.

VOREY-SUR-ARZON 43800 Haute-Loire **RN 103 Maps 18-A3 and 17-A3**
♈⊗ **LE RELAIS DE LA BASCULE** (N° RR MAR 16 920) (Mme
Tirtaine) place des Moulettes ☎ 71-03-41-67.

VOULX 77940 Seine-et-Marne **RD 219 Map 9-B2**
⊗⊷ **LA BRUYÈRE** (No RR AOU 22 914) (M. Alban **Baldran**) 72,
Grande-Rue ☎ 64-31-92-41. Bar. Closed Sun evening, 15–28 Feb,
16 Aug–6 Sept. Coaches welcome. Rest. seats 160. Restaurant:
home cooking. Specialities: huitres, escargots, tête de veau,
grillades. Menu 82–115F. Children's menu. À la carte. Evening
meals until 9.30pm.

WAILLY BEAUCAMP 62170 Pas-de-Calais **RN 1 Map 5-A3**

♈⊗ **LE CHAILLOTE** (N° RR SEPT 27 389) (M. Jean-Luc **Sieradzke**) German, English, Italian, Polish spoken. Filling station nearby open 8am–7pm.

WANCOURT 62128 Pas-de-Calais **Map 5-B3 see Arras**

WASSELONNE 67310 Bas-Rhin **RN 4 Map 10-B2**

♈⊗ **AU ROCHER** (N° RR NOV 27 446) (M. André Hecter) 18, route de
⌂ Strasbourg ☎ 88-87-06-72 ⇥ 8 with TV. Open 6.30am–9.30pm. Restaurant: home cooking. Specialities: boeuf bourguignon. Menu 60–100F. Children's menu. À la carte. Lunch 11.30am–2.30pm. Dinner 7–9pm. Credit cards accepted. Traditional décor. Rest. seats 60 in 2 rooms. ⊢ Parking. Closed Sun. German, English spoken. Sights: Strasbourg, cathedral.

WINGLES 62410 Pas-de-Calais **RD 165 Map 5-A1**

♈⊗ **CAFE DES ROUTIERS** (N° RR MAI 27 615) (Mme Martine
⌂ **Morelle**) 37 Grand Place ☎ 21-69-52-88. Dinner to 8pm. Closed Sun, Aug ⇥ 9 at 80F.

WITTELSHEIM-GRAFFENWALD 68310 Haut-Rhin **RN 83 Map 10-B3**

♈⊗ **HOTEL DES VOSGES** (N° RR OCT 26 351) (M. **Riedle**) rue de
⌂ Reiningue ☎ 89-55-10-20 ⇥ 13 110–140F. Closed Sun. Evening meals to 9pm. Open 5am–11pm. Coaches welcome. Rest. seats 80. German spoken. Home cooking. Children's menu. À la carte. Credit cards accepted. Parking.

WOIPPY 57140 Moselle **RN 412 Maps 6-B3 and 10-A1**

♈⊗ **LE CHARDON LORRAIN** (N° RR JUN 23 333) (Mme Françoise **de Cecco**) 58, rue de Metz ☎ 87-30-46-61 ⇥ 3. Closed Sun, 20 Dec–15 Jan. Coaches welcome. Rest. seats 70. Evening meals until 9pm. Parking.

WOLFGANTZEN 68600 Haut-Rhin **Map 10-B2**

♈⊗ **A L'AGNEAU D'OR** (N° RR JAN 25 247) (M. Etienne **Weimburger**) 37, rue Principale ☎ 89-72-86-66. Closed Wed, Feb. German, Alsatian spoken.

WORMHOUDT 59470 Nord **RN 16 Map 5-A2**

♈⊗ **CAFE DE LA FORGE** (N° RR JUN 14 405) (M. Guy **Depriester**) 84, Grand Place ☎ 28-65-62-33. Closed 15–31 Aug. Evening meals to 9pm.

YEBLES 77390 Seine-et-Marne **RN 19 Map 1-B3**

♈⊗ **RELAIS DE L'EST** (N° RR OCT 26 680) (André and Maria
⌂ **Boussuge Nune**) ☎ 64-06-00-40. ⇥ 11. Closed Sun. Portuguese, Spanish spoken.

YENNE 73170 Savoie **2-A/B3**

♈⊗ **RELAIS DE MONTAPLAN** (N° RR DEC 27 475) (Mme Michèle **Remy**) Landrecin ☎ 79-36-72-50. Dinner to 10pm. Closed Sun. Filling station 200m.

YERVILLE 76760 Seine-Maritime **RN 29 Maps 4-A3**

♈⊗ **L'ESCALE ROUTIERE** (N° RR DEC 25 771) (M Christian **Dela-
⌂ haye**) route d'Yvetot ☎ 35-96-80-45. **Minitel**. Closed 6pm Fri–noon Sat, Aug. Restaurant: regional home cooking. Menu 55F.

YMONVILLE

Yerville continued

Menu à la carte. Open 6am–10.30pm. Lunch 11–3pm. Dinner 7.30–10pm. Credit cards accepted. ⊨ Hotel bedrooms nearby. Coaches welcome. Rest. seats 124. Parking.

YMONVILLE 28150 Eure-et-Loir **RN 154 Map 9-B1**

♈⊗ **LE RELAIS DE BEAUCE** (N° RR SEPT 26 997) (Mme Martine **Millochau**) 'La Michellerie' ☎ 37-32-26-34. Restaurant: home cooking. Menu to 50F. Dinner to 10pm. Closed Sat, Sun, Aug. Credit cards accepted. Rest. seats 92. Parking. Sights: Chatres Cathedral, maison de Picassiette à Chatres, moulin à vent.

YSSINGEAUX LA GUILDE 43200 Haute-Loire **RN 88 – RD 105 Map 18-A3**

♈⊗ **LA PETITE AUBERGE** (N° RR JUN 16 996) (Mme **Delabre**) ☎
⌂ 71-59-05-32 ⊨ 4. Closed Sun low season, July. Coaches welcome. Rest. seats 70. Evening meals until 11pm. English spoken.

YUTZ 57110 Moselle **RN 53 Bis Map 10-A1**

♈⊗ **CHEZ CHANTAL ET NOEL** (N° RR DEC 26 754) (M. Noël
⌂ **Rubeillon**) 140, rue Nationale ☎ 82-56-00-28. Closed Sat, Sun, Aug. Home cooking. Menu 54F. Lunch 11.30am–3pm. Coaches welcome. Rest. seats 60. Evening meals 7–10pm. Credit cards accepted. Modern décor ⊨ 8 70F per person. ⊨ Parking.

YVETOT 76190 Seine-Maritime **Map 4-A3**

♈⊗ **HOTEL DE FECAMP** (No RR AUG 27 589) (**Corbineau-Lamare**)
⌂ 25 rue Clouis Cappon ☎ 35-95-44-40 ⊨ 5 at 120–150F. Full-board 170F. Parking.

YVRE-L'ÉVEQUE 72530 Sarthe **RN 23 Map 8-B2**

♈⊗ **CAFE DE BENER** (N° RR JUN 25 007) (Mme Annick **Simon**) 25, route du Mans Bener ☎ 43-84-54-63. Closed Wed 2pm, Aug. Coaches welcome. No meals on Sun.

BELGIUM

ADUINKERKE 8660

⚏ **DIENSTSTATION 297** (N° RR JUN 550000085) (Mme Marie **Roose**) Duiniterkenweg 1 ☎ 058/41-19-18. Telex 058/41-59-36. Restaurant: open 6am–10pm. Closed Sun and 24 Dec–2 Jan. English, French and Dutch spoken.

ANTWERP 2040

🍽⚏ **TOTAL SERVICE STATION DELWAIDEDOK ANTWERP-SEBAAN – HOEK LAAGEIND STABROEK DELWAIDEDOK KAAI 730** (N° RR 550000109) ☎ 03/568-88-08 – 03/568-88-09. **Minitel**. Closed Sat evening, Sun evening 8pm–6am. Free showers. Shop, credit cards accepted. French, Dutch, English, German spoken.

BANDE 6951

⚏ **LES ROUTIERS SERVICE STATION TOTAL SEPT** (N° RR 550000114) Nle 4, 47 Nationale 4. Direction: Luxembourg ☎ 084/34-44-24. **Minitel**. Closed Mon. Credit cards accepted. Shop open 7am–10pm. Free coffee. French, Dutch spoken.

BARCHON 4511

🍽⚏ **SERVICE STATION TOTAL RESTAURANT LES ROUTIERS** (N° RR SEPT 550000115) rue Lieutenant Jungling, 1 Autotroute E 40 Barchon exit (No 36) ☎ 041/87-47-27. Open 24 hours. Credit cards accepted. Free showers and coffee. French, Dutch, German spoken. Sights: Chantilly (20km), Senlis (28km), L'Isle-Adam (10km), L'Abbaye de Royaumont (10km), Beauvais (35km).

BRULY DE COUVIN 6402 Prov. Namur

🍽⊗ **CHEZ PIERRE** (N° RR AVR 22 759) (M. Pierre **Libens**) 65, rue Grande ☎ 060/37-72-02. Closed Mon. English, German, Dutch spoken.

BRUSSELS 1210

⊗⚏ **TOTAL SERVICE STATION** (N° RR JANV 550000104) Port de Bruxelles, avenue du Port 132, Porte de Bruxelles TIR ☎ 024/26-0-54. Closed Sat 1pm to Sun. Free showers and coffee. Shop. Credit cards accepted. Dutch, French spoken.

GHENT 9020

⚏ **TOTAL SERVICE STATION** (N° RR 550000107) Port Arthurlaan Gent/Zeehaven ☎ 091/51-61-44. Shop open 7am–9pm. Closed Sun. Free coffee. Credit cards accepted. Dutch, French spoken.

GOETSENHOVEN 3311

⊗⚏ **TOTAL SERVICE STATION AE 40** (N° RR 550000102) Directions: Brussels/Liège ☎ 016/76-72-45. Open 24 hrs. Free coffee. Credit cards accepted. Shop. Dutch, French spoken.

KWAADMECHELEN

KWAADMECHELEN 3968
⊗🚿 **TOTAL SERVICE STATION LES ROUTIERS** (N° RR SEPT 5 50000112) Sluisstraat 1 A-Autoroute A-13 25 ☎ 013/66-54-06. Open 7am–10pm. Closed Sun. German, French, Dutch spoken. Showers and coffee free. Credit cards accepted. Shop.

LAAKDAL/EINDHOUT 3999
⊗🚿 **TOTAL SERVICE STATION LES ROUTIERS** (N° RR 550000111) Hezemeer 1 Autoroute A13 sortie nr 24 ☎ 014/30-19-35. Shop open 7am–10pm. Free showers and coffee. Credit cards accepted. Closed Sun. French, Dutch, English, German spoken.

MARCHE EN FAMENNE 5400 Duruisseau
🚿 **TOTAL SERVICE STATION LES ROUTIERS** (N° RR 550000113) Route de Namur 73 National 4. Direction: Brussels ☎ 084/31-17-25. Shop open 7am–10pm. Credit cards accepted. Free coffee. French, Dutch spoken.

MEER HOOGSTRATEN 2321
⊗🚿 **TOTAL SERVICE STATION GRENSEWEG** (N° RR 550000106) E 19 D2 Grenszone, Industiezone ☎ 03/315-88-98. Closed Sat, Sun. Free showers, and coffee. Shop open 6am–10pm. Credit cards accepted. Dutch, French spoken.

MENEN-REKKEM 8530
🍴🚿 **TOTAL SERVICE STATION KORTRIJK/LAR** (N° RR 550000108) Riijksweg 746 Pecq/Geluwe N 746. Transportzone LAR ☎ 056/40-00-02. **Minitel.** Open 24 hrs. Closed Sat midday to Mon 6am. Rest room. Free showers. Shop. Open 24 hrs. Credit cards accepted. French, Dutch spoken.

NEUVILLE 5600
🍴⊗ **LA QUERCINETTE** (N° RR FEV 27 778) (M. Michel **Paquet**) 34 route de Mariembourg ☎ 071/66-78-91. English, Spanish, Portuguese spoken. Restaurant: regional home cooking. Specialities: poisson, gibiers (in season). Menu to 300FB. Children's menu. À la carte. Dinner to 11pm. Closed Tues, Feb. Credit cards accepted. Traditional décor. Rest. seats 220 in 3 rooms. Garden terrace. ⊢ Filling station nearby open 24 hrs. Fishing. Mini golf. Children's playground. Sights: grottes de Neptune, museum de la bière, barage de l'eau d'Heure (7km).

NOIREFONTAINE 6831 **RN 26, 28 and 47**
⊗ **LE RELAIS DES ROUTIERS** (N° RR MAI 19 777) (M. **Marqua**) route de Bouillon ☎ 061/46-63-74. Closed Sun (except Jul/Aug). Dinner to 10pm.

ROTSELAAR 3110
⊗🚿 **TOTAL SERVICE STATION ROTSELAAR** (N° RR 550000105) AUT A2 ☎ 016/44-82-70. Open 24 hrs. Shop. Credit cards accepted. Free coffee. Dutch, French spoken.

RUISBROEK 1610
🚿 **STATION SERVICE TOTAL RUISBROEK** (N° RR JUIL 55 0000110) RN Brussels/Paris ☎ 02/876-73-63 and 02/378-34-00. Open 24 hrs. English, Dutch spoken. Showers. Shop. Credit cards accepted. Coffee free.

VILVORDE 1800

♀⊗ **MONICO** (N° RR JANV 25 253) (M. **Pollet**) 548 Schaarbeeck Lei
☎ 02/252-06-85. Restaurant: home cooking. Menu to 50F. Children's menu. À la carte. Lunch 12–2pm. Dinner 7–10pm. Closed
Sat, Sun. Credit cards accepted. Traditional décor. Rest. seats 60.
Garden terrace. Parking.

ZEEBRUGGE 8380

⊗♬ **TOTAL SERVICE STATION BARON** (N° RR 550000103) N 31 de
Maerelaan 74 ☎ 050/54-54-61. **Minitel**. Open 24 hrs. Free showers. Shop. Free coffee. Credit cards accepted. Dutch, French,
English, German spoken.

ITALY

CAMPODARSEGO 35011
LES ROUTIERS (N° RR MARS 23163) (Sig. Diego **Savaretto**)
Via Antoniana 128, Padova ☎ 040-55-41-13.

GLOSSARY

The following list is not intended as a substitute for a phrase book or French dictionary, but as a quick and easy reference guide in a restaurant or hotel, or whilst travelling.

GREETINGS/GENERAL CONVERSATION

Good Morning	Bonjour
Goodbye	Au Revoir
Please	S'il vous plait
Thank you	Merci
Do you speak English?	Parlez-vous anglais?
I don't understand	Je ne comprends pas
Sorry/Excuse me	Je vous prie de m'excuser
Yes, No	Oui, Non
I come from England	Je viens d'Angleterre
Scotland	d'Écosse
Wales	du Pays de Galles
Ireland	d'Irelande
United States	des États-Unis

A L'HOTEL

Can you recommend a hotel?	Pouvez-vous m'indiquer un bon hotel?
Do you have a room available?	Avez-vous une chambre libre?
I would like to reserve a twin room with bathroom	Je voudrais reserver une chambre à deux lits avec salle de bain
At what time is dinner?	A quelle heure servez-vous le diner?
A table for four please	Je voudrais une table pour quartre personnes
Can I have the menu please?	Voulez-vous me donner le menu?
Where are the toilets?	Où sont les toilettes?
Could you prepare my bill please?	Pouvez-vous me preparer la note?
How much do I owe you?	Combien vous dois-je?

WHERE IS . . . ?

Where is the police station?	Où se trouve la gendarmerie?
Where is . . . Road/Street?	Où se trouve la rue . . . ?
Where is the British Embassy?	L'ambassade de Grande Bretagne?
How do I get to the bank?	Comment aller à la banque?
How do I get to the Post Office?	Comment aller à la poste?
Where can I find a post box?	Comment puis-je trouver une boite aux lettres?

ACCIDENT/ILLNESS

I have had an accident	J'ai eu un accident
There are people injured	Il y a des blessés
Call an ambulance	Appelez une ambulance
Where can I find a doctor?	Où puis-je trouver un docteur?
Where is the nearest chemist?	Où est la pharmacie la plus proche?

| I am ill. I have a temperature | Je suis malade. J'ai de la fièvre |
| Do you have any asprin? | Avez-vous des medicaments? |

GETTING TO A GARAGE

How far is the nearest garage?	À quelle distance se trouve la garage la plus proche?
Is it far?	Est-ce loin?
Do I go straight on?	Faut-il aller tout droit?
Turn around/Do a U turn	Faire demi-tour
Do I have to turn left?	Dois-je tourner à gauche?
right?	à droite?
At which crossroads must I turn?	A quel croisement dois-je tourner?
At which traffic lights do I turn?	Je tourne a quel feu tricolore?
Fill her up, please	Le plein, s'il vous plait

IN CASE OF BREAKDOWN

I have broken down	Je suis en panne
I have a flat tyre	J'ai un pneu crevé
It's overheating	Cela surchauffe
The battery needs recharging	Les batteries ont besoin d'être rechargées
The ... does not work	Le/la ... ne marche pas
The ... is broken	Le/la ... est cassé(e)
Will it take long?	Ce sera vite fait?

Axle	Essieu
Battery	Batterie
Brake	Frein
Carburettor	Carburateur
Choke	Starter
Clutch	Embrayage
Distributor	Allumeur
Engine	Moteur
Exhaust pipe	Tuyau d'échappement
Fan belt	Courroie
Fuel tank	Réservoir de carburant
Gear box	Boite de vitesses
Headlight	Phare
Horn	Avertisseur
Ignition	Allumage
Indicator	(Feu) Clignotant
Oil	Huile
Radiator	Radiateur
Silencer	Silencieux
Spark plug	Bougie
Steering	Direction
Steering wheel	Volant
Suspension	Suspension
Tyre	Pneu
Wheel	Roue
Windscreen	Pare-brise
Windscreen-wiper	Essuie-glace

UNDERSTANDING THE MENU
Les Viandes

Meat

Le Boeuf	beef
Charolais	best cut
Chateaubriand	double fillet steak

Contrefilet	sirloin
Entrecôte	rib steak
Faux Filet	sirloin steak
Filet	fillet
L'Agneau	lamb
Le Porc	pork
Jambon	ham
Jambon cru	raw smoked ham
Veau	veal
Foie	liver
Foie gras	goose liver
Ris	sweetbreads
Rognons	kidneys
Tripes	tripe

Volaille/Gibier — Poultry/Game

Caille	quail
Canard	duck
Dindon	turkey
Faisan	pheasant
Liévre	hare
Oie	goose
Perdreau	partridge
Pintade	guinea-fowl
Poulet	chicken

Les Poissons/Coquillages — Fish/Shellfish

Coquille St Jacques	scallop
Crabe	crab
Crevette	prawn
Daurade	sea bream
Écrevisse	crayfish
Fletan	halibut
Fruits de mer	seafood
Homard	lobster
Huitre	oyster
Limand	lemon sole
Lotte de mer	monkfish
Maquereau	mackerel
Morue	salt cod
Moule	mussel
Plie	plaice
Raie	skate
Saumon	salmon
Seiche	squid
Sole	sole
St. Pierre	John Dory
Thon	tuna
Truite	trout

Les Fruits — Fruit
Les Légumes — Vegetables
Les Herbes/Épices — Herbs/Spices

Ail	garlic
Ananas	pineapple
Aneth	dill
Abricot	apricot
Artichaut	artichoke
Asperge	asparagus

Avocat	avocado
Banane	banana
Basilic	basil
Cassis	blackcurrant
Cerise	cherry
Champignon	mushroom
Chou	cabbage
Choufleur	cauliflower
Ciboulette	chive
Citron	lemon
Citron vert	lime
Concombre	cucumber
Coriandre	coriander
Cornichon	gherkin
Courgette	courgette
Cresson	watercress
Échalote	shallot
Endive	chicory
Épinards	spinach
Estragon	tarragon
Fenouil	fennel
Fève	broad bean
Fraise	strawberry
Framboise	raspberry
Gingembre	ginger
Groseille	gooseberry
Haricot vert	French bean
Laitue	lettuce
Menthe	mint
Mure	blackberry
Muscade	nutmeg
Myrtille	blueberry
Oignon	onion
Oseille	sorrel
Pamplemousse	grapefruit
Pêche	peach
Persil	parsley
Petit pois	pea
Poire	pear
Poireau	leak
Poivre	pepper
Poivron	green, red, yellow pepper
Pomme	apple
Pomme de terre	potato
Prune	plum
Pruneau	prune
Radis	radish
Raisin	grape
Romarin	rosemary
Safran	saffron
Thym	thyme
Tomate	tomato
Truffe	truffle

APPLICATION FORM

If you use the Guide regularly, then it would certainly be in your interest to join Club Bon Viveur and receive the numerous benefits on offer.

Remember what they are . . .

- Discounts at over 300 Les Routiers restaurants and hotels in Britain
- £2 off additional copies of both Les Routiers Guides
- Discounts off motoring services and insurance with Europ Assistance
- Discounts off holidays in the Paris and France brochures booked through Jet Tours and the French Travel Service
- Newsletters including promotional offers

We are always pleased to hear your comments on any restaurants and hotels you have visited. On the reverse of this page, there is the opportunity to give your opinion.

To join Club Bon Viveur, simply complete the form below and return it to us with the annual subscription fee of £12.00.

Name _____

Address _____

_____

_____

I enclose a cheque for £12.00 (payable to Routiers Ltd) ☐
OR
Please debit my Access/Visa Card for the amount of
£12.00. ☐

Card No. .... Expiry Date _____

Signature ....

Return to: Club Bon Viveur, 25-27 Vanston Place, London SW6 1AZ.
Please allow 28 days for delivery.

YOUR OPINION

Do you have a favourite pub, restaurant or hotel which you would like to recommend to us, which is not already Les Routiers recommended? If it is worthy of nomination, please let us know on the form below so that, with their consent, we may arrange for an inspector to call.

Alternatively, if you visit a Les Routiers establishment which you think is worthy of a Les Routiers Award or, if you are dissatisfied with an establishment, we would like to hear your comments.

With your help, we can maintain Les Routiers standards, and all correspondence will be treated in strictest confidence.

Name of Establishment: _____

Address/Location: _____

_____

Type of Establishment (please circle):

Restaurant   Public House   Wine Bar/Bistro   Hotel   B&B

Please circle: Nomination   OR   Complaint

Comments: _____

_____

_____

_____